INTRODUCTION TO
THE THEORETICAL AND EXPERIMENTAL ANALYSIS
OF STRESS AND STRAIN

McGRAW-HILL SERIES IN MECHANICAL ENGINEERING

Robert N. Drake and Stephen J. Kline, *Consulting Editors*

Beggs · Mechanism

Cambel and Jennings · Gas Dynamics

Durelli, Phillips, and Tsao · Introduction to the Theoretical and Experimental Analysis of Stress and Strain

Ham, Crane, and Rogers · Mechanics of Machinery

Hartman · Dynamics of Machinery

Jacobson and Ayre · Engineering Vibrations

Phelan · Fundamentals of Mechanical Design

Sabersky · Engineering Thermodynamics

Shigley · Machine Design

Stoecker · Refrigeration and Air Conditioning

The Series was established in 1954 under the Consulting Editorship of Richard G. Folsom, who continued in this capacity until he assumed the Presidency of Rensselaer Polytechnic Institute in 1958.

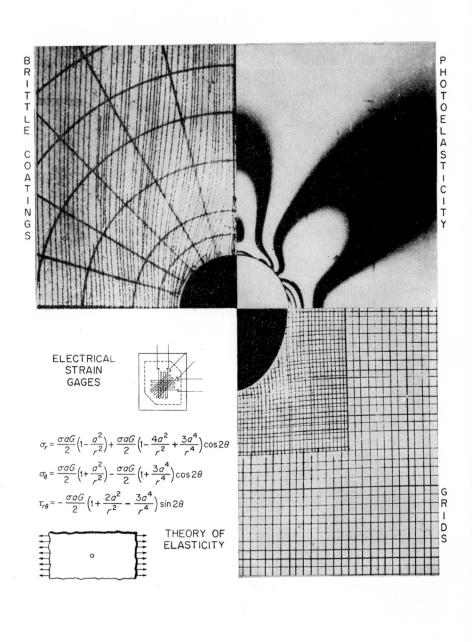

BRITTLE COATINGS

PHOTOELASTICITY

ELECTRICAL
STRAIN
GAGES

GRIDS

$$\sigma_r = \frac{\sigma a G}{2}\left(1-\frac{a^2}{r^2}\right)+\frac{\sigma a G}{2}\left(1-\frac{4a^2}{r^2}+\frac{3a^4}{r^4}\right)\cos 2\theta$$

$$\sigma_\theta = \frac{\sigma a G}{2}\left(1+\frac{a^2}{r^2}\right)-\frac{\sigma a G}{2}\left(1+\frac{3a^4}{r^4}\right)\cos 2\theta$$

$$\tau_{r\theta} = -\frac{\sigma a G}{2}\left(1+\frac{2a^2}{r^2}-\frac{3a^4}{r^4}\right)\sin 2\theta$$

THEORY OF
ELASTICITY

Introduction to the Theoretical and Experimental Analysis of Stress and Strain

A. J. DURELLI

Professor, Illinois Institute of Technology
Supervisor, Armour Research Foundation

E. A. PHILLIPS

Research Engineer
Standard Railway Equipment Manufacturing Company

C. H. TSAO

Member, Technical Staff, Systems Development Laboratories
Hughes Aircraft Company

McGRAW-HILL BOOK COMPANY, INC.

New York   Toronto   London

1958

INTRODUCTION TO THE THEORETICAL AND EXPERIMENTAL
ANALYSIS OF STRESS AND STRAIN

PREFACE

This book has been written for use as a text by students with the background usually found in college seniors and graduates and is an outgrowth of a course given to such students at the École Polytechnique in Montreal, and at the Illinois Institute of Technology in Chicago. The book is intended to be only an introduction to the field of stress analysis, giving an over-all picture and a balanced description of the several methods used: it is not intended to replace the full course on theory of elasticity, photo-elasticity, etc. It is expected that after this course the student will be in a good position to select those methods in stress analysis which should be studied more thoroughly.

An effort has been made to develop the book in a systematic manner. The theory of elasticity is presented from the general three-dimensional point of view, and although the conventional parallelepiped approach is used, references are made whenever necessary to the underlying philosophy of the rigorous theoretical development. More emphasis has been placed on this chapter than is common in experimental-stress-analysis courses. It is the conviction of the authors that the training of engineers in stress analysis requires an understanding, limited in scope but fundamental, of the principles of the theory of elasticity. All experimental techniques are based on those principles, and an erroneous conception of the elastic phenomenon will seriously handicap any stress analyst, whatever his skill may be in a particular technique.

Much thought was given to the presentation of this chapter. It is realized that psychologically it is often better to start with simple cases and to advance stepwise to the more complicated cases. It was decided, however, that in this book a logical science should be developed in a logical manner, starting from the most general and going to the particular by simplification. Therefore, all developments of the theory of elasticity are presented in three dimensions from the beginning.

The authors considered also that the theory of elasticity is not only the necessary background of all experimental methods but also one of the analysis methods, and should be presented to the students as such. A few elementary problems are solved with the theory of elasticity, and the Kirsch solution of the infinite plate with a circular hole is developed in detail. The objective of this development is to show the student how an elastic problem can be solved completely and rigorously by means of theory.

To keep the unity between the different chapters, it was considered convenient to approach the solution of one problem using all the available theoretical and experimental methods. The problem of the plate with a circular hole, under a unidimensional state of stress, presents a complex stress distribution which can be solved in many different ways. This allows comparisons between the methods and the development of criteria for their application.

Technical details of the methods have been underemphasized in the book, the philosophy being that the student can learn them easily in the laboratory if he is well acquainted with the fundamental principles of the method. Several of the experimental methods require tools, but the companies making them available also furnish literature wherein the necessary technical details are extensively explained.

Although it is the purpose of the authors to give a balanced presentation of the field of stress analysis, some chapters have been emphasized. This is particularly true of the brittle-coating and brittle-material methods, the reason being that the presentation of these methods has been underemphasized in most books published so far, and also that the authors have made a more important original contribution in these areas. It is unfortunate, however, that the developments in these methods are very recent and many points have not been completely clarified. The presentation of the material is therefore less definite and will probably require greater effort on the part of the reader. Some emphasis has been put also on the chapter dealing with the geometric representation of stresses. Much of the material included in this chapter is not easily available in the English literature, and it was considered that the more complete presentation would be useful, not only to students, but also to research workers interested in the fields of plasticity and failure.

An effort is made in the book to develop the critical spirit of the student toward the methods used in the standard books on strength of materials and, in general, toward the results the designer will find in engineering handbooks. Most of the formulas used in the field of strength of materials are good only for particular cases, and the assumptions on which they are based strongly limit their field of application. The use of those formulas outside their field may introduce very serious errors.

A similar critical spirit should be developed toward the theory of elasticity when all the complexities of the physical cases are kept in mind. The theory of elasticity is only an approximation to reality and also breaks down when assumptions such as the divisibility of matter in infinitesimal particles do not hold.

A strong effort has also been made to give examples of the application of basic concepts to the solution of problems of industrial interest. Nothing is more frustrating to a reader than to analyze, without end, what happens on a thin sheet with an empty circular hole, or in a round disk under diametral compression, without ever relating this knowledge to everyday problems in engineering. The necessary sacrifices in accuracy in this kind of work have to be acknowledged and accepted as part of the approach to the solution of technical problems.

In the present volume only the chapters dealing with theory of elasticity, grids, mechanical strain gages, and brittle coatings have been included. It is intended to publish the material dealing with other methods of stress analysis in future volumes.

About the Definition of the Terms Used. Attention should be called to the fact that many of the terms which are used in the book to express fundamental concepts do not always have a unique meaning in common use. Some of the terms are misnomers, and others are probably not the best that could be found. The words "theory of elasticity," for example, do not represent as they should a theory of the elasticity of materials, but rather a theory about stress and strain distribution when the materials are elastic. "Photoelasticity" does not deal with the elasticity of light but uses a light property, double refraction, to measure maximum shear stresses. In civil engineering, "stress analysis" often means moment and load analysis in structures. "Experimental stress analysis" very seldom is an analysis of stresses, but an analysis of strains, and the word "analytical," when used as a synonym of "theoretical," leads to inconsistencies such as "analytical stress analysis." With the exception of the last instance—there is no reason for the word "theoretical" to be supplanted by the word "analytical"—the book follows the accepted expressions. It was believed that any gain in accuracy would have been invalidated by the resulting confusion.

About the Teamwork of the Authors. The stress-analysis field is new and includes so many diversified techniques that a single person could scarcely cover them all efficiently. It was considered convenient, therefore, to divide the work among several persons who would work as a team to keep the chapters well coordinated.

The development of the chapters on the theory of stress, the theory of strain, geometric representations in three and in two dimensions, and mechanical strain gages has been mainly the work of E. A. Phillips. The development of the chapters on the theory of elasticity, the properties of special families of curves, dimensional analysis, stresses and strains in brittle coatings, and the grid method has been mainly the work of C. H. Tsao. E. A. Phillips and C. H. Tsao together contributed to the chapters on applications of elasticity theory to two- and three-dimensional problems. Several of the tests reported in the brittle-coatings chapters were conducted by S. Okubo. The computations of most of the stress loci using Kirsch's equations were conducted by N. W. Carey. The chapter on statistical applications has been written by J. W. Dally, who also contributed to the chapter on properties of brittle coatings. The introduction to brittle-coating methods has been written by A. S. Kobayashi. The development of the Preface, of the chapters on properties and applications of brittle coatings, and of the chapter on fundamental concepts has been mainly the work of A. J. Durelli, who also was in charge of the organization of the book and of the direction of the writing. A. J. Durelli also supervised the experimental work and was in charge of the courses on stress analysis, the notes of which formed the basis for the development of the book.

Credit should be given to V. Parks and K. Hofer for proofreading and many valuable suggestions.

A. J. DURELLI
E. A. PHILLIPS
C. H. TSAO

CONTENTS

LIST OF SYMBOLS†

†F, L, T, t denote force, length, time, and temperature, respectively. The symbol 1 denotes a dimensionless quantity.

A	Area (L^2)
A	Total sum of squares
$A(x_1,x_2)$	Area under Gaussian curve between x_1 and x_2
AM	Arithmetic mean of several measurements
a	Acceleration (LT^{-2})
B	Sum of squares between columns, in statistics
C	Curve
C	Residual sum of squares, in statistics
$\cos(n,x)$, $\cos(n,y)$, $\cos(n,z)$	Cosines of the angles between the directions n, x; n, y; and n, z (1)
d	Smallest possible reading on a scale (L)
DS	Deformation sensitivity (L)
E	Modulus of elasticity (FL^{-2})
E_m	Modulus of elasticity of a model (FL^{-2})
E_p	Modulus of elasticity of a prototype (FL^{-2})
E_c	Modulus of elasticity of a coating (FL^{-2})
E_s	Modulus of elasticity of a specimen (FL^{-2})
$\mathbf{E}$, $\mathbf{E}'$, $\mathbf{E}''$	Strain tensor, deviator strain tensor, and spherical strain tensor
F, f	Forces (F)
$F(x_1,x_2)$	Absolute frequency of occurrence of the variable between x_1 and x_2
F_0	Ratio of mean squares
F_x, F_y, F_z	x, y, and z components of a force (F)
$f(x_1,x_2)$	Relative frequency of occurrence of the variable between x_1 and x_2
G	Shear modulus of elasticity (FL^{-2})
I	Area moment of inertia (L^4)
I	Mass moment of inertia (FLT^2)
I_1, I_1', I_1''	First invariant of stress tensors $\mathbf{S}$, $\mathbf{S}'$, $\mathbf{S}''$ (FL^{-2})
I_2, I_2', I_2''	Second invariant of stress tensors $\mathbf{S}$, $\mathbf{S}'$, $\mathbf{S}''$ (F^2L^{-4})
I_3, I_3', I_3''	Third invariant of stress tensors $\mathbf{S}$, $\mathbf{S}'$, $\mathbf{S}''$ (F^3L^{-6})
J_1, J_1', J_1''	First invariant of strain tensors $\mathbf{E}$, $\mathbf{E}'$, $\mathbf{E}''$ (L/L)
J_2, J_2', J_2''	Second invariant of strain tensors $\mathbf{E}$, $\mathbf{E}'$, $\mathbf{E}''$ (L^2/L^2)
J_3, J_3', J_3''	Third invariant of strain tensors $\mathbf{E}$, $\mathbf{E}'$, $\mathbf{E}''$ (L^3/L^3)
K	Bulk modulus of elasticity (FL^{-2})
k	$\sigma_1/(\sigma_u - \sigma_R^c)$ at the instant when cracks perpendicular to σ_2 are about to appear in a coating (1)
L	Range
L, l, l_0	Lengths (L)

xvii

l Direction cosine (1)

M_x, M_y, M_z x, y, and z components of a moment (FL)

m_ϵ, m_σ Scale factors for strain and stress in the Mohr's-circle construction

m Strain-gage mechanical multiplication (1)

m Arithmetic mean of many measurements

m Direction cosine (1)

m Mass (FT^2L^{-1})

$\mathfrak{M}$ Momentum (FT)

N Number of measurements of a quantity (1)

n A large number of measurements of a quantity (1)

n Direction cosine (1)

P Power (FLT^{-1})

p Pressure (FL^{-2})

p Probable error of a single observation

p_0 Probable error of the mean

p_{oct} Resultant stress acting on an octahedral plane (FL^{-2})

p_{nx}, p_{ny}, p_{nz} x, y, and z components of p_n (FL^{-2})

p_n Resultant stress acting on an oblique plane with normal n (FL^{-2})

q Number of degrees of freedom

R General region

R^2 Multiple correlation coefficient

r, θ Polar coordinates $(L, 1)$

r_1 Ratio of lengths in structures (1)

r_2 Ratio of concentrated loads, acting on structures (1)

r_3 Ratio of loads distributed on a line, acting on structures (1)

r_4 Ratio of loads distributed on surfaces, acting on structures (1)

r_5 Ratio of loads distributed on volumes, acting on structures (1)

r_6 Ratio of displacements, on structures (1)

S Estimate of the standard deviation

S Surface (L^2)

$\mathbf{S, S', S''}$ Stress tensor, deviator stress tensor, and sperical stress tensor

SS Strain sensitivity (L/L)

S_ϵ Standard error of the estimate

S_n Resultant strain acting on an oblique plane with normal n

S_u, S_v Isostatics or arc displacement along isostatics (L)

S_1, S_2, S_3 Principal normal components of the deviator stress tensor (FL^{-2})

S_x, S_y, S_z Normal components of the deviator stress tensor (FL^{-2})

T Energy (FL)

t Time (T)

t Thickness (L)

t A statistical ratio

t_0 Brittle-coating test temperature (t)

t_r Brittle-coating refrigerating temperature (t)

u, v, w x, y, and z components of displacement (L)

u A coded value of a variable

$\bar{u}, \bar{v}, \bar{w}$ x, y, and z components of applied boundary displacements (L)

V Volume (L^3)

V Coefficient of variation

v Velocity (LT^{-1})

v Variance

W Work (FL)

w Width (L)

X A measurement

$\bar{X}$ Arithmetic mean of a number of measurements

$\bar{\bar{X}}$ The grand mean

X, Y, Z x, y, and z components of body force intensity (FL^{-3})

$\bar{X}_n, \bar{Y}_n, \bar{Z}_n$ x, y, and z components of applied surface force per unit area (FL^{-2})

x, y, z Cartesian coordinates (L)

X_{1r} The estimate of the dependent variable X_1

$[x^2]$ The reduced sum of squares

α Angular acceleration (T^{-2})

$\alpha, \beta, \theta, \psi$ Angles (1)

α Ratio between load necessary to crack a coating perpendicular to σ_2 and the load necessary to crack the same coating, at the same point, perpendicular to σ_1 (1)

β Ratio in a brittle-coating test between the initial high load in the relaxation test, minus the low load producing cracks perpendicular to σ_2, and the direct load producing cracks perpendicular to σ_1 (1)

γ Coefficient of linear thermal expansion $[(L/L)t^{-1}]$

γ Gradient of strain in a coating, in the direction of the crack $(L/L/L)$

γ Specific weight (FL^{-3})

γ_n Shear strain corresponding to direction n (1)

$\gamma_{P_0P_1, P_0P_2}$ Decrease of angle between line segments P_0P_1 and P_0P_2 (1)

$\left.\begin{array}{l} \gamma_{zy} = \gamma_{yz} \\ \gamma_{yz} = \gamma_{zy} \\ \gamma_{zx} = \gamma_{xz} \end{array}\right\}$ x, y, z cartesian shear-strain components (1)

γ_{oct} Octahedral shear strain (1)

ϵ Volume dilatation $= \epsilon_x + \epsilon_y + \epsilon_z$ (L/L)

ϵ_{P_0P} Unit elongation or normal strain in direction P_0P (L/L)

ϵ_{oct} Octahedral normal strain (L/L)

ϵ_m Mean normal strain of the spherical strain tensor $= (\epsilon_x + \epsilon_y + \epsilon_z)/3$ (L/L)

ϵ_n Normal strain corresponding to direction n (L/L)

$\bar{\epsilon}$ Natural strain (L/L)

$\epsilon_x, \epsilon_y, \epsilon_z$ x, y, z cartesian normal strain components (L/L)

$\epsilon_1, \epsilon_2, \epsilon_3$ Principal normal strains (L/L)

ϵ_1^c Principal strain in a coating in the direction of ϵ_1^s produced by external load (L/L)

ϵ_1^s Algebraically larger principal strain in a specimen (L/L)

ϵ_2^c Principal strain in a coating in the direction of ϵ_2^s produced by external load (L/L)

ϵ_2^s Algebraically smaller principal strain in a specimen (L/L)

ϵ_s Strain sensitivity of a coating. Minimum strain required to crack a coating on a unidimensionally loaded specimen when the strain gradient is 0.0002 (in./in.)/in. (L/L)

ϵ_s^d Strain sensitivity of a coating under direct loading (L/L)

ϵ_s^r Strain sensitivity of a coating under relaxation loading (L/L)

ϵ_a Strain sensitivity of a coating at the specific strain gradient x (L/L)

θ_P Angle between positive x direction and principal direction n (1)

λ Lamé's constant (FL^{-2})

ν Poisson's ratio (1)

ν_c Poisson's ratio of a coating (1)

ν_s Poisson's ratio of a specimen (1)

ξ, η, ζ Alternative rectangular coordinates (L)

ρ Mass density $(FL^{-4}T^2)$

ρ_u, ρ_v Radii of curvature of isostatics S_u and S_v (L)

σ, σ_X Statistical standard deviation

$\sigma_{\bar{X}}$ Standard error of the mean

σ_n Component of p_n acting normal to an oblique plane with normal n (FL^{-2})

σ_{oct} Octahedral normal stress—component of p_{oct} acting normal to the octahedral plane (FL^{-2})

σ_{aG} Normal stress in a field of uniform tension or compression (FL^{-2})

σ_u, σ_v Principal normal stresses where $\sigma_u \geq \sigma_v$ (FL^{-2})

$\sigma_x, \sigma_y, \sigma_z$ Normal stresses acting on planes perpendicular to the x, y, and z axes. Also principal normal stresses when x, y, z axes are principal (FL^{-2})

$\sigma_1, \sigma_2, \sigma_3$ Principal normal stresses (FL^{-2})

$\sigma_r, \sigma_\theta, \tau_{r\theta}$ Normal and shear-stress components in polar coordinates (FL^{-2})

σ_1^c Principal stress in a coating in the direction of σ_1^s produced by external load (FL^{-2})

σ_1^s Algebraically larger principal stress in a specimen (FL^{-2})

σ_2^c Principal stress in a coating in the direction of σ_2^s produced by external load (FL^{-2})

σ_2^s Algebraically smaller principal stress in a specimen (FL^{-2})

σ_u Ultimate strength of a coating (FL^{-2})

σ_R^c Residual stress in a coating (FL^{-2})

σ_0^d Minimum σ_1^s required to crack a coating in the direct-loading test when σ_2^s is zero (FL^{-2})

σ_0^r Minimum σ_1^s required to crack a coating in the relaxation-loading test when σ_2^s is zero (FL^{-2})

σ_H^c Thermal hydrostatic tension in a coating (FL^{-2})

σ_m Normal stress in a model (FL^{-2})

σ_m Mean normal stress of the spherical stress tensor $= (\sigma_x + \sigma_y + \sigma_z)/3$ (FL^{-2})

σ_p Normal stress in a prototype (FL^{-2})

τ_n Components of p_n acting parallel to an oblique plane with normal n (FL^{-2})

τ_{oct} Octahedral shear stress (Component of p_{oct} acting parallel to the octahedral plane) (FL^{-2})

$\left.\begin{array}{l} \tau_{xy} = \tau_{yx} \\ \tau_{yz} = \tau_{zy} \\ \tau_{zx} = \tau_{xz} \end{array}\right\}$ x, y, and z cartesian shear-stress components (FL^{-2})

ϕ Stress function

ω Angular velocity (T^{-1})

$\omega_x, \omega_y, \omega_z$ x, y, z cartesian rotation components of an infinitesimal rigid displacement (1)

INTRODUCTION

Problems of the Transmission of Forces. The problems of the engineer are fundamentally the problems of a more efficient utilization of forces in nature. Particularly, civil and mechanical engineers use the forces present in bodies which resist deformations and allow the transmission of outside forces from one point of the space to another.

In the solution of this problem of the transmission of forces, there are two phases: matter and shape. Of these, the study of the nature of the materials and of the improvement of their properties constitutes the first part of the engineering sciences and is sometimes the more important. Among other items it includes the development of new types of high-strength steels, and of plastics a short time ago unknown. It also includes the development of the new methods of treating wood to produce strengths as high as those of plywood.

The second part of the engineering sciences is the study of the shapes to be given to the materials. Although often considered independently of the first part, there does exist a relationship between the shape of a material and its properties. The good engineer will give to each material that shape which is most appropriate to its properties.

This point was not well realized some years ago by those who patterned reinforced-concrete structures after steel structures and similarly designed steel structures with the appearance and shape of wooden structures. It is true, in some cases (inside the elastic range in some two-dimensional problems, for instance), that the shape is independent of the properties of the material. However, this is so because the problem of the stress distribution, which often determines the shape, is in these cases independent of the properties.

Nature of Materials to Be Used and of Loads to Be Transmitted. When the engineer approaches the solution of the problem of the transmission of forces from one point of the space to another, he will find that the loads to be transmitted are either in movement or at a standstill. Most of the time, both kinds of loads will be acting together. This approach to the solution of the problem, then, will be either static or dynamic, according to the type of loads involved.

The engineer will also find that the materials possess several character-

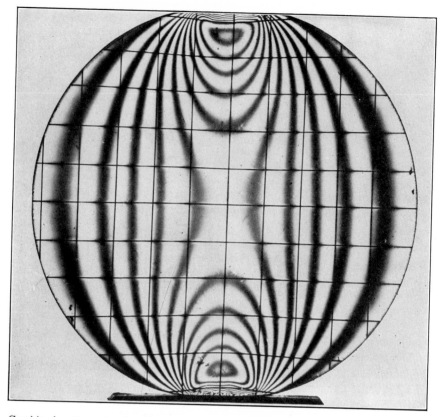

Combined pattern showing isochromatics and grid distortions. The information contained in this photograph gives more data than that necessary to solve completely
the stress analysis of the disk under diametral loading. Two physical phenomena are
related at all points on the disk: strain and birefringence. (Grid distortions are noticeable to the naked eye.)

istic properties and that among these properties, elasticity is relatively
easy to determine. Many materials behave first elastically, then, as the
amount of the load increases, plastically, and finally break. Although
not all materials follow this pattern of behavior, it is common in engineering
materials and permits a well-developed and relatively easy study of what
happens inside the elastic field.

Therefore, as the nature of the loads determines whether the engineer
will use a static or dynamic approach to the solution of the problem of
transmission of forces, so the nature of the material used requires an elastic
or plastic analysis, or a knowledge of the rupture conditions, or, depending
on the case, all three.

The study of the stress distribution produced by static and dynamic loads in the elastic and plastic ranges of materials, or of their rupture conditions, can be developed either theoretically or experimentally. A few words should be said here about the characteristics of these two approaches and about their advantages and limitations.

Theory and Experiment. Between the nature of rational work and the nature of experimental work there exists a well-defined qualitative difference. Rational, or theoretical, work reasons from the general to the particular; experimental work reasons from the particular to the general. The one is the antithesis of the other. Rational work, or, in the case of engineering

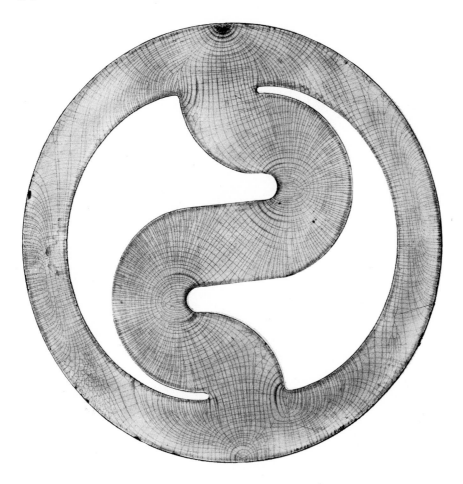

Physical evidence that the two principal stresses at each point are perpendicular to each other. Two families of isostatics obtained from a brittle-coating test conducted on a CR39 model diametrically loaded under compression.

sciences, mathematical work, is logical, abstract, and, if properly conducted, rigorous.   One starts with a few hypotheses and from these derives a series of statements which rest one upon the other.   The validity of the conclusion is conditioned by the validity of the assumptions with respect to physical reality.   The rational mind is not satisfied with individual cases or particular laws; rather, it looks for general principles from which conclusions may be deduced.

Experimental work, on the other hand, is more modest.   The experimental man studies individual cases and by means of induction obtains conclusions only after many tests.   The conclusions obtained in this way apply only to the range covered by the cases studied.

The critical spirit requires that the engineer adopt different attitudes

Detail of figure on page xxiii.

when he appraises the results of rational work from the attitudes required when he faces the interpretation of experimental work. The engineer should ask the theoretician to what extent his hypothesis corresponds to the physical cases, and whether his conclusions do not fall outside the limit of applicability of the hypothesis. On the other hand, experimental work should be judged mainly from the point of view of the precision of the instruments of measurement. The conditions under which the test has been conducted should also be considered, and in the case of laboratory work it should be noted how closely the service conditions have been reproduced. The engineer must also be careful in avoiding extrapolation of the conclusions to cases outside the field investigated.

The mathematical approach to the solution of physical problems may in some instances lose contact with reality. It is interesting to quote here the criticism of this approach made by a French professor, who writes:*

> Mathematicians have ruined everything, overflowing their unique stupidity on those sciences which are the strangest to their usual business. The mathematician is horrified by reality . . . he sacrifices common sense. To generalize, he reduces nature to schemes . . . vacuum is his element, form his god . . . . We should develop in our students a flexible mind, we always have time to add the algebra which too often is only the trade of an intelligent technician. It is easier to go wrong looking at an equation than looking at the phenomenon it represents.

Others go to the opposite extreme in this way of thinking: for them, there is no other way of doing research than by experimentation. "The word experiment is so fundamental in the field of research as to form both the basis and the definition of it . . . research consists essentially in experimentation," says T. A. Boyd.† Henri Poincaré had already written something similar: "The experiment is the only source of truth; only experiments can teach us something new; only they can give us certitude. Those two points nobody can argue."‡ Frank B. Jewett is quoted by Boyd as saying: "All human progress in the arts has necessarily been the results of experiment."† This mistrust of logic is widespread in the United States. The former vice-president of General Motors, Charles F. Kettering, reminded engineers in a speech a few years ago: "The inventor should beware of logic, because logic is an organized form of going wrong with confidence."

The dangers threatening the experimental mind are not smaller than those threatening the logical mind. Robert Hutchins, former president

---

*H. Bouasse, "Théorie de l'élasticité. Résistance des matériaux," p. xi, Delagrave, Paris, 1920.

†T. A. Boyd, "Research, the Pathfinder of Science and Industry," p. 6, Appleton-Century-Crofts, Inc., New York, 1935.

‡Henri Poincaré, "Science et hypothèse," p. 167, E. Flammarion, Paris, 1905.

of the University of Chicago, tells the following anecdote in one of his contributions to the study of education in the United States:†

Everything that goes by the name of science does not deserve the reverence we pay it. Take, for example, the striking conclusions of the paper read at the last meeting of the American Association for the Advancement of Science . . . . According to *Science* [the author of the research] found that early in the winter, trees prevent snow from reaching the ground. He also discovered that snow in the forest lasted from one to three weeks longer than it does in the open.

One of the instructors at the Massachusetts Institute of Technology received a report from one of his students in which the student stated: "During the First World War, the proof was made that fliers with a compass could find their way easier than fliers without it." The conclusion is certainly correct, but it seems strange that a war and the "experiment" were necessary to realize it.

The experiment is often so intimately tied to logic that a flaw in the logic may be the cause of a wrong experimental result. Maurois tells in one of his books the following anecdote, popular in Oxford. After drinking whisky and soda, a student observes that his ideas have become confused and that he cannot speak fluently. Another time he drinks gin and soda and experiences the same effects. For the third time he performs the experiment, this time changing gin for brandy. Still his ideas become confused, and still he cannot speak fluently. The conclusion is obvious. The common element was soda.

Since in France the emphasis has been on theoretical developments and in the United States on experimental analysis, it is symptomatic that a French professor points out the danger of theory disconnected from physical reality and that the president of an American university points out the danger of the lack of logical reasoning.

People who dislike theories make them, however, without knowing it, just as Molière's bourgeois learned he was talking in prose, much to his surprise. Today it is impossible to build without a theory. It may happen, however, that the unconsciously accepted theory is not a good one. Although the number of equations in a book is not a sign of its value, neither is their absence a sign of the author's intelligence.

It is just as difficult today to build without experiments. People who dislike experiments have to rely on them directly or indirectly, at least to validate their assumptions.

Theoretical and Experimental Stress Analysis. There seem to have been three stages in the development of stress-analysis knowledge. The first was an empirical period, when knowledge was obtained by intuition or by rough

†Robert Maynard Hutchins, Education for Freedom. *Harper's Magazine*, vol. 183, p. 513, Oct., 1941.

approximations. The second stage involved the mathematical reasoning of the theory of elasticity. This second stage represents a very important development because theories can "foresee," by setting general laws. This stage could not have been the final one, since the conclusions of theoretical reasoning had to be applied to the physical world. This last stage has been called "experimental stress analysis."

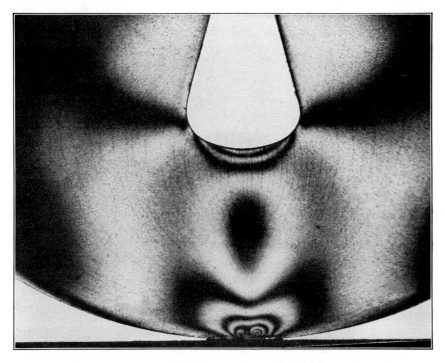

Simultaneous isostatic and isochromatic patterns. All the information necessary to solve completely the stress analysis is contained in this photograph.

From the point of view of intellectual training, it is convenient that a man be in the position of reaching a sound conclusion by theoretical means. From the point of view of the results to be obtained, however, it does not matter whether the conclusion is reached by intuition, by experimenting, or by rigorous calculation. An engineer can design a component by getting approximate formulas from a handbook, or by developing rigorously a theory of elasticity approach, or by using some of the experimental-stress-analysis techniques, or by following a feeling of what is the right shape to be given to a component to make it light and

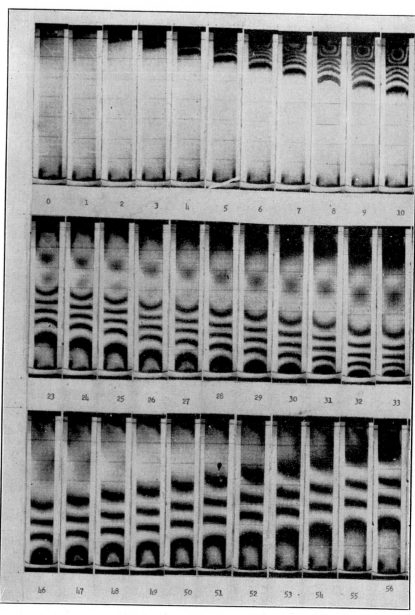

Stress wave propagating along a rectangular bar. Series of photographs of isochromatics produced by a dynamic load acting normal to the top surface of a bar of

urethene rubber (Hysol 8705). The time interval between pictures is **76** microseconds.

strong. Or he may use several of these ways. What is important is that the component be light and strong, and not that the engineer be a good theoretician. It is true, however, that, in today's stage of scientific development, the chances of obtaining a good design are much better when the engineer is a good theoretician.

Today we are witnessing the development of a more synthetic approach to stress-analysis knowledge, in which intuition, reasoning, and experiments are better correlated. None of the three stages can be exclusive. We shall always need the theory of elasticity for the general principles which will permit the complete solution of certain problems and foresee the solution of others. We shall always need experiments to check our theories and to solve problems we have not been able to solve theoretically. Finally, we shall always need intuition, either to discover a mathematical solution or to determine the best way of devising an experiment.

Sometimes experimental developments go ahead of theoretical developments. One instance is in the study of the stress distribution in finite plates produced by triangular or rectangular discontinuities with rounded corners, when the plates are loaded in the plane. Theoretical solution of the case seems difficult; yet it is easily solved by means of photoelasticity. Sometimes theoretical developments go ahead of experimental developments, as, for example, in the study of the distribution of stress around circular holes in infinite plates loaded in the plane. Kirsch obtained his solution in 1890, much before any experimental tool with enough precision was available. Even today, with the exception of photoelasticity, there is no experimental tool giving results as accurate as those obtained by Kirsch, if we assume the material behaving according to the assumptions of the theory of elasticity.

Often, however, the theoretical assumptions of homogeneity and infinite divisibility of matter do not correspond to the physical behavior of the engineering materials. In a contemplated second volume, without actually going into a detailed analysis of plastic deformations and of theories of failures, attention will be called to the fact that stress analysis is only a step in the prediction of failure conditions, or absence thereof, and apparent inconsistencies between stress-analysis results and failure results, even in brittle materials, will be pointed out.

PART 1

MATHEMATICAL METHOD OF ANALYSIS

CHAPTER 1

THEORY OF STRESS

1.1. Introduction. In this chapter the concept of stress is introduced through a series of definitions which, it is hoped, will conform with intuitive concepts of the term. Once these basic definitions are established, many properties of stress will be logically developed. The reader should attempt to gain primarily, as an end result of reading the chapter, a better intuitive view of the mechanism of stress relations throughout a body and secondarily an understanding, but not necessarily a memorization, of the equations as preparation for developments in the following chapters.

An important notion regarding the range of applicability of the concepts established and developed in the first two chapters is that the discussions are not restricted to elastic bodies or even to solid bodies. Any continuous distribution of matter is acceptable, such as a steel beam, a piece of tar, or a liquid. Major restrictions as to the nature of the material composing the bodies appear in Chap. 4, but in the meantime there is satisfaction in keeping good account of the broad scope of the subject matter and in narrowing it down only when absolutely necessary to permit the mathematical developments to continue.

1.2. Definitions. The objective of this section is to define the terms body forces, surface forces, stresses, normal stresses, and shear stresses and to formulate a means of expressing these quantities mathematically.

For this purpose consider an arbitrarily shaped body (Fig. 1.1), which is subjected to a system of loads indicated schematically by the four unlabeled arrows. No restrictions are necessary on the material or materials composing the body except that, as a prerequisite to the mathematics to be used, it be continuous, i.e., no discrete points or sets of points will be supposed to exist in the medium. As a result, the theory to be developed will not provide any information on the complicated load distributions occurring among particles of crystal or molecular size. It can, however, be expected to compare favorably with physical behavior in the sense of "average" load distributions over elements composed of many smaller particles; and experiments which in general only measure "averages" show this to be the case. Hence, the assumption of continuity of matter is an unimportant restriction from the point of view of obtaining practical results.

The system of loads acting on the body will be catalogued into two groups, (1) body forces, which act throughout the body and are not produced by physical contact with other bodies; and (2) surface forces, which act on exterior surfaces of the body and result from contact with matter external to the body.

Body-force intensities will be designated as forces per unit volume. Examples of body forces are those produced by gravitational, electromagnetic, or inertia force fields. Let the x, y, and z components of the body-force intensity be called X, Y, and Z, respectively. If an element of volume ΔV has the resultant forces ΔF_x, ΔF_y, and ΔF_z acting on it in the cartesian directions, the cartesian body-force intensity components acting at a point within ΔV are defined as

$$X = \lim_{\Delta V \to 0} \frac{\Delta F_x}{\Delta V}$$

$$Y = \lim_{\Delta V \to 0} \frac{\Delta F_y}{\Delta V}$$

$$Z = \lim_{\Delta V \to 0} \frac{\Delta F_z}{\Delta V}$$

In the case of surface forces, the distinction between exterior and interior surfaces must be made clear. An exterior surface is any surface comprising a part of the *bounding* surface of the body and includes, for example, the surface surrounding an internal cavity. A case of surface forces acting on such an "exterior" surface is that of gas pressure exerted inside a hollow sphere. In contrast, an interior surface is created only by an imaginary cut through the body and lies, prior to such a cut, entirely inside the boundaries of the body.

The applied loads acting on the exterior surface of the body are described in terms of forces per unit area and, as such, are called applied stresses. The x, y, and z components of the applied stresses acting on the surface at a point P are defined as

$$\bar{X}_n = \lim_{\Delta S \to 0} \frac{\Delta F_x}{\Delta S}$$

$$\bar{Y}_n = \lim_{\Delta S \to 0} \frac{\Delta F_y}{\Delta S}$$

$$\bar{Z}_n = \lim_{\Delta S \to 0} \frac{\Delta F_z}{\Delta S}$$

where ΔF_x, ΔF_y, ΔF_z are the resultant cartesian components of force acting on the element of surface ΔS containing P. These stress components can be represented at the surface point P by vectors having lengths and directions corresponding, respectively, to the magnitudes and directions of the stress components.

Consider now another type of surface forces, viz., those forces acting on imaginary internal surfaces in the body. In general, the function of the theory of elasticity is to mathematically incorporate the loadings on a body with the geometry of the body (and with the properties of the material composing the body, if necessary) so as to obtain a knowledge of these "internal" forces.

Suppose an imaginary cut is taken through the body (Fig. 1.1) and a system of forces, equivalent to the force system acting before the cut was

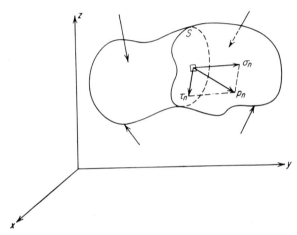

Fig. 1.1. In an arbitrarily shaped body, the resultant of the stresses acting on an element of the internal surface S created by an imaginary cut is shown as a vector p_n. σ_n is the normal component of the stress p_n, acting in the direction of the normal to S; and τ_n is the tangential or shear component of p_n, acting in the plane S.

made, is applied to one of the exposed surfaces. Taken as forces per unit area, these correspond dimensionally to the applied stresses described above and are so treated, even as regards notation; but here they are internal by nature, or "induced stresses," since they are induced throughout the body by the applied stresses on the external surfaces and by the body forces. The three cartesian components p_{nx}, p_{ny}, and p_{nz} of these stresses acting on a small element of area on the surface are defined as†

†This notation scheme will be carried throughout the text; all stresses will be represented by lower-case symbols having, as a first subscript, a letter denoting the direction of the outer normal to the plane on which they act and, as a second subscript, a letter giving the direction along which the stresses act. In this case, n is used as a first subscript to signify the normal to an arbitrarily oriented surface element. An exception to this rule is the case of applied stresses which are shown above as $\bar{X}_n$, $\bar{Y}_n$, $\bar{Z}_n$.

$$p_{nx} = \lim_{\Delta S \to 0} \frac{\Delta F_x}{\Delta S}$$

$$p_{ny} = \lim_{\Delta S \to 0} \frac{\Delta F_y}{\Delta S}$$

$$p_{nz} = \lim_{S \to 0} \frac{\Delta F_z}{\Delta S}$$

Their resultant will be called p_n, and its magnitude and direction can be obtained from the following (see Fig. 1.2).[†]

$$p_n = \sqrt{p_{nx}^2 + p_{ny}^2 + p_{nz}^2}$$

$$\cos (p_n, x) = \frac{p_{nx}}{p_n}$$

$$\cos (p_n, y) = \frac{p_{ny}}{p_n} \qquad (1.1)$$

$$\cos (p_n, z) = \frac{p_{nz}}{p_n}$$

The resultant stress can also be broken down into two components, one normal to the plane (denoted by σ_n and called a normal stress [‡]) and one parallel to the plane (denoted by τ_n and called a shear stress). Since σ_n is the projection of p_n onto the normal direction, its magnitude is given by

$$\sigma_n = p_n \cos (p_n, n)$$

where $\cos (p_n, n)$, by the established convention, is the cosine of the angle between the directions of p_n and n.

A useful rule which will be repeatedly used in the first few chapters can be now applied, namely, that the cosine of an angle between two lines is the sum of the pairwise products of the direction cosines of the two lines,[¶] thus:

$$\cos (p_n, n) = \cos (p_n, x) \cos (n, x) + \cos (p_n, y) \cos (n, y)$$

$$+ \cos (p_n, z) \cos (n, z) \qquad (1.2)$$

Substituting this into the above equation for σ_n and using Eqs. (1.1), the normal stress is seen to be

$$\sigma_n = p_{nx} \cos (n, x) + p_{ny} \cos (n, y) + p_{nz} \cos (n, z) \qquad (1.3)$$

[†] $\cos (p_n, x)$ is the cosine of the angle between the positive direction of p_n and the x axis. This convention for cosine notations will be used throughout.

[‡] σ_n and τ_n are, more accurately, stress "components" of p_n; however, after the introductory paragraphs, the discussion will center almost completely around stress components and not the resultant stress p_n; thus, it will be convenient to drop the term component whenever no confusion arises in so doing.

[¶] See R. Courant, "Differential and Integral Calculus," vol. II, p. 12, Interscience Publishers, Inc., New York, 1936.

The magnitude of the shear stress can be determined from the relation

$$\tau_n^2 + \sigma_n^2 = p_n^2 \tag{1.4}$$

Figure 1.2 indicates the three described methods of representing the stress acting on the surface element.

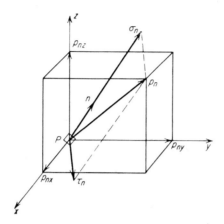

FIG. 1.2. Three methods of representing the stress acting on a surface element with outer normal n. The direction and magnitude of the resultant stress p_n; its components σ_n and τ_n in the directions normal and tangential to the surface; or its components p_{nx}, p_{ny}, p_{nz} in the cartesian directions can be given.

1.3. The Nine Cartesian Stress Components: Notation and Sign Conventions. Suppose a cut through the body is taken parallel to one of the cartesian planes, say, the yz plane (Fig. 1.3). The cartesian stress components at a point P on the exposed surface can be designated p_{xx}, p_{xy}, and p_{xz}, where the first subscript is changed from n to x since the x axis is parallel to the direction of the normal to the plane. These stress components are normal and shear stresses; hence they can be replaced by the σ and τ notation. In the case of normal stresses, the two subscripts are identical and are replaced by single ones, i.e.,

$$p_{xx} = p_x = \sigma_{xx} = \sigma_x$$

On the surface facing the negative x direction there are similarly three cartesian stress components, which by Newton's third law are equal in magnitude but opposite in sense to those on the opposite surface. These are shown in Fig. 1.3 as dotted arrows and are given symbols identical to their opposites.

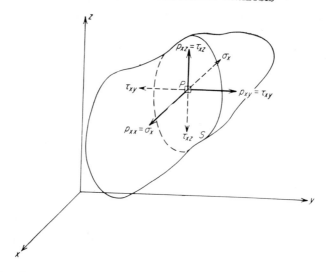

FIG. 1.3. Imaginary surface S taken parallel to the yz plane. On this surface, there are three cartesian components of the resultant stress, identified by σ_x, τ_{xy}, and τ_{xz}.

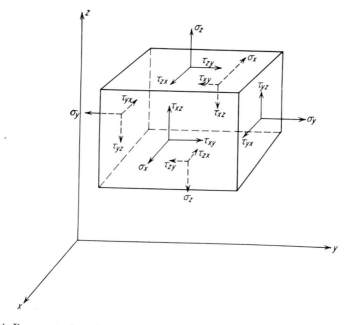

FIG. 1.4. Representation of the cartesian components of stress occurring at a point P on planes parallel to the cartesian planes. All the stresses, as shown, are considered positive.

If the surfaces parallel to the other cartesian planes are examined, two figures similar to Fig. 1.3 can be drawn and the results summed up in a composite picture (Fig. 1.4) by using a rectangular parallelepiped which is imagined to be entirely located at P. The stresses as drawn are considered positive.

A summary of the rules of notation and sign conventions is as follows:

The normal stresses σ_x, σ_y, σ_z are considered positive when directed outward from the surface and negative when directed inward to the surface. Positive normal stresses are called tensile stresses, and negative ones are called compressive stresses. This terminology and sign convention applies to all normal stresses regardless of the orientation of the surfaces on which they act.

The shear stresses τ_{xy}, τ_{yx}, τ_{yz}, τ_{zy}, τ_{zx}, and τ_{xz} are positive when directed in a positive cartesian direction while acting on a plane whose outer normal points in a positive cartesian direction, or when directed in a negative cartesian direction while acting on a plane whose outer normal points in a negative cartesian direction. They are negative if their sense is reversed from these directions. This sign convention, unlike that for the normal stresses, is meaningful only when planes parallel to coordinate planes are being considered.

The subscripts for the shear stresses follow the rule that the first subscript denotes the direction of the outer normal to the plane on which the stress acts, and the second subscript denotes the direction toward which the stress acts.

In the case of normal stresses, a single subscript is used. This denotes both the outer normal to the plane on which the stress acts and the direction in which it acts. Occasionally, when no confusion will arise, this subscript will be dropped in the case of stresses acting on the general oblique plane with outer normal n. Right-handed coordinate systems will be employed throughout.

1.4. The State of Stress at a Point. One cannot ask for the stress at a given point in the body since, as has been seen, there are an infinite number of stresses in existence at any point, one resultant stress corresponding to each distinctly inclined plane passing through the point. The request must be made for either the stress at the point which acts on a given plane through the point or for the "state of stress" at the point, i.e., for the stresses acting on all planes. Both of these requests can be answered very simply if the stresses at the point which act on the planes parallel to the cartesian coordinate planes are known. This will be shown next.

Suppose that the nine cartesian stress components σ_x, σ_y, σ_z, τ_{xy}, τ_{yx}, τ_{yz}, τ_{zy}, τ_{zx}, τ_{xz} are known at point P, and it is desired to find the stresses acting on the surface through P whose outer normal n has the direction cosines cos (n,x), cos (n,y), cos (n,z). Let the surface ABC in Fig. 1.5 be such a surface, and let P be so placed that points A, B, C, and P form a tetrahedron with three sides parallel to the three coordinate planes. All

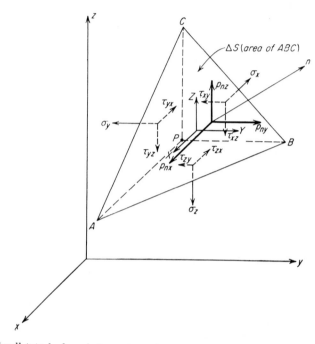

Fig. 1.5. Small tetrahedronal element cut from the body at P with all acting stresses. The condition of equilibrium with respect to forces in the three coordinate directions allows determination of the three stresses p_{nx}, p_{ny}, and p_{nz}, in terms of the cartesian components of stresses acting on the planes parallel to the coordinate planes, the body-force-intensity components, and the direction cosines of the normal n.

the cartesian stress components acting on the tetrahedronal element are shown: the nine components acting on APB, APC, and BPC, the body-force-field-intensity cartesian components, and the unknown stress on the side ABC (given here by its three cartesian components).

If the tetrahedron considered is very small, the stresses can be supposed to act uniformly over their respective sides and the body-force field can also be assumed constant throughout the element. If ΔS is the area of side ABC, the x component of force acting on the side BCP is given by $\sigma_x \Delta S \cos (n,x)$. Other force components in the x direction can be similarly written. The x component of the body-force field is $X \Delta S\, h/3$, where $\Delta S\, h/3$ is the volume of the tetrahedron and h is the perpendicular distance from P to the side ABC. These forces acting in the x direction must be in equilibrium so that

$$p_{nx} \, \Delta S + \frac{X \, \Delta S \, h}{3} = \sigma_x \, \Delta S \, \cos (n,x) + \tau_{yx} \, \Delta S \, \cos (n,y) + \tau_{zx} \, \Delta S \, \cos (n,z)$$

ΔS is common to all terms and can be canceled. It is further possible to neglect the term involving $\Delta S \, h$ as compared with all other terms in the equation because the tetrahedron is small. This gives the first of the equations below, the second and third being obtainable from similar force summations in the y and z directions.†

$$p_{nx} = \sigma_x \, \cos (n,x) + \tau_{yx} \, \cos (n,y) + \tau_{zx} \, \cos (n,z)$$

$$p_{ny} = \tau_{xy} \, \cos (n,x) + \sigma_y \, \cos (n,y) + \tau_{zy} \, \cos (n,z) \qquad (1.5)$$

$$p_{nz} = \tau_{xz} \, \cos (n,x) + \tau_{yz} \, \cos (n,y) + \sigma_z \, \cos (n,z)$$

These equations completely characterize the state of stress at a point in terms of the nine cartesian stress components.

Without too much additional trouble, these equations can be derived by using a tetrahedron of finite size on which the stresses and body-force intensities are allowed to vary over the surfaces or volume on which they act.‡ The element is shrunk down to zero size after the equations of equilibrium are written.

1.5. The Equations of Equilibrium. Leaving temporarily the analysis of the stresses at a single point, an investigation will be made of the equilibrium conditions that must exist for the entire stress field in the body. The derivation will be simple, and the reader who seeks more elaborate reasoning is referred to texts on the theory of elasticity.¶ The results obtained here are of course identical to those developed through the use of more rigorous mathematical methods.

Suppose a rectangular parallelepiped with edges dx, dy, and dz parallel to the coordinate axes is cut from the body at point $P(x,y,z)$ (Fig. 1.6), and the stresses and body forces acting on the element before its removal are restored.

The element is assumed to be small so that these loadings are essentially uniform and representable in the first approximation by single average

†It will be noticed that the second and third of Eqs. (1.5) can be obtained from the first through a cyclic permutation, i.e., advancing x to y, y to z, and z to x. Most equations in the theory in the first few chapters will be seen to appear in sets of three where this rule applies.

‡I. S. Sokolnikoff, "Mathematical Theory of Elasticity," 1st ed., p. 39, McGraw-Hill Book Company, Inc., New York, 1946.

¶*Ibid.*, pp. 41–43. Also, A. E. H. Love, "A Treatise on the Mathematical Theory of Elasticity," p. 84, 4th ed., Dover Publications, New York, 1944.

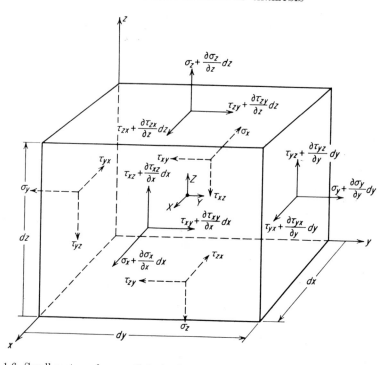

Fig. 1.6. Small rectangular parallelepiped removed from the body at point P for the purpose of establishing the equations of equilibrium. Stresses and body forces acting on the element and the variations of the stresses across the element are shown.

loads in the center of their areas of application. The differences between the loads on opposite sides of the element are increments $(\partial \sigma_x / \partial x)\, dx, \cdots$.

Consider the following six conditions of equilibrium:

$$\sum F_x = 0$$
$$\sum F_y = 0$$
$$\sum F_z = 0$$
$$\sum M_x = 0 \qquad (1.6)$$
$$\sum M_y = 0$$
$$\sum M_z = 0$$

Applying the first condition to the parallelepiped, one obtains

$$\sum F_x = \left(\sigma_x + \frac{\partial \sigma_x}{\partial x}\, dx \right) dy\, dz - \sigma_x\, dy\, dz + \left(\tau_{yx} + \frac{\partial \tau_{yx}}{\partial y}\, dy \right) dz\, dx$$

$$- \tau_{yx}\, dz\, dx + \left(\tau_{zx} + \frac{\partial \tau_{zx}}{\partial z}\, dz \right) dx\, dy - \tau_{zx}\, dx\, dy + X\, dx\, dy\, dz = 0$$

After some cancellations and division by $dx\,dy\,dz$, the first of the following three equations is obtained. The second and third conditions of equilibrium lead to the other two equations.

$$\frac{\partial \sigma_x}{\partial x} + \frac{\partial \tau_{yx}}{\partial y} + \frac{\partial \tau_{zx}}{\partial z} + X = 0$$

$$\frac{\partial \tau_{xy}}{\partial x} + \frac{\partial \sigma_y}{\partial y} + \frac{\partial \tau_{zy}}{\partial z} + Y = 0 \qquad (1.7)$$

$$\frac{\partial \tau_{xz}}{\partial x} + \frac{\partial \tau_{yz}}{\partial y} + \frac{\partial \sigma_z}{\partial z} + Z = 0$$

These are called the equations of equilibrium and are "field" equations in the sense that they connect the stresses from point to point. The nine cartesian stress components that vary continuously from point to point must, in a solution to any problem, satisfy the three above conditions. Note again that, as in Eqs. (1.5), successive equations in Eqs. (1.7) can be obtained through cyclic permutation of x, y, and z.

1.6. Equality of Shear Stresses on Perpendicular Planes. Continuing the analysis of equilibrium of the parallelepiped, the moment equations in Eqs. (1.6) are next applied. Since the parallelepiped is in equilibrium, the sum of the moments taken with respect to any axis is zero. It is slightly more convenient to choose axes parallel to the xyz coordinate axes shown in Fig. 1.6 and which pass through the center of the parallelepiped.

The axis parallel to the x axis is considered first:

$$\sum M_x = \tau_{yz}\,dx\,dz\,\frac{dy}{2} + \left(\tau_{yz} + \frac{\partial \tau_{yz}}{\partial y}\,dy\right)dx\,dz\,\frac{dy}{2}$$

$$- \tau_{zy}\,dx\,dy\,\frac{dz}{2} - \left(\tau_{zy} + \frac{\partial \tau_{zy}}{\partial z}\,dz\right)dx\,dy\,\frac{dz}{2} = 0$$

Two pairs of terms combine, and the equation becomes, after division by $dx\,dy\,dz$,

$$\tau_{yz} + \frac{\partial \tau_{yz}}{\partial y}\frac{dy}{2} - \tau_{zy} - \frac{\partial \tau_{zy}}{\partial z}\frac{dz}{2} = 0$$

Since the parallelepiped is very small, the terms involving differentials can be neglected as compared to the terms τ_{yz} and τ_{zy}, so that finally

$$\tau_{yz} = \tau_{zy}$$

Similar treatment of the remaining two moment equations gives two similar conditions; in total

$$\tau_{zy} = \tau_{yz}$$
$$\tau_{yz} = \tau_{zy} \tag{1.8}$$
$$\tau_{zx} = \tau_{xz}$$

Thus, there are three simple relations between the nine cartesian stress components characterizing the state of stress at any point. The order of the indices on the shear stresses can be subsequently regarded as immaterial, with the result that future discussion need only regard six stress components, that is, σ_x, σ_y, σ_z, $\tau_{xy} = \tau_{yx}$, $\tau_{yz} = \tau_{zy}$, $\tau_{zx} = \tau_{xz}$.

1.7. Some Direction-cosine Relationships. Consider the cosines of the nine angles between the axes of two orthogonal coordinate systems $Oxyz$ and $Ox'y'z'$ (Fig. 1.7). By application of the proposition stated by

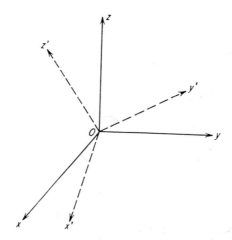

Fig. 1.7. Two orthogonal coordinate systems for which the direction-cosine relations (1.9) and (1.10) hold true.

Eq. (1.2), it can be shown that the direction cosines are connected by six fundamental relations, which are given below for future reference.

$$\cos^2(x,x') + \cos^2(x,y') + \cos^2(x,z') = 1$$
$$\cos^2(y,x') + \cos^2(y,y') + \cos^2(y,z') = 1 \tag{1.9}$$
$$\cos^2(z,x') + \cos^2(z,y') + \cos^2(z,z') = 1$$

$$\cos(x,x')\cos(y,x') + \cos(x,y')\cos(y,y') + \cos(x,z')\cos(y,z') = 0$$
$$\cos(y,x')\cos(z,x') + \cos(y,y')\cos(z,y') + \cos(y,z')\cos(z,z') = 0 \tag{1.10}$$
$$\cos(z,x')\cos(x,x') + \cos(z,y')\cos(x,y') + \cos(z,z')\cos(x,z') = 0$$

1.8. The Laws of Stress Transformation.   Equations (1.5) are restrictive in the sense that they give only the cartesian components of the stresses acting on the inclined plane, that is, p_{nx}, p_{ny}, p_{nz}.   Another useful triad of stress components on this plane, the normal-stress component and two mutually perpendicular shear-stress components, can be obtained as functions of σ_x, σ_y, σ_z, τ_{xy}, τ_{yz}, τ_{zx}.

Let a new orthogonal coordinate system $O'x'y'z'$ be placed with origin at P having the x' axis coincident with the normal n to the plane and the y' and z' axes (which must run parallel to the plane with normal n) coincident with the directions of the desired shear stresses.   Such a coordinate system is shown in Fig. 1.8, where again, as in Fig. 1.5, the plane ABC is imagined to pass through point P since the tetrahedron is very small.   By the previously established rules of notation, the required

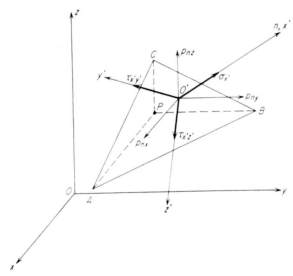

FIG. 1.8. Small tetrahedronal element cut from the body at P.   The three mutually perpendicular stress components $\sigma_{x'}$, $\tau_{x'y'}$, $\tau_{x'z'}$ acting on the inclined plane are shown. The laws of stress transformation [Eqs. (1.12)] give these in terms of σ_x, σ_y, σ_z, τ_{xy}, τ_{yz}, τ_{zx}. The figure is comparable with Fig. 1.5, where the arrangement was for the determination of the triad of stresses p_{nx}, p_{ny}, p_{nz}.

stresses, shown by heavy lines in the figure, can be denoted by $\sigma_{x'}$, $\tau_{x'y'}$, and $\tau_{x'z'}$; for example, $\tau_{x'y'}$ is the shear stress directed in the y' direction and acting on a plane through P whose normal is directed in the x' direction.

Since the normal direction coincides with the x' direction, Eqs. (1.5) can be rewritten as follows:

$$p_{nx} = \sigma_x \; \cos{(x',x)} + \tau_{yx} \cos{(x',y)} + \tau_{zx} \cos{(x',z)}$$

$$p_{ny} = \tau_{xy} \cos{(x',x)} + \sigma_y \; \cos{(x',y)} + \tau_{zy} \cos{(x',z)} \qquad (1.11)$$

$$p_{nz} = \tau_{xz} \cos{(x',x)} + \tau_{yz} \cos{(x',y)} + \sigma_z \; \cos{(x',z)}$$

The stress $\sigma_{x'}$ must be equal to the sum of the projections of p_{nx}, p_{ny}, and p_{nz} onto the x' axis,

$$\sigma_{x'} = p_{nx} \cos{(x',x)} + p_{ny} \cos{(x',y)} + p_{nz} \cos{(x',z)}$$

Similarly

$$\tau_{x'y'} = p_{nx} \cos{(y',x)} + p_{ny} \cos{(y',y)} + p_{nz} \cos{(y',z)}$$

When Eqs. (1.11) and (1.8) are substituted into these, Eqs. (1.12a) and (1.12d) below are obtained. The remaining four equations can be derived in an entirely similar way by using two more tetrahedrons with inclined planes having outer normals parallel to the y' and z' axes.

$$\sigma_{x'} = \sigma_x \cos^2{(x',x)} + \sigma_y \cos^2{(x',y)} + \sigma_z \cos^2{(x',z)}$$
$$+ 2\tau_{xy} \cos{(x',x)} \cos{(x',y)} + 2\tau_{yz} \cos{(x',y)} \cos{(x',z)}$$
$$+ 2\tau_{zx} \cos{(x',z)} \cos{(x',x)} \qquad (1.12a)$$

$$\sigma_{y'} = \sigma_y \cos^2{(y',y)} + \sigma_z \cos^2{(y',z)} + \sigma_x \cos^2{(y',x)}$$
$$+ 2\tau_{yz} \cos{(y',y)} \cos{(y',z)} + 2\tau_{zx} \cos{(y',z)} \cos{(y',x)}$$
$$+ 2\tau_{xy} \cos{(y',x)} \cos{(y',y)} \qquad (1.12b)$$

$$\sigma_{z'} = \sigma_z \cos^2{(z',z)} + \sigma_x \cos^2{(z',x)} + \sigma_y \cos^2{(z',y)}$$
$$+ 2\tau_{zx} \cos{(z',z)} \cos{(z',x)} + 2\tau_{xy} \cos{(z',x)} \cos{(z',y)}$$
$$+ 2\tau_{yz} \cos{(z',y)} \cos{(z',z)} \qquad (1.12c)$$

$$\tau_{x'y'} = \sigma_x \cos{(x',x)} \cos{(y',x)} + \sigma_y \cos{(x',y)} \cos{(y',y)}$$
$$+ \sigma_z \cos{(x',z)} \cos{(y',z)}$$
$$+ \tau_{xy}[\cos{(x',x)} \cos{(y',y)} + \cos{(x',y)} \cos{(y',x)}]$$
$$+ \tau_{yz}[\cos{(x',y)} \cos{(y',z)} + \cos{(x',z)} \cos{(y',y)}]$$
$$+ \tau_{zx}[\cos{(x',z)} \cos{(y',x)} + \cos{(x',x)} \cos{(y',z)}] \qquad (1.12d)$$

$$\tau_{y'z'} = \sigma_y \cos{(y',y)} \cos{(z',y)} + \sigma_z \cos{(y',z)} \cos{(z',z)}$$
$$+ \sigma_x \cos{(y',x)} \cos{(z',x)}$$
$$+ \tau_{yz}[\cos{(y',y)} \cos{(z',z)} + \cos{(y',z)} \cos{(z',y)}]$$
$$+ \tau_{zx}[\cos{(y',z)} \cos{(z',x)} + \cos{(y',x)} \cos{(z',z)}]$$
$$+ \tau_{xy}[\cos{(y',x)} \cos{(z',y)} + \cos{(y',y)} \cos{(z',x)}] \qquad (1.12e)$$

$$\tau_{z'x'} = \sigma_z \cos(z',z) \cos(x',z) + \sigma_x \cos(z',x) \cos(x',x)$$

$$+ \sigma_y \cos(z',y) \cos(x',y)$$

$$+ \tau_{zx}[\cos(z',z) \cos(x',x) + \cos(z',x) \cos(x',z)]$$

$$+ \tau_{xy}[\cos(z',x) \cos(x',y) + \cos(z',y) \cos(x',x)]$$

$$+ \tau_{yz}[\cos(z',y) \cos(x',z) + \cos(z',z) \cos(x',y)] \qquad (1.12f)$$

It is important to note again the meaning of these equations. Equation (1.12d), for instance, can be used to find the shear stress acting in the y' direction on a surface having an outer normal directed in the x' direction if the six cartesian stress components σ_x, σ_y, σ_z, τ_{xy}, τ_{yz}, τ_{zx} at the point and the orientation of the coordinate system $O'x'y'z'$ are known. These equations will play a part in future developments and are therefore written out in full for reference.

1.9. Principal Stresses, Planes, and Directions: Definitions and Properties. Equations (1.5) or (1.12) describe the state of stress at a point. Some important consequences of these stress-transformation laws will be studied in this section. The derivation will be analytical, although conclusions, identical to those to be established here, are easily seen from geometrical representations of the equations. The reader who is more receptive to visual aids in understanding is referred to Chap. 3.

Consider the laws (1.12) which give the normal and shear stresses on an arbitrary plane. If the six cartesian stress components at the point are known, consider the question of whether or not there exist planes on which the shear stresses are zero, or, stated in another way, whether or not planes exist on which the total resultant stress acting is a normal stress.

If there are such planes, the resultant normal stress acting on each of them must possess the property that its x, y, and z components are, respectively, equal to p_{nx}, p_{ny}, and p_{nz} (see, for instance, Fig. 1.2 for $\tau_n = 0$ and $p_n = \sigma_n$). For convenience in distinguishing these "special" planes from all others, let the direction cosines of their outer normals be designated by $\cos(n_i,x)$, $\cos(n_i,y)$, and $\cos(n_i,z)$ and the normal stresses acting on them by σ_i. The above property can be stated in terms of these symbols as

$$\sigma_i \cos(n_i,x) = p_{ix}$$

$$\sigma_i \cos(n_i,y) = p_{iy} \qquad (1.13)$$

$$\sigma_i \cos(n_i,z) = p_{iz}$$

Substituting Eqs. (1.5) into these and rearranging,

$$(\sigma_x - \sigma_i) \cos (n_i,x) + \tau_{yx} \cos (n_i,y) + \tau_{zx} \cos (n_i,z) = 0$$

$$\tau_{xy} \cos (n_i,x) + (\sigma_y - \sigma_i) \cos (n_i,y) + \tau_{zy} \cos (n_i,z) = 0 \qquad (1.14)$$

$$\tau_{xz} \cos (n_i,x) + \tau_{yz} \cos (n_i,y) + (\sigma_z - \sigma_i) \cos (n_i,z) = 0$$

It can be shown[†] that a nontrivial solution for the three unknowns $\cos (n_i,x)$, $\cos (n_i,y)$, $\cos (n_i,z)$ can exist only if the determinant of their coefficients is zero, i.e.,

$$\begin{vmatrix} \sigma_x - \sigma_i & \tau_{yx} & \tau_{zx} \\ \tau_{xy} & \sigma_y - \sigma_i & \tau_{zy} \\ \tau_{xz} & \tau_{yz} & \sigma_z - \sigma_i \end{vmatrix} = 0 \qquad (1.15)$$

The problem now becomes that of determining whether or not there exist any values of σ_i that satisfy Eq. (1.15). If there are such values, then Eqs. (1.14) can be solved for the direction cosines corresponding to each of them; and the original question, as to the possibility of existence of planes free from shear stresses, is answered.

Expanding Eq. (1.15),

$$\sigma_i^3 - (\sigma_x + \sigma_y + \sigma_z)\sigma_i^2$$
$$+ (\sigma_x\sigma_y + \sigma_y\sigma_z + \sigma_z\sigma_x - \tau_{xy}^2 - \tau_{yz}^2 - \tau_{zx}^2)\sigma_i$$
$$- (\sigma_x\sigma_y\sigma_z - \sigma_x\tau_{yz}^2 - \sigma_y\tau_{zx}^2 - \sigma_z\tau_{xy}^2 + 2\tau_{xy}\tau_{yz}\tau_{zx}) = 0 \qquad (1.16)$$

As a side note it is interesting to take cognizance of the two-dimensional counterpart of this equation by setting all the z stress components equal to zero. The three roots (call them σ_1, σ_2, and σ_3) become

$$\sigma_1, \sigma_2 = \frac{\sigma_x + \sigma_y}{2} \pm \sqrt{\left(\frac{\sigma_x - \sigma_y}{2}\right)^2 + \tau_{xy}^2}$$

$$\sigma_3 = 0 \qquad (1.17)$$

The expression for σ_1 and σ_2 is seen to be the familiar equation encountered in the field of elementary strength of materials for the determination of the normal stresses acting on shear-free planes.

Going back to the general three-dimensional problem, it is necessary now to check whether or not the roots σ_1, σ_2, σ_3 are real numbers in Eq. (1.16). One root is seen to be real from the following considerations: The left-hand side becomes positive if σ_i is taken as a large enough positive number and negative if σ_i is taken as a large enough negative number. Hence, there must exist at least one real value of σ_i that will make the

†Courant, *op. cit.*, vol. II, p. 23.

left-hand side zero; i.e., there exists one real value of σ_i which will satisfy the equation. Call this root σ_3.

To determine whether the remaining two roots are real, suppose the analysis beginning with Eqs. (1.14) is repeated using a new coordinate system $O'x'y'z'$, so chosen that the z' axis coincides with the line of action of the normal stress σ_3, just shown to be real; that is, $\sigma_{z'} = \sigma_3$ and $\tau_{y'z'} = \tau_{z'x'} = 0$. Equations (1.14) become

$$(\sigma_{x'} - \sigma_i) \cos(n_i, x') + \tau_{y'x'} \cos(n_i, y') = 0$$

$$\tau_{x'y'} \cos(n_i, x') + (\sigma_{y'} - \sigma_i) \cos(n_i, y') = 0$$

$$(\sigma_{z'} - \sigma_i) \cos(n_i, z') = 0$$

As before, a nontrivial solution for the direction cosines can exist only if

$$\begin{vmatrix} \sigma_{x'} - \sigma_i & \tau_{y'x'} & 0 \\ \tau_{x'y'} & \sigma_{y'} - \sigma_i & 0 \\ 0 & 0 & \sigma_{z'} - \sigma_i \end{vmatrix} = 0$$

or

$$(\sigma_{z'} - \sigma_i)[\sigma_i^2 - (\sigma_{x'} + \sigma_{y'})\sigma_i + (\sigma_{x'}\sigma_{y'} - \tau_{x'y'}^2)] = 0$$

One root of this equation is $\sigma_{z'} = \sigma_3$ as would be expected. The remaining roots are

$$\sigma_1, \sigma_2 = \frac{\sigma_{x'} + \sigma_{y'}}{2} \pm \sqrt{\frac{(\sigma_{x'} - \sigma_{y'})^2}{4} + \tau_{x'y'}^2} \qquad (1.18)$$

These are clearly real, since the discriminant cannot be negative.

All three roots of Eq. (1.16) are therefore real, and it can be concluded that there is associated with every state of stress at a point, a possibility of three, but not more than three, distinct normal stresses occurring on planes free from shear stresses. These stresses are called *principal stresses*; the planes on which they act are called *principal planes*; and the directions of the outer normals to these principal planes are called *principal directions*. It will next be shown that there can always be found a set of three mutually perpendicular principal directions for any given state of stress. Equations (1.3) and (1.5) can be combined to the form,

$$\sigma_n = \sigma_x \cos^2(n, x) + \sigma_y \cos^2(n, y) + \sigma_z \cos^2(n, z)$$

$$+ 2\tau_{xy} \cos(n, x) \cos(n, y) + 2\tau_{yz} \cos(n, y) \cos(n, z) \qquad (a)$$

$$+ 2\tau_{zz} \cos(n, z) \cos(n, x)$$

Consider now a quadric surface which has the property that the length of a line OP, parallel to the normal direction n and extending from the origin

O of the $Oxyz$ coordinate system to a point P on the surface, is equal to the reciprocal of the square root of the absolute value of the stress σ_n; i.e.,

$$OP = \frac{1}{\sqrt{|\sigma_n|}}$$

The coordinates of point P are

$$x = OP \cos (n,x)$$

$$y = OP \cos (n,y)$$

$$z = OP \cos (n,z)$$

If the direction cosines in these equations and the value

$$\sigma_n = \pm \frac{1}{(OP)^2}$$

are substituted into Eq. (a), the result is

$$\sigma_x x^2 + \sigma_y y^2 + \sigma_z z^2 + 2\tau_{xy}xy + 2\tau_{yz}yz + 2\tau_{zx}zx = \pm 1 \qquad (b)$$

This represents a particular quadric surface for any given state of stress. If the coordinate system is rotated, the coefficients (i.e., the stresses) will change; but, of course, the states of stress and the quadric are unaltered. A well-known theorem in the geometry of surfaces† states that it is always possible, in the case of such a general second-degree quadratic surface, to find an orthogonal coordinate system such that the coefficients of the last three terms in Eq. (b) become zero. This is equivalent to stating that there always exists an orthogonal coordinate system, say $Ox'y'z'$, such that the shear stresses $\tau_{x'y'}$, $\tau_{y'z'}$, $\tau_{z'x'}$ are zero. The coordinate axes Ox', Oy', Oz' are principal directions by the above definition; and the associated coordinate system is called a *principal coordinate system*.

The next section outlines the method of determining the principal directions after calculating the principal stresses from Eq. (1.16).

Three cases arise regarding the roots of Eq. (1.16). They can be visualized readily in Sec. 3.5, where further analysis of the quadric surface is made; at this time, they are just discussed.

Case 1. If the three roots of Eq. (1.16) have distinct values ($\sigma_1 \neq \sigma_2$, $\sigma_2 \neq \sigma_3$, $\sigma_3 \neq \sigma_1$), the three corresponding principal stresses occur on a single set of mutually perpendicular principal planes. This case is illustrated in Fig. 1.9a. In this case, there are shear stresses on all planes having orientations different from those of the planes shown.

Case 2. If two of the three roots of Eq. (1.16) are equal (say $\sigma_1 \neq \sigma_2 = \sigma_3$), *all* planes perpendicular to the principal planes on which σ_1

†See C. Smith, "Solid Geometry," p. 47, Macmillan and Co., Ltd., London, 1946.

acts are principal planes acted on by the principal stress $\sigma_2 = \sigma_3$. Figure 1.9b schematically represents this case.

Case 3. If the three roots of Eq. (1.16) are equal (say $\sigma_1 = \sigma_2 = \sigma_3 = \sigma_n$), every plane is a principal plane acted on by the principal stress σ_n. This state of stress, Fig. 1.9c, in which no shear stresses act on any plane, is called hydrostatic, and is encountered chiefly in the field of fluid mechanics.

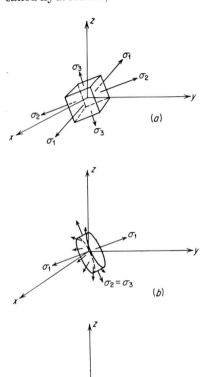

FIG. 1.9. Schematic representation of principal planes existing at a point. Three cases:

(a) $\sigma_1 \neq \sigma_2$, $\sigma_2 \neq \sigma_3$, $\sigma_3 \neq \sigma_1$
(b) $\sigma_1 \neq \sigma_2 = \sigma_3$.
(c) $\sigma_1 = \sigma_2 = \sigma_3 = \sigma_n$

1.10. Principal Stresses, Planes, and Directions: Method of Determination. When the cartesian stress components at a point are known and it is desired to obtain the principal stresses and directions (the latter determine the principal planes), the following procedure can be used:

The three roots of Eq. (1.16) are first calculated. If they are equal, there is no calculation required because, as stated in Case 3, the cartesian stress components would have been $\sigma_x = \sigma_y = \sigma_z = \sigma_n$, $\tau_{xy} = \tau_{yz} = \tau_{zx} = 0$, and the state of stress would have been known to be hydrostatic. If two roots are equal, it is necessary only to substitute the third unequal root in Eqs. (1.14) to obtain the principal direction corresponding to it, for, by Case 2, all other directions perpendicular to the calculated one are principal. If all three roots are different, it is necessary to determine only two of the three principal directions, and the third, by Case 1, is perpendicular to these two.

The method of obtaining any one principal direction corresponding to a particular principal stress is as follows: Suppose that a particular value of σ_i (say, σ_1), as calculated from Eq. (1.16), is substituted into Eqs. (1.14). The three unknowns, $\cos(n_1,x)$, $\cos(n_1,y)$, and $\cos(n_1,z)$, are determined by using Eq. (1.16) in its determinant form

$$\begin{vmatrix} \sigma_x - \sigma_1 & \tau_{yx} & \tau_{zx} \\ \tau_{xy} & \sigma_y - \sigma_1 & \tau_{zy} \\ \tau_{xz} & \tau_{yz} & \sigma_z - \sigma_1 \end{vmatrix} = 0$$

Calling

$$A = \begin{vmatrix} \sigma_y - \sigma_1 & \tau_{zy} \\ \tau_{yz} & \sigma_z - \sigma_1 \end{vmatrix} \qquad B = - \begin{vmatrix} \tau_{xy} & \tau_{zy} \\ \tau_{xz} & \sigma_z - \sigma_1 \end{vmatrix} \qquad C = \begin{vmatrix} \tau_{xy} & \sigma_y - \sigma_1 \\ \tau_{xz} & \tau_{yz} \end{vmatrix}$$

the nontrivial solution of Eqs. (1.14) can be written as

$$\frac{\cos(n_1,x)}{A} = \frac{\cos(n_1,y)}{B} = \frac{\cos(n_1,z)}{C} = K \qquad (1.19)$$

where K is a constant (not zero) to be determined. This can be verified by direct substitution into Eqs. (1.14). There will result three equations in terms of the stresses which will be seen by inspection to reduce to the identities $0 = 0$. The subsidiary condition [see Eqs. (1.9)]

$$\cos^2(n_1,x) + \cos^2(n_1,y) + \cos^2(n_1,z) = 1$$

determines K, since by Eq. (1.19) it becomes

$$A^2 K^2 + B^2 K^2 + C^2 K^2 = 1$$

or

$$K = \pm \frac{1}{\sqrt{A^2 + B^2 + C^2}}$$

Thus,

$$\cos(n_1,x) = \frac{A}{\sqrt{A^2 + B^2 + C^2}} \qquad \cos(n_1,y) = \frac{B}{\sqrt{A^2 + B^2 + C^2}}$$

$$\cos(n_1,z) = \frac{C}{\sqrt{A^2 + B^2 + C^2}}$$

(1.20)

These are the three direction cosines of the outer normal to the plane on which the principal stress σ_1 acts. The plus sign in front of the radical is chosen since the negative sign merely indicates a normal of opposite sense, and it is known that opposite planes have identical stresses acting on them.

When $\sigma_z = \tau_{yz} = \tau_{zz} = 0$, the stress system is called a two-dimensional, or plane-stress, system. It is so commonly encountered that it is considered useful to rewrite the equations of this section for this specific case. If the principal direction corresponding to, say, σ_1 is to be determined, Eqs. (1.20) reduce to

$$\cos(n_1, x) = \frac{\sigma_1 - \sigma_y}{\sqrt{(\sigma_1 - \sigma_y)^2 + \tau_{xy}^2}} \tag{1.20a}$$

$$\cos(n_1, y) = \frac{\tau_{xy}}{\sqrt{(\sigma_1 - \sigma_y)^2 + \tau_{xy}^2}} \tag{1.20b}$$

$$\cos(n_1, z) = 0$$

Let the angle $\theta_p = (n_1, x)$, so that

$$\cos(n_1, x) = \cos\theta_p$$

$$\cos(n_1, y) = \cos\left(\frac{\pi}{2} - \theta_p\right) = \sin\theta_p$$

Then, using Eqs. (1.20a) and (1.20b) above,

$$\sin 2\theta_p = 2\sin\theta_p \cos\theta_p$$

$$= 2\frac{\tau_{xy}(\sigma_1 - \sigma_y)}{(\sigma_1 - \sigma_y)^2 + \tau_{xy}^2}$$

The principal stress σ_1 is expressed in terms of the cartesian stresses in Eqs. (1.17). Substitution of this into the above yields, after some algebra,

$$\sin 2\theta_p = \frac{\tau_{xy}}{\sqrt{[(\sigma_x - \sigma_y)/2]^2 + \tau_{xy}^2}} \tag{1.20c}$$

Similarly

$$\cos 2\theta_p = 2\cos^2\theta_p - 1$$

$$= \frac{2(\sigma_1 - \sigma_y)^2}{(\sigma_1 - \sigma_y)^2 + \tau_{xy}^2} - 1$$

$$= \frac{(\sigma_x - \sigma_y)/2}{\sqrt{[(\sigma_x - \sigma_y)/2]^2 + \tau_{xy}^2}} \tag{1.20d}$$

Equations (1.20c) and (1.20d) together combine to give

$$\tan 2\theta_p = \frac{2\tau_{xy}}{\sigma_x - \sigma_y} \qquad (1.20e)$$

Except for a minus sign, Eqs. (1.20e) and (1.20c) compare with Eqs. (7.15) and (7.16) in the Mohr's-circle discussion (Sec. 7.4). The minus sign appearing in the latter equations arises from the reversed shear-stress sign convention adopted specifically for the Mohr's-circle construction. [See paragraph immediately preceding Eqs. (7.13).]

1.11. Invariants of Stress. As it is now known that the cubic equation (1.16) has three real roots representing the three principal stresses, some further conclusions can be made regarding the coefficients in the equation. It will be observed that the principal stresses, i.e., roots of the equation, depend only on the state of stress at the point and do not depend on the orientation of the xyz coordinate system. Hence the coefficients

$$I_1 = \sigma_x + \sigma_y + \sigma_z \qquad (1.21a)$$

$$I_2 = \sigma_x\sigma_y + \sigma_y\sigma_z + \sigma_z\sigma_x - \tau_{xy}^2 - \tau_{yz}^2 - \tau_{zx}^2 \qquad (1.21b)$$

$$I_3 = \sigma_x\sigma_y\sigma_z - \sigma_x\tau_{yz}^2 - \sigma_y\tau_{zx}^2 - \sigma_z\tau_{xy}^2 + 2\tau_{xy}\tau_{yz}\tau_{zx}$$

$$= \begin{vmatrix} \sigma_x & \tau_{xy} & \tau_{xz} \\ \tau_{yx} & \sigma_y & \tau_{yz} \\ \tau_{zx} & \tau_{zy} & \sigma_z \end{vmatrix} \qquad (1.21c)$$

will not change with a change in the coordinate-system orientation. The quantities I_1, I_2, and I_3 are called the three invariants of stress. If the $Oxyz$ coordinate system is taken as the principal coordinate system, the shear-stress components vanish and the stress invariants take the form

$$I_1 = \sigma_1 + \sigma_2 + \sigma_3 \qquad (1.22a)$$

$$I_2 = \sigma_1\sigma_2 + \sigma_2\sigma_3 + \sigma_3\sigma_1 \qquad (1.22b)$$

$$I_3 = \sigma_1\sigma_2\sigma_3 \qquad (1.22c)$$

1.12. Equations of the State of Stress Referred to the Principal Coordinate System. If the $Pxyz$ coordinate system is so oriented that its axes coincide with the principal directions at a point, the equations representing the state of stress at the point simplify considerably. Assume that the orientation is such that

$$\sigma_x = \sigma_1 \qquad \sigma_y = \sigma_2 \qquad \sigma_z = \sigma_3 \qquad \tau_{xy} = \tau_{yz} = \tau_{zz} = 0$$

where σ_1, σ_2, σ_3 are the three principal stresses.

Equations (1.1) remain the same,

$$p_n = \sqrt{p_{nx}^2 + p_{ny}^2 + p_{nz}^2} \qquad (1.23)$$

Equations (1.5) become

$$p_{nx} = \sigma_1 \cos{(n,x)}$$

$$p_{ny} = \sigma_2 \cos{(n,y)} \tag{1.24}$$

$$p_{nz} = \sigma_3 \cos{(n,z)}$$

Equations for the resultant, normal, and shear stresses acting on an oblique plane through the point can now be written in terms of the principal stresses. Thus, substituting Eqs. (1.24) in Eq. (1.23) for the resultant stress, substituting Eqs. (1.24) in Eq. (1.3) for the normal stress, and recopying Eq. (1.4) for the shear stress, the result is

$$p_n = \sqrt{\sigma_1^2 \cos^2{(n,x)} + \sigma_2^2 \cos^2{(n,y)} + \sigma_3^2 \cos^2{(n,z)}}$$

$$\sigma_n = \sigma_1 \cos^2{(n,x)} + \sigma_2 \cos^2{(n,y)} + \sigma_3 \cos^2{(n,z)} \tag{1.25}$$

$$\tau_n = \sqrt{p_n^2 - \sigma_n^2}$$

By the above, it is seen that τ_n can be further expressed as

$$\tau_n^2 = \sigma_1^2 \cos^2{(n,x)} + \sigma_2^2 \cos^2{(n,y)} + \sigma_3^2 \cos^2{(n,z)}$$
$$- \left[\sigma_1 \cos^2{(n,x)} + \sigma_2 \cos^2{(n,y)} + \sigma_3 \cos^2{(n,z)}\right]^2$$

and it can be verified easily, by recalling that the sum of the squares of the three direction cosines is unity, that an alternate expression for τ_n is

$$\tau_n^2 = (\sigma_1 - \sigma_2)^2 \cos^2{(n,x)} \cos^2{(n,y)}$$
$$+ (\sigma_2 - \sigma_3)^2 \cos^2{(n,y)} \cos^2{(n,z)}$$
$$+ (\sigma_3 - \sigma_1)^2 \cos^2{(n,z)} \cos^2{(n,x)} \tag{1.26}$$

Finally, the laws of stress transformation [Eqs. (1.12)] can be referred to the principal coordinate system,

$$\sigma_{x'} = \sigma_1 \cos^2{(x',x)} + \sigma_2 \cos^2{(x',y)} + \sigma_3 \cos^2{(x',z)}$$

$$\sigma_{y'} = \sigma_1 \cos^2{(y',x)} + \sigma_2 \cos^2{(y',y)} + \sigma_3 \cos^2{(y',z)}$$

$$\sigma_{z'} = \sigma_1 \cos^2{(z',x)} + \sigma_2 \cos^2{(z',y)} + \sigma_3 \cos^2{(z',z)}$$

$$\tau_{x'y'} = \sigma_1 \cos{(x',x)} \cos{(y',x)} + \sigma_2 \cos{(x',y)} \cos{(y',y)}$$
$$+ \sigma_3 \cos{(x',z)} \cos{(y',z)} \tag{1.27}$$

$$\tau_{y'z'} = \sigma_1 \cos{(y',x)} \cos{(z',x)} + \sigma_2 \cos{(y',y)} \cos{(z',y)}$$
$$+ \sigma_3 \cos{(y',z)} \cos{(z',z)}$$

$$\tau_{z'x'} = \sigma_1 \cos{(z',x)} \cos{(x',x)} + \sigma_2 \cos{(z',y)} \cos{(x',y)}$$
$$+ \sigma_3 \cos{(z',z)} \cos{(x',z)}$$

1.13. Octahedral Stresses.   Consider at a point a state of stress characterized by the three principal stresses σ_1, σ_2, and σ_3.

As in the previous section, the principal coordinate system at the point can, with no loss of generality, be taken as the $Pxyz$ cartesian coordinate system.   Further, consider the eight inclined planes† passing through the point whose normals n have the direction cosines

$$\cos(n,x) = \pm \frac{1}{\sqrt{3}}$$

$$\cos(n,y) = \pm \frac{1}{\sqrt{3}}$$

$$\cos(n,z) = \pm \frac{1}{\sqrt{3}}$$

Although these eight planes pass through the point at which the state of stress under discussion occurs, they may be drawn in the form of a regular octahedron around the point for better visualization.   This is done in Fig. 1.10.   The acute angles between the normals to the octahedral planes and the coordinate axes are equal to

$$\arccos \frac{1}{\sqrt{3}} = 54°45'$$

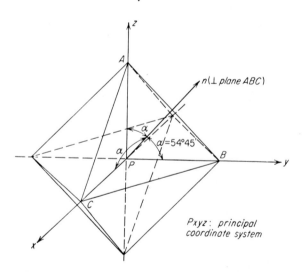

Fig. 1.10. The eight octahedral planes.   The direction cosines of the normals to each plane are $\pm 1/\sqrt{3}$.

†The eight planes are established by taking all possible combinations of the plus and minus signs.

The resultant stress and its normal and shear components acting on any one of these eight planes are, by Eqs. (1.25) and (1.26),

$$p_{oct} = \sqrt{\frac{\sigma_1^2 + \sigma_2^2 + \sigma_3^2}{3}} \tag{1.28}$$

$$\sigma_{oct} = \frac{\sigma_1 + \sigma_2 + \sigma_3}{3} \tag{1.29}$$

$$\tau_{oct} = \tfrac{1}{3}\sqrt{(\sigma_1 - \sigma_2)^2 + (\sigma_2 - \sigma_3)^2 + (\sigma_3 - \sigma_1)^2} \tag{1.30}$$

The stresses σ_{oct} and τ_{oct} are called the octahedral normal and shear stress, respectively. It will be seen in the chapter on failure theories that the octahedral shear stress has importance as a criterion for the beginning of yielding (plastic flow) in a body which is increasingly stressed.

An alternate expression for τ_{oct} is

$$\tau_{oct} = \tfrac{1}{3}\sqrt{2(\sigma_1 + \sigma_2 + \sigma_3)^2 - 6(\sigma_1\sigma_2 + \sigma_2\sigma_3 + \sigma_3\sigma_1)} \tag{1.31}$$

This can be verified by equating the above to Eq. (1.30).

If the $Pxyz$ coordinate system is not principal, the six stress components σ_x, σ_y, σ_z, τ_{xy}, τ_{yz}, τ_{zx}, and not the principal stresses, may be known at the point. Recalling that the three stress invariants [Eqs. (1.22)] are equal to their respective forms in Eqs. (1.21), and observing that the expressions (1.29) and (1.31) contain only the first and second stress invariants, the octahedral normal and shear stresses can be immediately expressed in terms of the cartesian stress components; thus,

$$\sigma_{oct} = \frac{\sigma_x + \sigma_y + \sigma_z}{3} \tag{1.32}$$

$$\tau_{oct} = \tfrac{1}{3}\sqrt{2(\sigma_x + \sigma_y + \sigma_z)^2 - 6(\sigma_x\sigma_y + \sigma_y\sigma_z + \sigma_z\sigma_x - \tau_{xy}^2 - \tau_{yz}^2 - \tau_{zz}^2)} \tag{1.33}$$

Another form for τ_{oct} can be easily shown from the above to be

$$\tau_{oct} = \tfrac{1}{3}\sqrt{(\sigma_x - \sigma_y)^2 + (\sigma_y - \sigma_z)^2 + (\sigma_z - \sigma_x)^2 + 6(\tau_{xy}^2 + \tau_{yz}^2 + \tau_{zz}^2)} \tag{1.34}$$

1.14. Decomposition of a State of Stress into Hydrostatic and Pure-shear Components. The theory of this section is fundamental to the study of plasticity, and it is becoming increasingly important in the study of failure of materials.

The nine cartesian stress components appearing as coefficients in the stress-transformation equations (1.5) can be represented by a tensor,[†] say, S; thus

†A discussion of tensors is beyond the scope of this text. It will suffice here to consider a tensor as simply a three-column, three-row array of stress components such as represented in Eq. (1.35).

$$S = \begin{bmatrix} \sigma_x & \tau_{xy} & \tau_{xz} \\ \tau_{yx} & \sigma_y & \tau_{yz} \\ \tau_{zx} & \tau_{zy} & \sigma_z \end{bmatrix} \tag{1.35}$$

If the $P.xyz$ coordinate system is principal, the tensor becomes

$$S = \begin{bmatrix} \sigma_1 & 0 & 0 \\ 0 & \sigma_2 & 0 \\ 0 & 0 & \sigma_3 \end{bmatrix} \tag{1.36}$$

Now the superposition of any two states of stress at a point leads to a third state of stress having stress components equal to the sum of the corresponding stress components of the two superposed states of stress. This property is a consequence of the linearity of the transformation equations (1.5) or (1.12). By virtue of this property, the stress tensor will now be split into two tensors, each of which represents a special type of state of stress. The superposition of these two will then give a state of stress which is represented by the tensor S.

Consider the stress tensor

$$S'' = \begin{bmatrix} \sigma_m & 0 & 0 \\ 0 & \sigma_m & 0 \\ 0 & 0 & \sigma_m \end{bmatrix} \tag{1.37}$$

where σ_m is defined as the mean normal stress,

$$\begin{aligned} \sigma_m &= \tfrac{1}{3}I_1 \\ &= \tfrac{1}{3}(\sigma_x + \sigma_y + \sigma_z) \\ &= \tfrac{1}{3}(\sigma_1 + \sigma_2 + \sigma_3) \end{aligned} \tag{1.38}$$

This represents a hydrostatic state of stress (see Case 3, Sec. 1.9). It is otherwise referred to as the *spherical stress tensor*, since it represents a spherical state of stress in the sense that the stress components do not change with a coordinate-system rotation.

Consider next the stress tensor

$$S' = \begin{bmatrix} \sigma_x - \sigma_m & \tau_{xy} & \tau_{xz} \\ \tau_{yx} & \sigma_y - \sigma_m & \tau_{yz} \\ \tau_{zx} & \tau_{zy} & \sigma_z - \sigma_m \end{bmatrix} \tag{1.39}$$

or, if the $Pxyz$ coordinate system is principal,

$$S' = \begin{bmatrix} \sigma_1 - \sigma_m & 0 & 0 \\ 0 & \sigma_2 - \sigma_m & 0 \\ 0 & 0 & \sigma_3 - \sigma_m \end{bmatrix} \qquad (1.40)$$

This represents a pure-shear state of stress,† since the first stress invariant of S',

$$\begin{aligned} I_1' &= (\sigma_x - \sigma_m) + (\sigma_y - \sigma_m) + (\sigma_z - \sigma_m) \\ &= I_1 - 3\sigma_m \\ &= I_1 - 3 \times \tfrac{1}{3}I_1 \\ &= 0 \end{aligned}$$

The tensor S' is otherwise referred to as the *deviator stress tensor*.

It can be seen by the superposition property discussed at the beginning of this section that

$$S = S' + S'' \qquad (1.41)$$

Equation (1.41) states that any given state of stress S be decomposed into a hydrostatic component S'' and a pure-shear component S'.

The invariants of the spherical stress tensor are, by Eqs. (1.22),

$$\begin{aligned} I_1'' &= 3\sigma_m \\ I_2'' &= 3\sigma_m^2 \\ I_3'' &= \sigma_m^3 \end{aligned} \qquad (1.42)$$

and the invariants of the deviator stress tensor are

$$\begin{aligned} I_1' &= 0 \\ I_2' &= -\tfrac{1}{6}[(\sigma_1 - \sigma_2)^2 + (\sigma_2 - \sigma_3)^2 + (\sigma_3 - \sigma_1)^2] \\ I_3' &= \tfrac{1}{27}[(2\sigma_1 - \sigma_2 - \sigma_3)(2\sigma_2 - \sigma_3 - \sigma_1)(2\sigma_3 - \sigma_1 - \sigma_2)] \end{aligned} \qquad (1.43)$$

† A state of stress is said to be a state of pure-shear stress if there exists some orientation of the $Pxyz$ coordinate system corresponding to which $\sigma_x = \sigma_y = \sigma_z = 0$, i.e., corresponding to which the matrix of the stress tensor takes the form

$$\begin{bmatrix} 0 & \tau_{xy} & \tau_{xz} \\ \tau_{yx} & 0 & \tau_{yz} \\ \tau_{zx} & \tau_{zy} & 0 \end{bmatrix}$$

It can be shown that a necessary and sufficient condition for a state of stress to be one of pure shear is that the first stress invariant $I_1 = \sigma_x + \sigma_y + \sigma_z = 0$. The necessity is obvious by the above definition of a state of pure shear. The proof of the sufficiency is lengthy. One way to carry it out is to refer to the stress quadric of Cauchy (see Sec. 3.5 and Exercise 3.1).

Other useful related concepts are defined as follows:
Normal components of the deviator stress tensor,

$$S_x = \sigma_x - \sigma_m$$
$$S_y = \sigma_y - \sigma_m \tag{1.44}$$
$$S_z = \sigma_z - \sigma_m$$

Principal normal components of the deviator stress tensor,

$$S_1 = \sigma_1 - \sigma_m$$
$$S_2 = \sigma_2 - \sigma_m \tag{1.45}$$
$$S_3 = \sigma_3 - \sigma_m$$

Principal shear stresses,

$$\tau_1 = \tfrac{1}{2}(\sigma_2 - \sigma_3) = \tfrac{1}{2}(S_2 - S_3)$$
$$\tau_2 = \tfrac{1}{2}(\sigma_3 - \sigma_1) = \tfrac{1}{2}(S_3 - S_1) \tag{1.46}$$
$$\tau_3 = \tfrac{1}{2}(\sigma_1 - \sigma_2) = \tfrac{1}{2}(S_1 - S_2)$$

The latter will be seen to be the shear stresses represented by the maximum ordinates of the three Mohr's circles (see Sec. 3.7 and Fig. 3.3).

1.15. The Lamé-Maxwell Equations: Equations of Equilibrium along Isostatics for the Case of Plane Stress. The Lamé-Maxwell equations derived in this section are particularly important in the photoelastic and brittle-coating methods of stress analysis. In preparation for their determination the concept of isostatics must first be discussed. In all that follows, a plane-stress field ($\sigma_z = \tau_{yz} = \tau_{zx} = 0$) will be assumed.

Isostatics, or *principal stress trajectories,* are curves which are everywhere tangent to the principal directions. Since at every point there are two mutually perpendicular principal directions in the xy plane, two mutually perpendicular isostatics pass through each point and the system of isostatics consists of a system of two orthogonal families of curves. Some of the properties of isostatics are discussed in Sec. 8.3, but it will suffice here only to define them.

Referring to Fig. 1.11, two isostatics, say, S_u, and S_v, are shown passing through a point P. Let the Pxy coordinate system be chosen with origin at P and axes tangent to the curves S_u and S_v. This is a principal coordinate system at P. Let a fixed reference coordinate system $Px'y'$ be also located at P, and call θ the angle between the x and x' axes. Equations (1.27) apply and reduce to:

$$\sigma_{x'} = \sigma_1 \cos^2 \theta + \sigma_2 \sin^2 \theta$$
$$\sigma_{y'} = \sigma_1 \sin^2 \theta + \sigma_2 \cos^2 \theta$$
$$\tau_{x'y'} = \frac{\sigma_1 - \sigma_2}{2} \sin 2\theta \tag{a}$$

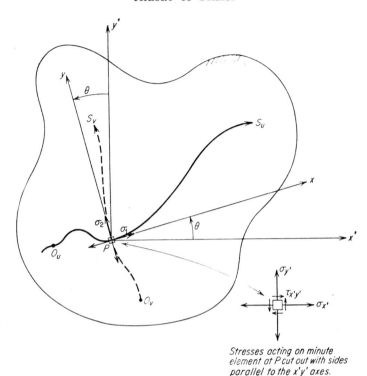

Stresses acting on minute
element at P cut out with sides
parallel to the x'y' axes.

FIG. 1.11. Setup for derivation of Lamé-Maxwell equations. The curves S_u and S_v are isostatics. The axes x, y are taken parallel to the tangents to S_u and S_v at P and are hence principal axes. The axes x', y' are fixed axes.

Now $\sigma_{x'}$, $\sigma_{y'}$, and $\tau_{x'y'}$ in general vary continuously from point to point in the $Px'y'$ coordinate frame; so the equilibrium equations (1.7) apply and can be written

$$\frac{\partial \sigma_{x'}}{\partial x'} + \frac{\partial \tau_{x'y'}}{\partial y'} = 0$$

$$\frac{\partial \tau_{x'y'}}{\partial x'} + \frac{\partial \sigma_{y'}}{\partial y'} = 0$$

(b)

Equations (a) also apply at every point, so that σ_1, σ_2, and θ are functions of position in the $Px'y'$ coordinate system; thus, substituting (a) into (b),

$$\frac{\partial \sigma_1}{\partial x'} \cos^2 \theta - \sigma_1 \sin 2\theta \frac{\partial \theta}{\partial x'} + \frac{\partial \sigma_2}{\partial x'} \sin^2 \theta + \sigma_2 \sin 2\theta \frac{\partial \theta}{\partial x'}$$

(c)

$$+ \frac{\partial \sigma_1}{\partial y'} \frac{\sin 2\theta}{2} + \sigma_1 \cos 2\theta \frac{\partial \theta}{\partial y'} - \frac{\partial \sigma_2}{\partial y'} \frac{\sin 2\theta}{2} - \sigma_2 \cos 2\theta \frac{\partial \theta}{\partial y'} = 0$$

$$\frac{\partial \sigma_1}{\partial x'} \frac{\sin 2\theta}{2} + \sigma_1 \cos 2\theta \frac{\partial \theta}{\partial x'} - \frac{\partial \sigma_2}{\partial x'} \frac{\sin 2\theta}{2} - \sigma_2 \cos 2\theta \frac{\partial \theta}{\partial x'}$$

$$+ \frac{\partial \sigma_1}{\partial y'} \sin^2 \theta + \sigma_1 \sin 2\theta \frac{\partial \theta}{\partial y'} + \frac{\partial \sigma_2}{\partial y'} \cos^2 \theta - \sigma_2 \sin 2\theta \frac{\partial \theta}{\partial y'} = 0 \qquad (c)$$

The arc displacement along the isostatics can be thought of as distance along the curves measured from some points of origin, say O_u and O_v (Fig. 1.11). If the $Px'y'$ axes are now chosen coincident with the xy principal axes at the point P, the angle θ becomes zero and differentiation with respect to x' and y' becomes analogous to differentiation with respect to distances along the curves S_u and S_v.

If such is the case, Eqs. (c) reduce to

$$\frac{\partial \sigma_1}{\partial S_u} + \sigma_1 \frac{\partial \theta}{\partial S_v} - \sigma_2 \frac{\partial \theta}{\partial S_v} = 0$$

$$\sigma_1 \frac{\partial \theta}{\partial S_u} - \sigma_2 \frac{\partial \theta}{\partial S_u} + \frac{\partial \sigma_2}{\partial S_v} = 0 \qquad (d)$$

The curvature of a curve is defined as the rate at which the tangent turns with respect to displacement along the curve,† and the radius of curvature is the reciprocal of the curvature. Calling ρ_u and ρ_v the radii of curvature of the isostatics S_u and S_v, this means that

$$\frac{1}{\rho_u} = \frac{\partial \theta}{\partial S_u}$$

$$\frac{1}{\rho_v} = \frac{\partial \theta}{\partial S_v}$$

Equations (d) thus take the form

$$\frac{\partial \sigma_1}{\partial S_u} = -\frac{\sigma_1 - \sigma_2}{\rho_v}$$

$$\frac{\partial \sigma_2}{\partial S_v} = -\frac{\sigma_1 - \sigma_2}{\rho_u} \qquad (1.47)$$

which are the Lamé-Maxwell equations.

The positive and negative senses of ρ_u and ρ_v are illustrated in Fig. 1.12. These result directly from the definition of the curvature and the convention that the angle θ is measured counterclockwise from a fixed direction to the tangent to the curve.

The integration of Eqs. (1.47) allows the determination of the value of a principal stress when the shear stress and the isostatic fields are

---

†See any discussion on the geometry of space curves, e.g., E. B. Wilson, "Advanced Calculus," p. 82, Ginn & Company, Boston, 1912.

known. As mentioned before, this will be found very important in photo-elasticity.

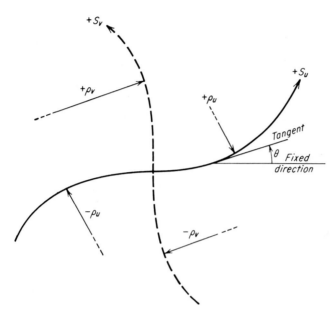

Fɪɢ. 1.12. Sign conventions for the radii of curvature used in the Lamé-Maxwell equations. The angle θ is measured counterclockwise from a fixed direction to the tangent to the curve. ρ is positive when θ increases with an increase in arc displacement and is negative when θ decreases with an increase in arc displacement.

1.16. Physical Evidence of the Perpendicularity of the Principal Stresses.
It is difficult to show in three-dimensional problems the correlation between theoretical developments and experimental data on the perpendicularity of the three principal stresses. It is advisable, however, that the reader be in a position to visualize the physical meaning of the elastic phenomena as the theory of elasticity develops. If we think for a moment of the three-dimensional problem as simplified to two dimensions by having all the z components of stress equal to zero (as was pointed out in Sec. 1.15), it is possible to show by the use of a brittle coating two sets of lines which are perpendicular to each other at every point (see Fig. 1.13). It will be proved later that the coating fails perpendicularly to the maximum principal stress. One set of lines shown in the figure was produced at the time the model was loaded. The second set was obtained when the model was unloaded, by techniques which will be explained later. This set is perpendicular to the second principal stress. Within experimental error the two sets of lines obtained are perpendicular to each other everywhere.

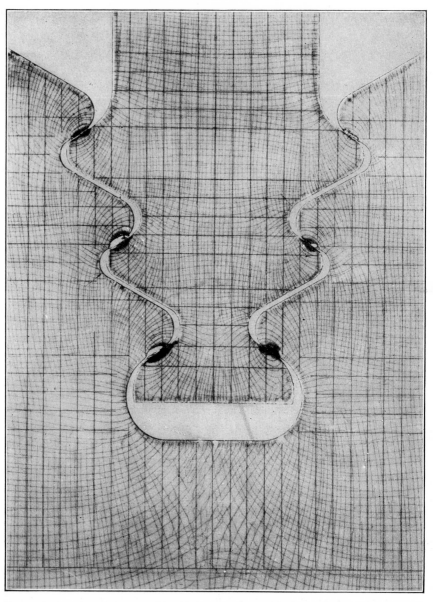

FIG. 1.13. Plastic model of a turbine blade dovetail joint showing brittle coating cracks. The two sets of cracks are perpendicular to each other at every point. This correlates with the theoretical requirements of principal stresses being perpendicular to each other.

Exercises

1.1. Find the principal stresses and directions corresponding to the given state of stress $\sigma_x = 0.5$, $\sigma_y = 0.7$, $\sigma_z = 0.6$; $\tau_{xy} = 1$, $\tau_{yz} = 1.2$, $\tau_{zx} = 0.8$. *Ans.* $\sigma_1 = 2.62$, $\sigma_2 = -0.24$, $\sigma_3 = -0.58$; $\cos(n_1,x) = 0.516$, $\cos(n_1,y) = 0.631$, $\cos(n_1,z) = 0.579$; $\cos(n_2,x) = -0.815$, $\cos(n_2,y) = 0.152$, $\cos(n_2,z) = 0.560$; $\cos(n_3,x) = 0.258$, $\cos(n_3,y) = -0.760$, $\cos(n_3,z) = 0.597$.

1.2. (a) Find the octahedral normal and shear stress corresponding to the given state of stress in Exercise 1.1. (b) Find the orientation of the octahedral plane whose normal, say, N_1 lies in the first octant of the principal coordinate system. *Hint.* Refer to the rule stated by Eq. (1.2). *Ans.* (a) $\sigma_{oct} = 0.6$; $\tau_{oct} = \sqrt{2.06}$. (b) $\cos(N_1,x) = -0.041/\sqrt{3}$, $\cos(N_1,y) = 0.023/\sqrt{3}$, $\cos(N_1,z) = 1.736/\sqrt{3}$.

1.3. Derive Eqs. (1.20c) and (1.20d) from Eqs. (1.20a) and (1.20b) and Eqs. (1.17).

1.4. Establish Eqs. (1.43).

CHAPTER 2

THEORY OF STRAIN

2.1. Introduction. The theory of strain is developed in this chapter. A large portion of the mathematical developments is only instrumental in obtaining the final equations, but it is important to follow these developments carefully since strain, a purely geometric quantity, is difficult to visualize in three dimensions. It will be seen that the equations characterizing the state of strain at a point appear similar to those in the chapter on stress and that the two concepts can subsequently be treated identically mathematically. Of primary value, also, is a clear understanding of the significance of the two basic restrictions that must be imposed on the general displacement equations to obtain this similarity.

2.2. General Displacements. Consider a body R composed of a continuous distribution of matter. Let the body be referred to the $Oxyz$ coordinate system (Fig. 2.1), and let $P_0(x_0, y_0, z_0)$ and $P(x, y, z)$ be any two

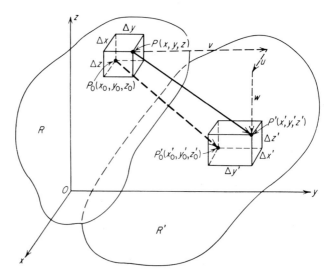

FIG. 2.1. Initial and final positions of the point P_0 and a neighboring point P in a region R that is transformed to the region R'. The boxes in R and R' are drawn only to locate P and P' with respect to P_0 and P_0'; and hence the box in R' is not to be mistaken as representing the transformed appearance of the box shown in R.

points in the body. Suppose all points in the body are displaced to new positions so that R acquires the configuration R', with point P moving to P' and point P_0 to P'_0. This general transformation can be decomposed into (1) a rigid displacement wherein relative distances between all points in the body remain unchanged and (2) a deformation wherein the relative distances are changed. It will be found very shortly that, except for a special case, the discussion will be restricted to only small local regions in the body. Hence, the end results will describe rigid displacements and deformations of only these small regions characterized by the base point P_0; however, as functions of the coordinates of P_0, they will cover the behavior of all local regions and, hence, the entire body.

Let $u(x,y,z)$, $v(x,y,z)$, and $w(x,y,z)$ be, respectively, the x, y, and z components of the displacement of point $P(x,y,z)$. The location of the transformed point $P'(x',y',z')$ can then be given in terms of x, y, and z by the expressions

$$x' = x + u(x,y,z)$$
$$y' = y + v(x,y,z) \qquad (2.1)$$
$$z' = z + w(x,y,z)$$

Using the notation

$$\Delta x = x - x_0$$
$$\Delta y = y - y_0 \qquad (2.2)$$
$$\Delta z = z - z_0$$

Eqs. (2.1) can be written

$$x' = x + u(x_0 + \Delta x, y_0 + \Delta y, z_0 + \Delta z)$$
$$y' = y + v(x_0 + \Delta x, y_0 + \Delta y, z_0 + \Delta z)$$
$$z' = z + w(x_0 + \Delta x, y_0 + \Delta y, z_0 + \Delta z)$$

The functions u, v, w can be expanded in a Taylor's series† about P_0, so that

$$x' = x + u(x_0,y_0,z_0) + \left(\frac{\partial u}{\partial x}\right)_{P_0} \Delta x + \left(\frac{\partial u}{\partial y}\right)_{P_0} \Delta y + \left(\frac{\partial u}{\partial z}\right)_{P_0} \Delta z + \cdots$$

$$y' = y + v(x_0,y_0,z_0) + \left(\frac{\partial v}{\partial x}\right)_{P_0} \Delta x + \left(\frac{\partial v}{\partial y}\right)_{P_0} \Delta y + \left(\frac{\partial v}{\partial z}\right)_{P_0} \Delta z + \cdots \quad (2.3)$$

$$z' = z + w(x_0,y_0,z_0) + \left(\frac{\partial w}{\partial x}\right)_{P_0} \Delta x + \left(\frac{\partial w}{\partial y}\right)_{P_0} \Delta y + \left(\frac{\partial w}{\partial z}\right)_{P_0} \Delta z + \cdots$$

†See R. Courant, "Differential and Integral Calculus," vol. II, p. 80, Interscience Publishers, Inc., New York, 1936.

The development can be easily continued if terms beyond those shown in the above series are negligible with respect to those shown. Put in the form of a requirement, this means that either (1) derivatives of u, v, w of higher order than the first or (2) higher products and powers of Δx, Δy, Δz must be small enough to make subsequent terms in the series negligible compared with those shown. The first case is equivalent to requiring that, throughout the region R, the variation of u, v, w in any direction be nearly constant. The second possibility means that the study must be restricted to a small neighborhood around P_0. Either one of these requirements could be imposed to permit the development to be continued with a "broken-off" or "linearized" series. The second will be chosen here, and the first case (called homogeneous deformation) will be discussed later in Sec. 2.8. This linearization constitutes the first of the two restrictions referred to in Sec. 2.1.

2.3. First Restriction: Confinement of the Analysis to a Small Neighborhood around a Point. Confining the study now to a small neighborhood around P_0, the series can be broken off after the terms shown. The local coordinates of P, that is, Δx, Δy, Δz, can be eliminated by using Eqs. (2.2), so that the location of P' is given only in terms of the coordinates of P and P_0, thus:

$$x' = u(x_0,y_0,z_0) - \left(\frac{\partial u}{\partial x}\right)_{P_0} x_0 - \left(\frac{\partial u}{\partial y}\right)_{P_0} y_0 - \left(\frac{\partial u}{\partial z}\right)_{P_0} z_0$$
$$+ \left[1 + \left(\frac{\partial u}{\partial x}\right)_{P_0}\right] x + \left(\frac{\partial u}{\partial y}\right)_{P_0} y + \left(\frac{\partial u}{\partial z}\right)_{P_0} z$$

$$y' = v(x_0,y_0,z_0) - \left(\frac{\partial v}{\partial x}\right)_{P_0} x_0 - \left(\frac{\partial v}{\partial y}\right)_{P_0} y_0 - \left(\frac{\partial v}{\partial z}\right)_{P_0} z_0$$
$$+ \left(\frac{\partial v}{\partial x}\right)_{P_0} x + \left[1 + \left(\frac{\partial v}{\partial y}\right)_{P_0}\right] y + \left(\frac{\partial v}{\partial z}\right)_{P_0} z$$

$$z' = w(x_0,y_0,z_0) - \left(\frac{\partial w}{\partial x}\right)_{P_0} x_0 - \left(\frac{\partial w}{\partial y}\right)_{P_0} y_0 - \left(\frac{\partial w}{\partial z}\right)_{P_0} z_0$$
$$+ \left(\frac{\partial w}{\partial x}\right)_{P_0} x + \left(\frac{\partial w}{\partial y}\right)_{P_0} y + \left[1 + \left(\frac{\partial w}{\partial z}\right)_{P_0}\right] z$$

The first four terms on the right-hand sides of these equations are constants for a fixed base point P_0 and therefore represent a translation component of the transformation of the small region. For brevity they can be replaced by the symbols U_{P_0}, V_{P_0}, and W_{P_0}, so that

$$x' = U_{P_0} + \left[1 + \left(\frac{\partial u}{\partial x}\right)_{P_0}\right] x + \left(\frac{\partial u}{\partial y}\right)_{P_0} y + \left(\frac{\partial u}{\partial z}\right)_{P_0} z$$

$$y' = V_{P_o} + \left(\frac{\partial v}{\partial x}\right)_{P_o} x + \left[1 + \left(\frac{\partial v}{\partial y}\right)_{P_o}\right]y + \left(\frac{\partial v}{\partial z}\right)_{P_o} z \qquad (2.4)$$

$$z' = W_{P_o} + \left(\frac{\partial w}{\partial x}\right)_{P_o} x + \left(\frac{\partial w}{\partial y}\right)_{P_o} y + \left[1 + \left(\frac{\partial w}{\partial z}\right)_{P_o}\right]z$$

It is convenient to rewrite Eqs. (2.4) in a second form for future reference. Noting in Fig. 2.1 that

$$\Delta x' = x' - x_0'$$
$$\Delta y' = y' - y_0'$$
$$\Delta z' = z' - z_0'$$

and that P_0 is transformed into P_0' by the same equations (2.1) that transform P into P', that is,

$$x_0' = x_0 + u(x_0,y_0,z_0)$$
$$y_0' = y_0 + v(x_0,y_0,z_0)$$
$$z_0' = z_0 + w(x_0,y_0,z_0)$$

Eqs. (2.4) can be written

$$\Delta x' = \left[1 + \left(\frac{\partial u}{\partial x}\right)_{P_o}\right]\Delta x + \left(\frac{\partial u}{\partial y}\right)_{P_o}\Delta y + \left(\frac{\partial u}{\partial z}\right)_{P_o}\Delta z$$

$$\Delta y' = \left(\frac{\partial v}{\partial x}\right)_{P_o}\Delta x + \left[1 + \left(\frac{\partial v}{\partial y}\right)_{P_o}\right]\Delta y + \left(\frac{\partial v}{\partial z}\right)_{P_o}\Delta z \qquad (2.5)$$

$$\Delta z' = \left(\frac{\partial w}{\partial x}\right)_{P_o}\Delta x + \left(\frac{\partial w}{\partial y}\right)_{P_o}\Delta y + \left[1 + \left(\frac{\partial w}{\partial z}\right)_{P_o}\right]\Delta z$$

The relations (2.4) or (2.5) have only linear terms in the variables and hence are called linear transformations. If the transformations are inverted, i.e., the right-hand-side variables are solved for, it will be found that the expressions are also linear in terms of the left-hand-side variables.

Such linear transformations possess many properties. Some of the more important properties that aid in the understanding of the mechanisms of strain will be considered.

1. Planes are carried into planes. Small plane segments in the neighborhood of P_0 (Fig. 2.1) are carried into plane segments in the neighborhood of P_0'. To prove this, consider all the points near P_0 that lie on a plane, say, $Ax + By + Cz + D = 0$, that is, whose coordinates satisfy this equation. The equation of the transformed plane can be written by replacing x, y, and z in the above by their values as obtained from Eqs. (2.4), and since these values are linear functions of x', y', and z', the equation of the transformed plane has the form $A'x' + B'y' + C'z' + D' = 0$, where the primed constants are functions of A, B, C, and D. The coordinates of the transformed points will satisfy this second equation; hence, the transformed points lie on a plane.

2. Straight lines are carried into straight lines. This follows from (1) since a straight line may be regarded as the intersection of two planes.

3. Parallel planes are carried into parallel planes. If this were not so, the two transformed planes would intersect and would therefore define a line; and by (2) the original planes would have to intersect at points corresponding to the transformed points on this line. This is impossible since the original planes are parallel.

4. Parallel lines are carried into parallel lines. This follows from (1) and (3) by noting that two parallel lines can be thought of as being defined by three planes, two of which are parallel.

These properties reveal that a small rectangular parallelepiped transforms, in the most general case, to a parallelepiped such as is shown in Fig. 2.2.

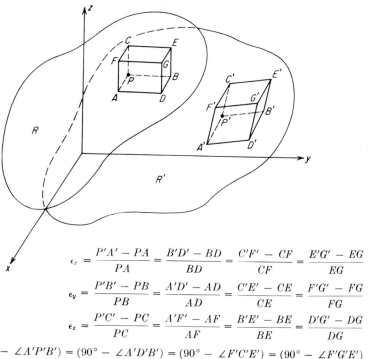

$$\epsilon_x = \frac{P'A' - PA}{PA} = \frac{B'D' - BD}{BD} = \frac{C'F' - CF}{CF} = \frac{E'G' - EG}{EG}$$

$$\epsilon_y = \frac{P'B' - PB}{PB} = \frac{A'D' - AD}{AD} = \frac{C'E' - CE}{CE} = \frac{F'G' - FG}{FG}$$

$$\epsilon_z = \frac{P'C' - PC}{PC} = \frac{A'F' - AF}{AF} = \frac{B'E' - BE}{BE} = \frac{D'G' - DG}{DG}$$

$$\gamma_{xy} = (90° - \angle A'P'B') = (90° - \angle A'D'B') = (90° - \angle F'C'E') = (90° - \angle F'G'E')$$
$$\gamma_{yz} = (90° - \angle B'P'C') = (90° - \angle B'E'C') = (90° - \angle D'A'F') = (90° - \angle D'G'F')$$
$$\gamma_{zx} = (90° - \angle C'P'A') = (90° - \angle C'F'A') = (90° - \angle F'B'D') = (90° - \angle E'G'D')$$

FIG. 2.2. Pictorial representation of the distortion and displacement of a small rectangular parallelepiped, and physical significance of the six components of strain resulting from the assumption of small deformations [transformation (2.4) or (2.5)]. The sides of the parallelepiped in its original position are parallel to the coordinate planes.

2.4. Second Restriction: Infinitesimal Deformations. It will now be assumed that the displacement components u, v, w and their derivatives are small enough to allow products and higher powers of these components to be neglected with respect to these quantities themselves. This is called the assumption of infinitesimal deformations. No changes result in the form of the basic transformation laws, Eqs. (2.4) or (2.5); however, the assumption has considerable influence on their meaning. The most important consequence of the assumption is seen from the following:

Suppose a second displacement field with components u', v', w' is applied to R' (Fig. 2.3) so that the region is further transformed to a region R'', with points P_0' and P' going to P_0'' and P''. The transformation laws will be similar in form to Eqs. (2.4), viz.,

$$x'' = U'_{P_0'} + \left[1 + \left(\frac{\partial u'}{\partial x}\right)_{P_0'}\right]x' + \left(\frac{\partial u'}{\partial y}\right)_{P_0'}y' + \left(\frac{\partial u'}{\partial z}\right)_{P_0'}z'$$

$$y'' = V'_{P_0'} + \left(\frac{\partial v'}{\partial x}\right)_{P_0'}x' + \left[1 + \left(\frac{\partial v'}{\partial y}\right)_{P_0'}\right]y' + \left(\frac{\partial v'}{\partial z}\right)_{P_0'}z' \qquad (2.6)$$

$$z'' = W'_{P_0'} + \left(\frac{\partial w'}{\partial x}\right)_{P_0'}x' + \left(\frac{\partial w'}{\partial y}\right)_{P_0'}y' + \left[1 + \left(\frac{\partial w'}{\partial z}\right)_{P_0'}\right]z'$$

The coordinates of P'' can be solved for in terms of those of the original point P by substituting Eqs. (2.4) into Eqs. (2.6). The task is lengthy,

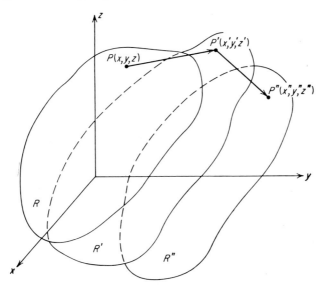

FIG. 2.3. Two successive transformations applied to the region R. The first displacement field u, v, w transforms the general point P in R to the point P' in R', and the second displacement field u', v', w', applied to R', transforms P' to the point P'' in R''.

and only the final result for x'' (after discarding all higher-order terms) is given:†

$$x'' = U_{P_0} + U'_{P_0} + \left[1 + \left(\frac{\partial u}{\partial x} \right)_{P_0} + \left(\frac{\partial u'}{\partial x} \right)_{P_0} \right] x$$

$$+ \left[\left(\frac{\partial u}{\partial y} \right)_{P_0} + \left(\frac{\partial u'}{\partial y} \right)_{P_0} \right] y$$

$$+ \left[\left(\frac{\partial u}{\partial z} \right)_{P_0} + \left(\frac{\partial u'}{\partial z} \right)_{P_0} \right] z \qquad (2.7)$$

If the order of application of the two transformations is now reversed (i.e., the displacement field u', v', w' is first applied to the region R followed by the application of the displacement field u, v, w), the point P would in general end up as a point, say, P''', in a region R'''. If the calculations are carried out for the x coordinate of P''', the result is

$$x''' = U'_{P_0} + U_{P_0} + \left[1 + \left(\frac{\partial u'}{\partial x} \right)_{P_0} + \left(\frac{\partial u}{\partial x} \right)_{P_0} \right] x$$

$$+ \left[\left(\frac{\partial u'}{\partial y} \right)_{P_0} + \left(\frac{\partial u}{\partial y} \right)_{P_0} \right] y$$

$$+ \left[\left(\frac{\partial u'}{\partial z} \right)_{P_0} + \left(\frac{\partial u}{\partial z} \right)_{P_0} \right] z \qquad (2.8)$$

---

†The calculations will actually show that the primed terms in Eq. (2.7) are evaluated at P'_0; however, the assumption of infinitesimal deformations makes the choice between P_0 and P'_0 for evaluation of the terms immaterial, e.g.,

$$\left(\frac{\partial u'}{\partial x} \right)_{P_0'} = \left(\frac{\partial u'}{\partial x} \right)_{(x_0', y_0', z_0')} = \left(\frac{\partial u'}{\partial x} \right)_{(x_0 + u_0, y_0 + v_0, z_0 + w_0)}$$

where

$$u_0 = u(x_0, y_0, z_0)$$
$$v_0 = v(x_0, y_0, z_0)$$
$$w_0 = w(x_0, y_0, z_0)$$

So, by Taylor's expansion,

$$\left(\frac{\partial u'}{\partial x} \right)_{P_0'} = \left(\frac{\partial u'}{\partial x} \right)_{P_0} + \left[\frac{\partial}{\partial x} \left(\frac{\partial u'}{\partial x} \right) \right]_{P_0} u_0 + \left[\frac{\partial}{\partial y} \left(\frac{\partial u'}{\partial x} \right) \right]_{P_0} v_0$$

$$+ \left[\frac{\partial}{\partial z} \left(\frac{\partial u'}{\partial x} \right) \right]_{P_0} w_0 + \cdots$$

and since all terms except the first on the right-hand side are negligible,

$$\left(\frac{\partial u'}{\partial x} \right)_{P_0'} = \left(\frac{\partial u'}{\partial x} \right)_{P_0}$$

This is identical to Eq. (2.7). The same result is obtained for the y and z coordinates of P''', so that the conclusion can be made that, under the assumption of infinitesimal deformations, the order of application of the two displacement fields has no effect on the final configuration.

The property is recognizable as the "principle of superposition" and is the underlying principle of the so-called "linear" theory of elasticity, which is treated in this text. Clearly there is no restriction on the number or on the order of application of displacement fields successively applied since linearity of the transformation equations is always assured by the assumption of small deformations. Advancement into nonlinear elasticity theory is possible by allowing larger deformations; but, in such a case, Eqs. (2.7) and (2.8) will not agree, and superposition is no longer possible.

2.5. Changes in Lengths of Straight-line Segments and Transformation of Angles between Straight-line Segments under the Assumption of Infinitesimal Deformations. It was pointed out that planes and straight lines in a local region of R are carried into planes and straight lines in the corresponding local region of R' by the transformations (2.5). A closer study will now be made of the nature of the transformation of straight-line segments and of the angles between them under the assumption of infinitesimal deformations. Since straight lines are known to transform into straight lines, it will only be necessary to discuss the movements of the two end points of a straight-line segment.

a. The Change in Length per Unit Length of a Line Segment. Let points P and P_0 be taken as the end points of a general line segment in the small region around P_0 (Fig. 2.1). The change in length per unit length of this line segment will be denoted by the symbol $\epsilon_{P_0 P} = (P_0'P' - P_0 P)/P_0 P$ and will be called a unit elongation, or normal strain. The square of the length of the transformed line is $(P_0'P')^2 = (\Delta x')^2 + (\Delta y')^2 + (\Delta z')^2$. Substituting Eqs. (2.5) into the above, and neglecting (by the assumption of infinitesimal deformations) products and squares of the derivatives, this becomes

$$(P_0'P')^2 = \left[1 + 2\left(\frac{\partial u}{\partial x}\right)_{P_0}\right](\Delta x)^2 + \left[1 + 2\left(\frac{\partial v}{\partial y}\right)_{P_0}\right](\Delta y)^2$$

$$+ \left[1 + 2\left(\frac{\partial w}{\partial z}\right)_{P_0}\right](\Delta z)^2 + 2\left[\left(\frac{\partial u}{\partial y}\right)_{P_0} + \left(\frac{\partial v}{\partial x}\right)_{P_0}\right]\Delta x\,\Delta y$$

$$+ 2\left[\left(\frac{\partial v}{\partial z}\right)_{P_0} + \left(\frac{\partial w}{\partial y}\right)_{P_0}\right]\Delta y\,\Delta z + 2\left[\left(\frac{\partial w}{\partial x}\right)_{P_0} + \left(\frac{\partial u}{\partial z}\right)_{P_0}\right]\Delta z\,\Delta x$$

Letting l, m, and n be the direction cosines of the original line P_0P† and

†That is, $l = \cos(P_0P,x)$, $m = \cos(P_0P,y)$, $n = \cos(P_0P,z)$.

using the relation $(P_0P)^2 = (\Delta x)^2 + (\Delta y)^2 + (\Delta z)^2$, this equation after some rearrangements takes the form:

$$(1 + \epsilon_{P_0P})^2 = 1 + 2\left(\frac{\partial u}{\partial x}\right)_{P_0} l^2 + 2\left(\frac{\partial v}{\partial y}\right)_{P_0} m^2 + 2\left(\frac{\partial w}{\partial z}\right)_{P_0} n^2$$

$$+ 2\left[\left(\frac{\partial u}{\partial y}\right)_{P_0} + \left(\frac{\partial v}{\partial x}\right)_{P_0}\right] lm + 2\left[\left(\frac{\partial v}{\partial z}\right)_{P_0} + \left(\frac{\partial w}{\partial y}\right)_{P_0}\right] mn$$

$$+ 2\left[\left(\frac{\partial w}{\partial x}\right)_{P_0} + \left(\frac{\partial u}{\partial z}\right)_{P_0}\right] nl$$

Now ϵ_{P_0P} is of the same order of magnitude as the displacement derivatives; hence, its square can be neglected when the left-hand side of the above equation is expanded, so that finally

$$\epsilon_{P_0P} = \left(\frac{\partial u}{\partial x}\right)_{P_0} l^2 + \left(\frac{\partial v}{\partial y}\right)_{P_0} m^2 + \left(\frac{\partial w}{\partial z}\right)_{P_0} n^2$$

$$+ \left[\left(\frac{\partial u}{\partial y}\right)_{P_0} + \left(\frac{\partial v}{\partial x}\right)_{P_0}\right] lm + \left[\left(\frac{\partial v}{\partial z}\right)_{P_0} + \left(\frac{\partial w}{\partial y}\right)_{P_0}\right] mn$$

$$+ \left[\left(\frac{\partial w}{\partial x}\right)_{P_0} + \left(\frac{\partial u}{\partial z}\right)_{P_0}\right] nl \qquad (2.9)$$

   b. *The Transformation of the Angle between Two Line Segments.* Consider next the two line segments P_0P_1 and P_0P_2, where P_1 and P_2 are two points in the neighborhood of P_0. Let l_1, m_1, n_1 and l_2, m_2, n_2 be the direction cosines of the lines P_0P_1 and P_0P_2, respectively; and let l_1', m_1', n_1' and l_2', m_2', n_2' be the direction cosines of the transformed line segments $P_0'P_1'$ and $P_0'P_2'$, respectively, i.e.,

$$l_1 = \frac{\Delta x_1}{P_0P_1} \qquad m_1 = \frac{\Delta y_1}{P_0P_1} \qquad n_1 = \frac{\Delta z_1}{P_0P_1}$$

$$l_2 = \frac{\Delta x_2}{P_0P_2} \qquad m_2 = \frac{\Delta y_2}{P_0P_2} \qquad n_2 = \frac{\Delta z_2}{P_0P_2}$$

$$l_1' = \frac{\Delta x_1'}{P_0'P_1'} \qquad m_1' = \frac{\Delta y_1'}{P_0'P_1'} \qquad n_1' = \frac{\Delta z_1'}{P_0'P_1'}$$

$$l_2' = \frac{\Delta x_2'}{P_0'P_2'} \qquad m_2' = \frac{\Delta y_2'}{P_0'P_2'} \qquad n_2' = \frac{\Delta z_2'}{P_0'P_2'}$$

The cosines of the angle between the two lines after deformation is the sum of the pairwise products of their individual direction cosines [see Eq. (1.2)]; hence

$$\cos(P_0'P_1', P_0'P_2') = l_1'l_2' + m_1'm_2' + n_1'n_2'$$

$$= \frac{1}{(P_0'P_1')(P_0'P_2')}(\Delta x_1' \, \Delta x_2' + \Delta y_1' \, \Delta y_2' + \Delta z_1' \, \Delta z_2')$$

Using Eqs. (2.5), and neglecting (by the assumption of infinitesimal deformations) products and squares of the derivatives,

$$\cos\left(P_0'P_1', P_0'P_2'\right) = \frac{1}{(P_0'P_1')(P_0'P_2')} \left\{ \left[1 + 2\left(\frac{\partial u}{\partial x}\right)_{P_0} \right] \Delta x_1 \, \Delta x_2 \right.$$

$$+ \left[1 + 2\left(\frac{\partial v}{\partial y}\right)_{P_0} \right] \Delta y_1 \, \Delta y_2 + \left[1 + 2\left(\frac{\partial w}{\partial z}\right)_{P_0} \right] \Delta z_1 \, \Delta z_2$$

$$+ \left[\left(\frac{\partial u}{\partial y}\right)_{P_0} + \left(\frac{\partial v}{\partial x}\right)_{P_0} \right] (\Delta x_1 \, \Delta y_2 + \Delta x_2 \, \Delta y_1)$$

$$+ \left[\left(\frac{\partial v}{\partial z}\right)_{P_0} + \left(\frac{\partial w}{\partial y}\right)_{P_0} \right] (\Delta y_1 \, \Delta z_2 + \Delta y_2 \, \Delta z_1)$$

$$\left. + \left[\left(\frac{\partial w}{\partial x}\right)_{P_0} + \left(\frac{\partial u}{\partial z}\right)_{P_0} \right] (\Delta z_1 \, \Delta x_2 + \Delta z_2 \, \Delta x_1) \right\}$$

$$= \frac{(P_0P_1)(P_0P_2)}{(P_0'P_1')(P_0'P_2')} \left\{ \left[1 + 2\left(\frac{\partial u}{\partial x}\right)_{P_0} \right] l_1 l_2 + \left[1 + 2\left(\frac{\partial v}{\partial y}\right)_{P_0} \right] m_1 m_2 \right.$$

$$+ \left[1 + 2\left(\frac{\partial w}{\partial z}\right)_{P_0} \right] n_1 n_2 + \left[\left(\frac{\partial u}{\partial y}\right)_{P_0} + \left(\frac{\partial v}{\partial x}\right)_{P_0} \right] (l_1 m_2 + l_2 m_1)$$

$$+ \left[\left(\frac{\partial v}{\partial z}\right)_{P_0} + \left(\frac{\partial w}{\partial y}\right)_{P_0} \right] (m_1 n_2 + m_2 n_1)$$

$$\left. + \left[\left(\frac{\partial w}{\partial x}\right)_{P_0} + \left(\frac{\partial u}{\partial z}\right)_{P_0} \right] (n_1 l_2 + n_2 l_1) \right\}$$

Now

$$\frac{(P_0P_1)(P_0P_2)}{(P_0'P_1')(P_0'P_2')} = \frac{1}{\left(1 + \dfrac{P_0'P_1' - P_0P_1}{P_0P_1}\right)\left(1 + \dfrac{P_0'P_2' - P_0P_2}{P_0P_2}\right)}$$

$$= \frac{1}{(1 + \epsilon_{P_0P_1})(1 + \epsilon_{P_0P_2})}$$

$$\approx \frac{1}{1 + \epsilon_{P_0P_1} + \epsilon_{P_0P_2}} \approx 1 - \epsilon_{P_0P_1} - \epsilon_{P_0P_2}$$

where $\epsilon_{P_0P_1}$ and $\epsilon_{P_0P_2}$ are the unit elongations of the lines P_0P_1 and P_0P_2. Using the above and neglecting products of the strains and the displacement derivatives, the equation for the cosine of the angle after deformation can be written

$$\cos(P_0'P_1', P_0'P_2') = (1 - \epsilon_{P_0P_1} - \epsilon_{P_0P_2})\Big\{(l_1 l_2 + m_1 m_2 + n_1 n_2)$$

$$+ 2\left[\left(\frac{\partial u}{\partial x}\right)_{P_0} l_1 l_2 + \left(\frac{\partial v}{\partial y}\right)_{P_0} m_1 m_2 + \left(\frac{\partial w}{\partial z}\right)_{P_0} n_1 n_2\right]$$

$$+ \left[\left(\frac{\partial u}{\partial y}\right)_{P_0} + \left(\frac{\partial v}{\partial x}\right)_{P_2}\right](l_1 m_2 + l_2 m_1) + \left[\left(\frac{\partial v}{\partial z}\right)_{P_0} + \left(\frac{\partial w}{\partial y}\right)_{P_0}\right](m_1 n_2 + m_2 n_1)$$

$$+ \left[\left(\frac{\partial w}{\partial x}\right)_{P_0} + \left(\frac{\partial u}{\partial z}\right)_{P_0}\right](n_1 l_2 + n_2 l_1)\Big\} \tag{2.10}$$

The cosine of the original angle is

$$\cos(P_0 P_1, P_0 P_2) = l_1 l_2 + m_1 m_2 + n_1 n_2$$

and the change in the angle, if desired, can be calculated from this equation and Eq. (2.10).

2.6. The Cartesian Components of Strain: Definitions and Physical Significance. Consider now, some special cases of Eq. (2.9). If the line segment $P_0 P$ is originally parallel to the x axis, $l = 1$, $m = n = 0$; and Eq. (2.9) reduces to

$$\epsilon_{P_0 P} = (\epsilon_x)_{P_0} = \left(\frac{\partial u}{\partial x}\right)_{P_0}$$

where the subscript x refers to the orientation of the original line segment. Similarly, $(\epsilon_y)_{P_0}$ and $(\epsilon_z)_{P_0}$ are the changes in lengths per unit length of line segments initially parallel to the y and z axes. Since the results are unaffected if the evaluation is made at any other point in the small region (cf. footnote, page 42), it can be assumed that the evaluations are at point $P(x,y,z)$. Then no subscripts P_0 are necessary, and

$$\epsilon_x = \frac{\partial u}{\partial x} \qquad \epsilon_y = \frac{\partial v}{\partial y} \qquad \epsilon_z = \frac{\partial w}{\partial z} \tag{2.11}$$

These are the normal components of strain in the cartesian directions, and they represent changes in lengths per unit length of line segments in the neighborhood of P which are originally parallel to the x, y, and z axes, respectively.

Equation (2.10) may be similarly treated. Suppose the original line segments $P_0 P_1$ and $P_0 P_2$ are parallel to the x and y axes, respectively. Then $l_1 = m_2 = 1$, and $m_1 = n_1 = l_2 = n_2 = 0$, and the equation reduces to

$$\cos(P_0'P_1', P_0'P_2') = \left(\frac{\partial u}{\partial y}\right)_{P_0} + \left(\frac{\partial v}{\partial x}\right)_{P_0}$$

Let $(\gamma_{xy})_{P_0}$ be the angle which when subtracted from 90° gives the angle between the transformed line segments, i.e.,

$$\cos(P_0'P_1', P_0'P_2') = \cos\left[\frac{\pi}{2} - (\gamma_{xy})_{P_0}\right] = \sin(\gamma_{xy})_{P_0} \tag{2.12}$$

However, since $(\gamma_{xy})_{P_0}$ is small, $\sin (\gamma_{xy})_{P_0} \cong (\gamma_{xy})_{P_0}$ so that

$$(\gamma_{xy})_{P_0} = \left(\frac{\partial u}{\partial y}\right)_{P_0} + \left(\frac{\partial v}{\partial x}\right)_{P_0}$$

The term $(\gamma_{xy})_{P_0}$ is known as a shear strain. Similar treatment for initial line segments parallel to the y and z axes and the z and x axes give the shear strains γ_{yz} and γ_{zx}. Thus [dropping the subscript P_0 as was done prior to Eqs. (2.11)]

$$\gamma_{xy} = \frac{\partial u}{\partial y} + \frac{\partial v}{\partial x}$$

$$\gamma_{yz} = \frac{\partial v}{\partial z} + \frac{\partial w}{\partial y} \qquad (2.13)$$

$$\gamma_{zx} = \frac{\partial w}{\partial x} + \frac{\partial u}{\partial z}$$

In physical meaning, the shear-strain components γ_{xy}, γ_{yz}, and γ_{zx} represent the decrease in the right angles between two line segments in the neighborhood of $P(x,y,z)$ initially parallel to the x and y, y and z, and z and x axes, respectively. It is seen by Eq. (2.12) that a positive shear strain corresponds to a decrease in the right angle during deformation, and vice versa.

The six components of strain ϵ_x, ϵ_y, ϵ_z, γ_{xy}, γ_{yz}, γ_{zx} are illustrated in Fig. 2.2, where the deformation of a small, initially rectangular parallelepiped is shown. It should be noted that opposite sides of the element remain parallel after deformation owing to the restriction of the study to a small region in R which renders the law of transformation linear. The additional restriction of small deformations makes possible the introduction of the six components of strain having the physical significances shown.

It is useful to rewrite Eqs. (2.9) and (2.10) using the strain definitions in this section.

$$\epsilon_{P_0P} = \epsilon_x l^2 + \epsilon_y m^2 + \epsilon_z n^2 + \gamma_{xy}lm + \gamma_{yz}mn + \gamma_{zx}nl \qquad (2.14)$$

$$\gamma_{P_0P_1,P_0P_2} = (1 - \epsilon' - \epsilon'')[(l_1l_2 + m_1m_2 + n_1n_2)$$

$$+ 2(\epsilon_x l_1l_2 + \epsilon_y m_1m_2 + \epsilon_z n_1n_2) + \gamma_{xy}(l_1m_2 + l_2m_1)$$

$$+ \gamma_{yz}(m_1n_2 + m_2n_1) + \gamma_{zx}(n_1l_2 + n_2l_1)] \qquad (2.15)$$

Equation (2.14) gives the unit elongation of a line segment (originally having direction cosines l, m, and n) located in the neighborhood of point $P(x,y,z)$ in terms of the six cartesian strain components existing at the point. Equation (2.15) gives the decrease (if $\gamma_{P_0P_1,P_0P_2}$ is positive) of the original angle between any two line segments (originally having direction cosines l_1, m_1, n_1, and l_2, m_2, n_2) located near point $P(x,y,z)$ in terms of their unit elongations ϵ' and ϵ'' and the six cartesian strain components existing at the point.

2.7. Rigid Displacements of Local Regions under the Assumption of Infinitesimal Deformations. In addition to studying the changes in lengths of line segments and of the angles between line segments in a local region around P (which is now taken as the base point instead of P_0), it is helpful to determine the conditions under which the transformations (2.5) represent an infinitesimal rigid displacement of the entire local region. The transformations will be seen to be divisible into two parts, one representing a pure deformation and the other a rigid displacement of the local region around P. As the latter does not give rise to stresses, it is usually neglected in theoretical work; however, it is necessary to know something of its nature and to be able to recognize it when it appears in mathematical formulas. The concept of rigid displacements also underlies several experimental approaches to stress-analysis problems, e.g., problems of thermal stresses and others of the dislocation type.

One way to specify the condition of a rigid displacement is to require that relative distances between all points in the neighborhood of P remain unaltered.

If $P_1(x_1,y_1,z_1)$ and, $P_2(x_2,y_2,z_2)$ are any two points in the neighborhood of $P(x,y,z)$, the requirement is that $(P_1P_2)^2 = (P_1'P_2')^2$, or that

$$(x_2 - x_1)^2 + (y_2 - y_1)^2 + (z_2 - z_1)^2 = (x_2' - x_1')^2 + (y_2' - y_2')^2 + (z_2' - z_1')^2$$

By writing Eqs. (2.2) for points P_1 and P_2 and subtracting, this can be transformed to

$$(\Delta x_2 - \Delta x_1)^2 + (\Delta y_2 - \Delta y_1)^2 + (\Delta z_2 - \Delta z_1)^2$$
$$= (\Delta x_2' - \Delta x_1')^2 + (\Delta y_2' - \Delta y_1')^2 + (\Delta z_2' - \Delta z_1')^2$$

By Eqs. (2.5) and the assumption of infinitesimal deformations, this becomes

$$(\Delta x_2 - \Delta x_1)^2 + (\Delta y_2 - \Delta y_1)^2 + (\Delta z_2 - \Delta z_1)^2 = \left(1 + 2\frac{\partial u}{\partial x}\right)(\Delta x_2 - \Delta x_1)^2$$

$$+ \left(1 + 2\frac{\partial v}{\partial y}\right)(\Delta y_2 - \Delta y_1)^2 + \left(1 + 2\frac{\partial w}{\partial z}\right)(\Delta z_2 - \Delta z_1)^2$$

$$+ \left(\frac{\partial u}{\partial y} + \frac{\partial v}{\partial x}\right)(\Delta x_2 - \Delta x_1)(\Delta y_2 - \Delta y_1)$$

$$+ \left(\frac{\partial v}{\partial z} + \frac{\partial w}{\partial y}\right)(\Delta y_2 - \Delta y_1)(\Delta z_2 - \Delta z_1)$$

$$+ \left(\frac{\partial w}{\partial x} + \frac{\partial u}{\partial z}\right)(\Delta z_2 - \Delta z_1)(\Delta x_2 - \Delta x_1)$$

Since $\Delta x_2 - \Delta x_1$, $\Delta y_2 - \Delta y_1$, $\Delta z_2 - \Delta z_1$ are arbitrary, the condition for a rigid displacement is satisfied if, and only if,

$$\frac{\partial u}{\partial x} = \frac{\partial v}{\partial y} = \frac{\partial w}{\partial z} = \frac{\partial u}{\partial y} + \frac{\partial v}{\partial x} = \frac{\partial v}{\partial z} + \frac{\partial w}{\partial y} = \frac{\partial w}{\partial x} + \frac{\partial u}{\partial z} = 0$$

and thus, by the definitions in the preceding section, it is satisfied if, and only if, the six cartesian strain components at the point are zero, i.e.,

$$\epsilon_x = \epsilon_y = \epsilon_z = \gamma_{xy} = \gamma_{yz} = \gamma_{zz} = 0 \qquad (2.16)$$

The general transformation of the local neighborhood around P [Eqs. (2.5)] can be rewritten

$$\Delta x' - \Delta x = \frac{1}{2}\left(\frac{\partial u}{\partial y} - \frac{\partial v}{\partial x}\right)\Delta y - \frac{1}{2}\left(\frac{\partial w}{\partial x} - \frac{\partial u}{\partial z}\right)\Delta z + \epsilon_x \Delta x + \frac{\gamma_{xy}}{2}\Delta y + \frac{\gamma_{xz}}{2}\Delta z$$

$$\Delta y' - \Delta y = \frac{1}{2}\left(\frac{\partial v}{\partial z} - \frac{\partial w}{\partial y}\right)\Delta z - \frac{1}{2}\left(\frac{\partial u}{\partial y} - \frac{\partial v}{\partial x}\right)\Delta x + \frac{\gamma_{yx}}{2}\Delta x + \epsilon_y \Delta y + \frac{\gamma_{yz}}{2}\Delta z$$

$$\Delta z' - \Delta z = \frac{1}{2}\left(\frac{\partial w}{\partial x} - \frac{\partial u}{\partial z}\right)\Delta x - \frac{1}{2}\left(\frac{\partial v}{\partial z} - \frac{\partial w}{\partial y}\right)\Delta y + \frac{\gamma_{zz}}{2}\Delta x + \frac{\gamma_{zy}}{2}\Delta y + \epsilon_z \Delta z$$

Thus, by Eq. (2.16) and the above, it is seen that an infinitesimal rigid displacement of the local region around P is given by the equations

$$\Delta x' - \Delta x = \frac{1}{2}\left(\frac{\partial u}{\partial y} - \frac{\partial v}{\partial x}\right)\Delta y - \frac{1}{2}\left(\frac{\partial w}{\partial x} - \frac{\partial u}{\partial z}\right)\Delta z$$

$$\Delta y' - \Delta y = \frac{1}{2}\left(\frac{\partial v}{\partial z} - \frac{\partial w}{\partial y}\right)\Delta z - \frac{1}{2}\left(\frac{\partial u}{\partial y} - \frac{\partial v}{\partial x}\right)\Delta x \qquad (2.17)$$

$$\Delta z' - \Delta z = \frac{1}{2}\left(\frac{\partial w}{\partial x} - \frac{\partial u}{\partial z}\right)\Delta x - \frac{1}{2}\left(\frac{\partial v}{\partial z} - \frac{\partial w}{\partial y}\right)\Delta y$$

and a pure deformation of the region is given by

$$\Delta x' - \Delta x = \epsilon_x \Delta x + \frac{\gamma_{xy}}{2}\Delta y + \frac{\gamma_{xz}}{2}\Delta z$$

$$\Delta y' - \Delta y = \frac{\gamma_{yx}}{2}\Delta x + \epsilon_y \Delta y + \frac{\gamma_{yz}}{2}\Delta z \qquad (2.18)$$

$$\Delta z' - \Delta z = \frac{\gamma_{zz}}{2}\Delta x + \frac{\gamma_{zy}}{2}\Delta y + \epsilon_z \Delta z$$

Calling

$$\omega_x = \frac{1}{2}\left(\frac{\partial w}{\partial y} - \frac{\partial v}{\partial z}\right)$$

$$\omega_y = \frac{1}{2}\left(\frac{\partial u}{\partial z} - \frac{\partial w}{\partial x}\right) \qquad (2.19)$$

$$\omega_z = \frac{1}{2}\left(\frac{\partial v}{\partial x} - \frac{\partial u}{\partial y}\right)$$

the rotation components of the infinitesimal rigid displacement of the local region, Eqs. (2.17) become

$$\Delta x' - \Delta x = \omega_y \, \Delta z - \omega_z \, \Delta y$$
$$\Delta y' - \Delta y = \omega_z \, \Delta x - \omega_x \, \Delta z \qquad (2.20)$$
$$\Delta z' - \Delta z = \omega_x \, \Delta y - \omega_y \, \Delta x$$

The rotation components ω_x, ω_y, ω_z are the small angles of rotation about the x, y, and z axes, respectively, that the local region around P undergoes during its rigid displacement. They are positive when the rotation is counterclockwise when viewed along the coordinate axes toward the origin. The following will show these facts:

In a body R consider a small rectangular region S having points P_1 and P in its opposite corners. The projection of this on the xy plane is shown in Fig. 2.4. Let R' be the strained configuration of R, and suppose the small region S is rigidly displaced to the tilted region S' during this deformation; i.e., while various portions of R may be strained, it is assumed that the strain components evaluated at the particular region S are

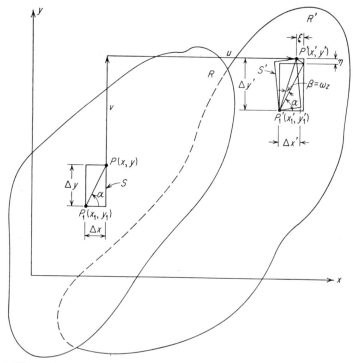

Fig. 2.4. Illustration of the translation and rotation of a small rectangular region S when the strain components at P (or P_1 since S is small), ϵ_x, ϵ_y, ϵ_z, γ_{xy}, γ_{yz}, γ_{zx}, are all zero during a general deformation of the body R to R'.

zero as in Eq. (2.16). The deformation of R is shown much larger in the figure than would be allowed under the assumption of infinitesimal deformations; however, this is done for clarity's sake only.

The rigid transformation of S can be divided into a translation (during which all points within it move the small amounts $x_1' - x_1 = u_1$ and $y_1' - y_1 = v_1$ in the x and y directions, respectively) and a counterclockwise rotation through the small angle ω_z. The displacements of point P are, then,†

$$u = x' - x = x_1' - x_1 + \xi = u_1 + \xi$$

$$v = y' - y = y_1' - y_1 + \eta = v_1 + \eta$$

Since the angle of rotation ω_z is small by the assumption of infinitesimal deformations and the line P_1P does not change length in transforming to $P_1'P'$, the geometry of the figure leads to the relations

$$\xi = -P_1'P'\omega_z \sin\alpha = -P_1P\omega_z \sin\alpha = -(y - y_1)\omega_z \qquad (a)$$

$$\eta = P_1'P'\omega_z \cos\alpha = P_1P\omega_z \cos\alpha = (x - x_1)\omega_z$$

Therefore,

$$u = u_1 - (y - y_1)\omega_z \qquad (b)$$

$$v = v_1 + (x - x_1)\omega_z$$

Since u, v_1, x_1, y_1, and ω_z are constant within the region S, their derivatives with respect to x and y are zero for variations within S, and hence, by Eqs. (b), the quantity

$$\frac{1}{2}\left(\frac{\partial v}{\partial x} - \frac{\partial u}{\partial y}\right) = \frac{1}{2}[\omega_z - (-\omega_z)] = \omega_z$$

This can be similarly done for ω_y and ω_x, and it thus verifies the statement that the components given by Eqs. (2.19) are the small counterclockwise angles of rotation (when viewed along the coordinate axes toward the origin) of the small neighborhood of point $P(x,y,z)$ during an infinitesimal rigid displacement of the region.

The figure also makes it possible to visualize the geometry of Eqs. (2.20). By the figure and Eqs. (a) above,

$$\xi = \Delta x' - \Delta x = -\Delta y\,\omega_z$$

$$\eta = \Delta y' - \Delta y = \Delta x\,\omega_z$$

These are two of the six terms in Eqs. (2.20). The remaining four terms can be similarly established by taking projections on the yz and zx planes.

2.8. Homogeneous Deformation. In Sec. 2.2, reference was made to the fact that, if derivatives of u, v, w higher than the first, were negligible in the general transformation laws (2.3), the series could be considered

† ξ and η are positive when representing displacements in the positive coordinate directions; hence $+\xi$ in this equation is actually a negative quantity.

sufficiently accurate by including only the terms shown. It was also seen that this linearization could be effected in a second manner, viz., by restricting the study to a small neighborhood of the base point P_0.

Consider the physical significance of the former. In view of the definitions of the cartesian strain components just discussed, the supposition that derivatives of u, v, w higher than the first are negligible implies that the strains are nearly constant throughout the region. This means that, physically, all parts of the body are subjected to nearly the same strain. In such a case, the body is said to be under a state of homogeneous deformation.

A very simple example is the case of uniaxial tension or compression in which, say, a long bar or rod is uniformly stretched or shortened.

It is clear that the case of homogeneous deformation is covered by all the equations and definitions subsequent to Eqs. (2.3); for example, the properties discussed at the end of Sec. 2.3 apply: planes remain planes during deformation, straight lines remain straight lines, etc. Since these same properties hold true for the displacement field within very small local regions in a body that is not homogeneously deformed, the deformation field within these small regions can therefore also be considered essentially homogeneous.

Thus the restriction applied in Sec. 2.3 can be stated more generally to cover both cases as a restriction of the study to a region of such size that the deformation field within it is homogeneous.

2.9. The Laws of Strain Transformation. In the study of stresses, it was seen that there are three normal stresses σ_x, σ_y, σ_z and three shear stresses τ_{xy}, τ_{yz}, τ_{zx} representing the stresses acting on planes parallel to the cartesian planes. In this chapter, three normal strains ϵ_x, ϵ_y, ϵ_z and three shear strains γ_{xy}, γ_{yz}, γ_{zx} have been found to characterize the behavior of line segments originally parallel to the cartesian axes. It might be expected that some further comparisons are possible between stresses and strains.

It has not been necessary to specify the location of the base point with respect to the origin of the coordinate system; hence no generality is lost if the origin is chosen at the base point P. Suppose this is done and a second orthogonal coordinate system $Px'y'z'$ is introduced with the x' axis paralleling the line segment PP_1 (Fig. 2.5a).

The normal strain of PP_1 can be called $\epsilon_{x'}$ and can be written in terms of the x, y, z components of strain by Eq. (2.14),

$$\epsilon_{x'} = \epsilon_x \cos^2(x',x) + \epsilon_y \cos^2(x',y) + \epsilon_z \cos^2(x',z) + \gamma_{xy} \cos(x',x)\cos(x',y)$$
$$+ \gamma_{yz} \cos(x',y)\cos(x',z) + \gamma_{zx} \cos(x',z)\cos(x',x) \qquad (2.21a)$$

If PP_1 is taken parallel to the y' and then the z' axes, two more similar equations can be obtained for $\epsilon_{y'}$, and $\epsilon_{z'}$.

Consider, next, two line segments PP_1 and PP_2 which are parallel to the x' and y' axes, respectively (Fig. 2.5b). The shear strain between these two lines is given by Eq. (2.15). By Eq. (1.10), $l_1 l_2 + m_1 m_2 + n_1 n_2 = 0$, and if the products of strains are again neglected the equation reduces to

$$
\begin{aligned}
\gamma_{x'y'} = {} & 2\epsilon_x \cos(x',x) \cos(y',x) + 2\epsilon_y \cos(x',y) \cos(y',y) \\
& + 2\epsilon_z \cos(x',z) \cos(y',z) \\
& + \gamma_{xy}[\cos(x',x) \cos(y',y) + \cos(x',y) \cos(y',x)] \\
& + \gamma_{yz}[\cos(x',y) \cos(y',z) + \cos(x',z) \cos(y',y)] \\
& + \gamma_{zx}[\cos(x',z) \cos(y',x) + \cos(x',x) \cos(y',z)] \qquad (2.21b)
\end{aligned}
$$

Two similar equations can be written for $\gamma_{y'z'}$ and $\gamma_{z'x'}$ by cyclic permutation.

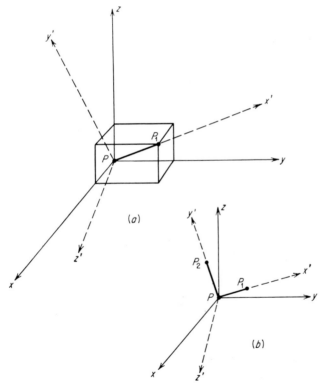

(a)

(b)

Fig. 2.5. Two orthogonal coordinate systems with origin at P for which the strain transformations (2.21a) and (2.21b) apply. In (a) the unit elongation of $PP_1(\epsilon_{x'})$ is given by Eq. (2.21a) in terms of the six x, y, z cartesian components of strain, and in (b) the decrease in the right angle P_1PP_2 (shear strain $\gamma_{x'y'}$) is given by Eq. (2.21b) in terms of the six x, y, z strain components. This figure is the strain counterpart of Fig. 1.8 for stresses.

Comparison of these equations to Eqs. (1.12) shows the transformation of strain to be governed by laws identical in form to those for stresses. In fact, the replacements

$$p_n \leftrightarrow S_n$$

$$\sigma_x \leftrightarrow \epsilon_x$$

$$\sigma_y \leftrightarrow \epsilon_y$$

$$\sigma_z \leftrightarrow \epsilon_z \qquad (2.22)$$

$$2\tau_{xy} \leftrightarrow \gamma_{xy}$$

$$2\tau_{yz} \leftrightarrow \gamma_{yz}$$

$$2\tau_{zx} \leftrightarrow \gamma_{zx}$$

will transform Eqs. (1.12) into the six equations just derived for strain, or vice versa. It follows that all the consequences of Eqs. (1.12) discussed in the chapter on stress have their counterpart in terms of strain. Some of the more important will be treated in the next section.

2.10. Principal Strains, Planes, and Directions: Definitions and Properties. Since the laws of stress and strain transformation at a point are identical in form, principal strains, planes, and directions must exist for strain in a manner analogous to those for stresses. It is only necessary to restate the results in Sec. 1.9 in terms of strains; however, some additional remarks on the physical significance of these concepts are useful.

The characteristic equation (1.16) can be written by (2.22)

$$\epsilon_i^3 - (\epsilon_x + \epsilon_y + \epsilon_z)\epsilon_i^2 + \left[\epsilon_x\epsilon_y + \epsilon_y\epsilon_z + \epsilon_z\epsilon_x - \left(\frac{\gamma_{xy}}{2}\right)^2 - \left(\frac{\gamma_{yz}}{2}\right)^2 - \left(\frac{\gamma_{zx}}{2}\right)^2 \right]\epsilon_i$$

$$- \left[\epsilon_x\epsilon_y\epsilon_z - \epsilon_x\left(\frac{\gamma_{yz}}{2}\right)^2 - \epsilon_y\left(\frac{\gamma_{zx}}{2}\right)^2 - \epsilon_z\left(\frac{\gamma_{xy}}{2}\right)^2 + \frac{\gamma_{xy}\gamma_{yz}\gamma_{zx}}{4} \right] = 0 \qquad (2.23)$$

where the three roots, say, ϵ_1, ϵ_2, ϵ_3, are three principal strains. As in the case of stresses, there are three possibilities.

Case 1. If ϵ_1, ϵ_2, and ϵ_3 are all different, there exists only one set of three mutually perpendicular principal directions of strain. These three principal strains are the change in lengths per unit length of line segments initially oriented in these three directions. The right angle initially formed by any one of these principal directions and another line remains a right angle, while all other original right angles do not remain right angles. Another way of stating this is that the three principal planes remain mutually perpendicular, while no other two originally perpendicular planes do. A rectangular parallelepiped whose sides are initially parallel to these three principal directions will transform to another rectangular parallelepiped, while one of any other original orientation will not remain rectangular.

Case 2. If two of the roots are equal, say, $\epsilon_1 \neq \epsilon_2 = \epsilon_3$, there are an infinite number of principal directions of strain. The direction of the line segment undergoing the strain ϵ_1 and all directions perpendicular to it are principal in this case. All planes normal to these directions are principal planes, i.e., the perpendicularity between any two of them is preserved during the deformation.

Case 3. If all three roots are equal, every direction is a principal direction of strain. All line segments undergo the same strain $\epsilon_1 = \epsilon_2 = \epsilon_3 = \epsilon_n$, and all right angles remain right angles during deformation.

Calculation of the principal directions and planes of strain is identical to the procedure outlined in Sec. 1.10 for stresses.

2.11. The Volume Dilatation. By adding Eq. (2.21a) and the two similar equations for $\epsilon_{y'}$ and $\epsilon_{z'}$ and using the direction cosine relations (1.9) and (1.10), the equation

$$\epsilon_{x'} + \epsilon_{y'} + \epsilon_{z'} = \epsilon_x + \epsilon_y + \epsilon_z$$

results. Thus, the sum of any three mutually perpendicular normal strains at a point is a constant, independent of the coordinate-system orientation.

The change in volume per unit volume of any small element of volume is given, under the assumption of infinitesimal deformations, by this sum. It is called the volume dilatation and is denoted by the symbol ϵ. This can be shown by considering a small rectangular parallelepiped in R that transforms to an oblique parallelepiped in R' (Fig. 2.2). The volume dilatation, by the above definition, is

$$\epsilon = \frac{\Delta V}{V} = \frac{V' - V}{V}$$

where V and V' are, respectively, the original and transformed volumes of the parallelepiped. The final volume is given approximately by $(1 + \epsilon_x)(1 + \epsilon_y)(1 + \epsilon_z)\, \Delta x\, \Delta y\, \Delta z$ so that

$$\epsilon = \frac{(1 + \epsilon_x)(1 + \epsilon_y)(1 + \epsilon_z) - 1}{1}$$

Expanding and neglecting products of strains higher than the first, this becomes

$$\epsilon = \epsilon_x + \epsilon_y + \epsilon_z \tag{2.24}$$

2.12. Continuity of Displacements. Consider the region inside the narrow strip ABC (Fig. 2.6). Let the displacement u be a discontinuous function of x. For example, let

$$u = -1 \quad \text{for} \quad 0 \leq x \leq 5$$

$$u = +1 \quad \text{for} \quad 5 < x \leq 10$$

Under such a displacement, the portions AB and BC move to $A'B'$ and $B''C'$, respectively, and are separated by a gap. A discontinuous displacement u is therefore seen to produce a gap in the final geometry. Obviously the necessary and sufficient condition that no gap exists in the final geometry is that all three displacement components u, v, and w are continuous functions of the space coordinates x, y, and z.

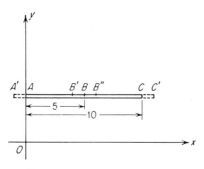

Fig. 2.6. A discontinuous displacement u in the strip ABC would produce a gap at some point B.

2.13. Equations of Compatibility. From Eqs. (2.11) and (2.13) it is seen that the six strain components ϵ_x, ϵ_y, . . . , are space derivatives of the three displacement components u, v, and w. If the latter are given as continuous functions of the space coordinates x, y, and z, the six strain components can always be uniquely determined by means of the six equations given by Eqs. (2.11) and (2.13). The question now arises as to what would happen if the six strain components are given and the three displacement components are desired. Here we still have six equations, Eqs. (2.11) and (2.13). But, instead of six unknowns, we have only three unknowns. With algebraic equations we know that, for three unknowns, three equations are generally necessary and sufficient to obtain a solution. Six equations will be three too many, because the solutions of the unknowns obtained from the first three equations generally will not satisfy the last three equations. No solution can exist unless the coefficients of these six equations satisfy certain specific relations so that the solutions obtained from the first three equations are identical to those from the last three equations. From the above discussion on algebraic equations it seems reasonable to expect that in general no displacement components can satisfy the six partial-differential equations (2.11) and (2.13), unless the given strain components satisfy some specific relations. This can also be demonstrated from geometrical considerations. Let the body be divided into a large number of small cubes. These cubes will be distorted into parallelepipeds of different proportions according to the prescribed strain conditions. For these various parallelepipeds to fit their neighbors perfectly, the prescribed strain components must be of a particular type satisfying certain conditions. The strains which distort cubes into parallelepipeds that do not fit with each other are called incompatible strains. The ones that give compatible parallelepipeds are called compatible strains. The condition that strains must satisfy in order to be compatible is called the compatibility condition, and this is expressed mathematically by the compatibility equations. Geometrical considerations thus also lead us to expect the existence of some relationships between the strains if the corresponding displacement field is to be continuous and the distorted geometry is to have no gaps.

The relations between strains and displacements are summarized in the two following theorems applicable to infinitesimal deformations:

1. If the displacement components u, v, and w are continuous functions of the space coordinates x, y, and z, then the corresponding strain components obtained from the displacement-strain relations (2.11) and (2.13) satisfy the following six equations:

$$\frac{\partial^2 \epsilon_x}{\partial y^2} + \frac{\partial^2 \epsilon_y}{\partial x^2} = \frac{\partial^2 \gamma_{xy}}{\partial x\, \partial y}$$

$$\frac{\partial^2 \epsilon_y}{\partial z^2} + \frac{\partial^2 \epsilon_z}{\partial y^2} = \frac{\partial^2 \gamma_{yz}}{\partial y\, \partial z}$$

$$\frac{\partial^2 \epsilon_z}{\partial x^2} + \frac{\partial^2 \epsilon_x}{\partial z^2} = \frac{\partial^2 \gamma_{zx}}{\partial z\, \partial x}$$

$$2\frac{\partial^2 \epsilon_x}{\partial y\, \partial z} = \frac{\partial}{\partial x}\left(-\frac{\partial \gamma_{yz}}{\partial x} + \frac{\partial \gamma_{xz}}{\partial y} + \frac{\partial \gamma_{xy}}{\partial z}\right)$$

$$2\frac{\partial^2 \epsilon_y}{\partial z\, \partial x} = \frac{\partial}{\partial y}\left(\frac{\partial \gamma_{yz}}{\partial x} - \frac{\partial \gamma_{xz}}{\partial y} + \frac{\partial \gamma_{xy}}{\partial z}\right)$$

$$2\frac{\partial^2 \epsilon_z}{\partial x\, \partial y} = \frac{\partial}{\partial z}\left(\frac{\partial \gamma_{yz}}{\partial x} + \frac{\partial \gamma_{xz}}{\partial y} - \frac{\partial \gamma_{xy}}{\partial z}\right)$$

(2.25)

2. In a simply connected body, if the strain components satisfy Eqs. (2.25), then there exist an infinite number of sets of displacement components u, v, and w with the following properties:

(a) They are continuous functions of the space coordinates x, y, and z.

(b) Each set of displacement components satisfy the strain-displacement relations (2.11) and (2.13).

(c) These sets of displacement components differ from each other by rigid-body displacements only.

A simply connected body is one where every closed curve drawn in the body can be shrunk to a point without passing out of the boundaries of the body (Fig. 2.7). Thus a ring or a torus is not a simply connected body. The region inside a circle or between two concentric spheres is a simply connected region.

Equations (2.25), which are a measure of whether the strains are compatible or not, are called the compatibility equations.

The first theorem can be readily proved. Differentiating Eqs. (2.11) and (2.13), we have

$$\frac{\partial^2 \epsilon_x}{\partial y^2} = \frac{\partial^3 u}{\partial x\,\partial y^2}$$

$$\frac{\partial^2 \epsilon_y}{\partial x^2} = \frac{\partial^3 v}{\partial x^2\,\partial y}$$

$$\frac{\partial^2 \gamma_{xy}}{\partial x\,\partial y} = \frac{\partial^3 u}{\partial x\,\partial y^2} + \frac{\partial^3 v}{\partial x^2\,\partial y}$$

from which

$$\frac{\partial^2 \epsilon_x}{\partial y^2} + \frac{\partial^2 \epsilon_y}{\partial x^2} = \frac{\partial^2 \gamma_{xy}}{\partial x\,\partial y}$$

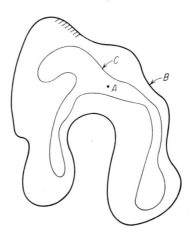

FIG. 2.7. Simply connected body. Any closed curve C drawn inside the body can be shrunk to a point A without passing out of the boundaries B.

The remaining five equations in Eqs. (2.25) can be proved in a similar manner.

The proof of the second theorem is beyond the scope of this book.[†]

†See I. S. Sokolnikoff, "Mathematical Theory of Elasticity," 1st ed., p. 24, McGraw-Hill Book Company, Inc., New York, 1946.

2.14. Finite Deformations. For large deformations, the products of strain components cannot be neglected with respect to the strains themselves as has been assumed in Sec. 2.4, and the relationships developed for infinitesimal strains become very poor approximations. For example, consider a rubber thread of length l_0 pulled to twice its initial length in two stages. In the first stage, the thread is pulled from l_0 to $1.5l_0$, and the strain is $(1.5l_0 - l_0)/l_0 = \frac{1}{2}$. In the second stage, the thread is pulled from $1.5l_0$ to $2l_0$, and the increase of strain is $(2l_0 - 1.5l_0)/1.5l_0 = \frac{1}{3}$. Hence the total strain is $\frac{1}{2} + \frac{1}{3} = 0.83$. By using the conventional formula for infinitesimal strains, the strain in the first stage will be $(1.5l_0 - l_0)/l_0 = \frac{1}{2}$, and the increase of strain in the second stage will be $(2l_0 - 1.5l_0)/l_0 = \frac{1}{2}$, so that the total strain is unity. Evidently the initial length at the beginning of the second stage is $1.5l_0$ and not l_0 so that the conventional formula derived on the assumption of infinitesimal strain is in appreciable error. Now if we divide the above pulling test into four stages, with one-fourth elongation taking place in each stage, then the changes of strain in the four stages will be $(1.25l_0 - l_0)/l_0$, $(1.50l_0 - 1.25l_0)/1.25l_0$, $(1.75l_0 - 1.50l_0)/1.50l_0$, and $(2l_0 - 1.75l_0)/1.75l_0$. The total strain will be 0.76. If we plot a curve $y = 1/x$ and erect ordinates at $x = l_0$, $1.25l_0$, $1.50l_0$, $1.75l_0$, and $2l_0$ (Fig. 2.8), then the total strains computed above from one-stage,

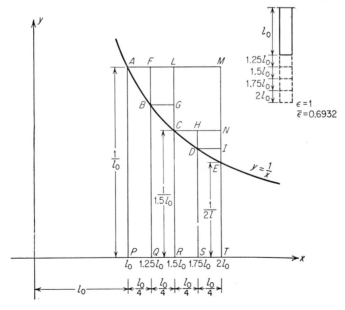

FIG. 2.8. Geometrical representation of natural strain. In a unidimensional strain where the total length of a specimen is increased from l_0 to $2l_0$ the natural strain is given by the area under the curve ACE.

two-stage, and four-stage elongation are equal to the areas of $PAMT$, $PALCNT$ and $PAFBGCHDIT$, respectively. Obviously, if we divide the pulling test into more stages, the zigzag line will come closer to the curve $ABCDE$. In the limit, if we divide the pulling test into an infinite number of stages, then the total strain will be equal to the area under the curve $ABCDE$,

$$\bar{\epsilon} = \int_{l_0}^{2l_0} \frac{1}{x} \, dx = [\ln x]_{l_0}^{2l_0} = \ln 2 = 0.693$$

where ln is the natural logarithm.

The strain calculated from an infinite number of subdivisions of deformations is called natural strain and is usually denoted by $\bar{\epsilon}$ in distinction to the conventional strain ϵ calculated from the formula based on infinitesimal deformation. For the general case of a bar pulled from an initial length l_0 to a final length l, by the same method shown above, we can obtain

$$\bar{\epsilon} = [\ln x]_{l_0}^{l} = \ln \frac{l}{l_0} = \ln (1 + \epsilon)$$

where ϵ denotes the conventional strain.

A comparison between the natural strain and conventional strain is given in Table 2.1. It is seen that for small deformations, these two strains have nearly equal values.

TABLE 2.1. COMPARISON BETWEEN NATURAL AND CONVENTIONAL STRAIN

ϵ	-1	-0.5	-0.1	-0.05	-0.01	0	0.01	0.05	0.1	0.5	1
$\bar{\epsilon}$	$-\infty$	-0.693	-0.1054	-0.0513	-0.01005	0	0.00995	0.04879	0.0953	0.4055	0.6932
Difference, %	∞	38.6	5.4	2.6	0.5	0	0.5	2.4	4.7	18.9	30.7

2.15. Octahedral Strains. Octahedral strains are analogous to octahedral stresses as defined in Sec. 1.13. Thus

$$\epsilon_{oct} = \frac{\epsilon_1 + \epsilon_2 + \epsilon_3}{3} \tag{2.26}$$

$$\gamma_{oct} = \tfrac{2}{3} \sqrt{(\epsilon_1 - \epsilon_2)^2 + (\epsilon_2 - \epsilon_3)^2 + (\epsilon_3 - \epsilon_1)^2} \tag{2.27}$$

Physically, the strain ϵ_{oct} is the change in length per unit length of line segments inclined at an angle 54°45′ to each of the three principal axes. The strain γ_{oct} represents the change in the original right angle between any one of these line segments and particular lines depending on the given state of strain lying in the octahedral planes.

2.16. Decomposition of a State of Strain into Pure Volumetric and Distortional Deformation Components. The discussion in this section parallels that in Sec. 1.14 for stresses.

The state of strain at a general point P can be represented by the strain tensor,

$$
\mathbf{E} = \begin{bmatrix}
\epsilon_x & \dfrac{\gamma_{xy}}{2} & \dfrac{\gamma_{xz}}{2} \\[2mm]
\dfrac{\gamma_{yx}}{2} & \epsilon_y & \dfrac{\gamma_{yz}}{2} \\[2mm]
\dfrac{\gamma_{zx}}{2} & \dfrac{\gamma_{zy}}{2} & \epsilon_z
\end{bmatrix}
\tag{2.28}
$$

If the $Pxyz$ coordinate system is principal, then

$$
\mathbf{E} = \begin{bmatrix}
\epsilon_1 & 0 & 0 \\
0 & \epsilon_2 & 0 \\
0 & 0 & \epsilon_3
\end{bmatrix}
\tag{2.29}
$$

By the same reasoning as given in Sec. (1.14) for stresses, the strain tensor $\mathbf{E}$ can be decomposed into two states of strain which, if superposed, are equivalent to the strain state $\mathbf{E}$. Thus

$$
\mathbf{E} = \mathbf{E}' + \mathbf{E}''
$$

The strain tensor $\mathbf{E}''$ is defined as

$$
\mathbf{E}'' = \begin{bmatrix}
\epsilon_m & 0 & 0 \\
0 & \epsilon_m & 0 \\
0 & 0 & \epsilon_m
\end{bmatrix}
\tag{2.30}
$$

where

$$
\begin{aligned}
\epsilon_m &= \tfrac{1}{3}(\epsilon_x + \epsilon_y + \epsilon_z) \\
&= \tfrac{1}{3}(\epsilon_1 + \epsilon_2 + \epsilon_3)
\end{aligned}
\tag{2.31}
$$

This represents a pure volumetric deformation since there are no shear strains and is referred to as the *spherical strain tensor*. The strain tensor $\mathbf{E}'$ is defined as

$$
\mathbf{E}' = \begin{bmatrix}
\epsilon_x - \epsilon_m & \dfrac{\gamma_{xy}}{2} & \dfrac{\gamma_{xz}}{2} \\[2mm]
\dfrac{\gamma_{yx}}{2} & \epsilon_y - \epsilon_m & \dfrac{\gamma_{yz}}{2} \\[2mm]
\dfrac{\gamma_{zx}}{2} & \dfrac{\gamma_{zy}}{2} & \epsilon_z - \epsilon_m
\end{bmatrix}
\tag{2.32}
$$

or if the $Pxyz$ coordinate system is principal,

$$\mathbf{E'} = \begin{bmatrix} \epsilon_1 - \epsilon_m & 0 & 0 \\ 0 & \epsilon_2 - \epsilon_m & 0 \\ 0 & 0 & \epsilon_3 - \epsilon_m \end{bmatrix} \tag{2.33}$$

This represents a pure distortion since there is no associated volumetric change. This is shown by applying Eq. (2.24), thus:

$$\epsilon' = (\epsilon_x - \epsilon_m) + (\epsilon_y - \epsilon_m) + (\epsilon_z - \epsilon_m)$$
$$= \epsilon_x + \epsilon_y + \epsilon_z - 3\epsilon_m$$
$$= 0$$

The tensor $\mathbf{E'}$ is otherwise referred to as the *deviator strain tensor*.

The strain invariants associated with the states of strain $\mathbf{E}$, $\mathbf{E'}$, and $\mathbf{E''}$ are [cf. Eqs. (1.22), (1.42), (1.43)]

$$J_1 = \epsilon_1 + \epsilon_2 + \epsilon_3$$
$$J_2 = \epsilon_1\epsilon_2 + \epsilon_2\epsilon_3 + \epsilon_3\epsilon_1 \tag{2.34}$$
$$J_3 = \epsilon_1\epsilon_2\epsilon_3$$

$$J_1' = 0$$
$$J_2' = -\tfrac{1}{6}[(\epsilon_1 - \epsilon_2)^2 + (\epsilon_2 - \epsilon_3)^2 + (\epsilon_3 - \epsilon_1)^2] \tag{2.35}$$
$$J_3' = \tfrac{1}{27}[(2\epsilon_1 - \epsilon_2 - \epsilon_3)(2\epsilon_2 - \epsilon_3 - \epsilon_1)(2\epsilon_3 - \epsilon_1 - \epsilon_2)]$$

$$J_1'' = 3\epsilon_m$$
$$J_2'' = 3\epsilon_m^2 \tag{2.36}$$
$$J_3'' = \epsilon_m^3$$

EXERCISE

2.1. Discuss the following displacement fields:

(a) $u = ax,$　　$v = ay,$　　$w = az$

(b) $u = ax,$　　$v = w = 0$

(c) $u = 2ay,$　　$v = w = 0$

CHAPTER 3

GEOMETRIC REPRESENTATIONS OF THE STATE OF STRESS AND STRAIN AT A POINT

3.1. Introduction. The state of stress at a point has been shown to be characterized by Eqs. (1.5) and (1.12), while the state of strain at a point has been seen to be governed by analogous equations (2.21). Some geometric methods of representing these laws are presented in this chapter. By means of these, additional insight will be gained into the previously discussed concepts of principal stresses (or strains) and principal planes and directions and also into some characteristics of the states of stress and strain hitherto not discussed. The representations discussed in this chapter apply to the three-dimensional state of stress and strain at a point. Methods of representing two-dimensional states of stress (i.e., when one of the principal stresses is zero) are treated in Chap. 7.

Since the equations referred to above are identical in form for both stresses and strains, the treatment can be carried out in terms of either; and, arbitrarily, stresses will be chosen. The replacements (2.22) are the only changes necessary to convert the discussion in this chapter into terms of strain.

To avoid repetition, some preliminary concepts and equations that will be used in connection with the geometric constructions will be discussed first.

Let σ_1, σ_2, σ_3 be the three principal stresses characterizing the state of stress at a point in the body, and for convenience let them be ordered in the manner $\sigma_1 \geq \sigma_2 \geq \sigma_3$. Consider a "local" cartesian-coordinate system centered at the point, with its x, y, and z axes parallel to the three principal directions corresponding to σ_1, σ_2, and σ_3, respectively. There is no loss of generality in carrying out the discussion for a coordinate system so oriented since it was established in Sec. 1.9 that the principal directions can be determined for any given state of stress. Using the above conventions, the cartesian stress components become

$$\sigma_x = \sigma_1 \qquad \sigma_y = \sigma_2 \qquad \sigma_z = \sigma_3 \qquad \tau_{xy} = \tau_{yz} = \tau_{zz} = 0$$

and Eqs. (1.5) simplify to

$$p_{nx} = \sigma_1 \cos(n,x)$$
$$p_{ny} = \sigma_2 \cos(n,y) \qquad\qquad (3.1)$$
$$p_{nz} = \sigma_3 \cos(n,z)$$

The resultant stress on any plane passing through the point,

$$p_n = \sqrt{p_{nx}^2 + p_{ny}^2 + p_{nz}^2} \tag{3.2}$$

can then be written

$$p_n = \sqrt{\sigma_1^2 \cos^2 (n,x) + \sigma_2^2 \cos^2 (n,y) + \sigma_3^2 \cos^2 (n,z)} \tag{3.3}$$

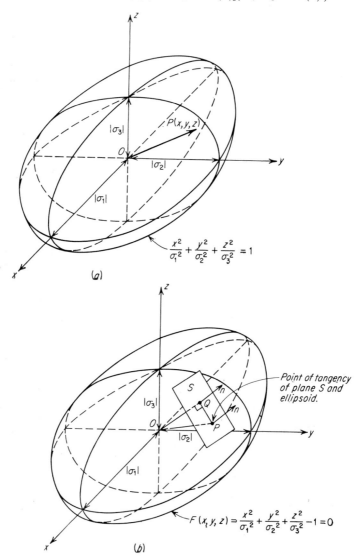

Fig. 3.1. Stress ellipsoid. In (a) the magnitude of the resultant stress p_n is represented by OP. In (b) OQ is drawn perpendicular to S, which is tangent to the ellipsoid. The magnitude of p_n is represented by OQ. The plane through the origin on which p_n acts is parallel to S and has the normal n.

Further, the normal stress acting on any plane passing through the point, as given by Eq. (1.3), can be written, using Eqs. (3.1),

$$\sigma_n = \sigma_1 \cos^2 (n,x) + \sigma_2 \cos^2 (n,y) + \sigma_3 \cos^2 (n,z) \tag{3.4}$$

3.2. The Stress Ellipsoid or Ellipsoid of Lamé. If Eqs. (3.1) are solved for the three direction cosines, then, squared and added, the equation

$$\frac{p_{nx}^2}{\sigma_1^2} + \frac{p_{ny}^2}{\sigma_2^2} + \frac{p_{nz}^2}{\sigma_3^2} = 1$$

is obtained since the sum of the squares of the direction cosines is equal to unity. This is the equation of an ellipsoid if referred to a coordinate system having p_{nx}, p_{ny}, and p_{nz} as cartesian axes. Considering these stress components synonymous with the coordinates x, y, and z of the local coordinate system at the point, the equation can be written

$$\frac{x^2}{\sigma_1^2} + \frac{y^2}{\sigma_2^2} + \frac{z^2}{\sigma_3^2} = 1 \tag{3.5}$$

The surface (3.5) is called the stress ellipsoid, or the ellipsoid of Lamé, and has the property that the radius vector from the origin O to a point $P(x,y,z) \equiv P(p_{nx},p_{ny},p_{nz})$ on the ellipsoid surface, and which has a length $p_n = \sqrt{p_{nx}^2 + p_{ny}^2 + p_{nz}^2}$, is equal to the magnitude of the resultant stress acting on some plane through point O. This is illustrated in Fig. 3.1a. An auxiliary construction of some kind is necessary in order to determine the plane.

The semiaxes have lengths equal to the magnitudes of the principal stresses at the point, and it can thus be concluded that the numerically largest and numerically smallest principal stresses at the point are at the same time the maximum and minimum of the resultant stresses acting on all planes through the point.

There are degenerate cases of the ellipsoid. When two of the principal stresses are equal, the ellipsoid becomes an ellipsoid of revolution about the axis parallel to the third, and when all three are equal, it becomes a sphere. The cases when one or two of the principal stresses are zero are treated in Sec. 7.2.

3.3. The Stress-director Surface. One of the auxiliary constructions which determines the plane on which the resultant stress represented by a particular radius vector of the stress ellipsoid acts is called the stress-director surface and is given by

$$\frac{x^2}{\sigma_1} + \frac{y^2}{\sigma_2} + \frac{z^2}{\sigma_3} = \pm 1 \tag{3.6}$$

When all the stresses σ_1, σ_2, σ_3 are positive, the plus sign must be chosen and the surface is an ellipsoid. When one or two are negative, both signs are taken and the surface splits up into two hyperboloids. When all are negative, the minus sign is chosen and the surface is again an ellipsoid.

The construction is used in the following way: The resultant stress p_n represented by a radius vector from the origin O to a point P on the stress ellipsoid acts on a plane through O that is parallel to the plane which is tangent to the stress-director surface at its point of intersection with the line OP. As it is difficult to visualize and use this construction in three dimensions, it will be more thoroughly discussed and proved in Chap. 7 for the two-dimensional case.

3.4. Tangent-plane Construction to the Stress Ellipsoid. This construction in connection with the stress ellipsoid allows the visualization of the magnitude of the resultant stress acting on any given plane. It does not, however, give the direction of the resultant stress. Let the given plane have a normal n. Referring to Fig. 3.1b, if a line is extended along n from the origin O to a point Q where it intersects at right angles a plane S tangent to the ellipsoid, the length of the line will be equal to the desired resultant stress.

To show the above property, consider Eq. (3.5) written in the form

$$F(x,y,z) = \frac{x^2}{\sigma_1^2} + \frac{y^2}{\sigma_2^2} + \frac{z^2}{\sigma_3^2} - 1 = 0$$

The cosines of the angles between the normal n at any point $P(x,y,z)$ on the surface $F(x,y,z) = 0$ and the x, y, z axes are given by†

$$\cos(n,x) = \frac{\partial F/\partial x}{R}$$

$$\cos(n,y) = \frac{\partial F/\partial y}{R} \tag{3.7}$$

$$\cos(n,z) = \frac{\partial F/\partial z}{R}$$

where

$$R = \sqrt{\left(\frac{\partial F}{\partial x}\right)^2 + \left(\frac{\partial F}{\partial y}\right)^2 + \left(\frac{\partial F}{\partial z}\right)^2}$$

Note that P in Fig. 3.1b now represents a generic point on the surface and does not in general coincide with the vector OP in Fig. 3.1a.

Applying this to the above ellipsoid, the direction cosines of the normal

---

†This is usually discussed in calculus texts treating the implicit representation of surfaces. See, for instance, R. Courant, "Differential and Integral Calculus," vol. II, p. 129, Interscience Publishers, Inc., New York, 1936.

n at the point of tangency of the plane S to the surface are

$$\cos (n,x) = \frac{x/\sigma_1^2}{\sqrt{x^2/\sigma_1^4 + y^2/\sigma_2^4 + z^2/\sigma_3^4}}$$

$$\cos (n,y) = \frac{y/\sigma_2^2}{\sqrt{x^2/\sigma_1^4 + y^2/\sigma_2^4 + z^2/\sigma_3^4}} \qquad (3.8)$$

$$\cos (n,z) = \frac{z/\sigma_3^2}{\sqrt{x^2/\sigma_1^4 + y^2/\sigma_2^4 + z^2/\sigma_3^4}}$$

These are also the direction cosines for the line OQ since OQ is parallel to n.

Now the direction cosines of the line OP are x/OP, y/OP, z/OP. The cosine of the angle between OP and OQ is the sum of the pairwise products of their individual direction cosines [see Eq. (1.2)], so that

$$\cos \angle POQ = \frac{x^2/\sigma_1^2 + y^2/\sigma_2^2 + z^2/\sigma_3^2}{OP\sqrt{x^2/\sigma_1^4 + y^2/\sigma_2^4 + z^2/\sigma_3^4}}$$

But since $\angle OQP$ is a right angle,

$$OQ = OP \cos \angle POQ = \frac{x^2/\sigma_1^2 + y^2/\sigma_2^2 + z^2/\sigma_3^2}{\sqrt{x^2/\sigma_1^4 + y^2/\sigma_2^4 + z^2/\sigma_3^4}}$$

By Eq. (3.5), the numerator in this last equation and its square root are equal, so that

$$OQ = \frac{\sqrt{x^2/\sigma_1^2 + y^2/\sigma_2^2 + z^2/\sigma_3^2}}{\sqrt{x^2/\sigma_1^4 + y^2/\sigma_2^4 + z^2/\sigma_3^4}}$$

$$= \sqrt{\frac{\sigma_1^2(x^2/\sigma_1^4) + \sigma_2^2(y^2/\sigma_2^4) + \sigma_3^2(z^2/\sigma_3^4)}{x^2/\sigma_1^4 + y^2/\sigma_2^4 + z^2/\sigma_3^4}}$$

and finally, by using Eqs. (3.8),

$$OQ = \sqrt{\sigma_1^2 \cos^2 (n,x) + \sigma_2^2 \cos^2 (n,y) + \sigma_3^2 \cos^2 (n,z)}$$

Comparison of this with Eq. (3.3) shows that

$$OQ = p_n$$

which was to be shown.

The ellipsoid can be used to visualize the results stated in the three cases in Sec. 1.9. Thus, if $\sigma_1 \neq \pm\sigma_2$, $\sigma_2 \neq \pm\sigma_3$, $\sigma_3 \neq \pm\sigma_1$, the lengths of the three principal semiaxes of the ellipsoid [which have, by (3.5), the lengths $|\sigma_1|$, $|\sigma_2|$, $|\sigma_3|$] are different. In this case, point Q can touch the surface of the ellipsoid in only six places, i.e., at the intersections of the surface and the coordinate axes. There are only three planes on which the resultant stress is perpendicular to the plane on which it acts. These planes are mutually perpendicular. There are only three principal directions and these are mutually perpendicular. This is the Case 1 discussed in Sec. 1.9 and depicted in Fig. 1.9a (except that in Fig. 1.9a the coordinate axes have not been taken as principal axes).

If two of the principal stresses are equal (say, $\pm\sigma_1 \neq \sigma_2 = \sigma_3$), then the ellipsoid is an ellipsoid of revolution about the x axis and point Q can touch the surface all along the circle $y^2 + z^2 = \sigma_2^2$ on the plane $x = 0$ and, also, at the two points of intersection of the surface with the x axis. Thus, the x axis is a principal direction (corresponding to σ_1), and all directions perpendicular to the x axis are principal directions (corresponding to $\sigma_2 = \sigma_3$). This corresponds to Case 2, Sec. 1.9. Figure 1.9b pictures this case if the coordinate system is rotated so that the x axis is coincident with the σ_1 direction.

If all three principal stresses are equal (say, $\sigma_1 = \sigma_2 = \sigma_3 = \sigma_n$), the ellipsoid degenerates to a sphere of radius $|\sigma_n|$ and point Q always lies on the surface. In this case, the distance OQ is always equal to the radius, so that all planes are principal planes. This is Case 3, Sec. 1.9, and is shown in Fig. 1.9c.

3.5. The Stress Quadric of Cauchy. As another example of methods for graphically representing the equations governing the state of stress at a point, consider the quadric surface

$$\sigma_1 x^2 + \sigma_2 y^2 + \sigma_3 z^2 = \pm 1 \qquad (3.9)$$

constructed in the local coordinate system at the point (Fig. 3.2). It will be shown that the length of a line OP running from the origin O to a point P on the surface is inversely proportional to the square root of the absolute value of the normal stress σ_n acting on a plane through the point whose normal n is coincident with the direction of OP.

To show this, consider the coordinates of P,

$$x = OP \cos (n,x)$$

$$y = OP \cos (n,y) \qquad (a)$$

$$z = OP \cos (n,z)$$

The equation of the surface (3.9) can be written

$$\sigma_1 \cos^2 (n,x) + \sigma_2 \cos^2 (n,y) + \sigma_3 \cos^2 (n,z) = \pm\frac{1}{(OP)^2}$$

Comparing this with Eq. (3.4), it is seen that

$$\sigma_n = \pm\frac{1}{(OP)^2} \qquad \text{or} \qquad OP = \frac{1}{\sqrt{|\sigma_n|}} \qquad (3.10)$$

which was to be shown.

The plus and minus signs in Eqs. (3.9) and (3.10) are necessary to take into account all possible combinations of the sign of the stress σ_n and of the principal stresses σ_1, σ_2, σ_3.

A discussion of these results is best accomplished by treating all possible cases separately.

Case 1. All Principal Stresses Positive, $\sigma_1 \geq \sigma_2 \geq \sigma_3 > 0$. Here the plus sign must be chosen in Eq. (3.9). The surface is an ellipsoid with

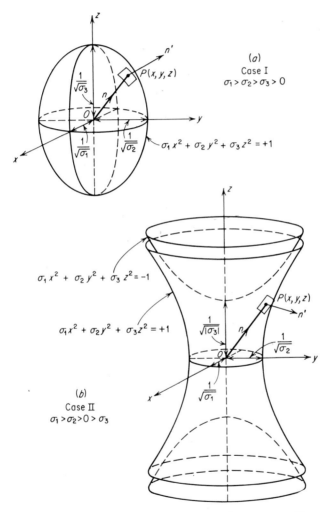

FIG. 3.2. Stress quadric of Cauchy. (*a*) All principal stresses positive and (*b*) one principal stress negative. The length of a line segment extending from O to a point P on the quadric surface is inversely proportional to the square root of the absolute value of the normal component of stress acting on a plane perpendicular to OP.

principal axes of lengths $2/\sqrt{\sigma_1}$, $2/\sqrt{\sigma_2}$, $2/\sqrt{\sigma_3}$, parallel to the principal directions of stresses (Fig. 3.2a). The smallest and largest principal axes are along the x and z axes, respectively, as a result of the ordering $\sigma_1 \geq \sigma_2 \geq \sigma_3$.

In particular, if two of the three principal stresses are equal, the surface becomes an ellipsoid of revolution, and if all three are equal, it becomes a sphere. It is interesting to note that, since the surface is bounded in all these possibilities, there exists no plane on which the normal stress σ_n is zero, i.e. on which only shear stresses act. To put this in another way, if all three principal stresses are tensile, then there are tensile stresses of some degree on every plane through the point.

Case 2. One Principal Stress Negative, $\sigma_1 \geq \sigma_2 > 0 > \sigma_3$. By the ordering convention $\sigma_1 \geq \sigma_2 \geq \sigma_3$ previously set up in Sec. 3.1, this is the only possible case of a single negative principal stress. Both signs in Eq. (3.9) are applicable, and the quadric surface splits into two parts, (1) a hyperboloid of one sheet (corresponding to the plus sign), and (2) a hyperboloid of two sheets (corresponding to the minus sign). This is illustrated in Fig. 3.2b. The cross section on the xy plane ($z = 0$) is the ellipse

$$\sigma_1 x^2 + \sigma_2 y^2 = 1$$

with largest principal axis in the y direction since $\sigma_1 > \sigma_2$.

By the theory of conic surfaces, the two conics are mutually asymptotic to the cone,†

$$\sigma_1 x^2 + \sigma_2 y^2 + \sigma_3 z^2 = 0$$

When the line OP approaches coincidence with a generator of the asymptotic cone, the point $P \rightarrow \infty$ and since $OP = 1/\sqrt{|\sigma_n|}$, $\sigma_n \rightarrow 0$. Hence, the normal stress is zero on planes perpendicular to the generators of the cone. There are an infinite number of such planes. All lines OP terminating on the surface of the hyperboloid of two sheets are perpendicular to planes on which negative normal stresses (compression) act, while lines terminating on the hyperboloid of one sheet correspond to planes on which positive (tensile) normal stresses act. The asymptotic cone represents the transition between these two cases.

Finally, if $\sigma_1 = \sigma_2 > 0 > \sigma_3$, the surfaces are hyperboloids of revolution.

Case 3. Two Principal Stresses Negative, $\sigma_1 > 0 > \sigma_2 \geq \sigma_3$. By reasoning similar to that in Case 2, the conic surface is split into two parts again, but here the x axis is the central axis, and all rays OP extending out to the hyperboloid of one sheet correspond to outer normals of planes having a compressive normal stress, and those extending out to the hyperboloid of two sheets correspond to planes of tensile stresses.

†Remembering that $\sigma_3 < 0$, this equation represents the cone as given more familiarly in solid analytical geometry in the form $x^2/a^2 + y^2/b^2 - z^2/c^2 = 0$.

Case 4. *All Principal Stresses Negative, $0 > \sigma_1 \geq \sigma_2 \geq \sigma_3$.* The negative sign must be taken in Eq. (3.9). This case is similar to Case 1 in all respects except that all stresses are negative.

Case 5. *One Principal Stress Zero.* *a.* $\sigma_1 \geq \sigma_2 > \sigma_3 = 0$. Equation (3.9) becomes independent of z, and the surface degenerates to a cylinder with sides parallel to the z axis. The cross section of the cylinder has the shape

$$\sigma_1 x^2 + \sigma_2 y^2 = 1$$

which is an ellipse or circle depending on whether $\sigma_1 \neq \sigma_2$ or $\sigma_1 = \sigma_2$.

b. $\sigma_1 > \sigma_2 = 0 > \sigma_3$. Both signs in Eq. (3.9) are applicable, and the equation becomes independent of y,

$$\sigma_1 x^2 + \sigma_3 z^2 = \pm 1$$

which (since $\sigma_3 < 0$) represents a double set of hyperbolic cylinders with sides parallel to the y axis and asymptotic to the planes

$$x = \pm \sqrt{\frac{|\sigma_3|}{\sigma_1}}\, z$$

Zero normal stresses are again evident (as in Case 2) when the ray OP lies in one of these asymptotic planes. If $|\sigma_3| = \sigma_1$, the asymptotic planes are inclined at 45° to the yz and xy planes.

c. $\sigma_1 = 0 > \sigma_2 \geq \sigma_3$. This is similar to Case 5a, except that the elliptic cylinder is parallel to the x axis and normal stresses are negative on all planes.

Cases 5a to c represent the state of stress at points in two-dimensional stress fields, and this is referred to again in Chap. 7.

Case 6. *Two Principal Stresses Zero.* *a.* $\sigma_1 > \sigma_2 = \sigma_3 = 0$. This degenerate case is that of a double set of infinite planes

$$\sigma_1 x^2 = 1 \qquad \text{or} \qquad x = \pm \sqrt{\frac{1}{\sigma_1}}$$

parallel to the yz plane.

b. $\sigma_1 = \sigma_2 = 0 > \sigma_3$. This is similar to the above. Here the two planes are given by

$$\sigma_3 z^2 = -1 \qquad \text{or} \qquad z = \pm \sqrt{\frac{1}{|\sigma_3|}}$$

and are parallel to the xy plane.

Cases 6a and b represent, respectively, uniaxial states of tension and compression.

3.6. The Stress Quadric of Cauchy: Orientation of Resultant Stress. The auxiliary surface construction given in Sec. 3.3 to be used in connection with the stress ellipsoid gives the resultant stress acting on a plane through a point in the body. The tangent plane construction discussed in Sec. 3.4 gives the magnitude only of the resultant stress acting on any given plane through the point. Finally, as has just been seen, the stress quadric of Cauchy gives the magnitude and sign of the normal component of stress acting on the plane. The following supplementary scheme, based on the quadric of Cauchy, will provide both the orientation and the sense of the resultant stress vector; and this, in combination with the magnitude and sense of the normal component of stress, will give the complete picture of the stress on any plane.

Consider the normal n' to the stress quadric surface at point P (Fig. 3.2a). As pointed out in Sec. 3.4, the direction cosines of this normal are proportional to $\partial F/\partial x$, $\partial F/\partial y$, $\partial F/\partial z$, where $F(x,y,z) = 0$ is the equation of the surface. For the quadric of Cauchy

$$F(x,y,z) = \sigma_1 x^2 + \sigma_2 y^2 + \sigma_3 z^2 \mp 1 = 0$$

so that

$$\frac{\partial F}{\partial x} = 2\sigma_1 x$$

$$\frac{\partial F}{\partial y} = 2\sigma_2 y$$

$$\frac{\partial F}{\partial z} = 2\sigma_3 z$$

By Eqs. (a), Sec. 3.5, and Eqs. (3.1) these can be written

$$\frac{\partial F}{\partial x} = 2\sigma_1 OP \cos (n,x) = 2OP p_{nx}$$

$$\frac{\partial F}{\partial y} = 2\sigma_2 OP \cos (n,y) = 2OP p_{ny}$$

$$\frac{\partial F}{\partial z} = 2\sigma_3 OP \cos (n,z) = 2OP p_{nz}$$

Therefore, the direction cosines of n' are proportional to p_{nx}, p_{ny}, p_{nz}, which means that n' is parallel to the resultant stress p_n acting on a plane with outer normal parallel to OP.

Again a pictorial confirmation of the results of Sec. 1.9 is possible. The three cases discussed at the end of that section were as follows:

Case 1. $\sigma_1 \neq \sigma_2$, $\sigma_2 \neq \sigma_3$, $\sigma_3 \neq \sigma_1$. In this case, the normal n' is parallel to OP only when the direction of OP coincides with a coordinate direction. By the above proposition these are therefore the only directions for which the normal stress is the resultant stress; thus, there are three, and only three, principal directions, and these are mutually perpendicular.

Case 2. $\sigma_1 \neq \sigma_2 = \sigma_3$. Here the quadric surface becomes a surface of revolution about the x axis, and the normal n' becomes parallel to OP whenever OP is perpendicular to the x axis and also when it coincides with the x axis. Thus, the x direction is a principal direction, and every direction normal to it is a principal direction.

Case 3. $\sigma_1 = \sigma_2 = \sigma_3$. The quadric surface degenerates to a sphere and n' is parallel to OP for every direction; hence all directions are principal.

3.7. Mohr's Circles. As a final example of graphical aids in the visualization of the state of stress at a point in a body, the three-dimensional counterpart of the familiar two-dimensional Mohr's circle will be discussed. The two-dimensional case will be covered in Chap. 7.

Besides providing one of the most convenient means of representing a state of stress, the construction will show some facts that are otherwise difficult to prove. It will show immediately the range of values within which the normal- and shear-stress components lie for a given state of stress. The maximum and minimum values of the normal stress σ_n and the shear stress τ_n for the given state of stress will then be directly evident.[†] Certainly Eqs. (1.5) or (1.12) defining the state of stress contain this information, and it would be possible to set up expressions for σ_n and τ_n from them, differentiate with respect to the direction cosines, and extract the desired maximum and minimum values of these stresses, including the orientation of the plane or planes on which they act. The process would, however, be lengthy.

By Eqs. (1.4) and (3.3),

$$p_n^2 = \sigma_n^2 + \tau_n^2 = \sigma_1^2 \cos^2{(n,x)} + \sigma_2^2 \cos^2{(n,y)} + \sigma_3^2 \cos^2{(n,z)} \qquad (a)$$

Rewriting Eqs. (3.4) and (1.9),

$$\sigma_n = \sigma_1 \cos^2{(n,x)} + \sigma_2 \cos^2{(n,y)} + \sigma_3 \cos^2{(n,z)} \qquad (b)$$

$$1 = \cos^2{(n,x)} + \cos^2{(n,y)} + \cos^2{(n,z)} \qquad (c)$$

These three equations can be solved for the three direction cosines by determinants, i.e.,

$$\cos^2{(n,x)} = \frac{\begin{vmatrix} \sigma_n^2 + \tau_n^2 & \sigma_2^2 & \sigma_3^2 \\ \sigma_n & \sigma_2 & \sigma_3 \\ 1 & 1 & 1 \end{vmatrix}}{D} \qquad \cos^2{(n,y)} = \frac{\begin{vmatrix} \sigma_1^2 & \sigma_n^2 + \tau_n^2 & \sigma_3^2 \\ \sigma_1 & \sigma_n & \sigma_3 \\ 1 & 1 & 1 \end{vmatrix}}{D}$$

$$\cos^2{(n,z)} = \frac{\begin{vmatrix} \sigma_1^2 & \sigma_2^2 & \sigma_n^2 + \tau_n^2 \\ \sigma_1 & \sigma_2 & \sigma_n \\ 1 & 1 & 1 \end{vmatrix}}{D}$$

[†] While σ_n has an algebraic sign, the shear stress τ_n does not (see Sec. 1.3); hence, there exists an algebraic maximum and minimum for σ_n but only numerical ones for τ_n.

where

$$D = \begin{vmatrix} \sigma_1^2 & \sigma_2^2 & \sigma_3^2 \\ \sigma_1 & \sigma_2 & \sigma_3 \\ 1 & 1 & 1 \end{vmatrix}$$

Three cases must be discussed.

Case 1. All Principal Stresses Different, $\sigma_1 > \sigma_2 > \sigma_3$. In this case $D \neq 0$, and the above expressions can be solved, with the results

$$\cos^2{(n,x)} = \frac{\tau_n^2 + (\sigma_n - \sigma_2)(\sigma_n - \sigma_3)}{(\sigma_1 - \sigma_2)(\sigma_1 - \sigma_3)}$$

$$\cos^2{(n,y)} = \frac{\tau_n^2 + (\sigma_n - \sigma_3)(\sigma_n - \sigma_1)}{(\sigma_2 - \sigma_3)(\sigma_2 - \sigma_1)} \qquad (3.11)$$

$$\cos^2{(n,z)} = \frac{\tau_n^2 + (\sigma_n - \sigma_1)(\sigma_n - \sigma_2)}{(\sigma_3 - \sigma_1)(\sigma_3 - \sigma_2)}$$

Consider the first of these rewritten in the form

$$\tau_n^2 + \sigma_n^2 - \sigma_n(\sigma_2 + \sigma_3) + \sigma_2\sigma_3 - \cos^2{(n,x)}(\sigma_1 - \sigma_2)(\sigma_1 - \sigma_3) = 0$$

or

$$\tau_n^2 + \left(\sigma_n - \frac{\sigma_2 + \sigma_3}{2}\right)^2 = \left(\frac{\sigma_2 - \sigma_3}{2}\right)^2 + \cos^2{(n,x)}(\sigma_1 - \sigma_2)(\sigma_1 - \sigma_3) \qquad (d)$$

or, after further algebra,

$$\tau_n^2 + \left(\sigma_n - \frac{\sigma_2 + \sigma_3}{2}\right)^2 = \left(\sigma_1 - \frac{\sigma_2 + \sigma_3}{2}\right)^2 \cos^2{(n,x)}$$

$$+ \left(\frac{\sigma_2 - \sigma_3}{2}\right)^2 [1 - \cos^2{(n,x)}] \qquad (3.12a)$$

For a given set of values of σ_1, σ_2, and σ_3, Eq. (3.12a) represents a family of circles in the $\sigma\tau$ plane with centers at $((\sigma_2 + \sigma_3)/2, 0)$. The direction cosine $\cos{(n,x)}$ is a parameter. Since $0 \leq \cos^2{(n,x)} \leq 1$, it is seen from Eq. (3.12a) that the family is bounded by the two limiting circles

$$\tau_n^2 + \left(\sigma_n - \frac{\sigma_2 + \sigma_3}{2}\right)^2 = \left(\frac{\sigma_2 - \sigma_3}{2}\right)^2 \qquad \text{for } \cos{(n,x)} = 0$$

$$\tau_n^2 + \left(\sigma_n - \frac{\sigma_2 + \sigma_3}{2}\right)^2 = \left(\sigma_1 - \frac{\sigma_2 + \sigma_3}{2}\right)^2 \qquad \text{for } \cos{(n,x)} = 1$$

These circles are shown in Fig. 3.3. Their radii are, respectively, $(\sigma_2 - \sigma_3)/2$ and $\sigma_1 - (\sigma_2 + \sigma_3)/2$.

Similar treatment of the remaining two equations of Eqs. (3.11) yields

$$\tau_n^2 + \left(\sigma_n - \frac{\sigma_3 + \sigma_1}{2}\right)^2 = \left(\sigma_2 - \frac{\sigma_3 + \sigma_1}{2}\right)^2 \cos^2 (n,y)$$

$$+ \left(\frac{\sigma_3 - \sigma_1}{2}\right)^2 [1 - \cos^2 (n,y)] \qquad (3.12b)$$

$$\tau_n^2 + \left(\sigma_n - \frac{\sigma_1 + \sigma_2}{2}\right)^2 = \left(\sigma_3 - \frac{\sigma_1 + \sigma_2}{2}\right)^2 \cos^2 (n,z)$$

$$+ \left(\frac{\sigma_1 - \sigma_2}{2}\right)^2 [1 - \cos^2 (n,z)] \qquad (3.12c)$$

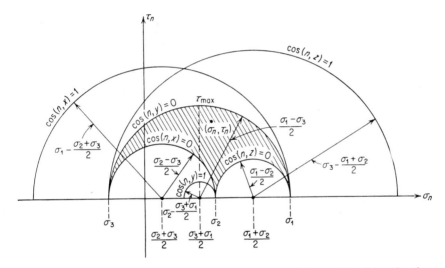

FIG. 3.3. Mohr's circles for the three-dimensional state of stress defined by the three principal stresses $\sigma_1 > \sigma_2 > \sigma_3$. The point representing the normal and shear components, σ_n and τ_n, of the resultant stress acting on any plane through the point must lie within the shaded region. The figure shows that there is no normal stress greater or less than the extreme principal stresses σ_1 and σ_3. The maximum shear stress is seen to be $(\sigma_1 - \sigma_3)/2$, and the normal stress acting on the plane on which the maximum shear stress acts is $(\sigma_1 + \sigma_3)/2$.

and these also represent families of circles, the first with centers at $((\sigma_3 + \sigma_1)/2,0)$ and the second with centers at $((\sigma_1 + \sigma_2)/2,0)$. The limiting circles for each of these families are also shown in the figure.

Any point (σ_n,τ_n) must lie inside each of the two limiting circles of each of the three families. Thus, the point can lie only within the shaded area shown since this is the only area common to the regions of each of the three families.

It is directly evident from the figure that

$$\sigma_{max} = \sigma_1 \qquad \sigma_{min} = \sigma_3$$

$$\tau_{max} = \frac{\sigma_1 - \sigma_3}{2} \qquad \tau_{min} = 0 \tag{3.13}$$

The minimum value of τ_n is zero since it has no algebraic sign.

The normal stress acting on the plane on which the shear stress is a maximum is seen to be

$$\sigma_{\tau,max} = \frac{\sigma_3 + \sigma_1}{2} \tag{3.14}$$

The direction cosines of the normal to the plane on which τ_{max} and $\sigma_{\tau,max}$ act can be obtained by substituting Eqs. (3.13) and (3.14) into Eqs. (3.11). The result is

$$\cos(n,x) = \pm \frac{1}{\sqrt{2}} \qquad \cos(n,y) = 0 \qquad \cos(n,z) = \pm \frac{1}{\sqrt{2}} \tag{3.15}$$

To summarize: For any given state of stress specified by the three principal stresses $\sigma_1 > \sigma_2 > \sigma_3$, the maximum shear stress $\tau_{max} = (\sigma_1 - \sigma_3)/2$ and occurs on each of two planes whose outer normals are perpendicular to the σ_2 direction and are inclined at 45° to the σ_1 and σ_3 directions. The normal stress acting on these two planes is $\sigma_{\tau,max} = (\sigma_3 + \sigma_1)/2$. The principal stresses σ_1 and σ_3 are at the same time the maximum and minimum normal stresses acting at the point.

It is also relatively simple from the construction to determine the values of σ_n and τ_n acting on any particular plane through the point, or, conversely, to find the plane (i.e., the direction cosines of its normal) on which a given set of normal and shear stresses acts. To show the procedure, consider the state of stress defined by given values of the principal stresses $\sigma_1 > \sigma_2 > \sigma_3$. For a given plane characterized by the direction cosines $\cos(n,x)$, $\cos(n,y)$, and $\cos(n,z)$ of its outer normal n, Equations (3.12a) to (3.12c) represent three particular circles. These can be drawn to scale with their proper centers, and their points of intersection will have coordinates σ_n and τ_n, which are the normal- and shear-stress components acting on the given plane (see Fig. 3.4). All three circles will cross at the same point since the direction-cosine relation (c) will have had to be observed. The radii of the circles for the construction are given, by the square roots of the right-hand sides of Eqs. (3.12a), (3.12b), and (3.12c), using the form of Eq. (d),

$$r_{23} = \sqrt{\left(\frac{\sigma_2 - \sigma_3}{2}\right)^2 + \cos^2 (n,x)(\sigma_1 - \sigma_2)(\sigma_1 - \sigma_3)}$$

$$r_{31} = \sqrt{\left(\frac{\sigma_3 - \sigma_1}{2}\right)^2 + \cos^2 (n,y)(\sigma_2 - \sigma_3)(\sigma_2 - \sigma_1)} \qquad (3.16)$$

$$r_{12} = \sqrt{\left(\frac{\sigma_1 - \sigma_2}{2}\right)^2 + \cos^2 (n,z)(\sigma_3 - \sigma_1)(\sigma_3 - \sigma_2)}$$

Actually the location of the point (σ_n, τ_n) can be obtained entirely graphically without calculating the lengths of the radii in Eqs. (3.16). Referring

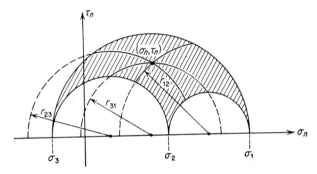

Fig. 3.4. Mohr's circles for the three-dimensional state of stress defined by the three principal stresses $\sigma_1 > \sigma_2 > \sigma_3$. The construction shows a method of locating the point (σ_n, τ_n) corresponding to a given set of direction cosines. The three radii r_{12}, r_{23}, r_{31} are computed from Eqs. (3.16).

to Fig. 3.5 (where three sketches of the same set of Mohr's circles are shown for clarity), it can be shown that $\angle ACB$ and $\angle AEF$ in Fig. 3.5a, the same-lettered angles in Fig. 3.5b, and the same-lettered angles in Fig. 3.5c are, respectively, equal to the angles whose direction cosines are $\cos (n,z)$, $\cos (n,x)$, and $\cos (n,y)$. Inspection will reveal that each of the three figures can be obtained from adjacent ones through cyclic permutation.

The first, Fig. 3.5a, will be proved; and the proof of the other two will follow by the cyclic properties mentioned above.

By the law of cosines applied to the triangle BCD,

$$(BD)^2 = (CD)^2 + (BC)^2 - 2(CD)(BC) \cos \angle ACB$$

Solving this for cos $\angle ACB$ and substituting the values

$$(BD)^2 = r_{12}^2 = \left(\frac{\sigma_1 - \sigma_2}{2}\right)^2 + \cos^2 (n,z)(\sigma_3 - \sigma_1)(\sigma_3 - \sigma_2)$$

$$CD = \frac{\sigma_1 - \sigma_2}{2}$$

$$BC = AC \cos \angle ACB = (\sigma_1 - \sigma_3) \cos \angle ACB$$

the result obtained, after some algebra, is that

$$\cos \angle ACB = \cos (n,z)$$

By drawing a line from point F to the point $((\sigma_2 + \sigma_3)/2,0)$ it can be shown in the very same way that $\angle AEF$ also equals the angle (n,z); and, as previously stated, the proofs in regard to Fig. 3.5b and c are also similar.

This construction can be summarized in a general way: Consider a state of stress defined by the three principal stresses $\sigma_1 > \sigma_2 > \sigma_3$, where the coordinate system at the point is oriented so that σ_1, σ_2, σ_3 act, respectively, in the x, y, and z directions. Mohr's circles can be drawn by locating the points σ_1, σ_2, and σ_3 on the σ_n axis and connecting them pairwise with circles. If, now, the stresses (σ_n,τ_n) acting on a plane characterized by the direction cosines cos (n,x), cos (n,y), and cos (n,z) are desired, the angles (n,x), (n,y), and (n,z) can be first determined† and then laid out, respectively, at the points σ_2, σ_3 (as in Fig. 3.5b), σ_3, σ_1 (as in Fig. 3.5c), and σ_1, σ_2 (as in Fig. 3.5a). Lines running from the two angles (n,x), so located, are then extended to their points of intersection with the $\sigma_1 - \sigma_2$ and $\sigma_3 - \sigma_1$ circles, and the distances from these points of intersection to the center of the $\sigma_2 - \sigma_3$ circle will both be the radius r_{23} as given in Eqs. (3.16). Similarly the distances from the center of the $\sigma_3 - \sigma_1$ circle to the intersections of lines extended from angles (n,y) and the $\sigma_2 - \sigma_3$ and $\sigma_1 - \sigma_2$ circles will be equal to r_{31}, and the distances from the center of the $\sigma_1 - \sigma_2$ circle to the intersections of lines extended from the angles (n,z) and the $\sigma_3 - \sigma_1$ and $\sigma_2 - \sigma_3$ circles will be equal to r_{12}. The desired stresses, σ_n and τ_n, are the coordinates of the point of intersection of the three arcs of radii r_{12}, r_{23}, and r_{31}.

The reverse procedure—finding the planes on which a given set of stresses (σ_n,τ_n) acts—is also possible.

Case 2. Two Principal Stresses Equal, $\sigma_1 = \sigma_2 > \sigma_3$. The case $\sigma_1 > \sigma_2 = \sigma_3$ can be discussed in a manner analogous to the case $\sigma_1 = \sigma_2 > \sigma_3$,

†They must all be made first-quadrant angles for use in the construction, and this can be done by adding or subtracting 180° or by changing their signs. This will not affect the result, as examination of the basic equations (a), (b), (c) will show.

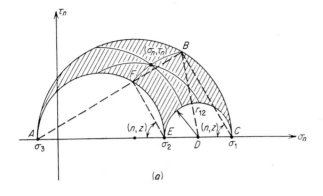

(a)

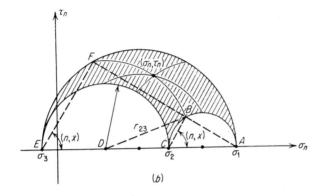

(b)

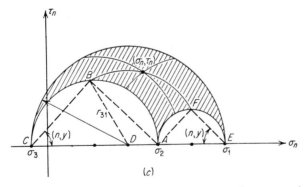

(c)

FIG. 3.5. Mohr's circles. Graphical method of determining the stresses (σ_n, τ_n) acting on a given plane.

and hence only the latter is discussed. The three equations (a), (b), and (c) become

$$\sigma_n^2 + \tau_n^2 = \sigma_1^2 \cos^2(n,x) + \sigma_1^2 \cos^2(n,y) + \sigma_3^2 \cos^2(n,z)$$

$$\sigma_n = \sigma_1 \cos^2(n,x) + \sigma_1 \cos^2(n,y) + \sigma_3 \cos^2(n,z) \qquad (e)$$

$$1 = \cos^2(n,x) + \cos^2(n,y) + \cos^2(n,z)$$

By the theory of equations, since the determinant of the coefficients of the direction cosines vanishes, a solution can exist only if the three quantities

$$\begin{vmatrix} \sigma_n^2 + \tau_n^2 & \sigma_1^2 & \sigma_3^2 \\ \sigma_n & \sigma_1 & \sigma_3 \\ 1 & 1 & 1 \end{vmatrix} \qquad \begin{vmatrix} \sigma_1^2 & \sigma_n^2 + \tau_n^2 & \sigma_3^2 \\ \sigma_1 & \sigma_n & \sigma_3 \\ 1 & 1 & 1 \end{vmatrix} \qquad \begin{vmatrix} \sigma_1^2 & \sigma_1^2 & \sigma_n^2 + \tau_n^2 \\ \sigma_1 & \sigma_1 & \sigma_n \\ 1 & 1 & 1 \end{vmatrix}$$

are zero. The third is zero since two columns are identical; and the first two, when set equal to zero, give the identical result,

$$\tau_n^2 + \left(\sigma_n - \frac{\sigma_1 + \sigma_3}{2}\right)^2 = \left(\frac{\sigma_1 - \sigma_3}{2}\right)^2$$

which implies that the point (σ_n, τ_n) must fall on the circle given by this equation. This is seen in Fig. 3.3 as the limiting case when $\sigma_2 \to \sigma_1$ so that the shaded area reduces to a semicircle joining σ_3 and σ_1. The graphical method for determining the stresses acting on a plane can, of course, still be applied; however, as there is rotational symmetry with respect to the z axis,† only the angle (n,z) need be plotted for the determination.

Case 3. All Three Principal Stresses Equal, $\sigma_1 = \sigma_2 = \sigma_3$. In this case Eqs. (a) to (c) reduce to

$$\sigma_n = \sigma_1 = \sigma_2 = \sigma_3$$

$$\tau_n = 0$$

or, as is evident in the figure, the circles reduce to the single point $(\sigma_n, 0)$. The stress acting on every plane through the point thus consists of only the normal stress σ_n.

EXERCISE

3.1. Prove that, if the first invariant corresponding to a given state of stress is zero, the state of stress is one of pure shear. *Hint.* The normal stress is zero on planes whose normals coincide with the generators of the asymptotic cone in the stress quadric of Cauchy. It remains to be shown that, corresponding to any one such nomral, the hypothesis that $I_1 = \sigma_1 + \sigma_2 + \sigma_3 = 0$ implies that there exist two other normals which also coincide with cone generators and which together with the given normal form an orthogonal triad.

†That is, σ_n and τ_n are independent of the angles (n,x) and (n,y). This is easily seen by manipulation of Eqs. (e).

CHAPTER 4

THEORY OF ELASTICITY

4.1. Introduction. The relationships between stresses themselves and between strains themselves developed in Chaps. 1 and 2 are obtained from purely theoretical considerations. They are general in character and applicable to bodies composed of a continuous distribution of matter. Since the elastic properties of materials were not used in their derivations, these relationships are valid for any type of material, be it steel, wax, or oil. The interrelationships between stresses and strains to be developed in this chapter, however, are based upon experimental laws. These laws vary from material to material. The science of mechanics is divided into several branches, each dealing with one specific class of materials. For instance, fluid mechanics treats gases and liquids, while theory of plasticity deals with solids loaded in the plastic range. The theory of elasticity, which will be treated in this chapter, deals only with solids loaded within the elastic range, and the relationships established in this chapter are therefore restricted to materials loaded within the elastic range.

4.2. Hooke's Law. Consider a slender steel bar of initial area A, subjected to an increasing tensile load F (Fig. 4.1). If the load is assumed to

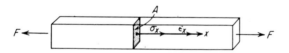

Fig. 4.1. Slender bar under uniaxial tension. The longitudinal stress is $F/A = \sigma_x$.

be distributed uniformly over the cross section and if the small change in the cross section caused by the load is neglected, then the longitudinal stress at any stage of the test is equal to F/A. If this stress is plotted against the longitudinal strain (change in length per unit initial length of the bar), we obtain a stress-strain diagram similar to the one shown in Fig. 4.2. The graph is very nearly a straight line up to a certain point P. The stress level at P is called the proportional limit because this stress

81

represents the limit below which the stresses are directly proportional to strains,

$$\sigma_z = E\epsilon_z \qquad (4.1)$$

where E is a constant of proportionality called the modulus of elasticity.

The greatest stress that can be applied without producing a permanent strain of 10^{-5} or more is often called the elastic limit. For steel the elastic limit very nearly coincides with the proportional limit so that the distinction between the two may be dropped.

Similar stress-strain curves can be obtained on many other materials. The values of modulus of elasticity and elastic limit of course vary from material to material. The range of stress below the elastic limit is usually referred to as the elastic range and that beyond the elastic limit as the plastic range. Equation (4.1), which establishes the proportionality between stress and strain in a simple tension or compression, was due to Hooke and is called Hooke's law.

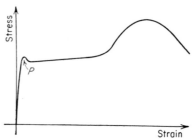

Fig. 4.2. Stress-strain curve of structural steel. Stress is proportional to strain up to the proportional limit P.

4.3. Generalized Hooke's Law. The question soon arises as to what is the relation between stresses and strains when the stress system is not a simple tension or compression. From Chap. 1 it is shown that any stress system can be defined by its six components, σ_x, σ_y, σ_z, τ_{xy}, τ_{yz}, τ_{zx}. From Chap. 2 it is shown that any strain system can be defined by its six components ϵ_x, ϵ_y, ϵ_z, γ_{xy}, γ_{yz}, γ_{zx}. A logical generalization of Hooke's law is obviously to make each stress component a linear function of the strain components. This was done by Cauchy, and the resulting law is called the generalized Hooke's law,

$$\sigma_x = C_{11}\epsilon_x + C_{12}\epsilon_y + C_{13}\epsilon_z + C_{14}\gamma_{xy} + C_{15}\gamma_{yz} + C_{16}\gamma_{zx}$$

$$\sigma_y = C_{21}\epsilon_x + C_{22}\epsilon_y + C_{23}\epsilon_z + C_{24}\gamma_{xy} + C_{25}\gamma_{yz} + C_{26}\gamma_{zx}$$

$$\cdots\cdots\cdots\cdots\cdots\cdots\cdots\cdots\cdots\cdots\cdots\cdots\cdots\cdots\cdots\cdots\cdots \qquad (4.2)$$

$$\tau_{zx} = C_{61}\epsilon_x + C_{62}\epsilon_y + C_{63}\epsilon_z + C_{64}\gamma_{xy} + C_{65}\gamma_{yz} + C_{66}\gamma_{zx}$$

where the 36 constants C_{11}, C_{12}, ... are called the elastic constants of the material. They are independent of stresses or strains.

4.4. Assumption of Isotropy and Homogeneity. A body is said to be isotropic if its elastic properties are the same in all directions. Hence, for isotropic bodies, the stress and strain components referred to a coordinate system $Ox'y'z'$ of any arbitrary orientation must be related by the same elastic constants C_{11}, C_{12}, ... In other words, for any orientation of the new coordinate system the following is true:

$$\sigma_{x'} = C_{11}\epsilon_{x'} + C_{12}\epsilon_{y'} + C_{13}\epsilon_{z'} + C_{14}\gamma_{x'y'} + C_{15}\gamma_{y'z'} + C_{16}\gamma_{z'x'}$$

$$\sigma_{y'} = C_{21}\epsilon_{x'} + C_{22}\epsilon_{y'} + C_{23}\epsilon_{z'} + C_{24}\gamma_{x'y'} + C_{25}\gamma_{y'z'} + C_{26}\gamma_{z'x'} \qquad (4.3)$$

$$\cdots\cdots\cdots\cdots\cdots\cdots\cdots\cdots\cdots\cdots\cdots\cdots\cdots\cdots\cdots\cdots\cdots\cdots\cdots\cdots$$

$$\tau_{z'x'} = C_{61}\epsilon_{x'} + C_{62}\epsilon_{y'} + C_{63}\epsilon_{z'} + C_{64}\gamma_{x'y'} + C_{65}\gamma_{y'z'} + C_{66}\gamma_{z'x'}$$

It can be shown† from strain-energy considerations that, in isotropic bodies, the 36 constants are not independent of each other. Certain relations exist between them so that there are 2, and only 2, independent elastic constants. In the following, we shall establish the relations between these 36 elastic constants and reduce the number of independent elastic constants from 36 to 2.

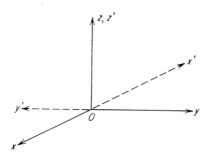

FIG. 4.3. New coordinate system $Ox'y'z'$ obtained by a rotation about Oz through an angle of $180°$. Here $\tau_{y'z'} = -\tau_{yz}$, $\tau_{z'x'} = -\tau_{zx}$ and $\gamma_{y'z'} = -\gamma_{yz}$, $\gamma_{z'x'} = -\gamma_{zx}$.

Let the new coordinate system $Ox'y'z'$ be the one obtained by a rotation of the old coordinate axes about Oz through an angle of $180°$ (Fig. 4.3); then by (1.12) and (2.21)

$$\sigma_{x'} = \sigma_x \qquad \sigma_{y'} = \sigma_y \qquad \sigma_{z'} = \sigma_z$$

$$\tau_{x'y'} = \tau_{xy} \qquad \tau_{y'z'} = -\tau_{yz} \qquad \tau_{z'x'} = -\tau_{zx} \qquad (4.4)$$

$$\epsilon_{x'} = \epsilon_x \qquad \epsilon_{y'} = \epsilon_y \qquad \epsilon_{z'} = \epsilon_z$$

$$\gamma_{x'y'} = \gamma_{xy} \qquad \gamma_{y'z'} = -\gamma_{yz} \qquad \gamma_{z'x'} = -\gamma_{zx}$$

† A. E. H. Love, "A Treatise on the Mathematical Theory of Elasticity," 4th ed., Dover Publications, New York, 1944.

By Eqs. (4.3) and (4.4), we have

$$\sigma_x = C_{11}\epsilon_x + C_{12}\epsilon_y + C_{13}\epsilon_z + C_{14}\gamma_{xy} - C_{15}\gamma_{yz} - C_{16}\gamma_{zx}$$

$$\sigma_y = C_{21}\epsilon_x + C_{22}\epsilon_y + C_{23}\epsilon_z + C_{24}\gamma_{xy} - C_{25}\gamma_{yz} - C_{26}\gamma_{zx}$$

$$\dots\dots\dots\dots\dots\dots\dots\dots\dots\dots\dots\dots\dots\dots\dots\dots\dots\dots$$ (4.5)

$$\tau_{zx} = -C_{61}\epsilon_x - C_{62}\epsilon_y - C_{63}\epsilon_z - C_{64}\gamma_{xy} + C_{65}\gamma_{yz} + C_{66}\gamma_{zx}$$

Comparing Eqs. (4.2) and (4.5), we have

$$C_{15} = -C_{15} \qquad C_{16} = -C_{16} \qquad \cdots$$

or

$$C_{15} = C_{16} = C_{25} = C_{26} = C_{35} = C_{36} = C_{45} = C_{46} = 0$$

$$C_{51} = C_{52} = C_{53} = C_{54} = C_{61} = C_{62} = C_{63} = C_{64} = 0$$

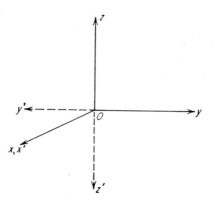

Fig. 4.4. New coordinate system $Ox'y'z'$ obtained by a rotation about Ox through an angle of $180°$. Here $\tau_{x'y'} = -\tau_{xy}$, $\tau_{z'x'} = -\tau_{zx}$ and $\gamma_{x'y'} = -\gamma_{xy}$, $\gamma_{z'x'} = -\gamma_{zx}$.

The generalized Hooke's law (4.2) now becomes

$$\sigma_x = C_{11}\epsilon_x + C_{12}\epsilon_y + C_{13}\epsilon_z + C_{14}\gamma_{xy}$$

$$\sigma_y = C_{21}\epsilon_x + C_{22}\epsilon_y + C_{23}\epsilon_z + C_{24}\gamma_{xy}$$

$$\sigma_z = C_{31}\epsilon_x + C_{32}\epsilon_y + C_{33}\epsilon_z + C_{34}\gamma_{xy}$$

$$\tau_{xy} = C_{41}\epsilon_x + C_{42}\epsilon_y + C_{43}\epsilon_z + C_{44}\gamma_{xy}$$ (4.6)

$$\tau_{yz} = C_{55}\gamma_{yz} + C_{56}\gamma_{zx}$$

$$\tau_{zx} = C_{65}\gamma_{yz} + C_{66}\gamma_{zx}$$

Next, let the new coordinate system be the one corresponding to a rotation about Ox through an angle of 180° (Fig. 4.4). Using the same procedure as above, we obtain $C_{14} = C_{24} = C_{34} = C_{41} = C_{42} = C_{43} = C_{56} = C_{65} = 0$.

Next, let the new coordinate system be the one corresponding to a rotation about Ox through an angle of 90°. By the same method as above we obtain

$$C_{12} = C_{13} \qquad C_{21} = C_{31} \qquad C_{23} = C_{32} \qquad C_{22} = C_{33} \qquad C_{44} = C_{66}$$

Similarly, by a rotation about Oz through an angle of 90°, we can obtain

$$C_{13} = C_{23} \qquad C_{31} = C_{32} \qquad C_{11} = C_{22} \qquad C_{44} = C_{55}$$

The generalized Hooke's law now becomes

$$\sigma_x = C_{11}\epsilon_x + C_{12}(\epsilon_y + \epsilon_z)$$

$$\sigma_y = C_{11}\epsilon_y + C_{12}(\epsilon_z + \epsilon_x)$$

$$\sigma_z = C_{11}\epsilon_z + C_{12}(\epsilon_x + \epsilon_y) \qquad (4.7)$$

$$\tau_{xy} = C_{44}\gamma_{xy}$$

$$\tau_{yz} = C_{44}\gamma_{yz}$$

$$\tau_{zx} = C_{44}\gamma_{zx}$$

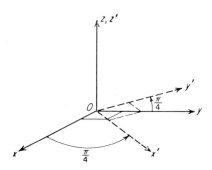

Fig. 4.5. New coordinate system $Ox'y'z'$ obtained by a rotation about Oz through an angle of 45°.

Finally, the new coordinate system is taken as the one corresponding to a rotation about Oz through an angle of 45° (Fig. 4.5). Here the laws of local transformation of stresses and of strains [Eqs. (1.12) and (2.21)] give

$$\sigma_{x'} = \tfrac{1}{2}\sigma_x + \tfrac{1}{2}\sigma_y + \tau_{xy}$$

$$\sigma_{y'} = \tfrac{1}{2}\sigma_x + \tfrac{1}{2}\sigma_y - \tau_{xy}$$

$$\sigma_{z'} = \sigma_z$$

$$\tau_{x'y'} = -\tfrac{1}{2}\sigma_x + \tfrac{1}{2}\sigma_y$$

$$\tau_{y'z'} = \frac{\sqrt{2}}{2}\,\tau_{yz} - \frac{\sqrt{2}}{2}\,\tau_{zx}$$

$$\tau_{z'x'} = \frac{\sqrt{2}}{2}\,\tau_{yz} + \frac{\sqrt{2}}{2}\,\tau_{zx}$$

$$\epsilon_{x'} = \tfrac{1}{2}\epsilon_x + \tfrac{1}{2}\epsilon_y + \tfrac{1}{2}\gamma_{xy}$$

$$\epsilon_{y'} = \tfrac{1}{2}\epsilon_x + \tfrac{1}{2}\epsilon_y - \tfrac{1}{2}\gamma_{xy}$$

$$\epsilon_{z'} = \epsilon_z$$

$$\tfrac{1}{2}\gamma_{x'y'} = -\tfrac{1}{2}\epsilon_x + \tfrac{1}{2}\epsilon_y$$

$$\tfrac{1}{2}\gamma_{y'z'} = \frac{\sqrt{2}}{4}\,\gamma_{yz} - \frac{\sqrt{2}}{4}\,\gamma_{zx}$$

$$\tfrac{1}{2}\gamma_{z'x'} = \frac{\sqrt{2}}{4}\,\gamma_{yz} + \frac{\sqrt{2}}{4}\,\gamma_{zx}$$

$$(4.8)$$

Owing to isotropy, Eqs. (4.7) applied to the new coordinate system give

$$\sigma_{x'} = C_{11}\epsilon_{x'} + C_{12}(\epsilon_{y'} + \epsilon_{z'})$$

$$\sigma_{y'} = C_{11}\epsilon_{y'} + C_{12}(\epsilon_{z'} + \epsilon_{x'})$$

$$\sigma_{z'} = C_{11}\epsilon_{z'} + C_{12}(\epsilon_{x'} + \epsilon_{y'})$$

$$\tau_{x'y'} = C_{44}\gamma_{x'y'}$$

$$\tau_{y'z'} = C_{44}\gamma_{y'z'}$$

$$\tau_{z'x'} = C_{44}\gamma_{z'x'}$$

$$(4.9)$$

Equations (4.8) are substituted into the first of Eqs. (4.9). We obtain

$$\tfrac{1}{2}(\sigma_x + \sigma_y) + \tau_{xy} = \sigma_{x'} = C_{11}(\tfrac{1}{2}\epsilon_x + \tfrac{1}{2}\epsilon_y + \tfrac{1}{2}\gamma_{xy})$$

$$+ C_{12}(\tfrac{1}{2}\epsilon_x + \tfrac{1}{2}\epsilon_y - \tfrac{1}{2}\gamma_{xy} + \epsilon_z)$$

The expressions for σ_x and σ_y in Eqs. (4.7) are substituted into the above equation to give

$$\tau_{xy} = \tfrac{1}{2}(C_{11} - C_{12})\gamma_{xy}$$

Comparing the above with the expression for τ_{xy} in Eqs. (4.7), we have

$$C_{44} = \tfrac{1}{2}(C_{11} - C_{12})$$

If we call $C_{12} = \lambda$, $C_{44} = G$, then we have the following stress-strain relations applicable to isotropic materials stressed below the proportional limit:

$$\sigma_x = (2G + \lambda)\epsilon_x + \lambda(\epsilon_y + \epsilon_z)$$
$$\sigma_y = (2G + \lambda)\epsilon_y + \lambda(\epsilon_z + \epsilon_x)$$
$$\sigma_z = (2G + \lambda)\epsilon_z + \lambda(\epsilon_x + \epsilon_y)$$
$$\tau_{xy} = G\gamma_{xy}$$
$$\tau_{yz} = G\gamma_{yz}$$
$$\tau_{zz} = G\gamma_{zz}$$

(4.10)

Equations (4.10) can be solved for the strains to give

$$\epsilon_x = \frac{\lambda + G}{G(3\lambda + 2G)}\sigma_x - \frac{\lambda}{2G(3\lambda + 2G)}(\sigma_y + \sigma_z)$$
$$\epsilon_y = \frac{\lambda + G}{G(3\lambda + 2G)}\sigma_y - \frac{\lambda}{2G(3\lambda + 2G)}(\sigma_z + \sigma_x)$$
$$\epsilon_z = \frac{\lambda + G}{G(3\lambda + 2G)}\sigma_z - \frac{\lambda}{2G(3\lambda + 2G)}(\sigma_x + \sigma_y)$$
$$\gamma_{xy} = \frac{1}{G}\tau_{xy}$$
$$\gamma_{yz} = \frac{1}{G}\tau_{yz}$$
$$\gamma_{zz} = \frac{1}{G}\tau_{zz}$$

(4.11)

The assumption of isotropy therefore reduces the number of elastic constants from 36 to 2. For isotropic but nonhomogeneous materials, the constants λ and G are functions of the space coordinates x, y, z and vary from point to point. For isotropic and homogeneous materials, these constants are not functions of the space coordinates and do not vary from point to point. They depend only on the particular material.

If the Ox, Oy, and Oz axes are chosen along the principal axes of stress, then $\tau_{xy} = \tau_{yz} = \tau_{zz} = 0$. From Eqs. (4.11) it follows that $\gamma_{xy} = \gamma_{yz} = \gamma_{zz} = 0$.

Hence Ox, Oy, and Oz axes are also the principal axes of strain. We have proved the following important theorem:

For isotropic elastic materials, the principal axes of stress and strain coincide.

4.5. Physical Significance of Elastic Constants. Consider the following special stress systems:

a. Pure-shear Two-dimensional Case. Here

$$\sigma_x = \sigma_y = \sigma_z = \tau_{yz} = \tau_{zx} = 0$$

$$\tau_{xy} = \text{applied shear stress}$$

By Eqs. (4.11),

$$\gamma_{xy} = \frac{1}{G}\tau_{xy}$$

The constant G is therefore the ratio of applied shear stress to the measured shear strain and can be determined in a torsion test of a circular cylinder. It is called the shear modulus of rigidity.

b. Uniaxial State of Stress. Here

$$\sigma_x = \text{applied uniaxial stress}$$

$$\sigma_y = \sigma_z = \tau_{xy} = \tau_{yz} = \tau_{zx} = 0$$

By Eqs. (4.11), we have

$$\epsilon_x = \frac{\lambda + G}{G(3\lambda + 2G)}\sigma_x$$

$$\epsilon_y = \epsilon_z = \frac{-\lambda}{2G(3\lambda + 2G)}\sigma_x \tag{4.12}$$

Comparing the above expression with Eq. (4.1), we have

$$\lambda = \frac{G(2G - E)}{E - 3G} \tag{4.13}$$

The constant E, called the modulus of elasticity, has been defined as the ratio of the applied uniaxial stress to the measured strain in a simple tension or compression test. The constant λ, called the Lamé's constant, has no physical significance. The relation between E, G, and λ is given by Eq. (4.13).

From Eqs. (4.12) it is seen that

$$\epsilon_y = \epsilon_z = \frac{-\lambda}{2(\lambda + G)}\epsilon_x = -\nu\epsilon_x$$

where

$$\nu = \frac{\lambda}{2(\lambda + G)} \tag{4.14}$$

The constant ν is the negative of the ratio of lateral strain to longitudinal strain under uniaxial longitudinal stress. It is called Poisson's ratio.

c. *Hydrostatic Compression.* Here

$$\sigma_x = \sigma_y = \sigma_z = -p \qquad p > 0$$

$$\tau_{xy} = \tau_{yz} = \tau_{zz} = 0$$

By Eqs. (4.11),

$$\epsilon_x = \epsilon_y = \epsilon_z = \frac{-1}{3\lambda + 2G} p$$

Using Eq. (2.24), the above equation becomes

$$p = \frac{-(3\lambda + 2G)}{3} \epsilon = -K\epsilon$$

where

$$K = \frac{3\lambda + 2G}{3} \tag{4.15}$$

The constant K is the ratio of applied hydrostatic pressure to the observed volume shrinkage per unit volume. It is called the bulk modulus of elasticity.

By means of Eqs. (4.13) to (4.15) it is possible to solve for all the constants λ, G, E, ν, and K if any two of them are given. These relations are shown in Table 4.1.

By choosing E and ν as the two basic elastic constants, Eqs. (4.10) and (4.11) can be written in the following form:

$$\epsilon_x = \frac{1}{E} [\sigma_x - \nu(\sigma_y + \sigma_z)]$$

$$\epsilon_y = \frac{1}{E} [\sigma_y - \nu(\sigma_z + \sigma_x)]$$

$$\epsilon_z = \frac{1}{E} [\sigma_z - \nu(\sigma_x + \sigma_y)]$$

$$\gamma_{xy} = \frac{2(1 + \nu)}{E} \tau_{xy} \tag{4.16}$$

$$\gamma_{yz} = \frac{2(1 + \nu)}{E} \tau_{yz}$$

$$\gamma_{zx} = \frac{2(1 + \nu)}{E} \tau_{zx}$$

TABLE 4.1. RELATIONS BETWEEN ELASTIC CONSTANTS IN ISOTROPIC MATERIALS

Elastic constant		λ	G	E	ν	K
Dimension		FL^{-2}	FL^{-2}	FL^{-2}	1	FL^{-2}
λ	G	$\cdots$	$\cdots$	$\dfrac{G(3\lambda+2G)}{\lambda+G}$	$\dfrac{\lambda}{2(\lambda+G)}$	$\dfrac{3\lambda+2G}{3}$
	E	$\cdots$	$\dfrac{A\dagger+(E-3\lambda)}{4}$	$\cdots$	$\dfrac{A-(E+\lambda)}{4\lambda}$	$\dfrac{A+(3\lambda+E)}{6}$
	ν	$\cdots$	$\dfrac{\lambda(1-2\nu)}{2\nu}$	$\dfrac{\lambda(1+\nu)(1-2\nu)}{\nu}$	$\cdots$	$\dfrac{\lambda(1+\nu)}{3\nu}$
	K	$\cdots$	$\dfrac{3(K-\lambda)}{2}$	$\dfrac{9K(K-\lambda)}{3K-\lambda}$	$\dfrac{\lambda}{3K-\lambda}$	$\cdots$
G	E	$\dfrac{G(2G-E)}{E-3G}$	$\cdots$	$\cdots$	$\dfrac{E-2G}{2G}$	$\dfrac{GE}{3(3G-E)}$
	ν	$\dfrac{2G\nu}{1-2\nu}$	$\cdots$	$2G(1+\nu)$	$\cdots$	$\dfrac{2G(1+\nu)}{3(1-2\nu)}$
	K	$\dfrac{3K-2G}{3}$	$\cdots$	$\dfrac{9KG}{3K+G}$	$\dfrac{3K-2G}{2(3K+G)}$	$\cdots$
E	ν	$\dfrac{\nu E}{(1+\nu)(1-2\nu)}$	$\dfrac{E}{2(1+\nu)}$	$\cdots$	$\cdots$	$\dfrac{E}{3(1-2\nu)}$
	K	$\dfrac{3K(3K-E)}{9K-E}$	$\dfrac{3EK}{9K-E}$	$\cdots$	$\dfrac{3K-E}{6K}$	$\cdots$
ν	K	$\dfrac{3K\nu}{1+\nu}$	$\dfrac{3K(1-2\nu)}{2(1+\nu)}$	$3K(1-2\nu)$	$\cdots$	$\cdots$

$\dagger\ A \equiv \sqrt{(E+\lambda)^2 + 8\lambda^2}$.

or

$$\sigma_x = \frac{E}{(1 + \nu)(1 - 2\nu)} [(1 - \nu)\epsilon_x + \nu(\epsilon_y + \epsilon_z)]$$

$$\sigma_y = \frac{E}{(1 + \nu)(1 - 2\nu)} [(1 - \nu)\epsilon_y + \nu(\epsilon_z + \epsilon_x)]$$

$$\sigma_z = \frac{E}{(1 + \nu)(1 - 2\nu)} [(1 - \nu)\epsilon_z + \nu(\epsilon_x + \epsilon_y)]$$

(4.17)

$$\tau_{xy} = \frac{E}{2(1 + \nu)} \gamma_{xy}$$

$$\tau_{yz} = \frac{E}{2(1 + \nu)} \gamma_{yz}$$

$$\tau_{zx} = \frac{E}{2(1 + \nu)} \gamma_{zx}$$

From physical considerations, it is obvious that G, E, and K must be positive quantities. From $G = 3K(1 - 2\nu)/2(1 + \nu)$, it follows that $-1 < \nu < \frac{1}{2}$. Table 4.2 gives average values of E, G, and ν obtained experimentally for some elastic materials. The values of E and G are given in millions of pounds per square inch.

TABLE 4.2. AVERAGE ELASTIC PROPERTIES OF MATERIALS

(Data are averages of values given in cited references)

Material	E	G	ν
Aluminum alloy[†].	10.0	3.8	0.33
Bakelite 61-893[‡].	0.62	—	0.36
Brass 70-30[†].	15.9	6.0	0.33
Carbon steels[†].	29.5	11.5	0.29
Cast iron[†].	16.5	6.7	0.25
Columbia resin CR-39[¶].	0.35	—	0.42
Concrete[§].	3.0	—	0.13
Copper[†].	15.6	5.8	0.36
Glass[†].	10.0		
Granite[†].	7.3		
Marblette[¶], annealed.	0.5	—	0.40
unannealed.	0.16	—	0.40
Malleable iron[†].	23.6	9.3	0.27

[†]L. S. Marks, "Mechanical Engineers' Handbook," 5th ed., McGraw-Hill Book Company, Inc., New York, 1951.

[‡]M. Hetényi, "Handbook of Experimental Stress Analysis," John Wiley & Sons, Inc., New York, 1950.

[¶]These are values immediately after loading, determined by tests conducted at Armour Research Foundation.

[§]R. J. Roark, "Formulas for Stress and Strain," 3d ed., McGraw-Hill Book Company, Inc., New York, 1954.

The stress-strain relations can be written as relations between the deviator and spherical stress and strain tensors discussed in Chaps. 1 and 2. To obtain these relations, add the first three of Eqs. (4.16),

$$\epsilon_x + \epsilon_y + \epsilon_z = \frac{1 - 2\nu}{E}(\sigma_x + \sigma_y + \sigma_z)$$

or, using Eqs. (1.38) and (2.31), and finally Table 4.1,

$$\epsilon_m = \frac{1}{3K}\sigma_m \tag{a}$$

Now observe from the stress-strain relations (4.10), which are identical to (4.17), that

$$\sigma_x = 2G\epsilon_x + \lambda(\epsilon_x + \epsilon_y + \epsilon_z)$$

$$\sigma_y = 2G\epsilon_y + \lambda(\epsilon_x + \epsilon_y + \epsilon_z)$$

$$\sigma_z = 2G\epsilon_z + \lambda(\epsilon_x + \epsilon_y + \epsilon_z)$$

$$\tau_{xy} = G\gamma_{xy}$$

$$\tau_{yz} = G\gamma_{yz}$$

$$\tau_{zx} = G\gamma_{zx}$$

By using Eq. (a) and Table 4.1, these can be converted to the form

$$\sigma_x - \sigma_m = 2G(\epsilon_x - \epsilon_m)$$

$$\sigma_y - \sigma_m = 2G(\epsilon_y - \epsilon_m)$$

$$\sigma_z - \sigma_m = 2G(\epsilon_z - \epsilon_m)$$

$$\tau_{xy} = 2G\frac{\gamma_{xy}}{2}$$

$$\tau_{yz} = 2G\frac{\gamma_{yz}}{2}$$

$$\tau_{zx} = 2G\frac{\gamma_{zx}}{2}$$

$$\tag{b}$$

Equations (a) and (b) can be seen by inspection of Eqs. (1.37), (1.39), (2.30), and (2.32), to be equivalent to the two tensor equations,

$$\mathbf{S}' = 2G\mathbf{E}'$$

$$\mathbf{S}'' = 3K\mathbf{E}'' \tag{c}$$

These state very concisely the stress-strain relations (4.16) or (4.17). Recalling that the shear modulus G represents the ratio of shear stress to shear strain in a state of pure shear, it is reasonable to expect that the stress and strain deviator tensors would be related through this constant. Similarly, since the bulk modulus K represents the ratio of applied hydrostatic pressure to the volume shrinkage per unit volume in a hydrostatic state of stress, it would be expected that this constant would link the spherical stress and strain tensors.

In either of Eqs. (c) it should be noted that if the strain tensor is written in determinant form, the constant multiplies every term in the determinant.

4.6. Fundamental Boundary-value Problems of Elasticity. Elasticity problems can be classified into three types according to whether the loading is applied through prescribed forces or prescribed displacements, or both. We shall first assume that body forces, if present, are always given. Then, if the normal and shear forces are given on the surfaces of a body, the problem is called the first boundary-value problem. If the displacements but not the forces are given on the surfaces of the body, the problem is called the second boundary-value problem. If forces are prescribed on some portions of the surface and displacements are prescribed on the other portions, the problem is called the mixed boundary-value problem. A tensile specimen stressed under a given force or a given elongation is an example of the first or second boundary-value problem, respectively. A specimen pulled to a given elongation while loaded laterally with a given force is an example of the mixed boundary-value problem. In all these elasticity problems, the quantities sought are the stresses, strains, and displacements along every direction, at every point in the body.

From the equations of the local transformations of stresses or strains at a point [Eqs. (1.12) and (2.21)] it is seen that the stresses and strains at any one point along any direction can be computed from the six stress components $(\sigma_x, \sigma_y, \sigma_z, \tau_{xy}, \tau_{yz}, \tau_{zx})$ and six strain components $(\epsilon_x, \epsilon_y, \epsilon_z, \gamma_{xy}, \gamma_{yz}, \gamma_{zx})$ at that point. From geometry it is evident that the displacement at any one point along any direction can be computed from the three displacement components (u, v, w) at that point. The problem therefore reduces to one of finding the six stress components, six strain components, and three displacement components at every point in the body. Obviously these components vary from point to point so that they are functions of the space coordinates x, y, z, as well as of the given loading. The problem is to obtain these functions.

4.7. Basic Conditions Which the Stresses, Strains, and Displacements Must Satisfy. The necessary and sufficient conditions which the components of stress, strain, and displacement must satisfy in order to constitute a solution of an elasticity problem are:

1. The stress-strain relations [Eqs. (4.16) or (4.17)].
2. The strain-displacement relations [Eqs. (2.11) and (2.13)].
3. The equilibrium equations [Eqs. (1.7)].

4. The displacements as continuous functions of the space coordinates x, y, z, so that neighboring points will be displaced to neighboring places and not be separated by a gap.

5. The prescribed boundary conditions at the surfaces of the body. The first four conditions must be satisfied at every point inside the body as well as on its surfaces. They are called the field conditions, or the field equations. The fifth one pertains only to the boundary and is called the boundary condition. For the first boundary-value problem, known forces are applied on the boundary. If we call $\bar{X}_n$, $\bar{Y}_n$, and $\bar{Z}_n$ the components of these applied forces per unit area, then, by Eqs. (1.5) the stress components at points on the boundary must satisfy these boundary conditions,

$$\sigma_x \ \cos (n,x) + \tau_{xy} \cos (n,y) + \tau_{xz} \cos (n,z) = \bar{X}_n$$

$$\tau_{xy} \cos (n,x) + \sigma_y \ \cos (n,y) + \tau_{zy} \cos (n,z) = \bar{Y}_n \qquad (4.18)$$

$$\tau_{zx} \cos (n,x) + \tau_{yz} \cos (n,y) + \sigma_z \ \cos (n,z) = \bar{Z}_n$$

where n is the direction of the outer normal of the boundary surface.

For the second boundary-value problem, known displacements are applied on the boundary. If we call $\bar{u}$, $\bar{v}$, and $\bar{w}$ the components of these applied displacements, then the displacement components at points on the boundary must satisfy these boundary conditions,

$$u = \bar{u}$$

$$v = \bar{v} \qquad (4.19)$$

$$w = \bar{w}$$

For the mixed boundary-value problem, the boundary conditions will be composed of Eqs. (4.18) on a portion of the boundary and Eqs. (4.19) on the rest of the boundary.

There is a total of fifteen field equations (six stress-strain relations, six strain-displacement relations, and three equilibrium equations) and fifteen unknowns (six stress components, six strain components, and three displacement components). Theoretically, these fifteen partial differential equations are necessary and sufficient to determine these fifteen unknowns. In the process, constants of integration will appear which are determined by the boundary conditions.

From the six stress-strain and six strain-displacement relations we can eliminate the six strain components and obtain six stress-displacement relations:

$$\frac{\partial u}{\partial x} = \frac{1}{E}\left[\sigma_x - \nu(\sigma_y + \sigma_z)\right] \qquad \frac{\partial u}{\partial y} + \frac{\partial v}{\partial x} = \frac{1}{G}\tau_{xy}$$

$$\frac{\partial v}{\partial y} = \frac{1}{E}\left[\sigma_y - \nu(\sigma_z + \sigma_x)\right] \qquad \frac{\partial v}{\partial z} + \frac{\partial w}{\partial y} = \frac{1}{G}\tau_{yz} \qquad (4.20)$$

$$\frac{\partial w}{\partial z} = \frac{1}{E}\left[\sigma_z - \nu(\sigma_x + \sigma_y)\right] \qquad \frac{\partial w}{\partial x} + \frac{\partial u}{\partial z} = \frac{1}{G}\tau_{zx}$$

or

$$\sigma_x = \lambda\epsilon + 2G\frac{\partial u}{\partial x} \qquad \tau_{xy} = G\left(\frac{\partial u}{\partial y} + \frac{\partial v}{\partial x}\right)$$

$$\sigma_y = \lambda\epsilon + 2G\frac{\partial v}{\partial y} \qquad \tau_{yz} = G\left(\frac{\partial v}{\partial z} + \frac{\partial w}{\partial y}\right) \qquad (4.21)$$

$$\sigma_z = \lambda\epsilon + 2G\frac{\partial w}{\partial z} \qquad \tau_{zx} = G\left(\frac{\partial w}{\partial x} + \frac{\partial u}{\partial z}\right)$$

Hence the problem is simplified into finding six stress components and three displacement components satisfying the six stress-displacement relations and three equilibrium equations in addition to the boundary condition. After the stress components and displacement components are obtained, the strain components can then be calculated from either the stress-strain or the strain-displacement relations.

In the chapter on strains, it was shown that in a simply connected region, if the strain components satisfy the six compatibility equations in strains (2.25), then there exist continuous-displacement components which satisfy the strain-displacement relations. Hence, for simply connected bodies, the elasticity problem can also be treated as one of finding six stress components and six strain components which satisfy the equilibrium, compatibility, and stress-strain relations in addition to the boundary conditions. After the stresses and strains are determined, then the displacements can be obtained from the latter by the strain-displacement relations.

For the twelve unknowns (six stress components, six strain components) we have fifteen equations (three equilibrium equations, six stress-strain relations, six compatibility equations). Since there are more equations than unknowns, it seems that in general no solution can be obtained. However, the six compatibility equations (2.25) are not independent of each other. By differentiating the first equation twice with respect to z, the second equation twice with respect to x, the third twice with respect to y, the fourth with respect to y and z, the fifth with respect to z and x, and the sixth with respect to x and y, six fourth-order partial-differential equations can be obtained. It can be easily shown that the first three of these six equations are equivalent to the last three so that only three are independent. Hence, for the twelve unknown stress and strain components we have actually only twelve equations (three equilibrium equations, six stress-strain relations, and three fourth-order compatibility equations). Solutions therefore can and do exist. It is usually simpler, however, to handle the six second-order compatibility equations rather than the three fourth-order equations. Furthermore, the fourth-order equations are not the exact equivalent of the second-order equations so that, if the former are to be used, certain other restrictions must be added.

4.8. Equations of Compatibility in Terms of Stresses. With the help of the stress-strain and equilibrium equations, the compatibility equations (2.25) can be transformed into relations between stress components. This will be done as follows. From the equations of equilibrium (1.7), we have

$$\frac{\partial \tau_{yz}}{\partial y} = -\left(\frac{\partial \sigma_z}{\partial z} + \frac{\partial \tau_{zx}}{\partial x} + Z\right)$$

$$\frac{\partial \tau_{yz}}{\partial z} = -\left(\frac{\partial \sigma_y}{\partial y} + \frac{\partial \tau_{xy}}{\partial x} + Y\right)$$

Differentiating the first of these equations with respect to z and the second with respect to y, and adding them together, we have

$$2\frac{\partial^2 \tau_{yz}}{\partial y\, \partial z} = -\frac{\partial^2 \sigma_z}{\partial z^2} - \frac{\partial^2 \sigma_y}{\partial y^2} - \frac{\partial}{\partial x}\left(\frac{\partial \tau_{zx}}{\partial z} + \frac{\partial \tau_{xy}}{\partial y}\right) - \frac{\partial Z}{\partial z} - \frac{\partial Y}{\partial y}$$

By using the first of the equilibrium equations, the above becomes

$$2\frac{\partial^2 \tau_{yz}}{\partial y\, \partial z} = \frac{\partial^2 \sigma_x}{\partial x^2} - \frac{\partial^2 \sigma_y}{\partial y^2} - \frac{\partial^2 \sigma_z}{\partial z^2} + \frac{\partial X}{\partial x} - \frac{\partial Y}{\partial y} - \frac{\partial Z}{\partial z} \qquad (4.22)$$

From the stress-strain relations and compatibility equations we can obtain

$$\frac{\partial^2 \epsilon_y}{\partial z^2} + \frac{\partial^2 \epsilon_z}{\partial y^2} = \frac{\partial^2 \gamma_{yz}}{\partial y\, \partial z}$$

$$E\epsilon_y = (1 + \nu)\sigma_y - 3\nu\sigma_m \qquad (4.23)$$

$$E\epsilon_z = (1 + \nu)\sigma_z - 3\nu\sigma_m$$

$$E\gamma_{yz} = 2(1 + \nu)\tau_{yz}$$

where, as in Eq. (1.38), $\sigma_m = \frac{1}{3}(\sigma_x + \sigma_y + \sigma_z)$. Eliminating τ_{yz}, ϵ_y, ϵ_z, and γ_{yz} from Eqs. (4.22) and (4.23), we have

$$(1 + \nu)\left(3\nabla^2\sigma_m - \nabla^2\sigma_x - 3\frac{\partial^2\sigma_m}{\partial x^2}\right) - 3\nu\left(\nabla^2\sigma_m - \frac{\partial^2\sigma_m}{\partial x^2}\right)$$

$$= (1 + \nu)\left(\frac{\partial X}{\partial x} - \frac{\partial Y}{\partial y} - \frac{\partial Z}{\partial z}\right) \qquad (4.24)$$

where

$$\nabla^2 = \frac{\partial^2}{\partial x^2} + \frac{\partial^2}{\partial y^2} + \frac{\partial^2}{\partial z^2}$$

Two more equations can be obtained similar to Eq. (4.24). Adding together these three equations, we obtain

$$3(1 - \nu)\nabla^2 \sigma_m = -(1 + \nu)\left(\frac{\partial X}{\partial x} + \frac{\partial Y}{\partial y} + \frac{\partial Z}{\partial z}\right)$$

Substituting this expression for $\nabla^2 \sigma_m$ in Eq. (4.24), we have

$$\nabla^2 \sigma_x + \frac{3}{1 + \nu}\frac{\partial^2 \sigma_m}{\partial x^2} = \frac{-\nu}{1 - \nu}\left(\frac{\partial X}{\partial x} + \frac{\partial Y}{\partial y} + \frac{\partial Z}{\partial z}\right) - 2\frac{\partial X}{\partial x} \quad (4.25)$$

We can obtain three equations of the above type, corresponding to the first three of the compatibility equations (2.25). Similarly the last three of the compatibility equations can be transformed into three equations of the following type:

$$\nabla^2 \tau_{yz} + \frac{3}{1 + \nu}\frac{\partial^2 \sigma_m}{\partial y\,\partial z} = -\left(\frac{\partial Y}{\partial z} + \frac{\partial Z}{\partial y}\right) \quad (4.26)$$

If the body forces are independent of location and, in particular, if there are no body forces, then Eqs. (4.25), (4.26) become

$$(1 + \nu)\nabla^2 \sigma_x + 3\frac{\partial^2 \sigma_m}{\partial x^2} = 0 \qquad (1 + \nu)\nabla^2 \tau_{yz} + 3\frac{\partial^2 \sigma_m}{\partial y\,\partial z} = 0$$

$$(1 + \nu)\nabla^2 \sigma_y + 3\frac{\partial^2 \sigma_m}{\partial y^2} = 0 \qquad (1 + \nu)\nabla^2 \tau_{zx} + 3\frac{\partial^2 \sigma_m}{\partial z\,\partial x} = 0 \quad (4.27)$$

$$(1 + \nu)\nabla^2 \sigma_z + 3\frac{\partial^2 \sigma_m}{\partial z^2} = 0 \qquad (1 + \nu)\nabla^2 \tau_{xy} + 3\frac{\partial^2 \sigma_m}{\partial x\,\partial y} = 0$$

Equations (4.25), (4.26) or Eqs. (4.27) are called compatibility equations in terms of stresses. If the stress components satisfy these equations as well as the equilibrium equations, then the strains obtained from these stress components by the stress-strain relations will be compatible so that the corresponding displacement components will be continuous. Hence, for the first boundary-value problem it becomes possible to work only on stresses. The problem simplifies into one of finding six stress components which satisfy the compatibility equations in terms of stresses (4.27) and the equilibrium equations (1.7) throughout the field and which satisfy the prescribed stress conditions on the boundary [Eqs. (4.18)]. After these stress components are obtained, the strain components and displacement components can be calculated easily from the stress-strain and strain-displacement relations. This simplification is not possible in the cases of the second and mixed boundary-value problems because the displacement as calculated from the stresses obtained in the above manner will not necessarily satisfy the prescribed displacement condition on the boundary.

4.9. Equations of Equilibrium in Terms of Displacements. Whereas the method of working on stresses is possible only for the first boundary-value problems, the method of working on displacements is applicable to all three boundary-value problems. This will be shown below.

By the stress-displacement relations, the equations of equilibrium can be expressed in terms of displacements

$$\nabla^2 u + \frac{1}{1-2\nu} \frac{\partial}{\partial x} \left(\frac{\partial u}{\partial x} + \frac{\partial v}{\partial y} + \frac{\partial w}{\partial z} \right) + \frac{X}{G} = 0$$

$$\nabla^2 v + \frac{1}{1-2\nu} \frac{\partial}{\partial y} \left(\frac{\partial u}{\partial x} + \frac{\partial v}{\partial y} + \frac{\partial w}{\partial z} \right) + \frac{Y}{G} = 0 \qquad (4.28)$$

$$\nabla^2 w + \frac{1}{1-2\nu} \frac{\partial}{\partial z} \left(\frac{\partial u}{\partial x} + \frac{\partial v}{\partial y} + \frac{\partial w}{\partial z} \right) + \frac{Z}{G} = 0$$

To obtain the boundary conditions in terms of displacements, Eqs. (4.21) are substituted into Eqs. (4.18).

$$\lambda\epsilon \cos(n,x) + G\left[2\frac{\partial u}{\partial x} \cos(n,x) + \left(\frac{\partial u}{\partial y} + \frac{\partial v}{\partial x} \right) \cos(n,y) \right.$$
$$\left. + \left(\frac{\partial u}{\partial z} + \frac{\partial w}{\partial x} \right) \cos(n,z) \right] = \bar{X}_n$$

$$\lambda\epsilon \cos(n,y) + G\left[2\frac{\partial v}{\partial y} \cos(n,y) + \left(\frac{\partial v}{\partial z} + \frac{\partial w}{\partial y} \right) \cos(n,z) \right. \qquad (4.29)$$
$$\left. + \left(\frac{\partial v}{\partial x} + \frac{\partial u}{\partial y} \right) \cos(n,x) \right] = \bar{Y}_n$$

$$\lambda\epsilon \cos(n,z) + G\left[2\frac{\partial w}{\partial z} \cos(n,z) + \left(\frac{\partial w}{\partial x} + \frac{\partial u}{\partial z} \right) \cos(n,x) \right.$$
$$\left. + \left(\frac{\partial w}{\partial y} + \frac{\partial v}{\partial z} \right) \cos(n,y) \right] = \bar{Z}_n$$

Equations (4.28) are called equilibrium equations in terms of displacements. If the displacement components satisfy these equations, then the stresses as calculated from the stress-displacement relations will satisfy the equilibrium equations (1.7). Hence, the second boundary-value problem simplifies into one of finding three displacement components satisfying the three equilibrium equations in terms of displacements (4.28) as well as the boundary conditions (4.19). Similarly the first boundary-value problem simplifies into one of finding three displacement components satisfying the field conditions (4.28) and the boundary conditions (4.29). The mixed boundary-value problem simplifies into one of finding three displacement components satisfying Eqs. (4.28) in the whole field, Eqs. (4.19) on a portion of the boundary, and Eqs. (4.29) on the rest of the boundary.

4.10. Basic Methods for Solving Elasticity Problems in Simply Connected Bodies. The basic methods used in solving the three types of boundary-value problems in elasticity can be summarized into the following:

1. Solve a system of fifteen equations (six stress-strain relations, six strain-displacement relations, and three equilibrium equations) for fifteen unknowns (six stress components, six strain components, and three displacement components) with the requirement that the stress components and the displacement components satisfy the boundary conditions.

2. Solve a system of nine equations (six stress-displacement relations and three equilibrium equations) for nine unknowns (six stress components and three displacement components) with the requirement that the stress components and the displacement components satisfy the boundary conditions.

3. Solve a system of three equations (equilibrium equations in terms of displacements) for three unknowns (three displacement components) with the requirement that the displacement components satisfy the boundary conditions.

4. Solve a system of fifteen equations (six stress-strain relations, six compatibility equations in strains, and three equilibrium equations) for twelve unknowns (six stress components and six strain components) with the requirement that the stress components satisfy the boundary conditions. This method can be used only for first boundary-value problems. Here the number of equations exceeds the number of unknowns by three. This is not a real excess because the six compatibility equations are essentially equivalent to three differential equations of a higher order. It is usually more convenient to work on the six lower-order equations than the three higher-order equations.

5. Solve a system of nine equations (six compatibility equations in stresses and three equilibrium equations) for six unknowns (six stress components) with the requirement that the stress components satisfy the boundary conditions. This method applies only to first boundary-value problems. The excess of equations to unknowns is again not a real one.

4.11. Elasticity Problems in Multiply Connected Bodies. For multiply connected regions, the compatibility equations, either in strain or in stress, are the necessary but insufficient conditions for continuous single-valued displacements. The correct solution must satisfy the compatibility equations, but a solution that satisfies the compatibility equations is not always the correct solution. To solve elasticity problems in multiply connected bodies, methods 1, 2, and 3 in Sec. 4.10 can be used without imposing any additional restrictions because the compatibility equations are not used. Methods 4 and 5 can still be used, but the stresses or strains thus obtained must be substituted into the strain-displacement or stress-displacement relations. The displacement components are then determined by the integration of these relations and inspected to see whether they are continuous and single-valued. In case of violations, the solutions of stresses and strains must be revised so as to make the displacement function come out to be continuous and single-valued.

Suitable cuts may be made in the body to render it simply connected. The cut line will then constitute a new boundary. The boundary condition at this new boundary is that the stress components and displacement components at the two sides of the cut line are the same. All the five methods listed in Sec. 4.10 then become applicable.

4.12. Principle of Superposition. The equilibrium equations (1.7), the stress-strain relations (4.17), the strain-displacement relations (2.11) and (2.13), and the boundary conditions (4.18) and (4.19) are all linear in character. In these equations, the components of stresses, strains, and displacements appear only in the first power. Hence, the principle of superposition is valid in all of the three fundamental elasticity problems. This can be readily verified in the following way:

Consider two first boundary-value problems. Let $\sigma_x^{(1)}$, $\sigma_y^{(1)}$, $\ldots$; $\epsilon_x^{(1)}$, $\epsilon_y^{(1)}$, $\ldots$; and $u^{(1)}$, $v^{(1)}$, $w^{(1)}$ be the components of stresses, strains, and displacements in a body loaded with body-force components $X^{(1)}$, $Y^{(1)}$, $Z^{(1)}$ and surface-force components $\bar{X}_n^{(1)}$, $\bar{Y}_n^{(1)}$, $\bar{Z}_n^{(1)}$. Let $\sigma_x^{(2)}$, $\sigma_y^{(2)}$, $\ldots$; $\epsilon_x^{(2)}$, $\epsilon_y^{(2)}$, $\ldots$; and $u^{(2)}$, $v^{(2)}$, $w^{(2)}$ be the components of stresses, strains, and displacements in the same body under the loads $X^{(2)}$, $Y^{(2)}$, $Z^{(2)}$ and $\bar{X}_n^{(2)}$, $\bar{Y}_n^{(2)}$, $\bar{Z}_n^{(2)}$. Consider the first of the equilibrium equations (1.7). Since $\sigma_x^{(1)}$, $\ldots$ and $\sigma_x^{(2)}$, $\ldots$ are solutions of the first and second loadings, we have

$$\frac{\partial \sigma_x^{(1)}}{\partial x} + \frac{\partial \tau_{xy}^{(1)}}{\partial y} + \frac{\partial \tau_{xz}^{(1)}}{\partial z} + X^{(1)} = 0$$

$$\frac{\partial \sigma_x^{(2)}}{\partial x} + \frac{\partial \tau_{xy}^{(2)}}{\partial y} + \frac{\partial \tau_{xz}^{(2)}}{\partial z} + X^{(2)} = 0$$

Adding these two equations, we have

$$\frac{\partial}{\partial x}(\sigma_x^{(1)} + \sigma_x^{(2)}) + \frac{\partial}{\partial y}(\tau_{xy}^{(1)} + \tau_{xy}^{(2)}) + \frac{\partial}{\partial z}(\tau_{xz}^{(1)} + \tau_{xz}^{(2)}) + (X^{(1)} + X^{(2)}) = 0$$

Hence, the combined solution $\sigma_x^{(1)} + \sigma_x^{(2)}$, $\sigma_y^{(1)} + \sigma_y^{(2)}$, $\ldots$; $\epsilon_x^{(1)} + \epsilon_x^{(2)}$, $\epsilon_y^{(1)} + \epsilon_y^{(2)}$, $\ldots$; and $u^{(1)} + u^{(2)}$, $v^{(1)} + v^{(2)}$, $\ldots$ satisfy the first of the three equilibrium equations for the body under the combined loads $X^{(1)} + X^{(2)}$, $Y^{(1)} + Y^{(2)}$, $Z^{(1)} + Z^{(2)}$, $\bar{X}_n^{(1)} + \bar{X}_n^{(2)}$, $\bar{Y}_n^{(1)} + \bar{Y}_n^{(2)}$, $\bar{Z}_n^{(1)} + \bar{Z}_n^{(2)}$. Similarly, the combined solution can be shown to satisfy the other two equations of equilibrium together with the stress-strain and strain-displacement relations. The combined solution is therefore the correct solution for the case where the body is under the combined load. Similarly the principle of superposition can be shown to be valid for the second boundary-value problem. For the mixed boundary-value problem, the principle of superposition cannot be readily applied unless the division of the boundary into the two portions, one under prescribed force, the other under prescribed displacement, is the same in the separate problems to be superposed.

4.13. Uniqueness of Solution. From experience we know that, under identical loadings, identical stresses will be produced. This has also been established mathematically in a theorem called the uniqueness theorem. To understand this theorem, the meaning of two terms, rigid-body displacement and nonrigid-body displacement, needs to be emphasized. Rigid-body displacement is the displacement usually treated in elementary dynamics. The body as a whole translates and rotates, while the distances between any two particles in the body remain unchanged. No strains and therefore no stresses are produced after such a displacement. Nonrigid-body displacement, or pure deformation, is the displacement referred to a set of coordinate axes inside the body and moving with the body. It is a measure of the change in distance between the particles in a body. Strains and therefore stresses always result from such a displacement. Any arbitrary displacement can be decomposed into two components, rigid- and nonrigid-body displacements (see Sec. 2.7).

We shall quote without proof the uniqueness theorem:† For the first boundary-value problem, there is a unique solution of stresses, strains, and nonrigid-body displacements. For the second and mixed boundary-value problems, there is a unique solution of stresses, strains, and displacements.

In the first boundary-value problem, no displacement is prescribed on the boundary; hence, the body can translate and rotate as a whole for any amount without violating the prescribed boundary conditions. This shows that there can be no unique solution for the rigid-body component of the total displacement. In the second and mixed boundary-value problem, the body must translate and rotate a specific amount to satisfy the prescribed displacements on the boundary. Unique solutions therefore

† See I. S. Sokolnikoff, "Mathematical Theory of Elasticity," 1st ed., McGraw-Hill Book Company, Inc., New York, 1946.

can and do exist for the rigid-body displacement, nonrigid-body displacement, as well as the total displacement.

4.14. The Inverse and Semi-inverse Methods of Solving Elasticity Problems. It has been shown that elasticity problems are essentially problems of obtaining solutions of groups of simultaneous partial-differential equations. Unfortunately, our present knowledge of pure mathematics has not advanced to the stage where we can solve these groups of simultaneous partial-differential equations directly and obtain the solutions of stresses, strains, and displacements. An inverse method is therefore commonly used. In this method, an educated guess on the final solution is made and checked against the basic equations and boundary conditions. This guess may be based on intuition, experiments, or existing solutions of similar problems. If all these conditions are satisfied, then the guessed solution is a correct solution, and, by the uniqueness theorem, the only correct solution. If some of these conditions are violated, then a revision must be made, based on the experience of the first trial. This revised guess is again checked for its correctness.

Often the educated guess is made on only some of the unknowns. The group of simultaneous equations thereby becomes simplified and is solved for the rest of the unknowns. The whole set of solutions is then checked for its correctness by means of the basic equations and boundary conditions. This method of solution in which initial assumptions about some of the unknowns are taken and the remaining unknowns solved is called the semi-inverse method. It is successful in many relatively simple problems. For complicated problems this method usually fails. It is to be pointed out that, at present, the majority of elasticity problems are still unsolved and experimental stress analysis is the usual method in dealing with such problems.

4.15. Saint-Venant's Principle. Frequently a solution can be obtained if the system of forces acting on a portion of the boundary is replaced by a statically equivalent system of forces acting on the same portion of the body. In such cases, a principle proposed by Saint-Venant is very useful. Briefly this principle states:

If a system of forces acting on one portion of the boundary is replaced by a statically equivalent system of forces acting on the same portion of the boundary, then the stresses, strains, and nonrigid-body displacements in the parts of the body sufficiently far removed from this portion of boundary remain approximately the same.

For example, the stress distribution of a straight bar of cross-sectional area A under a uniformly distributed load p at its two ends (Fig. 4.6a) can be obtained easily by the inverse method. We make a guess that the stresses at every point inside the body are

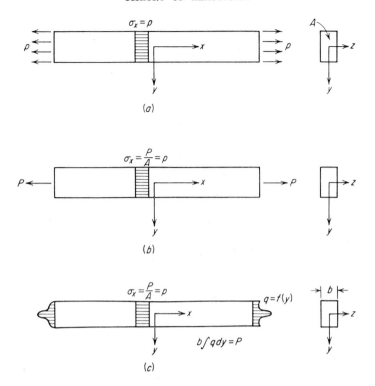

Fig. 4.6. Saint-Venant's principle applied to a straight bar under axial load.

$$\sigma_x = p \tag{4.30}$$

$$\sigma_y = \sigma_z = \tau_{xy} = \tau_{yz} = \tau_{zx} = 0$$

By inspection these stresses satisfy the equilibrium, compatibility, and boundary conditions, so that they are really the correct solution. Now suppose the bar is loaded at the ends by concentrated loads P instead of the distributed loads p (Fig. 4.6b). Then the stresses given by Eqs. (4.30) are no longer the correct solution because they do not satisfy the boundary conditions at the two ends. If the concentrated load P and the resultant of the distributed loads are equal in magnitude, have the same point of application, and act in the same direction so that they are statically equivalent, then Saint-Venant's principle states that the stresses at the portion of the bar sufficiently far away from the two ends, i.e., at the middle portions of the bar, will be approximately the same for these two loadings. Expressions (4.30) therefore also give the stresses at the portion of the bar away from the two ends when the load P at the ends is a concentrated load statically equivalent to the uniformly distributed load p.

By the same principle, expressions (4.30) are also valid in the regions away from the two ends for any load system which is statically equivalent to the uniformly distributed load p (Fig. 4.6c).

FIG. 4.7. Illustration of Saint-Venant's principle. The flat bar is under a concentrated load at one end and under a nonuniform and slightly nonsymmetric load at the other end. The central part of the bar (away from the ends a distance equal to about the width of the bar) is under a homogeneous state of stress. The figures show the order of the photoelastic fringes.

Figure 4.7 shows a bar supported by a steel block and loaded by a concentrated load at the top. It is seen from this photograph of the isochromatic photoelastic fringe pattern that the portion of the bar at a

Fig. 4.8. Brittle-coating-test verification of Saint-Venant's principle. The crack pattern in the notch strip becomes horizontal in the region at a distance of about $1\frac{1}{2}$ times the diameter of the notch.

distance of about one width away from the top and bottom shows uniform darkness. By photoelastic methods to be explained in a later contemplated volume, this has the interpretation that the vertical stresses are essentially uniform in this region. Figure 4.8 shows a notched strip under a uniformly distributed tensile load at its ends. It is seen that the crack pattern of the brittle coating sprayed on this strip becomes horizontal lines in the region at a distance of about $1\frac{1}{2}$ times the diameter of the notch away from the edge of these notches. By the methods explained later in the chapters on brittle coatings, this has the interpretation that the vertical stresses are essentially uniform in this region. Hence the disturbance of the notches extends only to a distance of about $1\frac{1}{2}$ their diameter. Another example of application of Saint-Venant's principle (to a beam under pure bending) may be found in Sec. 5.1.

EXERCISES

4.1. Prove that the elastic constants C_{12} and C_{13} in the generalized Hooke's law are equal for isotropic materials.

4.2. A solid sphere is placed in a tank filled with water under a uniform pressure p. Determine the stresses, strains, and displacements at every point in the sphere. If a larger sphere is used, would the pressure at its center be larger than that at the center of a smaller sphere? What are the stresses and strains in a body of irregular shape placed in the above tank? Neglect body forces.

CHAPTER 5

APPLICATION TO THREE-DIMENSIONAL PROBLEMS

5.1. Elastic Solution of Beams of Rectangular Cross Section, under Pure Bending. Let a beam of rectangular cross section be bent by two equal and opposite couples M (Fig. 5.1), and let us assume that body forces produce stresses which are negligible in comparison with those produced by applied forces. The problem will be solved by the semi-inverse method (see Sec. 4.14). The stress components as given by the elementary beam formula are

$$\sigma_x = \frac{My}{I} \tag{5.1}$$

$$\sigma_y = \sigma_z = \tau_{xy} = \tau_{yz} = \tau_{zz} = 0$$

where I is the area moment of inertia of the beam cross section with respect to the z axis.

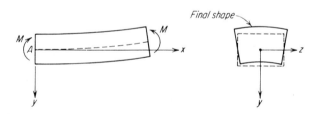

Fig. 5.1. Pure bending of a beam of rectangular cross section.

We shall take expressions (5.1) as our guess of the stresses and derive the strains and displacements from the basic equations. From Eqs. (5.1) and the stress-strain relations, we have

$$\epsilon_x = \frac{My}{EI} \qquad \epsilon_y = \epsilon_z = -\nu \frac{My}{EI} \tag{5.2}$$

$$\gamma_{xy} = \gamma_{yz} = \gamma_{zz} = 0$$

107

From Eqs. (5.2) and the strain-displacement relations we have

$$\frac{\partial u}{\partial x} = \frac{My}{EI} \qquad \frac{\partial v}{\partial y} = \frac{\partial w}{\partial z} = -\nu \frac{My}{EI}$$

$$\frac{\partial u}{\partial y} + \frac{\partial v}{\partial x} = \frac{\partial v}{\partial z} + \frac{\partial w}{\partial y} = \frac{\partial w}{\partial x} + \frac{\partial u}{\partial z} = 0$$

(5.3)

Equations (5.3) can be integrated to give

$$u = \frac{M}{EI} xy + C_1 y + C_2 z + C_4$$

$$v = -\frac{M}{2EI} [x^2 + \nu(y^2 - z^2)] - C_1 x + C_3 z + C_5 \qquad (5.4)$$

$$w = -\frac{\nu M}{EI} yz - C_2 x - C_3 y + C_6$$

where $C_1, C_2, \ldots, C_6$ are constants of integration, independent of x, y, z. Assume that point A, the centroid of the left end of the bar, is fixed and that in the neighborhood of this point an element of the x axis, and an element of the xy plane are also fixed. Thus we have, for $x = y = z = 0$,

$$u = v = w = 0$$

$$\frac{\partial v}{\partial x} = \frac{\partial w}{\partial x} = \frac{\partial w}{\partial y} = 0$$

Substituting these conditions into Eqs. (5.4), the six constants are all found to be equal to zero. Then

$$u = \frac{M}{EI} xy$$

$$v = -\frac{M}{2EI} [x^2 + \nu(y^2 - z^2)] \qquad (5.5)$$

$$w = -\frac{\nu M}{EI} yz$$

The stresses, strains, and displacements given by Eqs. (5.1), (5.2), and (5.5) then constitute our assumed solution. The next step is to check the validity of this assumed solution. By actual substitution it is seen that these do satisfy the stress-strain and strain-displacement relations and also the equilibrium equations. By inspection, the displacement is found to be a continuous function of x, y, z. The boundary conditions are also satisfied if (1) the centroid of the left end of the bar together with an element of the x axis and an element of the xy plane is fixed and (2) the end moments are applied through a system of forces distributed over the end surfaces in the same manner as is the stress σ_x given in Eqs. (5.1). Hence, the assumed solution is correct if (1) and (2) are fulfilled. It is to be pointed out that condition (1) is used only for fixing the rigid-body displacement. It has no influence on the nonrigid-body displacement and therefore on any of the strains and stresses either. The problem belongs to the first boundary-value type because no nonrigid-body displacements are prescribed on the boundary.

Let us study the deformed shape of transversal and longitudinal planes. From (2.1) and (5.5) for the deformed point $P'(x', y', z')$

$$x' = x + u = x + \frac{Mxy}{EI} \tag{a}$$

$$y' = y + v = y - \frac{M}{2EI} [x^2 + \nu(y^2 - z^2)] \tag{b}$$

$$z' = z + w = z - \frac{\nu M}{EI} yz \tag{c}$$

First consider the undeformed plane $x = a$. Substituting a for x into (a) and (b) and combining both equations:

$$x' = a + \frac{Ma}{EI} y' + \left(\frac{M}{EI}\right)^2 \left(\frac{a}{2}\right)[a^2 + \nu(y^2 - z^2)]$$

The term M/EI can be shown to be the reciprocal of the radius of curvature, and so using the same degree of qualification as used in Chap. 2 for infinitesimal deformations, M/EI must be small and terms containing $(M/EI)^2$ can be neglected.

The equation then represents a plane

$$x' = a + \frac{Ma}{EI} y'$$

This confirms the assumption of elementary beam theory that, in general, transversal cross sections will deform to inclined planes. Equation (c) acts within this plane to give the cross section the final shape shown in Fig. 5.1.

Another interesting property is shown by considering the undeformed plane $y = b$ and substituting (a) and (c) into (b):

$$y' = b - \frac{M}{2EI} \left\{ \left(x' - \frac{Mxb}{EI}\right)^2 + \nu \left[b^2 - \left(z' + \frac{M}{EI} bz\right)^2\right] \right\}$$

Again neglecting terms containing higher orders of M/EI, the equation reduces to

$$y' = b - \frac{M}{2EI} [x'^2 + \nu(b^2 - z'^2)]$$

From this equation it is seen that points on the same level and on the same hyperbola $x^2 - \nu z^2 = $ const will move to new places at the same distance from the original level and constitute a contour line. The contour lines of the deformed surface are therefore a family of hyperbolas

$$x^2 - \nu z^2 = \text{const}$$

as shown in Fig. 5.2.

The slope of the asymptotes is given by

$$\tan \alpha = \frac{1}{\sqrt{\nu}}$$

or

$$\nu = \cot^2 \alpha$$

It is possible to experimentally determine Poisson's ratio from the above theory. If the upper or lower surface of a beam under pure bending is polished and a glass plate put over it, the contour lines of the deformed beam can be obtained optically. The technique is based on the variable thickness of the air gap between the glass and beam surface.

Since the above example is a problem of the first boundary-value type, it can be solved also by means of the compatibility equations in terms of stresses. Again, we shall take expressions (5.1) as our guess of the stresses. By inspection we see that these stresses do satisfy the equilibrium and compatibility equations. Further, they satisfy the boundary conditions if

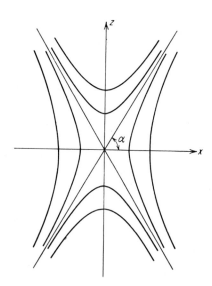

Fig. 5.2. Contour lines of the deformed top or bottom surface of a beam of rectangular cross section under pure bending.

the end moments are applied through a system of forces distributed over the end surfaces in the same manner as the stress σ_x given in Eqs. (5.1). Hence, the assumed solution of the stresses is correct. The correct strains and displacements are then computed from these stresses and are identical to the expressions given by Eqs. (5.2) and (5.5).

In case the end moments are not applied through a system of forces distributed over the end surfaces in the manner of σ_x given in Eqs. (5.1), then Saint-Venant's principle can be invoked and the stresses, strains, and displacements given above will be valid at the middle portion of the bar at least one-half times the depth of the bar away from the ends.

An experimental verification of the linearity of the stress distribution and of the application of Saint-Venant's principle is shown in Fig. 5.3. This photograph is a two-dimensional photoelastic isochromatic pattern. By photoelastic methods to be explained in a later contemplated volume, this pattern has the interpretation that the maximum shear-stress distribution across the height of the beam is linear in all the region between the two inside supports up to a distance from these supports of about one-half the height of the beam.

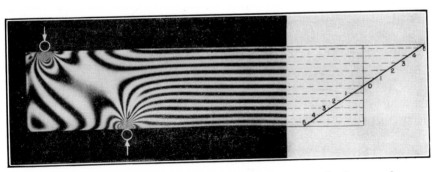

Fig. 5.3. Two-dimensional photoelasticity isochromatic pattern of a beam under pure bending. The distribution of maximum shear stress is verified to be linear across the height of the beam. Saint-Venant's principle applies at a distance, from the inside support toward the center of the beam, of less than one-half the height of the beam.

Another experimental verification can be seen in Fig. 5.4. According to Eqs. (5.1) the stresses σ_x and σ_y are principal stresses. This means that the direction of the principal stresses is longitudinal and transversal in the pure-bending field. As explained later in the chapter dealing with brittle coatings, the direction of failure of these coatings coincides with the direction of the principal stresses (isostatics). The geometric regularity of these lines is shown in Fig. 5.4, which corresponds to a beam loaded by means of pins located on the central axis. The isostatics are longitudinal

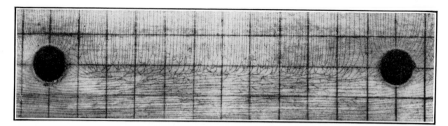

Fig. 5.4. Principal stress trajectories (isostatics) on the surface of a beam under pure bending. The direction of the principal stresses is verified to be longitudinal and transverse to the axis of the beam. The isostatics have been obtained using brittle coatings.

and transversal to the beam everywhere except at a distance from the center of the hole equal to less than one-half the height of the beam. It can also be seen in this figure that, because of a slight difference in the mechanical properties of the beam material, the neutral axis does not coincide exactly with the central axis of the beam.

5.2. Elastic Solution of a Prismatic Bar Standing under Its Own Weight. Consider a homogeneous bar of square cross section which is supported on a frictionless surface such as shown in Fig. 5.5. It is desired to find the stresses and displacements throughout the bar resulting from the gravity loading only. The body-force-intensity components will be

$$X = Y = 0 \qquad Z = -\gamma \qquad (5.6)$$

where γ is the weight per unit volume of the material.

The boundary conditions are [see Eqs. (4.18) and (4.19)]

$$\bar{w} = 0 \qquad \bar{X}_n = \bar{Y}_n = 0 \qquad \text{on } z = 0$$

and $\qquad \bar{X}_n = \bar{Y}_n = \bar{Z}_n = 0 \qquad \text{on remaining surfaces} \qquad (5.7)$

Consider the system of stresses

$$\sigma_x = \sigma_y = \tau_{xy} = \tau_{yz} = \tau_{zx} = 0 \qquad \sigma_z = -\gamma(l - z) \qquad (5.8)$$

It is easily seen that these stresses along with the body-force-intensity loadings in Eqs. (5.6) satisfy the equilibrium conditions (1.7) and the compatibility equations (4.27). This is therefore the correct solution for the stresses throughout the entire bar provided the boundary conditions are satisfied. The boundary conditions along the sides and top are clearly satisfied as are the conditions $\bar{X}_n = \bar{Y}_n = 0$ on the bottom surface. It remains to be seen whether the displacement condition $\bar{w} = 0$ on $z = 0$ is satisfied.

From the stress-strain relations (4.16), it is found that

$$\epsilon_x = \epsilon_y = \frac{\nu}{E}\gamma(l-z)$$

$$\epsilon_z = -\frac{\gamma}{E}(l-z) \tag{5.9}$$

$$\gamma_{xy} = \gamma_{yz} = \gamma_{zx} = 0$$

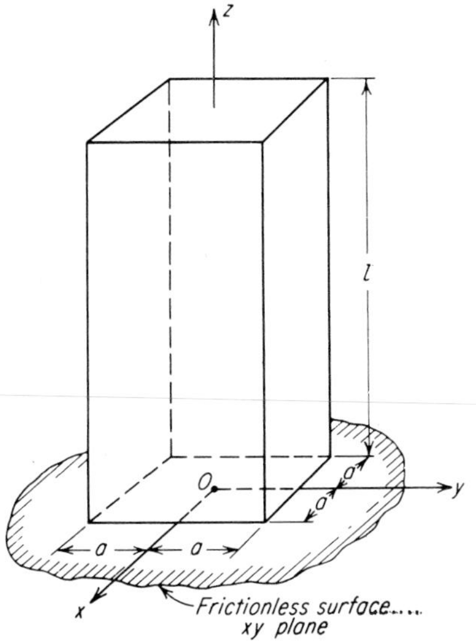

FIG. 5.5. Bar standing under its own weight.

From the strain-displacement relations (2.11) and (2.13) and the above,

$$\frac{\partial u}{\partial x} = \epsilon_x = \frac{\nu\gamma}{E}(l-z) \qquad \frac{\partial v}{\partial y} = \epsilon_y = \frac{\nu\gamma}{E}(l-z) \tag{5.10a}$$

$$\frac{\partial w}{\partial z} = \epsilon_z = -\frac{\gamma}{E}(l-z) \tag{5.10b}$$

$$\frac{\partial u}{\partial y} + \frac{\partial v}{\partial x} = \gamma_{xy} = 0 \qquad \frac{\partial v}{\partial z} + \frac{\partial w}{\partial y} = \gamma_{yz} = 0 \qquad \frac{\partial w}{\partial x} + \frac{\partial u}{\partial z} = \gamma_{zx} = 0 \tag{5.10c}$$

As can be verified by substitution, the solution of these equations is

$$u = \frac{\nu\gamma}{E}x(l-z) + C_1 y + C_2 z + C_3$$

$$v = \frac{\nu\gamma}{E}y(l-z) - C_1 x + C_4 z + C_5 \tag{5.11}$$

$$w = -\frac{\gamma}{E}\left(lz - \frac{z^2}{2}\right) + \frac{\nu\gamma}{2E}(x^2 + y^2) - C_2 x - C_4 y + C_6$$

where the coefficients C_1, C_2, ... , C_6 are constants of integration. Since the terms involving them do not contribute to any strains within the body [as is clear from the fact that none of these coefficients appear in Eqs. (5.9)], these terms represent a rigid displacement of the entire body. That is, the conditions for a rigid displacement [Eq. (2.16)] are satisfied for the portion of the displacement field involving these six constants.

These coefficients are therefore evaluated by simply fixing the bar rigidly at some arbitrary point, i.e., by fixing some point in the body and specifying the orientation of lines passing through the point. If this point is chosen as point O (Fig. 5.5), then

$$u = v = w = \frac{\partial u}{\partial z} = \frac{\partial v}{\partial z} = \frac{\partial v}{\partial x} = 0$$

at $x, y, z = 0$.

In this case all the constants become zero, and the displacement field takes the form

$$u = \frac{\nu\gamma}{E} x(l - z)$$

$$v = \frac{\nu\gamma}{E} y(l - z) \tag{5.12}$$

$$w = -\frac{\gamma}{E}\left(lz - \frac{z^2}{2}\right) + \frac{\nu\gamma}{2E}(x^2 + y^2)$$

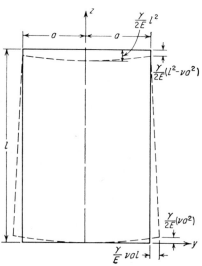

FIG. 5.6. Displacements of a bar standing under its own weight as given by the elasticity solutions (5.12). The displacements shown are those which occur in the plane $x = 0$.

The displacement field represented by these equations is illustrated in Fig. 5.6. The displacements are shown in the plane $x = 0$. All horizontal lines are deformed to parabolas, and vertical lines become inclined but remain straight. There is clearly a violation of the boundary condition $\bar{w} = 0$ at $z = 0$; and hence the assumed solution for stresses [Eqs. (5.8)] is incorrect with respect to this condition. If, instead of prescribing that $\bar{w} = 0$ on $z = 0$, the condition $\bar{Z}_n = -\gamma l$ is prescribed, i.e., suppose the actual physical bar had a uniform compressive stress distribution over its lower boundary,† the assumed stresses [Eqs. (5.8)] and the corresponding displacements [Eqs. (5.12)] would represent the true solution throughout the entire bar and the displacements shown in Fig. 5.6 would be those which would actually occur.

Going back to the boundary condition $\bar{w} = 0$ on $z = 0$, it should be noted that, by Saint-Venant's principle, the solution presented here is very accurate at locations some distance away from the bottom of the bar since the actual stress distribution along the bottom is statically equivalent to that given by the solutions (5.8).

This problem is illustrated experimentally in Fig. 5.7, where the photoelastic isochromatic pattern is shown for a gelatin block of square cross section standing under its own weight. As explained in the figure, some friction exists at the bottom boundary and some residual stresses are present along the other boundaries; however, as stated above by Saint-Venant's principle, the correlation with theory should be good for the central portion of the bar. The fringe orders are plotted along the right side; and, as predicted by the theory, which says the stress σ_z will increase linearly with depth [Eqs. (5.8)], the fringe orders, which are proportional to the stress σ_z, also increase linearly with depth.

A determination of the material fringe value f‡ can be made from this test. The weight of this model per unit volume was measured to be $\gamma = 0.036$ lb/in.³. Its height is $7\frac{7}{8}$ in. and its cross section is a 2 13/16-in. square. At a depth of, say, 6 in. in the model, the fringe order is seen to be about 4.5. The stress $\sigma_z = 6\gamma = 6 \times 0.036 = 0.216$ psi. The maximum

---

†This could be realized, for example, by standing the bar on a frictionless surface having a parabolic shape that would exactly fit the deformed surface as given by Eqs. (5.12) for $z = 0$.

‡This will be explained later in a contemplated volume on photoelasticity; however it will suffice here to remark that the fringe order n is proportional to the maximum shear stress τ_{max}, which occurs in the plane perpendicular to the line of sight, and is also proportional to the thickness t of the model; thus,

$$n = \frac{1}{f} t\tau_{max}$$

where $1/f$ is the constant of proportionality and f itself is called the material fringe value.

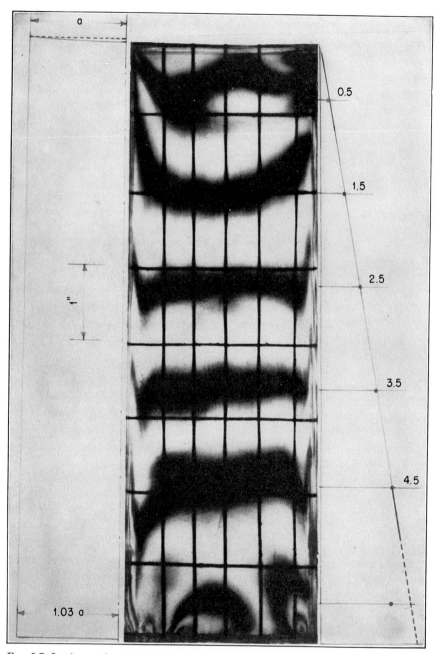

Fig. 5.7. Isochromatic pattern obtained from a gelatin block of square cross section, standing under its own weight. There are friction stresses at the bottom boundary and residual stresses on the vertical and top boundaries which limit the correlation with theory to the central part of the block. The curvature of the top boundary is visible on the photograph.

shear stress at this depth in the plane of observation is $\tau_{max} = \sigma_z/2 = 0.108$ psi.† By the equation in the second footnote on page 115,

$$f = \frac{\tau_{max}t}{n} = \frac{0.108 \times 2\frac{13}{16}}{4.5}$$

$$= 0.068 \frac{\text{psi-in.}}{\text{fringe}}$$

The modulus of elasticity E of the gelatin may be determined by measuring the vertical displacements of the top boundary or by measuring the lateral "spread" at the bottom. Measurements on the model in Fig. 5.7 showed that the width at the bottom was about 1.03 times that at the top. Noting the displacements given in Fig. 5.6, this ratio is seen to be $1 + \gamma\nu l/E$. Poisson's ratio for gelatin is approximately 0.5; hence

$$1 + \frac{\gamma\nu l}{E} = 1.03 = 1 + \frac{0.036 \times 0.5 \times 7\frac{7}{8}}{E}$$

or $E = 4.7$ psi

EXERCISES

5.1. Carry out rigorously the integration of Eqs. (5.3), and obtain Eqs. (5.4).

5.2. Carry out rigorously the integration of Eqs. (5.10), and obtain Eqs. (5.11).

†This is evident from observation of the Mohr's-circle construction (Chap. 3) but can also be deduced from Eq. (1.12e) by maximizing $\tau_{y'z'}$ with respect to the orientation of the $y'z'$ coordinate system.

CHAPTER 6

TWO-DIMENSIONAL PROBLEMS
IN THE THEORY OF ELASTICITY

6.1. Statement of the Plane Problem. Consider a homogeneous isotropic elastic body bounded by two parallel planes and one or more cylindrical surfaces whose generators are perpendicular to the bounding planes. The case where the region D occupied by the body is finite and simply connected is shown in Fig. 6.1. Let S_L denote the lateral boundary whose trace on the median plane $(z = 0)$ is the plane curve C. Let R denote the plane region bounded by C (Fig. 6.3). Let the body be loaded by surface forces on S_L only and by body forces. Let all these external loads be parallel to the bounding planes and constant in the z direction. Let the two components of the surface loads be denoted by $\bar{X}_n(x,y)$ and $\bar{Y}_n(x,y)$. The notations $\bar{X}_n(x,y)$ and $\bar{Y}_n(x,y)$ are used to denote that $\bar{X}_n$ and $\bar{Y}_n$ are functions of x and y only and not of z. Let the components of the body force be

$$X = -\frac{\partial \Omega}{\partial x}$$

$$Y = -\frac{\partial \Omega}{\partial y} \tag{6.1}$$

$$Z = 0$$

where

$$\Omega = \Omega(x,y)$$

The boundary conditions are, by Eqs. (4.18),

$$\sigma_z = \tau_{zx} = \tau_{zy} = 0 \qquad \text{on } z = \pm\frac{t}{2}$$

$$\left.\begin{array}{l} \sigma_x \cos(n,x) + \tau_{xy} \cos(n,y) = \bar{X}_n(x,y) \\[2mm] \tau_{xy} \cos(n,x) + \sigma_y \cos(n,y) = \bar{Y}_n(x,y) \\[2mm] \tau_{zx} \cos(n,x) + \tau_{zy} \cos(n,y) = 0 \end{array}\right\} \qquad \text{on } S_L \tag{6.2}$$

This special type of first boundary-value problem is called the plane problem, or the two-dimensional problem. A wide variety of practical problems falls in this category. To solve the plane problem, three different approaches or methods are commonly used. (The word "method" will be used in this text, although the word "approach" would be just as

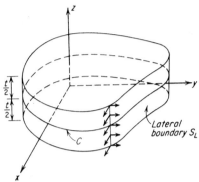

FIG. 6.1. Cylindrical body bounded by the planes $\pm t/2$ and the lateral surface S_L.

appropriate.) These are the plane-strain, plane-stress, and the generalized plane-stress methods. It must be recognized clearly that these methods constitute only attempts at solutions. It will be seen that, except in special cases, none of these approaches will constitute the exact elasticity solution, i.e., the one satisfying completely and rigorously all the basic equations and boundary conditions.

These three methods will be discussed in this chapter. First, however, the basic equations governing the plane problem will be set forth.

6.2. Basic Equations of the Plane Problem. The fundamental equations governing the plane problem can be deduced from the general equations given in Chap. 4. Noting that Z, the component in the z direction of the body force, is zero, we obtain from Eqs. (1.7), (4.25), and (4.26) the following equations of equilibrium and compatibility in terms of stresses. Equations of equilibrium,

$$\frac{\partial \sigma_x}{\partial x} + \frac{\partial \tau_{yx}}{\partial y} + \frac{\partial \tau_{zx}}{\partial z} + X = 0$$

$$\frac{\partial \tau_{xy}}{\partial x} + \frac{\partial \sigma_y}{\partial y} + \frac{\partial \tau_{zy}}{\partial z} + Y = 0 \tag{6.3}$$

$$\frac{\partial \tau_{xz}}{\partial x} + \frac{\partial \tau_{yz}}{\partial y} + \frac{\partial \sigma_z}{\partial z} = 0$$

Equations of compatibility in terms of stresses,

$$\nabla^2 \sigma_x + \frac{3}{1+\nu} \frac{\partial^2 \sigma_m}{\partial x^2} = \frac{-\nu}{1-\nu} \left(\frac{\partial X}{\partial x} + \frac{\partial Y}{\partial y} \right) - 2 \frac{\partial X}{\partial x}$$

$$\nabla^2 \sigma_y + \frac{3}{1+\nu} \frac{\partial^2 \sigma_m}{\partial y^2} = \frac{-\nu}{1-\nu} \left(\frac{\partial X}{\partial x} + \frac{\partial Y}{\partial y} \right) - 2 \frac{\partial Y}{\partial y}$$

$$\nabla^2 \sigma_z + \frac{3}{1+\nu} \frac{\partial^2 \sigma_m}{\partial z^2} = \frac{-\nu}{1-\nu} \left(\frac{\partial X}{\partial x} + \frac{\partial Y}{\partial y} \right)$$

$$\nabla^2 \tau_{xy} + \frac{3}{1+\nu} \frac{\partial^2 \sigma_m}{\partial x\, \partial y} = - \left(\frac{\partial Y}{\partial x} + \frac{\partial X}{\partial y} \right)$$

$$\nabla^2 \tau_{yz} + \frac{3}{1+\nu} \frac{\partial^2 \sigma_m}{\partial y\, \partial z} = 0$$

$$\nabla^2 \tau_{zx} + \frac{3}{1+\nu} \frac{\partial^2 \sigma_m}{\partial z\, \partial x} = 0$$

(6.4)

where
$$\sigma_m = \frac{\sigma_x + \sigma_y + \sigma_z}{3}$$

The problem is therefore one of finding a set of stress components satisfying Eqs. (6.3) and (6.4) in the whole region and Eqs. (6.2) on the boundary.

6.3. Plane-strain Method. In the plane-strain method, the semi-inverse approach will be used. The following assumptions on stresses are made:

$$\sigma_x = \sigma_x(x,y)$$

$$\sigma_y = \sigma_y(x,y)$$ (6.5)

$$\tau_{xy} = \tau_{xy}(x,y)$$

$$\sigma_z = \nu(\sigma_x + \sigma_y)$$
                                    (6.6)
$$\tau_{yz} = \tau_{zx} = 0$$

Substituting Eqs. (6.5) and 6.6) into the stress-strain relations, we obtain

$$\epsilon_x = \epsilon_x(x,y)$$

$$\epsilon_y = \epsilon_y(x,y)$$ (6.7)

$$\gamma_{xy} = \gamma_{xy}(x,y)$$

$$\epsilon_z = \gamma_{yz} = \gamma_{zx} = 0$$

As a consequence of assumptions (6.5) and (6.6) we therefore have: (1) All stress and strain components are functions of x and y only; they do not vary in the z direction. (2) All stress and strain components in the z direction vanish except σ_z, which is equal to $\nu(\sigma_x + \sigma_y)$. Because all strain components in the z direction vanish and the strain is two-dimensional, this method is called the plane-strain method.

Next, the validity of the assumptions (6.5) and (6.6) must be tested. Substituting these equations into the equilibrium equations (6.3), the third of the latter is identically satisfied. The other two become

$$\frac{\partial \sigma_x}{\partial x} + \frac{\partial \tau_{xy}}{\partial y} + X = 0$$

$$\frac{\partial \tau_{xy}}{\partial x} + \frac{\partial \sigma_y}{\partial y} + Y = 0$$

(6.8)

The equations of compatibility in terms of stresses [Eqs. (6.4)] become

$$\nabla^2 \sigma_x + \frac{\partial^2}{\partial x^2}(\sigma_x + \sigma_y) = \frac{-\nu}{1 - \nu}\left(\frac{\partial X}{\partial x} + \frac{\partial Y}{\partial y}\right) - 2\frac{\partial X}{\partial x}$$

$$\nabla^2 \sigma_y + \frac{\partial^2}{\partial y^2}(\sigma_x + \sigma_y) = \frac{-\nu}{1 - \nu}\left(\frac{\partial X}{\partial x} + \frac{\partial Y}{\partial y}\right) - 2\frac{\partial Y}{\partial y}$$

(6.9)

$$\nabla^2(\sigma_x + \sigma_y) = \frac{-1}{1 - \nu}\left(\frac{\partial X}{\partial x} + \frac{\partial Y}{\partial y}\right)$$

$$\nabla^2 \tau_{xy} + \frac{\partial^2}{\partial x\,\partial y}(\sigma_x + \sigma_y) = -\left(\frac{\partial Y}{\partial x} + \frac{\partial X}{\partial y}\right)$$

The fourth equation of (6.9) can be derived from Eqs. (6.8). Each of the other three can be derived from Eqs. (6.8) and one of the remaining two Eqs. (6.9). Hence satisfaction of any one of the first three compatibility equations is sufficient. Arbitrarily, then, the third equation, the simplest, will be used with Eqs. (6.8) to satisfy equilibrium and compatibility, and will be written

$$\left(\frac{\partial^2}{\partial x^2} + \frac{\partial^2}{\partial y^2}\right)(\sigma_x + \sigma_y) = \frac{-1}{1 - \nu}\left(\frac{\partial X}{\partial x} + \frac{\partial Y}{\partial y}\right)$$

(6.10)

To solve the differential equations (6.8) and (6.10) for the three unknowns σ_x, σ_y, and τ_{xy}, a new function of x and y only will be introduced. This new function, called Airy's stress function, and usually denoted by ϕ, is one of several functions which play an important part in solving problems in theory of elasticity. Although it can be used in any two-dimensional coordinate system, here for cartesian coordinates it is defined by the three following equations:

$$\sigma_x = \frac{\partial^2 \phi}{\partial y^2} + \Omega \qquad \sigma_y = \frac{\partial^2 \phi}{\partial x^2} + \Omega$$

$$\tau_{xy} = -\frac{\partial^2 \phi}{\partial x\,\partial y}$$

(6.11)

Since ϕ and Ω are functions of x and y only, σ_x, σ_y and τ_{xy} given by Eqs. (6.11) are also functions of x and y only; hence, there will be no violation of Eqs. (6.5). Substituting Eqs. (6.11) and (6.1) into (6.8), the latter are identically satisfied. Substituting Eqs. (6.11) and (6.1) into (6.10), we obtain

$$\nabla^4 \phi = -\frac{1 - 2\nu}{1 - \nu} \nabla^2 \Omega$$

where

$$\nabla^4 \phi \equiv \frac{\partial^4 \phi}{\partial x^4} + 2 \frac{\partial^4 \phi}{\partial x^2 \, \partial y^2} + \frac{\partial^4 \phi}{\partial y^4} \qquad (6.12)$$

$$\nabla^2 \Omega = -\left(\frac{\partial X}{\partial x} + \frac{\partial Y}{\partial y}\right)$$

The problem of solving three differential equations (6.8) and (6.10) is therefore reduced to that of solving one differential equation (6.12). After solving Eq. (6.12) for the Airy's stress function ϕ, then the stress components σ_x, σ_y, and τ_{xy} calculated from ϕ in Eqs. (6.11) together with the stress components σ_z, τ_{xz}, and τ_{yz} given in Eqs. (6.6) will satisfy the equilibrium and compatibility requirements. If the region is simply connected, then the solution will be the correct solution if it further meets the boundary conditions.

6.4. The Primary Problem in the Plane-strain Method. The boundary conditions of the plane problem [Eqs. (6.2)] can be divided into three parts.

$$\tau_{zx} = \tau_{zy} = 0 \qquad \text{on } z = \pm\frac{t}{2}$$

$$\tau_{zx} \cos(n,x) + \tau_{zy} \cos(n,y) = 0 \qquad \text{on } S_L \qquad (6.13)$$

$$\left.\begin{array}{l} \sigma_x \cos(n,x) + \tau_{xy} \cos(n,y) = X_n(x,y) \\[2mm] \tau_{xy} \cos(n,x) + \sigma_y \cos(n,y) = \bar{Y}_n(x,y) \end{array}\right\} \quad \text{on } S_L \qquad (6.14)$$

$$\sigma_z = 0 \qquad \text{on } z = \pm\frac{t}{2} \qquad (6.15)$$

The assumed stress system [Eqs. (6.6) and (6.11)] satisfy Eqs. (6.13) identically. By properly choosing ϕ, it can also be made to satisfy Eqs. (6.14). The assumed stress system, however, cannot satisfy Eq. (6.15) except under special cases where the sum $\sigma_x + \sigma_y$ happens to vanish throughout the body. The solution which satisfies equilibrium, compatibility, and the boundary conditions (6.13) and (6.14) is called the primary solution of the plane-strain method. The corresponding problem

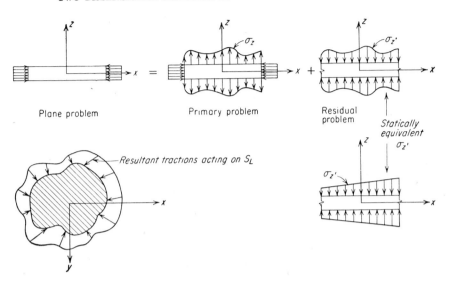

FIG. 6.2. Plane-strain method. The right side of the equality represents a typical solution to the plane problem. If, as shown, σ_z is not linear, the statically equivalent linear solution is useful far from the surface $z = \pm t/2$ (t must be much larger than shown, see Fig. 6.6.)

is called the primary problem of the plane-strain method. Since the primary solution violates Eq. (6.15), a residual problem has to be solved to remove this violation. The two solutions are then superposed together as shown in Fig. 6.2 to give the correct solution. The primary problem can be stated as follows:

Region. The whole body in the plane problem.

Body force. The given body force in the plane problem.

Boundary conditions,

$$\left.\begin{aligned} \tau_{zx} = \tau_{zy} = 0 \\ \sigma_z = \nu(\sigma_x + \sigma_y) \end{aligned}\right\} \quad \text{on } z = \pm\frac{t}{2}$$

$$\left.\begin{aligned} \tau_{zx} \cos(n,x) + \tau_{zy} \cos(n,y) = 0 \\ \sigma_x \cos(n,x) + \tau_{xy} \cos(n,y) = \bar{X}_n(x,y) \\ \tau_{xy} \cos(n,x) + \sigma_y \cos(n,y) = \bar{Y}_n(x,y) \end{aligned}\right\} \quad \text{on } S_L$$

The primary problem can be solved by finding a particular Airy's stress function ϕ which satisfies Eq. (6.12) and whose corresponding stresses given by Eqs. (6.11) satisfy the boundary conditions (6.14). After this ϕ is found, the stresses are given by Eqs. (6.11) and (6.6). Strains and displacements, if desired, can be calculated from the stresses by the stress-strain and strain-displacement relations.

6.5. The Residual Problem in the Plane-strain Method. The residual problem in the plane strain method can be stated as follows:

Region. Same as in the primary problem.

Body force. None.

Boundary conditions,

$$\left.\begin{array}{c} \tau_{zx} = \tau_{zy} = 0 \\[6pt] \sigma_z = -\sigma_z' \end{array}\right\} \quad \text{on } z = \pm\frac{t}{2}$$

Free boundary (no stresses) on S_L

Here σ_z' denotes the value of σ_z in the primary solution given by Eqs. (6.6) and (6.11). The residual problem will be discussed according to the form of the function σ_z'. A special case will be discussed first, followed by the general case.

Case 1. $\sigma_z' = ax + by + c$. Here σ_z' is a linear function of both x and y. A solution can be readily obtained by the inverse method. Assume the solution of the residual problem to be

$$\sigma_x = \sigma_y = \tau_{xy} = \tau_{yz} = \tau_{zx} = 0$$

$$\sigma_z = -\sigma_z' = -(ax + by + c) \tag{6.16}$$

By direct substitution it can be easily verified that these stresses satisfy equilibrium equations and the compatibility equations in terms of stresses. If we restrict our discussion to simply connected regions only, then the stresses given by Eqs. (6.16) is the correct solution of the residual problem. Adding this solution to the primary solution, the only effect is to cancel the normal stress in the z direction. Hence the true solution has the same stresses as the primary solution, except that the value of σ_z is identically zero instead of $\nu(\sigma_x + \sigma_y)$. Because σ_z is different between the true solution and the primary solution, all the normal strain components will be different between the true solution and the primary solution. The strains in the true solution are obtained from the stresses in the true solution by the stress-strain relations. These strains will not be two-dimensional or plane strains because the value of ϵ_z will not be zero.

For the case where $a = b = c = 0$, the residual problem does not exist, and the true solution will be the same as the primary solution. Here the value of σ_z' in the primary solution is zero. This agrees with the general conclusion reached above, which states that, for a linear σ_z', the true solution is the same as the primary solution with σ_z equal to zero. For this particular case, σ_z' vanishes, so that the strain in the true solution will be plane-strain. One example in which we find $a = b = c = 0$ is when $\nu = 0$.

Case 2. σ_z' is any function of x and y. No exact solution has been obtained for this general case.   But if the body is a long cylinder, i.e., if the thickness t is large compared with the lateral dimensions, then an approximate solution can be obtained which is valid in the middle portion of the cylinder.   This will be discussed below in detail.

Let $O'x'y'$ be the centroidal principal axes of the plane region R bounded by the curve C (Fig. 6.3).   For a linear distribution of σ_z given by $ax' + by' + c$, the resultant force F and the resultant moments about the $O'x'$ and $O'y'$ axes, $M_{x'}$ and $M_{y'}$, are given by

$$F = \iint_R (ax' + by' + c)\ dx'\ dy'$$

$$M_{x'} = \iint_R (ax' + by' + c)y'\ dx'\ dy'$$

$$M_{y'} = \iint_R (ax' + by' + c)x'\ dx'\ dy'$$

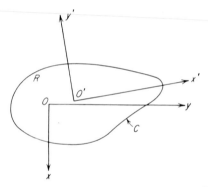

Fig. 6.3. Cross section of a cylindrical body.

Since $O'x'y'$ are the centroidal principal axes, the three integrals $\iint_R x'\ dx'\ dy'$, $\iint_R y'\ dx'\ dy'$, and $\iint_R x'y'\ dx'\ dy'$ all vanish.   Hence

$$F = cA$$
$$M_{x'} = bI_{x'} \tag{6.17}$$
$$M_{y'} = aI_{y'}$$

where A = area inside closed curve C
   $I_{x'}$ = moment of inertia of area about x' axis
   $I_{y'}$ = moment of inertia of area about y' axis

By choosing the proper values of a, b, and c, the linear σ_z can be made to have any values of F, $M_{x'}$, and $M_{y'}$.   In other words, there is a linear distribution of σ_z which is statically equivalent to any arbitrary distribution of σ_z. Furthermore, for any given values of F, $M_{x'}$, and $M_{y'}$, there is one, and only one, set of linear σ_z which is its static equivalent. By Saint-Venant's principle the stress in the middle portion of a long cylinder will not be appreciably affected if the boundary forces on the two end planes $z = \pm t/2$ are changed from the distribution of σ_z given by the primary solution into a statically equivalent linear σ_z. The latter has an exact solution, as shown in Case 1. Hence, in the middle portion of a long cylinder, the true solution is very nearly the same as the primary solution except that σ_z is the difference between the distribution of σ_z given by the primary solution and a statically equivalent linear distribution of σ_z computed by Eqs. (6.17). For the special case where σ_z of the primary solution is linear, the true distribution of σ_z will vanish because any two linear distributions which are statically equivalent must be identical to each other and their difference vanish. This agrees with the conclusion obtained in Case 1, although the latter is more broad and states that the solution is exact and applicable to the whole region. For the special case where σ_z of the primary solution is self-equilibrating, then the true solution is identical to the primary solution in the middle portion of a long cylinder.

6.6. Plane-stress Method. The plane problem can be approached in a way different from that of the plane-strain method. Instead of assuming a two-dimensional state of strain we shall assume a two-dimensional state of stress, or plane stress. Here we assume

$$\sigma_z = \tau_{zx} = \tau_{zy} = 0 \tag{6.18}$$

The equilibrium equations (6.3) are again simplified into Eqs. (6.8). The compatibility equations (6.4) become

$$\nabla^2 \sigma_x + \frac{3}{1+\nu} \frac{\partial^2 \sigma_m}{\partial x^2} = \frac{-\nu}{1-\nu} \left(\frac{\partial X}{\partial x} + \frac{\partial Y}{\partial y} \right) - 2 \frac{\partial X}{\partial x}$$

$$\nabla^2 \sigma_y + \frac{3}{1+\nu} \frac{\partial^2 \sigma_m}{\partial y^2} = \frac{-\nu}{1-\nu} \left(\frac{\partial X}{\partial x} + \frac{\partial Y}{\partial y} \right) - 2 \frac{\partial Y}{\partial y}$$

$$\frac{3}{1+\nu} \frac{\partial^2 \sigma_m}{\partial z^2} = \frac{-\nu}{1-\nu} \left(\frac{\partial X}{\partial x} + \frac{\partial Y}{\partial y} \right)$$

$$\nabla^2 \tau_{xy} + \frac{3}{1+\nu} \frac{\partial^2 \sigma_m}{\partial x \, \partial y} = -\left(\frac{\partial Y}{\partial x} + \frac{\partial X}{\partial y} \right) \tag{6.19}$$

$$\frac{\partial^2 \sigma_m}{\partial y \, \partial z} = 0$$

$$\frac{\partial^2 \sigma_m}{\partial z \, \partial x} = 0$$

where
$$\sigma_m = \frac{\sigma_x + \sigma_y}{3}$$

The problem is then to find three stress components σ_x, σ_y, and τ_{xy} which will satisfy Eqs. (6.8) and (6.19) in the whole region and Eqs. (6.2) on the boundary. By going through an involved process of integration, the following solution of Eqs. (6.8) and (6.19) can be obtained:

$$\sigma_x = \frac{\partial^2 \Phi}{\partial y^2} + \Omega$$

$$\sigma_y = \frac{\partial^2 \Phi}{\partial x^2} + \Omega$$

$$\tau_{xy} = -\frac{\partial^2 \Phi}{\partial x\, \partial y} \qquad (6.20)$$

$$\Phi = \phi' + \frac{\nu(t^2 - 12z^2)}{24(1 + \nu)}\left[\nabla^2\phi' + 2\Omega - \frac{1 + \nu}{2(1 - \nu)}(x^2 + y^2)\nabla^2\Omega\right]$$

$$\phi' = \phi'(x,y)$$

$$\nabla^4\phi' = -(1 - \nu)\nabla^2\Omega$$

$$\nabla^2\Omega = \text{const}$$

where

$$\nabla^4 = \frac{\partial^4}{\partial x^4} + \frac{\partial^4}{\partial y^4} + \frac{\partial^4}{\partial z^4} + 2\left(\frac{\partial^4}{\partial x^2 \partial y^2} + \frac{\partial^4}{\partial y^2 \partial z^2} + \frac{\partial^4}{\partial z^2 \partial x^2}\right)$$

Note that Ω defines the body force through Eqs. (6.1), so that the last equation in Eqs. (6.20) means the plane-stress method cannot be applied to plane problems where the given body force is not of the type $\nabla^2\Omega = \text{const}$. This is not a serious limitation since in most cases the body force is the weight of the body, so that $X = \text{const}$ and $Y = Z = 0$. Hence $\nabla^2\Omega = 0$, and the plane-stress method is applicable.

As is the case with all differential equations, although the process of obtaining a solution by integration is usually complicated, the process of testing the validity of any particular solution by differentiation is always simple. By direct substitution and differentiation, it can be proved that Eqs. (6.20) are a solution of Eqs. (6.8) and (6.19). The proof is quite lengthy and is left as an exercise for the student. From the above we therefore arrive at the conclusion that, for simply connected bodies, the stress system given by Eqs. (6.18) and (6.20) is the correct solution provided it satisfies the boundary conditions.

6.7. The Primary Problem in the Plane-stress Method. The boundary conditions (6.13) and (6.15) are identically satisfied by the stress system of Eqs. (6.18) and (6.20). But the boundary conditions (6.14) cannot be satisfied. This is obvious since the stress components σ_x, σ_y, and τ_{xy} in Eqs. (6.20) are functions of z, while the boundary forces $\bar{X}_n$ and $\bar{Y}_n$ are not. However, we note that

$$\int_{-t/2}^{t/2} (t^2 - 12z^2)\, dz = 0$$

$$\phi' = \phi'(x,y,$$

$$\Omega = \Omega(x,y)$$

so that from Eqs. (6.20), the mean values of Φ, σ_x, σ_y, and τ_{xy}, averaged throughout the thickness t, are

$$\frac{1}{t}\int_{-t/2}^{t/2} \Phi\, dz = \phi'$$

$$\frac{1}{t}\int_{-t/2}^{t/2} \sigma_x\, dz = \frac{1}{t}\int_{-t/2}^{t/2}\left(\frac{\partial^2 \Phi}{\partial y^2} + \Omega\right)dz = \frac{\partial^2 \phi'}{\partial y^2} + \Omega$$

$$\frac{1}{t}\int_{-t/2}^{t/2} \sigma_y\, dz = \frac{\partial^2 \phi'}{\partial x^2} + \Omega \qquad (6.21)$$

$$\frac{1}{t}\int_{-t/2}^{t/2} \tau_{xy}\, dz = -\frac{\partial^2 \phi'}{\partial x\, \partial y}$$

If we choose ϕ' such that
$$\nabla^4 \phi' = -(1 - \nu)\nabla^2\Omega \qquad \text{in whole body}$$

$$\left.\begin{aligned}
\left(\frac{\partial^2 \phi'}{\partial y^2} + \Omega\right)\cos(n,x) - \frac{\partial^2 \phi'}{\partial x\, \partial y}\cos(n,y) &= \bar{X}_n(x,y)\\[2mm]
-\frac{\partial^2 \phi'}{\partial x\, \partial y}\cos(n,x) + \left(\frac{\partial^2 \phi'}{\partial x^2} + \Omega\right)\cos(n,y) &= \bar{Y}_n(x,y)
\end{aligned}\right\} \text{ on } S_L \qquad (6.22)$$

then by Eqs. (6.21) and (6.22)

$$\left.\begin{aligned}
\frac{\cos(n,x)}{t}\int_{-t/2}^{t/2}\sigma_x\, dz + \frac{\cos(n,y)}{t}\int_{-t/2}^{t/2}\tau_{xy}\, dz &= \bar{X}_n(x,y)\\[2mm]
\frac{\cos(n,x)}{t}\int_{-t/2}^{t/2}\tau_{xy}\, dz + \frac{\cos(n,y)}{t}\int_{-t/2}^{t/2}\sigma_y\, dz &= \bar{Y}_n(x,y)
\end{aligned}\right\} \text{ on } S_L \qquad (6.23)$$

Equation (6.23) shows that the average stresses satisfy the boundary conditions (6.14). The solution which satisfies equilibrium, compatibility, and the boundary conditions (6.13), (6.15) and whose average stresses further satisfy the boundary conditions (6.14) is called the primary solution of the plane-stress method. The corresponding problem is called the primary problem of the plane-stress method. Since the primary solution violates Eqs. (6.14), a residual problem has to be solved to remove this violation. These two solutions are then added together as shown in Fig. 6.4 to give the correct solution. The primary problem can be stated as follows:

Region. The whole body in the plane problem.

Body force. The given body force in the plane problem. This body force must be of the type $\nabla^2 \Omega = $ const.

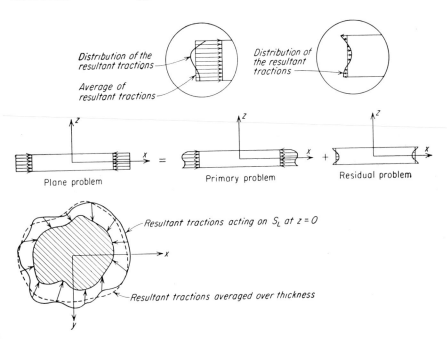

FIG. 6.4. Plane-stress method. A graphical picture of the plane-stress method.

Boundary conditions,

$$\tau_{zx} = \tau_{zy} = \sigma_z = 0 \qquad \text{on } z = \pm \frac{t}{2}$$

$$\tau_{zx} \cos (n,x) + \tau_{zy} \cos (n,y) = 0$$

$$\frac{\cos (n,x)}{t} \int_{-t/2}^{t/2} \sigma_x \, dz + \frac{\cos (n,y)}{t} \int_{-t/2}^{t/2} \tau_{xy} \, dz = \bar{X}_n(x,y)$$

$$\frac{\cos (n,x)}{t} \int_{-t/2}^{t/2} \tau_{xy} \, dz + \frac{\cos (n,y)}{t} \int_{-t/2}^{t/2} \sigma_y \, dz = \bar{Y}_n(x,y)$$

$$\text{on } S_L \qquad (6.24)$$

The primary solution can be solved by finding an Airy's function ϕ' which satisfies Eqs. (6.22). After this ϕ' is found, the stresses are given by Eqs. (6.18) and (6.20). Strains and displacements, if desired, can be calculated from the stresses by the stress-strain and strain-displacement relations.

6.8. The Residual Problem in the Plane-stress Method. The residual problem in the plane-stress method is set up to remove the difference between the boundary forces on S_L of the plane problem and those of the primary problem of the plane-stress method. By Eqs. (6.20),

$$\sigma_x = \frac{\partial^2 \phi'}{\partial y^2} + \Omega + \frac{\nu(t^2 - 12z^2)}{24(1+\nu)} \frac{\partial^2}{\partial y^2} \left[\nabla^2 \phi' + 2\Omega - \frac{1+\nu}{2(1-\nu)}(x^2+y^2)\nabla^2\Omega \right]$$

$$\tau_{xy} = -\frac{\partial^2 \phi'}{\partial x\, \partial y} - \frac{\nu(t^2 - 12z^2)}{24(1+\nu)} \frac{\partial^2}{\partial x\, \partial y} \left[\nabla^2 \phi' + 2\Omega - \frac{1+\nu}{2(1-\nu)}(x^2+y^2)\nabla^2\Omega \right]$$

By the aid of Eqs. (6.22), the above equations can be combined to give

$$\sigma_x \cos(n,x) + \tau_{xy} \cos(n,y) = \bar{X}_n(x,y)$$

$$+ \frac{\nu(t^2 - 12z^2)}{24(1+\nu)} \cos(n,x) \frac{\partial^2}{\partial y^2} \left[\nabla^2 \phi' + 2\Omega - \frac{1+\nu}{2(1-\nu)}(x^2+y^2)\nabla^2\Omega \right]$$

$$- \frac{\nu(t^2 - 12z^2)}{24(1+\nu)} \cos(n,y) \frac{\partial^2}{\partial x\, \partial y} \left[\nabla^2 \phi' + 2\Omega - \frac{1+\nu}{2(1-\nu)}(x^2+y^2)\nabla^2\Omega \right]$$

$$(6.25)$$

Similarly, we can obtain

$$\tau_{xy} \cos(n,x) + \sigma_y \cos(n,y) = \bar{Y}_n(x,y)$$

$$+ \frac{\nu(t^2 - 12z^2)}{24(1+\nu)} \cos(n,y) \frac{\partial^2}{\partial x^2} \left[\nabla^2 \phi' + 2\Omega - \frac{1+\nu}{2(1-\nu)}(x^2+y^2)\nabla^2\Omega \right]$$

$$- \frac{\nu(t^2 - 12z^2)}{24(1+\nu)} \cos(n,x) \frac{\partial^2}{\partial x\, \partial y} \left[\nabla^2 \phi' + 2\Omega - \frac{1+\nu}{2(1-\nu)}(x^2+y^2)\nabla^2\Omega \right]$$

$$(6.26)$$

Equations (6.25) and (6.26) represent the boundary forces on S_L in the primary solution. By comparing these with the boundary forces on S_L in the plane problem given by Eqs. (6.14) it is seen that the last two terms in both Eqs. (6.25) and (6.26) are the differences which must be removed. The residual problem of the plane-stress method can therefore be stated as follows:

Region. Same as in the primary problem.

Body force. None.

Boundary conditions,

$$\tau_{zx} = \tau_{zy} = \sigma_z = 0 \qquad \text{on } z = \pm\frac{t}{2}$$

$$\left.\begin{aligned}
\tau_{zx} \cos(n,x) + \tau_{zy} \cos(n,y) &= 0 \\
\sigma_z \cos(n,x) + \tau_{zy} \cos(n,y) &= -H \cos(n,x) \frac{\partial^2 J}{\partial y^2} \\
&\quad + H \cos(n,y) \frac{\partial^2 J}{\partial x\,\partial y} \\
\tau_{zy} \cos(n,x) + \sigma_y \cos(n,y) &= -H \cos(n,y) \frac{\partial^2 J}{\partial x^2} \\
&\quad + H \cos(n,x) \frac{\partial^2 J}{\partial x\,\partial y}
\end{aligned}\right\} \quad \text{on } S_L$$

$$(6.27)$$

where
$$H \equiv \frac{\nu(t^2 - 12z^2)}{24(1 + \nu)}$$

$$J \equiv \nabla^2\phi' + 2\Omega - \frac{1+\nu}{2(1-\nu)}(x^2 + y^2)\nabla^2\Omega$$

Three special cases of the residual problem will be discussed below:

Case 1. $\nu = 0$. From Eqs. (6.27) it is seen that the residual problem vanishes so that the primary solution is the true solution.

Case 2. $t = 0$. Since the value of z is limited between $-t/2$ and $t/2$, z vanishes under this case. The difference $t^2 - 12z^2$ also vanishes, and Eqs. (6.27) show that the residual problem does not exist. The primary solution is then the true solution. Obviously for thin plates, where the thickness t is small compared with lateral dimensions, the primary solution will be a very good approximation of the true solution.

Case 3. $J = ax + by + c$. Here J is a linear function of x and y so that all its second-order derivatives with respect to x and y vanish. Equations (6.27) show that the residual problem does not exist and the primary solution is the true solution.

6.9. The Generalized Plane-stress Solution. The stresses σ_x, σ_y, and τ_{zy} given by Eqs. (6.20) are functions of z so that they are not constant throughout the thickness. Now if the second term in the expression for Φ is omitted so that $\Phi = \phi'$, then the resulting stress system will be given by

$$\sigma_z = \tau_{zx} = \tau_{zy} = 0$$

$$\sigma_x = \frac{\partial^2\phi'}{\partial y^2} + \Omega$$

$$\sigma_y = \frac{\partial^2\phi'}{\partial x^2} + \Omega$$

$$(6.28)$$

$$\tau_{xy} = -\frac{\partial^2\phi'}{\partial x\,\partial y}$$

$$\phi' = \phi'(x,y)$$

$$\nabla^4\phi' = -(1-\nu)\nabla^2\Omega$$

$$\nabla^2\Omega = \text{const}$$

This stress system is called the generalized plane-stress solution of the plane problem. It can be easily verified that if ϕ' is chosen so that Eqs. (6.22) are satisfied, then this solution satisfies all the boundary conditions (6.13) to (6.15) but violates the compatibility equation (6.19). Except with the omission of the term involving $t^2 - 12z^2$, the generalized plane-stress solution is otherwise identical to the primary solution of the plane-stress method. The stresses in the generalized plane-stress solution do not depend on z and are therefore constant throughout the thickness of the plate. This property is also shared by the primary solution of the plane-strain method. Obviously the generalized plane-stress solution will be the correct solution if ν or t vanishes or if J is a linear function of x and y. For thin plates the generalized plane-stress solution is a good approximation of the true solution.

6.10. Discussion on the Plane-strain, Plane-stress, and Generalized Plane-stress Methods. Regarding the plane problem and the three methods used for its solution, the following can be said:

1. For a thin plate loaded on the lateral surface only (Fig. 6.5), the primary solution of the plane-stress method is very nearly the true solution. The plane-stress method is therefore the usual method used in solving

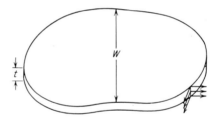

FIG. 6.5. Thin plate loaded on the lateral surface only. Thickness t is small compared with the least lateral dimension w.

plane problems involving thin plates. For a long cylinder loaded on the lateral surface (Fig. 6.6), the true values of σ_x, σ_y, and τ_{xy} in the middle portion of the cylinder are very nearly those given by the primary solution of the plane-strain method. These values are independent of the boundary conditions at the two ends of the long cylinder. In other words, the primary solution of the plane-strain method always gives very good values of σ_x, σ_y, and τ_{xy} in the middle portion of a long cylinder whether the two ends of the long cylinder are free, fixed, or partially fixed. The values of σ_z, ϵ_x, ϵ_y, and ϵ_z in the middle portion as well as in any other portions of the long cylinder will depend on the conditions of restraint at the two ends of the cylinder. The plane-strain method is therefore the usual method employed in solving for the stress components σ_x, σ_y, and τ_{xy} in the middle portion of long cylinders regardless of their end conditions.

2. From the differential equations on ϕ' and ϕ given by Eqs. (6.28) and (6.12) it is seen that $1 - \nu$ in the former corresponds to $(1 - 2\nu)/(1 - \nu)$ in the latter, or ν in the former corresponds to $\nu/(1 - \nu)$ in the latter. Hence the values of σ_x, σ_y, and τ_{xy} in the generalized plane-stress solution for a material having a Poisson's ratio of ν_1 are identical to the primary plane-strain solution for a material having a Poisson's ratio equal to $\nu_1/(1 - \nu_1)$. For the special cases where $\nu = 0$ or $\nabla^2\Omega = 0$, the two solutions have the same σ_x, σ_y, τ_{xy}, τ_{yz}, and τ_{zz}.

3. When $\nabla^2\Omega$ vanishes, Eqs. (6.12) and (6.28) show that ϕ, ϕ', and consequently the stresses σ_x, σ_y, and τ_{xy} in the primary plane-strain solution and in the generalized plane-stress solution will not depend on the

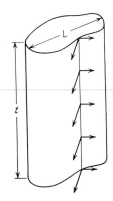

FIG. 6.6. Long cylinder loaded on the lateral surface. Thickness t is large compared with the largest lateral dimension L.

elastic constants ν and E. This is very useful in the field of experimental stress analysis. It proves that, in those plane problems where $\nabla^2\Omega$ vanishes, the models used in the experimental investigations need not be made of the same material as the prototype. Any elastic material loaded within the elastic range will be a satisfactory material for the model. The above conclusion naturally applies only to simply connected bodies because the equations of compatibility assure a continuous displacement field only for simply connected bodies. In multiply connected bodies, the above conclusion is in general incorrect. However, if the resultant of all the external loads on each of the boundary curves either vanishes or is a couple, then it can be shown that the stresses σ_x, σ_y, and τ_{xy} are still independent of the elastic constants, in plane problems where $\nabla^2\Omega$ vanishes.[†] The case of a ring under diametral compressions (Fig. 8.12) is one example of this class of plane problems. It should be pointed out that, in any

†For a proof, see E. Coker and L. Filon, "Treatise on Photoelasticity," pp. 501–524, Cambridge University Press, London, 2d ed., 1957.

plane problem, the strains will always depend on the elastic constants. Also, the value of σ_z in the primary plane-strain solution will always depend on ν unless the sum $\sigma_x + \sigma_y$ vanishes.

6.11. Use of Polar Coordinates in Solving Plane Problems Where There Are No Body Forces. It is often advantageous to solve plane problems by using polar coordinates in which the position of a point is defined by the distance r from the origin O and by the angle θ between r and the x axis. In terms of polar coordinates, all the equations derived previously in this chapter will take new forms. Those new equations connected with the primary plane-strain solution for plane problems without body force will be derived below.

Cartesian and polar coordinates are connected by the following relations:

$$x = r \cos \theta \qquad \tan \theta = \frac{y}{x}$$

$$y = r \sin \theta \qquad r^2 = x^2 + y^2 \tag{6.29}$$

The components of stress in the radial and tangential directions, σ_r, σ_θ, and $\tau_{r\theta}$, are related to σ_x, σ_y, and τ_{xy} by the local stress-transformation formulas (1.12); thus

$$\sigma_r = \sigma_x \cos^2 \theta + \sigma_y \sin^2 \theta + \tau_{xy} \sin 2\theta$$

$$\sigma_\theta = \sigma_x \sin^2 \theta + \sigma_y \cos^2 \theta - \tau_{xy} \sin 2\theta \tag{6.30}$$

$$\tau_{r\theta} = (\sigma_y - \sigma_x) \sin \theta \cos \theta + \tau_{xy} \cos 2\theta$$

or

$$\sigma_x = \sigma_r \cos^2 \theta + \sigma_\theta \sin^2 \theta - \tau_{r\theta} \sin 2\theta$$

$$\sigma_y = \sigma_r \sin^2 \theta + \sigma_\theta \cos^2 \theta + \tau_{r\theta} \sin 2\theta \tag{6.31}$$

$$\tau_{xy} = (\sigma_r - \sigma_\theta) \sin \theta \cos \theta + \tau_{r\theta} \cos 2\theta$$

The stress component σ_x varies from point to point; hence it is a function of both x, y and r, θ. From calculus we have

$$\frac{\partial \sigma_x}{\partial x} = \frac{\partial \sigma_x}{\partial r} \frac{\partial r}{\partial x} + \frac{\partial \sigma_x}{\partial \theta} \frac{\partial \theta}{\partial x}$$

$$\frac{\partial \sigma_y}{\partial y} = \frac{\partial \sigma_y}{\partial r} \frac{\partial r}{\partial y} + \frac{\partial \sigma_y}{\partial \theta} \frac{\partial \theta}{\partial y} \tag{6.32}$$

From Eqs. (6.29) we obtain

$$\frac{\partial r}{\partial x} = \frac{x}{r} = \cos \theta \qquad \frac{\partial \theta}{\partial x} = -\frac{y}{r^2} = -\frac{\sin \theta}{r}$$

$$\frac{\partial r}{\partial y} = \frac{y}{r} = \sin \theta \qquad \frac{\partial \theta}{\partial y} = \frac{x}{r^2} = \frac{\cos \theta}{r} \tag{6.33}$$

From Eqs. (6.31) to (6.33) we obtain

$$\frac{\partial \sigma_x}{\partial x} = \cos \theta \frac{\partial}{\partial r} (\sigma_r \cos^2 \theta + \sigma_\theta \sin^2 \theta - \tau_{r\theta} \sin 2\theta)$$

$$- \frac{\sin \theta}{r} \frac{\partial}{\partial \theta} (\sigma_r \sin^2 \theta + \sigma_\theta \cos^2 \theta - \tau_{r\theta} \sin 2\theta) \qquad (6.34)$$

$$\frac{\partial \sigma_y}{\partial y} = \sin \theta \frac{\partial}{\partial r} (\sigma_r \sin^2 \theta + \sigma_\theta \cos^2 \theta + \tau_{r\theta} \sin 2\theta)$$

$$+ \frac{\cos \theta}{r} \frac{\partial}{\partial \theta} (\sigma_r \sin^2 \theta + \sigma_\theta \cos^2 \theta + \tau_{r\theta} \sin 2\theta)$$

Similarly the derivatives of τ_{xy} with respect to x and y can be expressed in terms of σ_r, σ_θ, and $\tau_{r\theta}$ and their derivatives with respect to r and θ. After substitution and simplification and remembering that there are no body forces, the equations of equilibrium (6.8) become

$$\frac{\cos \theta}{r} \left(\sigma_r - \sigma_\theta + \frac{\partial \tau_{r\theta}}{\partial \theta} \right) + \cos \theta \frac{\partial \sigma_r}{\partial r}$$

$$- \sin \theta \frac{\partial \tau_{r\theta}}{\partial r} - \frac{\sin \theta}{r} \left(\frac{\partial \sigma_\theta}{\partial \theta} + 2\tau_{r\theta} \right) = 0 \qquad (6.35)$$

$$\frac{\sin \theta}{r} \left(\sigma_r - \sigma_\theta + \frac{\partial \tau_{r\theta}}{\partial \theta} \right) + \sin \theta \frac{\partial \sigma_r}{\partial r}$$

$$+ \cos \theta \frac{\partial \tau_{r\theta}}{\partial r} + \frac{\cos \theta}{r} \left(\frac{\partial \sigma_\theta}{\partial \theta} + 2\tau_{r\theta} \right) = 0$$

Equations (6.35) can be further simplified into

$$\frac{\partial \sigma_r}{\partial r} + \frac{1}{r} \frac{\partial \tau_{r\theta}}{\partial \theta} + \frac{\sigma_r - \sigma_\theta}{r} = 0 \qquad (6.36)$$

$$\frac{1}{r} \frac{\partial \sigma_\theta}{\partial \theta} + \frac{\partial \tau_{r\theta}}{\partial r} + \frac{2\tau_{r\theta}}{r} = 0$$

Equations (6.36) are the equations of equilibrium in polar coordinates. Since ϕ is a function of r and θ, we have

$$\frac{\partial \phi}{\partial x} = \frac{\partial \phi}{\partial r} \frac{\partial r}{\partial x} + \frac{\partial \phi}{\partial \theta} \frac{\partial \theta}{\partial x} = \cos \theta \frac{\partial \phi}{\partial r} - \frac{\sin \theta}{r} \frac{\partial \phi}{\partial \theta}$$

$$\frac{\partial^2 \phi}{\partial x^2} = \cos \theta \frac{\partial}{\partial r} \left(\frac{\partial \phi}{\partial x} \right) - \frac{\sin \theta}{r} \frac{\partial}{\partial \theta} \left(\frac{\partial \phi}{\partial x} \right)$$

$$= \cos^2 \theta \frac{\partial^2 \phi}{\partial r^2} - \frac{\sin 2\theta}{r} \frac{\partial^2 \phi}{\partial r \partial \theta} + \frac{\sin^2 \theta}{r^2} \frac{\partial^2 \phi}{\partial \theta^2} + \frac{\sin^2 \theta}{r} \frac{\partial \phi}{\partial r} + \frac{\sin 2\theta}{r^2} \frac{\partial \phi}{\partial \theta}$$

$$(6.37a)$$

Similarly

$$\frac{\partial^2 \phi}{\partial x \, \partial y} = \sin \theta \cos \theta \frac{\partial^2 \phi}{\partial r^2} + \frac{\cos 2\theta}{r} \frac{\partial^2 \phi}{\partial r \, \partial \theta} \qquad (6.37b)$$

$$- \frac{\sin \theta \cos \theta}{r^3} \frac{\partial^2 \phi}{\partial \theta^2} - \frac{\sin \theta \cos \theta}{r} \frac{\partial \phi}{\partial r} - \frac{\cos 2\theta}{r^2} \frac{\partial \phi}{\partial \theta}$$

$$\frac{\partial^2 \phi}{\partial y^2} = \sin^2 \theta \frac{\partial^2 \phi}{\partial r^2} + \frac{\sin 2\theta}{r} \frac{\partial^2 \phi}{\partial r \, \partial \theta} + \frac{\cos^2 \theta}{r^2} \frac{\partial^2 \phi}{\partial \theta^2}$$

$$+ \frac{\cos^2 \theta}{r} \frac{\partial \phi}{\partial r} - \frac{\sin 2\theta}{r^2} \frac{\partial \phi}{\partial \theta} \qquad (6.37c)$$

By addition

$$\frac{\partial^2 \phi}{\partial x^2} + \frac{\partial^2 \phi}{\partial y^2} = \frac{\partial^2 \phi}{\partial r^2} + \frac{1}{r} \frac{\partial \phi}{\partial r} + \frac{1}{r^2} \frac{\partial^2 \phi}{\partial \theta^2} \qquad (6.37d)$$

And by factoring (6.12)

$$\nabla^4 \phi \equiv \frac{\partial^4 \phi}{\partial x^4} + 2 \frac{\partial^4 \phi}{\partial x^2 \, \partial y^2} + \frac{\partial^4 \phi}{\partial y^4} \equiv \left(\frac{\partial^2}{\partial x^2} + \frac{\partial^2}{\partial y^2} \right) \left(\frac{\partial^2 \phi}{\partial x^2} + \frac{\partial^2 \phi}{\partial y^2} \right) \qquad (6.37e)$$

By Eqs. (6.30) and (6.37) Eqs. (6.11) and (6.12) are transformed into their new forms in polar coordinates,

$$\sigma_r = \frac{1}{r} \frac{\partial \phi}{\partial r} + \frac{1}{r^2} \frac{\partial^2 \phi}{\partial \theta^2}$$

$$\sigma_\theta = \frac{\partial^2 \phi}{\partial r^2} \qquad (6.38)$$

$$\tau_{r\theta} = \frac{1}{r^2} \frac{\partial \phi}{\partial \theta} - \frac{1}{r} \frac{\partial^2 \phi}{\partial r \, \partial \theta}$$

$$\nabla^4 \phi \equiv \left(\frac{\partial^2}{\partial r^2} + \frac{1}{r} \frac{\partial}{\partial r} + \frac{1}{r^2} \frac{\partial^2}{\partial \theta^2} \right) \left(\frac{\partial^2 \phi}{\partial r^2} + \frac{1}{r} \frac{\partial \phi}{\partial r} + \frac{1}{r^2} \frac{\partial^2 \phi}{\partial \theta^2} \right) = 0 \qquad (6.39)$$

The problem is then to find a stress function ϕ which satisfies Eq. (6.39) and whose corresponding stresses as computed by Eq. (6.38) satisfy the boundary conditions. After this ϕ is found, the stresses are given by Eqs. (6.38) and (6.6). As pointed out in Sec. 6.10, these stresses are identical to those in the generalized plane-stress solution except that σ_z will be $\nu(\sigma_x + \sigma_y)$ instead of zero.

6.12. Development of the Airy's Stress Function in Polar Coordinates. In the solution of plane problems the choice of ϕ is often the most difficult part of the problem. If body forces are neglected, Eq. (6.39) can be solved for several possible forms of ϕ. This equation is a fourth-order, biharmonic, partial differential type which can be solved using the separation of variables method.

Assume that the solution of (6.39) is of the form

$$\phi = F(r)G(\theta) \tag{6.40}$$

where

$$G(\theta) = \begin{cases} \sin n\theta \\ \cos n\theta \end{cases}$$

This form of representation indicates $G(\theta)$ may be $\sin n\theta$ or $\cos n\theta$, and by use of the bracket and the over and under position of the two terms it is possible to carry both forms through the solution of (6.39). Substituting (6.40) into (6.39) it is evident that

$$\frac{\partial^2 \phi}{\partial r^2} + \frac{1}{r}\frac{\partial \phi}{\partial r} + \frac{1}{r^2}\frac{\partial^2 \phi}{\partial \theta^2} = \left(\frac{d^2F(r)}{dr^2} + \frac{1}{r}\frac{dF(r)}{dr} - \frac{n^2 F(r)}{r^2}\right)\begin{cases}\sin n\theta \\ \cos n\theta\end{cases}$$

And by the same process the full substitution has the form

$$\nabla^4\phi = \left(\frac{d^2}{dr^2} + \frac{1}{r}\frac{d}{dr} - \frac{n^2}{r^2}\right)\left(\frac{d^2F(r)}{dr^2} + \frac{1}{r}\frac{dF(r)}{dr} - \frac{n^2 F(r)}{r^2}\right)\begin{cases}\sin n\theta \\ \cos n\theta\end{cases} = 0$$

and for an arbitrary θ it is necessary that

$$\frac{d^4F(r)}{dr^4} + \frac{2}{r}\frac{d^3F(r)}{dr^3} - \frac{1+2n^2}{r^2}\frac{d^2F(r)}{dr^2}$$
$$+ \frac{1+2n^2}{r^3}\frac{dF(r)}{dr} + \frac{n^4 - 4n^2}{r^4}F(r) = 0 \tag{6.41}$$

Equation (6.41) is an ordinary differential equation of the Euler type. To reduce this equation to a linear form with constant coefficients, a new variable t is chosen such that

$$t = \ln r \qquad r = e^t \qquad \frac{dt}{dr} = \frac{1}{r}$$

By the chain rule $\dfrac{dF}{dr} = \dfrac{dF}{dt}\dfrac{dt}{dr} = \dfrac{1}{r}\dfrac{dF}{dt}$

$$\frac{d^2F}{dr^2} = \frac{1}{r^2}\left(\frac{d^2F}{dt^2} - \frac{dF}{dt}\right)$$

$$\frac{d^3F}{dr^3} = \frac{1}{r^3}\left(\frac{d^3F}{dt^3} - 3\frac{d^2F}{dt^2} + 2\frac{dF}{dt}\right)$$

$$\frac{d^4F}{dr^4} = \frac{1}{r^4}\left(\frac{d^4F}{dt^4} - 6\frac{d^3F}{dt^3} + 11\frac{d^2F}{dt^2} - 3\frac{dF}{dt}\right)$$

Substituting these into (6.41), the Euler-type equation reduces to a linear equation with constant coefficients.

$$\frac{d^4F}{dt^4} - 4\frac{d^3F}{dt^3} + 2(2 - n^2)\frac{d^2F}{dt^2} + (3 + 4n^2)\frac{dF}{dt} + n^2(n^2 - 4)F = 0 \quad (6.42)$$

It can be shown† that Eq. (6.42) has solutions of the form

$$F = Ke^{\lambda t}$$

If this function and its derivatives are substituted into (6.42), and the common term $Ke^{\lambda t}$ factored out, the resulting polynomial in λ can be equated to zero.

$$\lambda^4 - 4\lambda^3 + 2(2 - n^2)\lambda^2 + (3 + 4n^2)\lambda + n^2(n^2 - 4) = 0$$

which has the roots

$$\lambda_1 = n \qquad \lambda_2 = -n \qquad \lambda_3 = 2 + n \qquad \lambda_4 = 2 - n$$

The solution of (6.41) must contain four arbitrary constants. It can be shown‡ that, if $n \geq 2$, the sum of the four terms represented by $Ke^{\lambda t}$ will be the general solution of the equation; and further, if $n = 0$ or $n = 1$, double roots exist and the general solution will have either the second or third form shown below.

$n \geq 2$

$$F(r)^{(n)} = a_n r^n + b_n r^{-n} + c_n r^{2+n} + d_n r^{2-n}$$

$n = 0$

$$F(r)^{(0)} = a_0 + b_0 \ln r + c_0 r^2 + d_0 r^2 \ln r \quad (6.43)$$

$n = 1$

$$F(r)^{(1)} = a_1 r + \frac{b_1}{r} + c_1 r^3 + d_1 r \ln r$$

where a, b, c, and d are arbitrary integration constants. It is clear now that $F(r)$ as expressed in (6.43) is of the proper form to combine with $G(\theta)$ to obtain a ϕ which meets the requirement $\nabla^4\phi = 0$. We can therefore write by Eqs. (6.43) and (6.40)

$$\phi^{(n)} = F(r)^{(n)}\begin{Bmatrix} \sin n\theta \\ \cos n\theta \end{Bmatrix} \quad (6.44)$$

By using Eq. (6.44) in Eq. (6.38) it is possible to compute σ_r, σ_θ, and $\tau_{r\theta}$ for each of the three forms given for ϕ in terms of the arbitrary constants $(b$, c, and $d)$, r, and $\begin{Bmatrix} \sin n\theta \\ \cos n\theta \end{Bmatrix}$. The three expressions for $\phi^{(n)}$ together with the associated relations for σ_r, σ_θ, and $\tau_{r\theta}$ are shown in equations

†L. R. Ford, "Differential Equations," p. 178, McGraw-Hill Book Company, Inc., New York, 1933.
‡*Ibid.*

(6.44) to (6.46). The radial and circumferential displacements u_r and u_θ are obtained by integrating the stress displacement equations. The terms containing the constants α_1, α_2, and α_3 refer to rigid displacements and need not be considered in most applications.

$$\phi^{(0)}(r) = a_0 + b_0 \ln r + c_0 r^2 + d_0 r^2 \ln r$$

$$\sigma_r = \frac{b_0}{r^2} + 2c_0 + d_0(1 + 2 \ln r)$$

$$\sigma_\theta = -\frac{b_0}{r^2} + 2c_0 + d_0(3 + 2 \ln r)$$

$$\tau_{r\theta} = 0 \tag{6.45}$$

$$u_r = \frac{1}{E}\left[-(1+\nu)\frac{b_0}{r} + 2(1-\nu)c_0 r + 2(1-\nu)d_0 r \ln r - (1+\nu)d_0 r\right]$$
$$+ \alpha_2 \cos \theta + \alpha_3 \sin \theta$$

$$u_\theta = \frac{1}{E}(4 d_0 r\theta) - \alpha_1 r - \alpha_2 \sin \theta + \alpha_3 \cos \theta$$

The stresses in this solution are independent of θ and the solution will be used in Chap. 9 to solve the problem of the thick-walled cylinder subjected to uniform internal and external pressure.

$$\phi^{(1)} = \left(a_1 r + \frac{b_1}{r} + c_1 r^3 + d_1 r \ln r\right)\begin{Bmatrix} \sin \theta \\ \cos \theta \end{Bmatrix}$$

$$\sigma_r = \left(-\frac{2b_1}{r^3} + 2c_1 r + \frac{d_1}{r}\right)\begin{Bmatrix} \sin \theta \\ \cos \theta \end{Bmatrix}$$

$$\sigma_\theta = \left(\frac{2b_1}{r^3} + 6c_1 r + \frac{d_1}{r}\right)\begin{Bmatrix} \sin \theta \\ \cos \theta \end{Bmatrix}$$

$$\tau_{r\theta} = \left(-\frac{2b_1}{r^3} + 2c_1 r + \frac{d_1}{r}\right)\begin{Bmatrix} -\cos \theta \\ \sin \theta \end{Bmatrix}$$

$$\tag{6.46}$$

$$u_r = \frac{1}{E}\left(\left[(1+\nu)\frac{b_1}{r^2} + (1-3\nu)c_1 r^2 - (1+\nu)d_1\right.\right.$$
$$\left.+ (1-\nu)d_1 \ln r\right]\begin{Bmatrix} \sin \theta \\ \cos \theta \end{Bmatrix} - [2 d_1 \theta]\begin{Bmatrix} \cos \theta \\ -\sin \theta \end{Bmatrix}\left.\right) + \alpha_2 \cos \theta + \alpha_3 \sin \theta$$

$$u_\theta = \frac{1}{E}\left(\left[-(1+\nu)\frac{b_1}{r^2} - (5+\nu)c_1 r^2 + (1-\nu)d_1 \ln r\right]\begin{Bmatrix} \cos \theta \\ -\sin \theta \end{Bmatrix}\right.$$
$$\left.+ [2 d_1 \theta]\begin{Bmatrix} \sin \theta \\ \cos \theta \end{Bmatrix}\right) - \alpha_1 r - \alpha_2 \sin \theta + \alpha_3 \cos \theta$$

Here the stresses are linear with respect to the sine and cosine of θ. A circular boundary acted on by a uniform system of parallel forces would produce this type of distribution.

$$\phi^{(n)} = (a_n r^n + b_n r^{-n} + c_n r^{2+n} + d_n r^{2-n})\begin{Bmatrix} \sin n\theta \\ \cos n\theta \end{Bmatrix} \qquad \text{for } n \geq 2$$

$$\sigma_r = [a_n(n - n^2)r^{n-2} - b_n(n + n^2)r^{-n-2} + c_n(2 + n - n^2)r^n$$

$$+ d_n(2 - n - n^2)r^{-n}]\begin{Bmatrix} \sin n\theta \\ \cos n\theta \end{Bmatrix}$$

$$\sigma_\theta = [a_n(n^2 - n)r^{n-2} + b_n(n^2 + n)r^{-n-2} + c_n(2 + 3n + n^2)r^n$$

$$+ d_n(2 - 3n + n^2)r^{-n}]\begin{Bmatrix} \sin n\theta \\ \cos n\theta \end{Bmatrix}$$

$$\tau_{r\theta} = [a_n(n^2 - n)r^{n-2} - b_n(n + n^2)r^{-n-2} + c_n(n + n^2)r^n$$

$$+ d_n(n - n^2)r^{-n}]\begin{Bmatrix} -\cos n\theta \\ \sin n\theta \end{Bmatrix} \qquad (6.47)$$

$$u_r = \frac{1}{E}\{-a_n(1 + \nu)nr^{n-1} + b_n(1 + \nu)nr^{-n-1}$$

$$+ c_n[4 - (1 + \nu)(2 + n)]r^{n+1} + d_n[4 - (1 + \nu)(2 - n)]r^{-n+1}\}\begin{Bmatrix} \sin n\theta \\ \cos n\theta \end{Bmatrix}$$

$$+ \alpha_2 \cos \theta + \alpha_3 \sin \theta$$

$$u_\theta = \frac{1}{E}\{-a_n(1 + \nu)nr^{n-1} - b_n(1 + \nu)nr^{-n-1}$$

$$- c_n[4 + (1 + \nu)n]r^{n+1} + d_n[4 - (1 + \nu)n]r^{-n+1}\}\begin{Bmatrix} \cos n\theta \\ -\sin n\theta \end{Bmatrix}$$

$$- \alpha_1 r - \alpha_2 \sin \theta + \alpha_3 \cos \theta$$

This stress function can be used in a manner identical to the two preceding stress functions. Examine the boundary conditions and note whether the stresses associated with ϕ^n are of the same form. Clearly, n can be assigned any value ≥ 2 to accommodate the distribution of stresses at the boundary. If the form of the stresses at the boundary is met, the constants a_n, b_n, c_n, and d_n can be solved for, from the boundary conditions as shown in an example problem in Chap. 9.

EXERCISES

6.1. Derive the first, second, and fourth of Eq. (6.9) from Eq. (6.8) and the third of Eq. (6.9).

6.2. Show that the stress systems (6.18) and (6.20) satisfy the equilibrium equations (6.8) and compatibility equations (6.19).

6.3. Derive the stress-strain relations for plane strain and plane stress from Eqs. (4.16) and (4.17), in the chapter on the theory of elasticity.

Ans.:

Plane strain	*Plane stress*

$$\epsilon_x = \frac{1 + \nu}{E}\left[(1 - \nu)\sigma_x - \nu\sigma_y\right] \qquad\qquad \epsilon_x = \frac{1}{E}(\sigma_x - \nu\sigma_y)$$

$$\epsilon_y = \frac{1 + \nu}{E}\left[(1 - \nu)\sigma_y - \nu\sigma_x\right] \qquad\qquad \epsilon_y = \frac{1}{E}(\sigma_y - \nu\sigma_x)$$

$$\epsilon_z = 0 \qquad\qquad\qquad\qquad\qquad \epsilon_z = -\frac{\nu}{E}(\sigma_x + \sigma_y)$$

$$\gamma_{xy} = \frac{2(1 + \nu)}{E}\tau_{xy} \qquad\qquad \gamma_{xy} = \frac{2(1 + \nu)}{E}\tau_{xy}$$

$$\gamma_{yz} = \gamma_{zx} = 0 \qquad\qquad\qquad \gamma_{yz} = \gamma_{zz} = 0$$

$$\sigma_x = \frac{E}{(1 + \nu)(1 - 2\nu)}\left[(1 - \nu)\epsilon_x + \nu\epsilon_y\right] \qquad \sigma_x = \frac{E}{1 - \nu^2}(\epsilon_x + \nu\epsilon_y)$$

$$\sigma_y = \frac{E}{(1 + \nu)(1 - 2\nu)}\left[(1 - \nu)\epsilon_y + \nu\epsilon_x\right] \qquad \sigma_y = \frac{E}{1 - \nu^2}(\epsilon_y + \nu\epsilon_x)$$

$$\sigma_z = \frac{\nu E}{(1 + \nu)(1 - 2\nu)}(\epsilon_x + \epsilon_y) \qquad\qquad \sigma_z = 0$$

$$\tau_{xy} = \frac{E}{2(1 + \nu)}\gamma_{xy} \qquad\qquad \tau_{xy} = \frac{E}{2(1 + \nu)}\gamma_{xy}$$

$$\tau_{yz} = \tau_{zz} = 0 \qquad\qquad\qquad \tau_{yz} = \tau_{zx} = 0$$

6.4. The instructor and the student will find it satisfying to obtain the equations of equilibrium in polar coordinates (6.36) directly from an element of a cylinder, rather than by applying the stress transformations to the equilibrium equations derived from the rectangular element.

CHAPTER 7

GEOMETRIC REPRESENTATIONS OF THE TWO-DIMENSIONAL STATE OF STRESS AND ASSOCIATED STATE OF STRAIN AT A POINT

7.1. Introduction. In the case of plane stress where, say,

$$\sigma_z = \tau_{zx} = \tau_{zy} = 0 \qquad (a)$$

the geometric representations of the state of stress at a point discussed in Chap. 3 simplify considerably. These will be taken up here along with other constructions which were not practical in the three-dimensional case. At the end of this chapter all the constructions discussed will be illustrated for one particular state of stress. The reader may find it useful to refer to these during the discussion of the individual methods of geometric representation.

It is convenient first to rewrite the equations governing the state of stress at a point for the plane-stress case above.

Assume a local cartesian-coordinate system with origin at the point and with x, y, and z axes parallel to the directions of the three principal stresses at the point, σ_1, σ_2, and σ_3, respectively. Let $\sigma_1 \geq \sigma_2$; then

$$\sigma_x = \sigma_1 \qquad \sigma_y = \sigma_2 \qquad \sigma_z = \sigma_3 = 0 \qquad \tau_{xy} = \tau_{yz} = \tau_{zz} = 0 \qquad (b)$$

and Eqs. (1.5) simplify to

$$p_{nx} = \sigma_1 \cos (n,x)$$
$$p_{ny} = \sigma_2 \cos (n,y) \qquad (7.1)$$
$$p_{nz} = 0$$

The terms involved in these equations are pictured in Fig. 7.1. If θ is designated as the counterclockwise angle from the positive x axis to the normal n to the surface of a small element at the point, the equations can be written

$$p_{nx} = \sigma_1 \cos \theta$$
$$p_{ny} = \sigma_2 \sin \theta \qquad (7.2)$$
$$p_{nz} = 0$$

Using this, the resultant stress

$$p_n = \sqrt{p_{nx}^2 + p_{ny}^2} \tag{7.3}$$

$$= \sqrt{\sigma_1^2 \cos^2 \theta + \sigma_2^2 \sin^2 \theta} \tag{7.4}$$

The normal stress acting on the plane with normal n, by Eqs. (1.3) and (7.2), or directly by Eq. (1.12a), is

$$\sigma_n = \sigma_1 \cos^2 \theta + \sigma_2 \sin^2 \theta \tag{7.5}$$

From Eq. (1.12d), the shear stress on the plane can also be written in terms of the principal stresses and the angle θ,

$$\tau_n = -\sigma_1 \cos \theta \sin \theta + \sigma_2 \sin \theta \cos \theta$$

$$= -(\sigma_1 - \sigma_2) \sin \theta \cos \theta \tag{7.6}$$

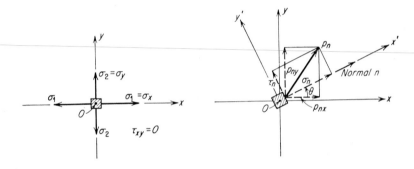

(a) Representation of principal stresses σ_1 and σ_2 acting on planes which pass through point O and face the x and y directions

(b) Same state of stress as in (a). Methods of representing stresses acting on a plane with normal inclined an angle θ from the positive x axis.

Fig. 7.1. Methods of representing the stresses on an inclined plane. If the Oxy coordinate system is oriented so that the principal stresses σ_1 and σ_2 act on planes through O facing the coordinate directions as in (a) above, then Eqs. (7.2), (7.4), (7.5), and (7.6) relate, respectively, the stresses p_{nx} and p_{ny}, p_n, σ_n, and τ_n acting on the inclined plane in (b) above to σ_1, σ_2, and the angle θ.

From the sign convention stated in Sec. 1.3 which underlies Eqs. (1.12), this shear stress, when positive, acts in the direction indicated in Fig. 7.1b, i.e., in a counterclockwise sense around the element, or in the direction of increasing θ.

The magnitude of the shear stress is also given by

$$\tau_n^2 + \sigma_n^2 = p_n^2 \tag{7.7}$$

When the x and y axes are not oriented in the principal directions, τ_{xy} is not zero and the equations for σ_n and τ_n are, from Eqs. (1.12a) and (1.12d),

$$\sigma_n = \sigma_x \cos^2 \theta + \sigma_y \sin^2 \theta + 2\tau_{xy} \sin \theta \cos \theta$$
$$\tau_n = -(\sigma_x - \sigma_y) \sin \theta \cos \theta + \tau_{xy}(\cos^2 \theta - \sin^2 \theta) \tag{7.8}$$

For this case of plane stress, $\cos(n,z) = 0$ and since $\tau_{zy} = \tau_{zx} = 0$, the strains $\gamma_{zy} = \gamma_{zx} = 0$ [see the stress-strain relations (4.16)]; and the equations corresponding to (7.8) in terms of strain are from Eqs. (2.21)

$$\epsilon_n = \epsilon_x \cos^2 \theta + \epsilon_y \sin^2 \theta + \gamma_{xy} \sin \theta \cos \theta$$
$$\frac{\gamma_n}{2} = -(\epsilon_x - \epsilon_y) \sin \theta \cos \theta + \frac{\gamma_{xy}}{2} (\cos^2 \theta - \sin^2 \theta) \tag{7.9}$$

7.2. The Stress Ellipse, or Ellipse of Lamé. Dividing the first of Eqs. (7.2) by σ_1, the second by σ_2, squaring, and adding, the equation of an ellipse

$$\frac{p_{nx}^2}{\sigma_1^2} + \frac{p_{ny}^2}{\sigma_2^2} = 1$$

is obtained. As in the three-dimensional counterpart [Eq. (3.5)] the local coordinates x and y at the point may be taken as synonymous with p_{nx} and p_{ny} (i.e., there is a local $p_{nx} \equiv x$, $p_{ny} \equiv y$ coordinate system at the point) so that the ellipse can be written

$$\frac{x^2}{\sigma_1^2} + \frac{y^2}{\sigma_2^2} = 1 \tag{7.10}$$

The length of the radius vector from the origin O to any point on the ellipse equals the magnitude of the resultant stress

$$p_n = \sqrt{x^2 + y^2} = \sqrt{p_{nx}^2 + p_{ny}^2}$$

acting on some plane through point O. In the case where $|\sigma_1| = |\sigma_2| = |\sigma_n|$, the ellipse becomes a circle of radius $|\sigma_n|$. Every radius vector has the same length, indicating that the magnitude of the resultant stress on every plane is the same and equal to $|\sigma_n|$. This applies to the case of a hydrostatic state of stress $\sigma_1 = \sigma_2$ and to the case of pure shear $\sigma_1 = -\sigma_2$.

When one of the principal stresses, say, σ_2, is zero, the ellipse reduces to a straight line of length $2\sigma_1$ along the x axis. All radius vectors of this degenerate ellipse lie on the x axis, and hence the resultant stress on any plane acts parallel to the x axis, as would be expected in this case of pure tension.

As pointed out in the discussion of the stress ellipsoid in the three-dimensional case, the plane on which the resultant stress p_n acts must be determined through some auxiliary construction. In a and c below, the magnitude of the resultant stress p_n is correlated with the plane on which p_n acts; in b the magnitude and direction of p_n is correlated with the plane on which it acts.

a. *Use of the Two Auxiliary Circles of Radii* $|\sigma_1|$ *and* $|\sigma_2|$. This is the simplest of the methods to determine graphically the plane upon which the resultant stress whose magnitude is represented by $p_n = OP$ acts. The method will be stated below and verified afterward.

Draw in conjunction with the stress ellipse either the small circle of radius $|\sigma_2|$ or the large circle of radius $|\sigma_1|$ with center at O (Fig. 7.2). The plane on which p_n, whose magnitude is represented by the length of

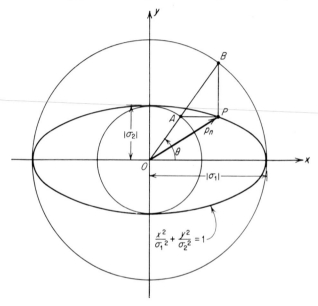

FIG. 7.2. Stress ellipse. Construction using two circles to correlate resultant stress whose magnitude is represented by $p_n = OP$ with plane on which it acts. The stress p_n acts on a plane whose normal is OA.

a radius vector OP, acts is found by extending a line parallel to either the x or the y axis from P until it intersects either the small or the large circle. Call these points of intersection A and B. The line OA will be coincident with OB and will be normal to the plane on which p_n acts.

The construction can be used in a reversed sense. If it is desired to find the resultant stress acting on a plane whose normal is inclined an angle θ from the x axis, the two circles of radii $|\sigma_1|$ and $|\sigma_2|$ can be drawn first. The line OAB at the inclination θ can next be drawn. The length of a line from O to the point of intersection of a horizontal line through A

and a vertical line through B will then represent the magnitude of the desired resultant stress.

The above properties are easily verified. Consider the two circles of radii $|\sigma_1|$ and $|\sigma_2|$ and the construction $OABP$. The x coordinate of B and the y coordinate of A are

$$x_B = |\sigma_1| \cos \theta = x_P$$
$$y_A = |\sigma_2| \sin \theta = y_P$$

(a)

Comparison of these to Eqs. (7.2) shows that the x and y coordinates of point P are equal in magnitude to the magnitudes of p_{nx} and p_{ny}, respectively, and hence OP has a length equal to the resultant stress p_n. Point P describes an ellipse as the angle θ is changed since, by eliminating θ from Eq. (a), the equation of the stress ellipse [Eq. (7.10)] is obtained.

The counterpart of this construction in the more general case of a three-dimensional state of stress would require the difficult visualization of three concentric spheres of radii $|\sigma_1|$, $|\sigma_2|$, $|\sigma_3|$, a radial line from the origin intersecting the spheres and three mutually perpendicular planes each passing through one of the points of intersections.

In the case where $|\sigma_1| = |\sigma_2| = |\sigma_n|$ the ellipse becomes a circle of radius $|\sigma_n|$ (coinciding with the two auxiliary circles). Every radius vector has the same length, and the magnitude of the resultant stress on every plane is the same and equal to $|\sigma_n|$. This corresponds to the hydrostatic state of stress $\sigma_1 = \sigma_2$ and the case of pure shear $\sigma_1 = -\sigma_2$.

When one of the principal stresses, say, σ_2, is zero, the ellipse reduces to a straight line along the x axis of length $2\sigma_1$. All radius vectors of this degenerate ellipse lie on the x axis, and hence the resultant stress on any plane acts parallel to the x axis, as would be expected in this case of pure tension.

b. *The Auxiliary Stress-director Curve.* This auxiliary construction, introduced in Sec. 3.3, reduces in the two-dimensional case to

$$\frac{x^2}{\sigma_1} + \frac{y^2}{\sigma_2} = \pm 1$$

(7.11)

When $\sigma_1 > \sigma_2 > 0$, the plus sign is chosen and the curve is an ellipse. This case is illustrated in Fig. 7.3. When one principal stress is negative, i.e., $\sigma_1 > 0 > \sigma_2$, the construction breaks up into two hyperbolas, one corresponding to the plus sign and one to the minus sign. This is similar to the behavior of the stress quadric of Cauchy discussed in Sec. 3.5. Finally, when both stresses are negative, the minus sign is chosen, and the curve is again an ellipse; however, it is to be remembered in this case that all normal stresses are negative.

The use of this construction can be described as follows (refer to Fig. 7.3):

The radius vector from O to a point P on the stress ellipse represents in magnitude and orientation the resultant stress vector acting on a plane whose normal parallels the normal to the stress-director curve at the latter's point of intersection with OP.

To prove this, let $P_0(x_0, y_0)$ be the point of intersection of OP and the stress director curve, and call ψ the angle between OP and the x axis. Then observe that, from the parametric equations of the stress ellipse, Eqs. (7.2), and from Fig. 7.3:

$$\cos \theta = \frac{p_{nx}}{\sigma_1} = \frac{OP \cos \psi}{\sigma_1} = \frac{OP}{OP_0} \frac{x_0}{\sigma_1}$$

$$\sin \theta = \frac{p_{ny}}{\sigma_2} = \frac{OP \sin \psi}{\sigma_2} = \frac{OP}{OP_0} \frac{y_0}{\sigma_2}$$

(a)

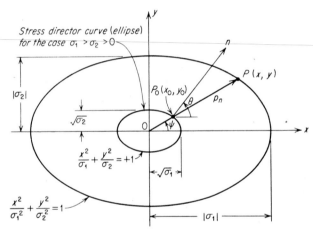

FIG. 7.3. Stress ellipse. Construction using auxiliary stress-director curve to correlate resultant stress $p_n = OP$ with plane on which it acts. The stress p_n acts on a plane whose normal is parallel to n, which is the normal to the stress-director curve at P_0.

where it is to be remembered that θ is the angle between the x axis and the normal n to the plane on which p_n acts.

Next consider the equation for the stress-director curve written in implicit form

$$f(x, y) = \frac{x^2}{\sigma_1} + \frac{y^2}{\sigma_2} \mp 1 = 0$$

By Eqs. (3.7), the cosine of the angle between the x axis and the normal to the curve $f(x, y) = 0$ at the point (x_0, y_0), and the cosine of the angle between the y axis and this normal, are given by

$$\cos (n,x) = \frac{\partial f/\partial x}{\sqrt{(\partial f/\partial x)^2 + (\partial f/\partial y)^2}}\bigg|_{(x_0,y_0)} = \frac{x_0/\sigma_1}{\sqrt{x_0^2/\sigma_1^2 + y_0^2/\sigma_2^2}}$$

$$\cos (n,y) = \frac{\partial f/\partial y}{\sqrt{(\partial f/\partial x)^2 + (\partial f/\partial y)^2}}\bigg|_{(x_0,y_0)} = \frac{y_0/\sigma_2}{\sqrt{x_0^2/\sigma_1^2 + y_0^2/\sigma_2^2}}$$ (b)

Now using the relations

$$\frac{OP}{OP_0} = \sqrt{\frac{x^2 + y^2}{x_0^2 + y_0^2}}$$

$$\frac{x}{y} = \frac{x_0}{y_0}$$

$$\frac{x^2}{\sigma_1^2} + \frac{y^2}{\sigma_2^2} = 1$$

it can be shown that

$$\frac{OP}{OP_0} = \frac{1}{\sqrt{x_0^2/\sigma_1^2 + y_0^2/\sigma_2^2}}$$

If this is substituted into Eqs. (a), and a comparison is made with Eqs. (b), it is seen that

$$\cos \theta = \cos (n,x)$$

$$\sin \theta = \cos (n,y)$$

and hence the statement as to the use of this construction is proved.

c. *Use of a Tangent Line.* This construction was discussed fully in Sec. 3.4 for the three-dimensional state of stress. Referring to Fig. 7.4, the resultant stress p_n acting on a plane whose normal is inclined at an angle θ from the x axis has a magnitude given by the distance OQ, where Q is the intersection of a line S tangent to the ellipse and perpendicular to OQ.

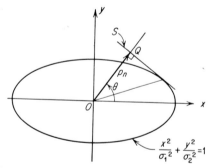

FIG. 7.4. Stress ellipse. Construction using tangent line to correlate resultant stress $p_n = OQ$ with plane on which it acts. The resultant stress p_n acts on a plane whose normal is inclined at an angle θ from the x axis.

The proof of this is the same as that given in Sec. 3.4 for the three-dimensional counterpart of this construction. In the special case when $\sigma_1 = \sigma_2$ or $\sigma_1 = -\sigma_2$, the ellipse becomes a circle.

7.3. Stress Quadric of Cauchy. This construction is fully treated in Sec. 3.5, and the plane-stress case corresponds to the special cases discussed there where one of the principal stresses was taken as zero.

7.4. Mohr's Circle for Stresses. The Mohr's circle is the most practical method of graphically describing the state of stress at a point. It will be more useful to develop it for the general case where the principal directions are not necessarily in the x and y directions. This can be reduced if desired to the special case where the x and y axes are in the principal directions, as was assumed in the discussion of the stress ellipse and the quadric of Cauchy.

Let us consider Eqs. (7.8) written in terms of the double angle 2θ,

$$\sigma_n = \frac{\sigma_x + \sigma_y}{2} + \frac{\sigma_x - \sigma_y}{2} \cos 2\theta + \tau_{xy} \sin 2\theta$$

$$\tau_n = -\frac{\sigma_x - \sigma_y}{2} \sin 2\theta + \tau_{xy} \cos 2\theta$$

(7.12)

The sign conventions for the terms in these equations are depicted in Fig. 7.5a and b and can be stated as follows: (1) The normal stresses σ_n, σ_x, and σ_y are positive when tensile; (2) the shear stress τ_{xy} is positive if, when acting on a plane whose normal has the positive coordinate direction, it acts toward the other positive coordinate direction, or if, when acting on a plane whose normal has the negative coordinate direction, it acts toward the other negative coordinate direction; and (3) the shear stress τ_n follows the same convention with respect to the rotated axes n and $n + 90°$ and hence is positive when acting counterclockwise on any surface whose outer normal n is inclined an angle θ from the x axis. These conventions are carried over from those underlying the three-dimensional equations (1.12).

Equations (7.12) are the equations of a circle in terms of the parameter 2θ. If the circle were drawn, it would be seen that, as the angle advances in one direction to denote various planes through the point (as in Fig. 7.5b), it advances in the circle construction in an opposite direction. The more common presentation of Mohr's circle† keeps these directions the same by reversing the sign convention for the shear stress. This change will also be made in this text in all further discussions of Mohr's circle; so the new shear-stress convention will be: τ_{xy} is positive if, when acting on a plane whose outer normal has the positive x direction, it

---

†For example, see S. Timoshenko and G. H. MacCullough, "Elements of Strength of Materials," 3d ed., Van Nostrand Company, Inc., New York, 1949.

acts toward the negative y direction (see Fig. 7.5c). On the plane whose normal n is inclined an angle θ from the x axis, a positive τ_n will correspondingly act toward the negative $n + 90°$ direction (see Fig. 7.5d).

Equations (7.12) can be rewritten for this convention by replacing all shear stresses by their negative, thus,

$$\sigma_n = \frac{\sigma_x + \sigma_y}{2} + \frac{\sigma_x - \sigma_y}{2} \cos 2\theta - \tau_{xy} \sin 2\theta$$

$$(7.13)$$

$$\tau_n = \frac{\sigma_x - \sigma_y}{2} \sin 2\theta + \tau_{xy} \cos 2\theta$$

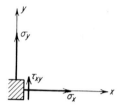

(a) Positive σ_x, σ_y, and τ_{xy} are used in Eqs. (7.12).

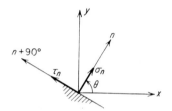

(b) Positive σ_n and τ_n as used in Eqs. (7.12).

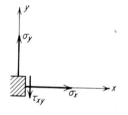

(c) Positive σ_x, σ_y, and τ_{xy} as used in Eqs. (7.13).

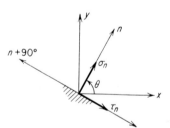

(d) Positive σ_n and τ_n as used in Eqs. (7.13).

FIG. 7.5. Sign conventions for Eqs. (7.12) and (7.13). Equations (7.13) and the conventions shown in (c) and (d) are the ones used in the discussion of Mohr's circle in this text.

These are the equations of a circle in the $\sigma_n \tau_n$ plane in terms of the parameter 2θ. This can be seen by eliminating the angle 2θ. Rewrite the equations

$$\sigma_n - \frac{\sigma_x + \sigma_y}{2} = \frac{\sigma_x - \sigma_y}{2} \cos 2\theta - \tau_{xy} \sin 2\theta$$

$$\tau_n = \frac{\sigma_x - \sigma_y}{2} \sin 2\theta + \tau_{xy} \cos 2\theta$$

square, and add,

$$\left(\sigma_n - \frac{\sigma_x + \sigma_y}{2}\right)^2 + \tau_n^2 = \left(\frac{\sigma_x - \sigma_y}{2}\right)^2 + \tau_{xy}^2$$

This is the equation of a circle of radius $\sqrt{((\sigma_x - \sigma_y)/2)^2 + \tau_{xy}^2}$ with center at $((\sigma_x + \sigma_y)/2, 0)$. This is drawn in Fig. 7.6. The parameter 2θ is the counterclockwise angle between the radius vector to point $Q(\sigma_x, \tau_{xy})$ and the radius vector to point $P(\sigma_n, \tau_n)$. This can be shown by expressing the abscissa σ_n and ordinate τ_n of point P in terms of σ_x, σ_y, and τ_{xy}. Thus,

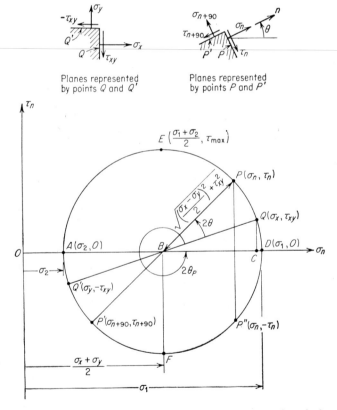

FIG. 7.6. Mohr's circle for stresses. Construction giving normal and shear stresses acting on any inclined plane in terms of the principal stresses σ_1 and σ_2 or the stresses σ_x, σ_y, τ_{xy} acting on planes facing the cartesian axes.

$$\sigma_n = OB + BP \cos(2\pi - 2\theta_P + 2\theta)$$

$$= OB + BP[\cos(2\pi - 2\theta_P)\cos 2\theta - \sin(2\pi - 2\theta_P)\sin 2\theta]$$

$$= OB + BP\left(\frac{BC}{BQ}\cos 2\theta - \frac{CQ}{BQ}\sin 2\theta\right)$$

$$= OB + BC \cos 2\theta - CQ \sin 2\theta$$

$$= \frac{\sigma_x + \sigma_y}{2} + \frac{\sigma_x - \sigma_y}{2}\cos 2\theta - \tau_{xy}\sin 2\theta$$

$$\tau_n = BP \sin(2\pi - 2\theta_P + 2\theta)$$

$$= BP[\sin(2\pi - 2\theta_P)\cos 2\theta + \cos(2\pi - 2\theta_P)\sin 2\theta]$$

$$= BP\left(\frac{CQ}{BQ}\cos 2\theta + \frac{BC}{BQ}\sin 2\theta\right)$$

$$= CQ \cos 2\theta + BC \sin 2\theta$$

$$= \tau_{xy}\cos 2\theta + \frac{\sigma_x - \sigma_y}{2}\sin 2\theta$$

which are exactly the expressions (7.13).

Had the local x and y coordinate axes been chosen in the principal directions at the point, $\sigma_x = \sigma_1$, $\sigma_y = \sigma_2$, and $\tau_{xy} = 0$, and points Q and Q' would fall on the σ_n axis.

There are many facts and useful results directly derivable from the construction.

a. *Expression for Principal Stresses.* Each point on the circle represents a particular plane through the point in the body and has coordinates representing the stresses acting on this plane; thus, it is evident that points D and A in Fig. 7.6, for which $\tau_n = 0$, correspond to the principal planes. The principal stresses are seen to be given by the expressions

$$\sigma_1, \sigma_2 = OB \pm BP$$

$$= \frac{\sigma_x + \sigma_y}{2} \pm \sqrt{\left(\frac{\sigma_x - \sigma_y}{2}\right)^2 + \tau_{xy}^2} \qquad (7.14)$$

Note that this is exactly Eq. (1.17), which was shown to be the special case of Eq. (1.16) when $\sigma_3 = \sigma_z = 0$. Equation (7.14) may also be obtained mathematically by differentiating the first of Eqs. (7.13) with respect to θ (or 2θ), equating the result to zero, solving for the angle 2θ, and substituting back into the original equation. It is evident from the circle that the principal stresses are at the same time the maximum and minimum stresses acting on any plane perpendicular to the xy plane and through the point.

b. *Orientation of Principal Planes.*   To find the orientation of the principal planes, it is necessary only to find the value of the angle in Fig. 7.6, say $2\theta_P$,† that brings point P in coincidence with point D.   Thus

$$\tan 2\theta_P = \tan (2\pi - \angle CBQ) = -\tan \angle CBQ = -\frac{CQ}{BC}$$

$$= -\frac{2\tau_{xy}}{\sigma_x - \sigma_y} \tag{7.15}$$

As pointed out in (a) above, differentiation of the first of Eqs. (7.13) will also yield the above result for the angle $2\theta_P$.

Since a given set of values of σ_x, σ_y, and τ_{xy} will yield two possible angles θ_P in Eq. (7.15), the auxiliary equation

$$\sin 2\theta_P = \sin (2\pi - \angle CBQ) = -\sin \angle CBQ = -\frac{CQ}{BQ}$$

$$= -\frac{\tau_{xy}}{\sqrt{\left(\dfrac{\sigma_x - \sigma_y}{2}\right)^2 + \tau_{xy}^2}} \tag{7.16}$$

can be used to specifically establish the plane on which the principal stress σ_1 acts.

Since points A and D are 180° apart, it is clear from the circle that the principal planes are 90° apart.

c. *Expression for Maximum Shear Stress and Orientation of Planes on Which It Acts.*   The maximum shear stress is represented by the ordinate of point E; thus,

$$\tau_{\max} = \sqrt{\left(\frac{\sigma_x - \sigma_y}{2}\right)^2 + \tau_{xy}^2} \tag{7.17}$$

and the angle $\theta_{\tau,\max}$ giving the orientation of the plane on which $\tau_{\max}$ acts is given by

$$\tan 2\theta_{\tau,\max} = \tan \left(\frac{\pi}{2} - \angle CBQ\right)$$

$$= \cot \angle CBQ = \frac{BC}{CQ}$$

$$= \frac{\sigma_x - \sigma_y}{2\tau_{xy}} \tag{7.18}$$

†Note that the subscript P on θ refers to the angle between the x axis and the principal axis and is not related to the point P as such.

which, for a given set of values of σ_x, σ_y, and τ_{xy}, can be used with the auxiliary equation

$$\sin 2\theta_{\tau . \max} = \sin \left(\frac{\pi}{2} - \angle CBQ \right)$$

$$= \cos \angle CBQ = \frac{BC}{BP}$$

$$= \frac{\sigma_x - \sigma_y}{2 \sqrt{\left(\frac{\sigma_x - \sigma_y}{2} \right)^2 + \tau_{xy}^2}} \qquad (7.19)$$

to specifically define the angle. It is seen from the circle that the maximum shear stress acts on a plane inclined at an angle of 45° to the principal planes, and also that the normal stress acting on this plane equals $(\sigma_1 + \sigma_2)/2$ or $(\sigma_x + \sigma_y)/2$.[†]

d. *The Pole Method for Determining Planes on Which Stresses Represented by Points on the Circle Act.* The conjugate point to point Q on Mohr's circle, say Q'' (Fig. 7.7), is called the pole and has a unique property. If a line is drawn from the pole to any point P on the circle, the stress components σ_n and τ_n, represented by the coordinates of P, act upon a plane whose normal has the same inclination from the x axis as the line $Q''P$ has from the line $Q''Q$.

To prove this, it is necessary only to show that $\angle PQ''Q$ is the angle θ. Since the triangle $BQ''P$ is an isosceles triangle, $\angle BQ''P$ must equal $\frac{1}{2}[\pi - (2\theta + \alpha)]$. By the same reasoning, $\angle BQ''Q$ equals $\frac{1}{2}(\pi - \alpha)$. The required angle $PQ''Q$ equals the difference

$$\angle BQ''Q - \angle BQ''P = \tfrac{1}{2}(\pi - \alpha) - \tfrac{1}{2}[\pi - (2\theta + \alpha)] = \theta$$

which was to be shown.

The pole can be used in two ways, provided the stresses σ_x, σ_y, τ_{xy}, and hence the pole's location, are known. First, by simply drawing lines from the pole to points on the circle, the stresses acting on planes parallel to these lines are immediately known. Second, the plane acted upon by a particular set of stresses is immediately established by the orientation of a line drawn from the point on the circle representing these stresses to the pole.

It is seen that the length of OP (Fig. 7.7) represents the magnitude of the resultant stress p_n acting on the plane parallel to $Q''P$; hence, it is also simple to visualize the direction of the resultant stress acting on

[†] It should be remembered that the maximum shear stress spoken of here is the maximum occurring only in the xy plane. If σ_1 and σ_2 are both greater than $\sigma_3 = \sigma_z$, which has been taken as zero, higher shears will actually occur than are indicated by Eq. (7.17) (see the discussion of Mohr's circle in three dimensions, Sec. 3.7).

any plane. It will have a length OP and will be inclined from the normal to the plane at an angle equal and opposite in sense to $\angle BOP$ (see the lower sketch in Fig. 7.7).

e. Other results. There are other miscellaneous results directly obtainable from Mohr's circle (Fig. 7.6).

1. The magnitude of the shears on mutually perpendicular planes is equal. This is true since the ordinates of P and P', two points representing perpendicular planes, are numerically equal.

2. The sum of the normal stresses on any two perpendicular planes is equal to $\sigma_1 + \sigma_2$. This follows since $\sigma_1 + \sigma_2$ is the sum of the abscissas of points P and P'.

3. The stresses acting on conjugate planes (i.e., planes inclined at equal but opposite angles from a principal plane) are equal except that the sense of the shear stress is reversed. This follows from comparison of the coordinates of points P and P'', two points representing conjugate planes.

4. When $\sigma_1 = \sigma_2$, the circle reduces to a point which indicates that the normal stress on every plane is the same and that the shear stress on every plane is zero. This is the case of a hydrostatic state of stress.

5. When $\sigma_1 = -\sigma_2$, the circle is centered at the origin and it is seen that there exist no normal stresses on the mutually perpendicular planes on which the shear stresses are numerically a maximum. This is a state of pure shear.

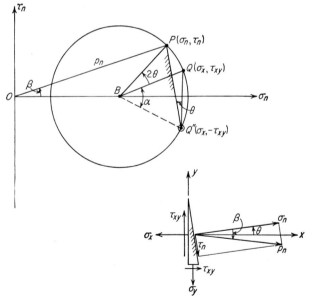

Fig. 7.7. The pole in Mohr's circle. For any point P the line PQ'' is parallel to the plane on which the stresses σ_n and τ_n act provided the x and σ_n axes are parallel.

7.5. Mohr's Circle for Strains. It was pointed out in Sec. 3.1 that the geometric methods of representing the state of stress at a point can be applied equally well to strains by replacing the stresses by their equivalents in strain terminology as given by Eq. (2.22). This rule also holds in this chapter, as is evident from a comparison of Eqs. (7.8) and (7.9).† By the equivalence of these two sets of equations, the Mohr's circle for strains can be immediately drawn and interpreted (Fig. 7.8).

For a given state of strain ϵ_x, ϵ_y, $\gamma_{xy}/2$, the points Q and Q' can be located using the following sign convention: The normal strains ϵ_x and ϵ_y, which

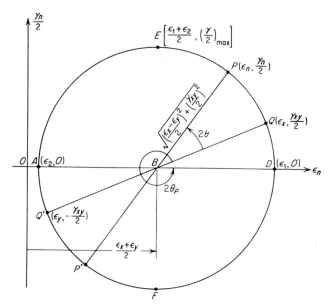

Fig. 7.8. Mohr's circle for strain. Construction giving normal and shear strains corresponding to any direction in terms of the principal strains ϵ_1 and ϵ_2 or the cartesian components ϵ_x, ϵ_y, $\gamma_{xy}/2$.

represent changes in lengths per unit lengths of small line segments initially parallel to the x and y axes at the point, are positive when the line segments increase in length in going from the unstrained to the strained state; and the shear strain $\gamma_{xy}/2$, which equals one-half the change in the right angle between two line segments initially parallel to the x and y axes, is positive when the angle increases. This is the reverse of the shear-strain convention used previously, and it is used to comply with the shear-stress convention used in the Mohr's circle for stresses. Having located points Q and Q', the

†An exception is that, although $\sigma_z = 0$ in the case of plane stress, the strain ϵ_z is not necessarily zero. This, of course, has no effect on the present discussions of the two-dimensional cases.

circle can be drawn by centering a compass at B, which is the intersection of QQ' and the ϵ_n axes. Various points around the circle have the coordinates shown, and the conclusions regarding principal directions, etc., reached in the discussion of Mohr's circle for stresses also apply here.

7.6. Mohr's Circles for Stress and Strain Combined. There are two methods of conveniently representing together the Mohr's circles for both stress and strain for a given state of plane stress. In one, a common origin of coordinates is used with two concentric circles; in the other, two different origins are used with a single circle.

To set up these dual representations, it is necessary to adjust the ratio of the scale factors for stress and strain. For this purpose, let 1 in. on the construction paper be equivalent to m_σ psi of stress and m_ϵ in./in. of strain.

Suppose it is first desired to represent a given state of stress and strain using a common origin and two concentric circles as shown in Fig. 7.9. The abscissa of the center of the stress circle is $(\sigma_x + \sigma_y)/2$, and that of the strain circle is $(\epsilon_x + \epsilon_y)/2$, and these must be made equal in the construction; i.e.,

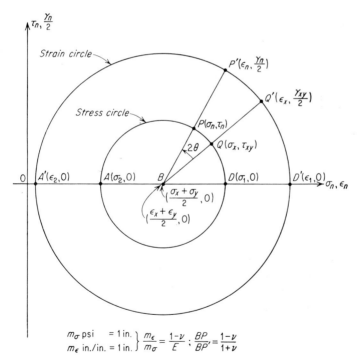

$$m_\sigma \text{ psi } = 1 \text{ in.} \atop m_\epsilon \text{ in./in.} = 1 \text{ in.} \Big\} \quad \frac{m_\epsilon}{m_\sigma} = \frac{1-\nu}{E} \; ; \; \frac{BP}{BP'} = \frac{1-\nu}{1+\nu}$$

FIG. 7.9. Mohr's circles for a state of stress and associated state of strain plotted from a common origin.

$$\frac{\sigma_x + \sigma_y}{2m_\sigma} = \frac{\epsilon_x + \epsilon_y}{2m_\epsilon}$$

or

$$\epsilon_x + \epsilon_y = \frac{m_\epsilon}{m_\sigma}(\sigma_x + \sigma_y) \qquad (a)$$

Now by adding the first two of the stress-strain relations [Eqs. (4.16)] (remembering that $\sigma_z = 0$),

$$\epsilon_x + \epsilon_y = \frac{1 - \nu}{E}(\sigma_x + \sigma_y) \qquad (b)$$

and by comparison of Eqs. (a) and (b) above

$$\frac{m_\epsilon}{m_\sigma} = \frac{1 - \nu}{E} \qquad (7.20)$$

Thus, if the elastic constants of the material are known and a particular scale is chosen for one of the circles, say, m_σ for the stress circle, the corresponding scale factor for the strain circle can be calculated from Eq. (7.20). By the stress-strain relations [Eqs. (4.16)], written for the principal stresses and strains,

$$\epsilon_1 - \epsilon_2 = (\sigma_1 - \sigma_2)\frac{1 + \nu}{E} \qquad (c)$$

and, using this, the ratio of the radii of the stress circle and the strain circle is seen to be

$$\frac{BP}{BP'} = \frac{(\sigma_1 - \sigma_2)/2m_\sigma}{(\epsilon_1 - \epsilon_2)/2m_\epsilon} = \frac{\sigma_1 - \sigma_2}{\epsilon_1 - \epsilon_2}\frac{1 - \nu}{E} = \frac{\sigma_1 - \sigma_2}{\sigma_1 - \sigma_2}\frac{E}{1 + \nu}\frac{1 - \nu}{E}$$

$$= \frac{1 - \nu}{1 + \nu} \qquad (7.21)$$

The construction has the following advantage: If the elastic constants of the material and a particular state of stress are known, the stress circle may be drawn to a given scale m_σ, and then from the center of the stress circle, point B, the strain circle can be drawn using a radius BP' which is equal to $(1 + \nu)/(1 - \nu)$ times the stress-circle radius BP. The strain components corresponding to any angle θ can then be taken directly from the strain circle using the scale $m_\epsilon = [(1 - \nu)/E]m_\sigma$. The reverse procedure is of course possible if the state of strain is known beforehand.

The second method of simultaneously representing a related state of stress and strain is through the use of the single circle as shown in Fig. 7.10. The necessary condition for the circles to have equal radii is

$$\frac{\sigma_1 - \sigma_2}{2m_\sigma} = \frac{\epsilon_1 - \epsilon_2}{2m_\epsilon}$$

or
$$\epsilon_1 - \epsilon_2 = \frac{m_\epsilon}{m_\sigma}(\sigma_1 - \sigma_2) \qquad (d)$$

Comparing Eqs. (c) and (d), it follows that

$$\frac{m_\epsilon}{m_\sigma} = \frac{1 + \nu}{E} \qquad (7.22)$$

The origins of coordinates must then be located according to the ratio

$$\frac{OB}{O'B} = \frac{(\sigma_x + \sigma_y)/2m_\sigma}{(\epsilon_x + \epsilon_y)/2m_\epsilon}$$

which, by Eqs. (b) and (7.22), can be written

$$\frac{OB}{O'B} = \frac{\sigma_x + \sigma_y}{\epsilon_x + \epsilon_y}\frac{1 + \nu}{E} = \frac{\sigma_x + \sigma_y}{\sigma_x + \sigma_y}\frac{E(1 + \nu)}{(1 - \nu)E}$$

$$= \frac{1 + \nu}{1 - \nu} \qquad (7.23)$$

By this method, if the elastic constants of the material are known and the state of stress is known at a point, the stress circle can be drawn

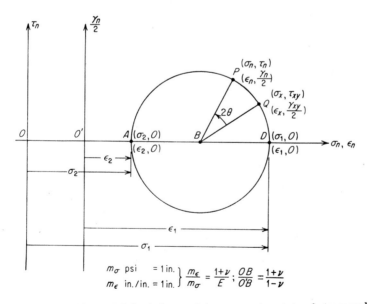

$$m_\sigma \text{ psi } = 1 \text{ in.} \left.\vphantom{\frac{m_\epsilon}{m_\sigma}}\right\} \frac{m_\epsilon}{m_\sigma} = \frac{1+\nu}{E} ; \frac{OB}{O'B} = \frac{1+\nu}{1-\nu}$$
$$m_\epsilon \text{ in./in. } = 1 \text{ in.}$$

FIG. 7.10. Two coincident Mohr's circles used to represent a state of stress and associated state of strain.

using any desired scale m_σ. The origin of the ϵ_n, $\gamma_n/2$ coordinate system is next located using Eq. (7.23); thus

$$OB = \frac{1 + \nu}{1 - \nu} O'B$$

The state of strain at the point is then given by the same circle as the stress circle provided the scale

$$m_\epsilon = \frac{1 + \nu}{E} m_\sigma$$

for strains is used.

7.7. The Dyadic Circle. This is another circle construction giving the same information as Mohr's circle; however, it is laid out differently. The construction is illustrated in Fig. 7.11, and reference is made to Eqs. (7.8) or (7.12), which are the equations it represents.

Suppose point O is the point in the body at which the state of stress is being considered, and suppose σ_x, σ_y, and τ_{xy} at the point are known. Choose the x and y directions, lay out any normal n at an angle θ from the x axis, and draw its perpendicular $n + 90°$. Locate point A with

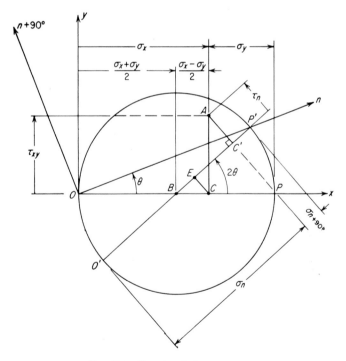

Fig. 7.11. Dyadic circle for stress.

coordinates σ_x and τ_{xy} in the Oxy coordinate system, and locate point B at a distance $(\sigma_x + \sigma_y)/2$ along the x axis. Draw the circle with B as center and radius OB. The stress σ_y is automatically established as the distance CP. From point P', the point of intersection of the n axis and the circle, draw the diameter $P'BO'$, and extend a perpendicular from A to this diameter. The stresses σ_n, $\sigma_{n+90°}$, and τ_n are then given by the lengths $O'C'$, $C'P'$, and $C'A$, respectively.

To show this, first observe that $\angle OP'B = \theta$ and $\angle OBP' = \pi - 2\theta$, so that $\angle PBP' = \pi - \angle OBP' = 2\theta$. Then

$$\sigma_n = O'B + BE + EC'$$

$$= OB + BC \cos 2\theta + AC \sin 2\theta$$

$$= \frac{\sigma_x + \sigma_y}{2} + \frac{\sigma_x - \sigma_y}{2} \cos 2\theta + \tau_{xy} \sin 2\theta$$

$$\sigma_{n+90°} = O'P' - O'C'$$

$$= \sigma_x + \sigma_y - \sigma_n$$

$$= \frac{\sigma_x + \sigma_y}{2} - \frac{\sigma_x - \sigma_y}{2} \cos 2\theta - \tau_{xy} \sin 2\theta$$

$$\tau_n = (-EC) + (AC' + EC)$$

$$= -BC \sin 2\theta + AC \cos 2\theta$$

$$= -\frac{\sigma_x - \sigma_y}{2} \sin 2\theta + \tau_{xy} \cos 2\theta$$

which are exactly Eqs. (7.12).†

All the properties derived from Mohr's circle can also be derived from the dyadic circle.

One interesting property is that the resultant stress p_n, which equals the length $O'A$ (see Fig. 7.12), acts in the direction of OQ, where Q is a point on the circle obtained by extending $O'A$ to the circle. To show this, consider the two right triangles $O'EO$ and $P'EQ$. These are similar triangles since $\angle O'EO = \angle P'EQ$ and $\angle EOO' = \angle EQP'$; and therefore

$$\frac{QE}{OE} = \frac{P'E}{O'E}$$

†The equation for $\sigma_{n+90°}$ can be written

$$\sigma_{n+90°} = \frac{\sigma_x + \sigma_y}{2} + \frac{\sigma_x - \sigma_y}{2} \cos 2(\theta + 90°) + \tau_{xy} \sin 2(\theta + 90°)$$

which is seen to be the same as the first of Eqs. (7.12), where θ is replaced by $\theta + 90°$.

Now, considering the triangles $O'EP'$ and OEQ, it is seen that they also are similar by virtue of the above ratio of sides and the fact that the triangles have the equal angles $\angle O'EP'$ and $\angle OEQ$. It thus follows that the two angles β are equal, and this establishes the above stated property.

7.8. Polar Representation of Stresses and Strains. This construction gives one of the most direct pictures of the state of stress and strain at a point. However, it is more difficult to draw it accurately than the Mohr's circle.

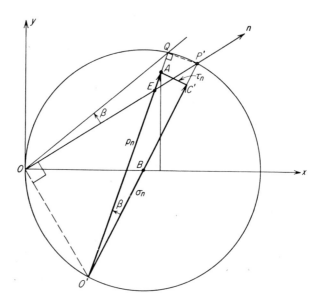

Fig. 7.12. Dyadic-circle. Construction for showing direction OQ in which stress $p_n = O'A$ acts.

Consider a local Oxy coordinate system with origin O at the point, and, as in the discussion of Mohr's circle, assume that the x and y axes do not necessarily coincide with the principal directions at the point. The construction consists of plotting, in a radial direction parallel to the outer normal of each plane through the point, the magnitudes of the normal and shear stresses and strains associated with each plane. The normal and shear stresses and the normal and shear strains are plotted separately, so there are two curves for the state of stress and two for the state of strain. It is noted that similar polar diagrams can be plotted on yz planes through the point if a more complete picture is desired.

As an example, consider the uniaxial state of stress

$$\sigma_x = 4{,}000 \text{ psi} \qquad \sigma_y = \sigma_z = \tau_{xy} = \tau_{yz} = \tau_{zx} = 0$$

By Eqs. (7.8)

$$\sigma_n = 4{,}000 \cos^2 \theta \qquad\qquad (a)$$

$$\tau_n = -4{,}000 \sin \theta \cos \theta \qquad\qquad (b)$$

the polar diagrams in Fig. 7.13a, b are constructed.
Using the stress-strain relations [Eqs. (4.16)],

$$\epsilon_x = \frac{1}{E} \sigma_x = \frac{4{,}000}{E}$$

$$\epsilon_y = \epsilon_z = -\frac{\nu}{E} \sigma_x = -\frac{4{,}000\nu}{E}$$

$$\gamma_{xy} = \gamma_{yz} = \gamma_{zx} = 0$$

Substituting these values into Eqs. (7.9),

$$\epsilon_n = \frac{4{,}000}{E} (\cos^2 \theta - \nu \sin^2 \theta) \qquad\qquad (c)$$

$$\frac{\gamma_n}{2} = -\frac{4{,}000}{E} \cos \theta \sin \theta(1 + \nu) \qquad\qquad (d)$$

These strain components are plotted in the polar manner in Figs. 7.13c and d for steel using $E = 29.5 \times 10^6$ psi and $\nu = 0.29$.

As is seen, the stresses and strains corresponding to any inclined plane are readily visualized. The four diagrams in the figure represent, respectively, radial plots of:

(a) The normal stress acting on planes perpendicular to the xy plane.

(b) The shear stress acting on planes perpendicular to the xy plane.

(c) The normal, or extensional, strain of line segments that are near the point and parallel to the xy plane.

(d) One-half the shear strain corresponding to all pairs of perpendicular line segments that are near the point and lie in the xy plane. The shear strain $\gamma_n/2$ equals one-half the change in the right angle (a decrease is positive) between a line segment inclined at an angle θ from the x axis and a line segment inclined at an angle $\theta + 90°$ from the x axis.

7.9. Polar Representation of Strain Using a Unit Circle as Reference. This is a method of graphically representing the state of strain at a point, and as will be seen, it has a direct physical interpretation. The construction consists in plotting the normal and shear strains corresponding to

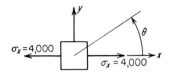

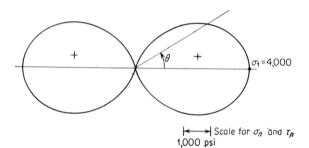

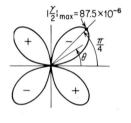

├──────┤ Scale for σ_n and τ_n
1,000 psi

(a) Normal stress σ_n.

(b) Shear stress τ_n using sign convention stated for Eqs. (7.12).

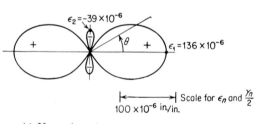

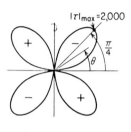

├────────────┤ Scale for ϵ_n and $\frac{\gamma_n}{2}$
100 ×10^{-6} in./in.

(c) Normal strain ϵ_n.

(d) Shear strain $\gamma_n/2$ using sign convention that $\gamma_n/2$ is positive when the right angle between the two lines inclined at θ and $\theta + 90°$ decreases in going from the unstrained to the strained state.

Fig. 7.13. Polar representation of the states of stress and strain at a point for the case of uniaxial tension. The figures for ϵ_n and $\gamma_n/2$ are plotted assuming $\nu = 0.29$ and $E = 29.5 \times 10^6$, typical values for steel.

each angle of inclination θ in a radial and tangential direction, respectively, from points on a reference unit circle. Thus, in Fig. 7.14, the normal strain ϵ_n as given by the first of Eqs. (7.9) is plotted as PP_1, and the shear strain $\gamma_n/2$ as given by the second of Eqs. (7.9) is plotted as P_1P_2, where

OP is inclined on angle θ from the x axis. The normal strains are plotted radially outward when positive and inward when negative, and the shear strains are plotted in a counterclockwise direction when positive and in a clockwise direction when negative.

If a circle is drawn in a two-dimensional homogeneous field of strain† on an actual body, Eqs. (7.9), which apply to all line segments within the region, will apply to all radii of the circle; and the deformed circle will be exactly the final curve obtained in the plot in Fig. 7.14. The original circle is assumed to have a unit radius so that the displacements of the points on its circumference will be equal to the strains (displacements per unit length). A physical representation of this phenomenon can be

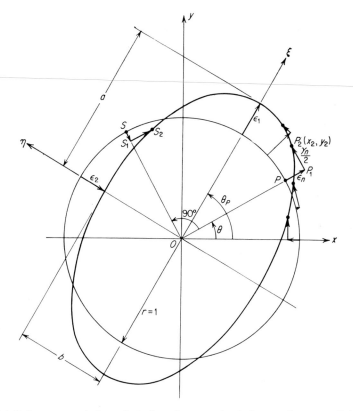

Fig. 7.14. Polar representation of strain using a unit circle as reference. Points on the circumference of such a circle drawn in a two-dimensional homogeneous field of strain on a body will be actually displaced as in the construction.

†See Sec. 2.8.

obtained by drawing a circle on a rubber sheet, as explained in the chapter dealing with grid methods. Figure 7.14a shows two such circles before and after deformation.

It can be seen that the convention for plotting shear strains follows from the three-dimensional shear-strain convention where γ_n is, when positive, equal to the decrease in the original right angle between line segments inclined at the angles θ and $\theta + 90°$ from the x axis. In this case, lines OP and OS become lines OP_2 and OS_2 after the deformation so that the 90° angle between them decreases. Thus, for a positive shear strain, the line P_1P_2 is drawn in a counterclockwise direction.

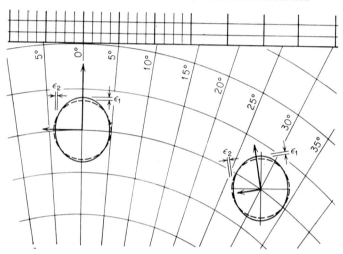

Fig. 7.14a. Deformation of circles drawn on a rubber sheet subjected to tension (see details in chapter on grid methods). The original (dotted circle) becomes an ellipse. The displacements of the points on the circle are proportional to the strains.

It will now be shown that the resultant curve is an ellipse; and, by drawing upon some of the properties of an ellipse, it will be shown that the principal axes of the ellipse have the same orientations as the principal axes of strain and that the major and minor semiprincipal axes, say, a and b, are equal respectively to $\epsilon_1 + 1$ and $\epsilon_2 + 1$, where ϵ_1 and ϵ_2 are the maximum and minimum principal strains.

Let the general point P on the unit circle in the figure have cartesian coordinates (x,y), and let P_2, the final position of point P, have coordinates (x_2,y_2). Then, from the figure,

$$x_2 = x + \epsilon_n \cos \theta - \frac{\gamma_n}{2} \sin \theta$$

$$y_2 = y + \epsilon_n \sin \theta + \frac{\gamma_n}{2} \cos \theta$$

Substituting for ϵ_n and $\gamma_n/2$ from Eqs. (7.9), which underlie the construction, and noting that $x = \cos\theta$ and $y = \sin\theta$, these can be written

$$x_2 = \cos\theta + \epsilon_x\cos^3\theta + \epsilon_y\sin^2\theta\cos\theta + \gamma_{xy}\sin\theta\cos^2\theta$$

$$+ (\epsilon_x - \epsilon_y)\sin^2\theta\cos\theta - \frac{\gamma_{xy}}{2}(\cos^2\theta\sin\theta - \sin^3\theta)$$

$$y_2 = \sin\theta + \epsilon_x\sin\theta\cos^2\theta + \epsilon_y\sin^3\theta + \gamma_{xy}\sin^2\theta\cos\theta$$

$$- (\epsilon_x - \epsilon_y)\sin\theta\cos^2\theta + \frac{\gamma_{xy}}{2}(\cos^3\theta - \sin^2\theta\cos\theta)$$

which reduce to

$$x_2 = (1 + \epsilon_x)\cos\theta + \frac{\gamma_{xy}}{2}\sin\theta \tag{a}$$

$$y_2 = (1 + \epsilon_y)\sin\theta + \frac{\gamma_{xy}}{2}\cos\theta \tag{b}$$

That these are the parametric equations of an ellipse can be seen by eliminating θ.

The term $\cos\theta$ can be eliminated to obtain an explicit expression for $\sin\theta$. The result is

$$\sin\theta = \frac{4y_2(1 + \epsilon_x) - 2x_2\gamma_{xy}}{4(1 + \epsilon_y)(1 + \epsilon_x) - \gamma_{xy}^2} \tag{c}$$

Through a similar procedure, an explicit expression for $\cos\theta$ can be obtained,

$$\cos\theta = \frac{4x_2(1 + \epsilon_y) - 2y_2\gamma_{xy}}{4(1 + \epsilon_x)(1 + \epsilon_y) - \gamma_{xy}^2} \tag{d}$$

If Eqs. (c) and (d) are squared and added, the parameter θ will be eliminated; and the resulting expression will be a second-degree expression in x_2 and y_2. Since it is known to represent a closed curve, it must be the equation of an ellipse.

In studying some of the properties of this ellipse, it is permissible to simplify its equation neglecting higher products and powers of the strain components as compared with the linear terms. When this is done, the equation of the ellipse obtained from Eqs. (c) and (d) above reduces to

$$(1 + 2\epsilon_y)x_2^2 + (1 + 2\epsilon_x)y_2^2 - 2\gamma_{xy}x_2y_2 - (1 + 2\epsilon_x + 2\epsilon_y) = 0 \tag{e}$$

By analytic-geometry theory, when a quadratic expression is written in the form

$$ax^2 + by^2 + 2cxy + d = 0$$

the term containing the product xy can be eliminated (i.e., the quadratic curve can be referred to a principal coordinate system) by rotating the coordinate axes through the angle θ_P defined by†

$$\tan 2\theta_P = \frac{2c}{a - b}$$

Applying this to Eq. (e), the required coordinate-system rotation is given by

$$\tan 2\theta_P = \frac{-2\gamma_{xy}}{(1 + 2\epsilon_y) - (1 + 2\epsilon_x)} = \frac{\gamma_{xy}}{\epsilon_x - \epsilon_y}$$

and also

$$\sin 2\theta_P = \frac{\gamma_{xy}}{\sqrt{(\epsilon_x - \epsilon_y)^2 + \gamma_{xy}^2}} \tag{7.24}$$

$$\cos 2\theta_P = \frac{\epsilon_x - \epsilon_y}{\sqrt{(\epsilon_x - \epsilon_y)^2 + \gamma_{xy}^2}}$$

Expressions for the x_2, y_2 coordinates in terms of the coordinates of the rotated system, say, ξ and η, are

$$x_2 = \xi \cos \theta_P - \eta \sin \theta_P$$

$$y_2 = \xi \sin \theta_P + \eta \cos \theta_P$$

The squares and cross products of these two equations give expressions for x_2^2, y_2^2, and $x_2 y_2$ in terms of θ_P. These can be transformed into terms of $2\theta_P$, substituted into Eq. (e), and the conditions (7.24) can be applied. The final result, after considerable algebra and after higher products and powers of the strains are neglected, is

$$\frac{\xi^2}{\left[1 + \dfrac{\epsilon_x + \epsilon_y}{2} + \sqrt{\left(\dfrac{\epsilon_x - \epsilon_y}{2}\right)^2 + \left(\dfrac{\gamma_{xy}}{2}\right)^2}\,\right]^2}$$

$$+ \frac{\eta^2}{\left[1 + \dfrac{\epsilon_x + \epsilon_y}{2} - \sqrt{\left(\dfrac{\epsilon_x - \epsilon_y}{2}\right)^2 + \left(\dfrac{\gamma_{xy}}{2}\right)^2}\,\right]^2} = 1$$

which can be written

$$\frac{\xi^2}{(1 + \epsilon_1)^2} + \frac{\eta^2}{(1 + \epsilon_2)^2} = 1 \tag{7.25}$$

Equation (7.25) is the equation of the ellipse of Fig. 7.14 referred to the principal axes ξ and η. As was to be shown, the angles of inclination θ_P

†See E. S. Smith, M. Salkover, and H. K. Justice, "Analytical Geometry," 2d ed., chap. 10, John Wiley & Sons, Inc., New York, 1954.

of the principal axes of the ellipse are the same as those corresponding to the principal directions of strain since Eqs. (7.24) are equivalent to Eqs. (7.15) and (7.16). (There is a difference in sign which is accounted for by the difference in shear-strain conventions leading to both sets of equations.) The same results can be established in an alternative manner. The radius vector to the point P_2 can be written in terms of ϵ_x, ϵ_y, γ_{xy}, and 2θ through the use of Eqs. (a) and (b). This can be differentiated with respect to θ and the resulting expression equated to zero to obtain the maximum and minimum values of r and the corresponding angles.

7.10. A Particular State of Stress and Strain Represented by All the Methods of This Chapter. The plane state of stress $\sigma_x = 4,000$ psi, $\sigma_y = -2,000$ psi, $\tau_{xy} = 0$ is illustrated in Fig. 7.15. The stress components σ_z, τ_{zy}, and τ_{zz} are zero, as are the strains γ_{zy} and γ_{zz}; however, by virtue of Poisson's ratio effect ϵ_z is not zero. In Figs. 7.16 to 7.25 this particular state of stress and its associated state of strain are represented by all the constructions discussed in this chapter.

In the constructions involving the sign of the shear stress and strain, the applicable sign convention is stated. Reference should be made to the appropriate section in the text for the complete explanation of each of the constructions.

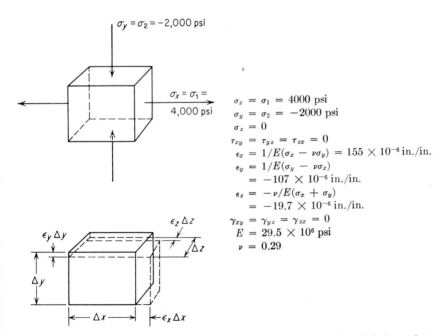

$$\sigma_x = \sigma_1 = 4000 \text{ psi}$$
$$\sigma_y = \sigma_2 = -2000 \text{ psi}$$
$$\sigma_z = 0$$
$$\tau_{xy} = \tau_{yz} = \tau_{zz} = 0$$
$$\epsilon_x = 1/E(\sigma_x - \nu\sigma_y) = 155 \times 10^{-6} \text{ in./in.}$$
$$\epsilon_y = 1/E(\sigma_y - \nu\sigma_x)$$
$$= -107 \times 10^{-6} \text{ in./in.}$$
$$\epsilon_z = -\nu/E(\sigma_x + \sigma_y)$$
$$= -19.7 \times 10^{-6} \text{ in./in.}$$
$$\gamma_{xy} = \gamma_{yz} = \gamma_{zz} = 0$$
$$E = 29.5 \times 10^6 \text{ psi}$$
$$\nu = 0.29$$

FIG. 7.15. Example of state of stress and associated state of strain which is used to illustrate all the methods of representation discussed in this chapter.

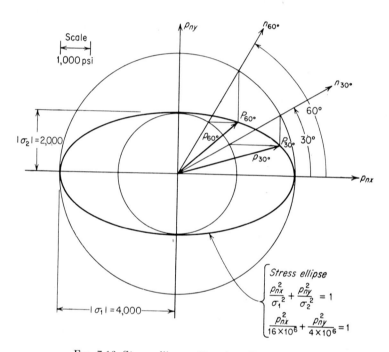

Fig. 7.16. Stress ellipse.   Use of auxiliary circles.

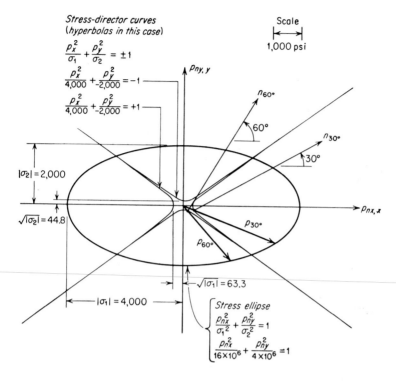

FIG. 7.17. Stress ellipse. Use of auxiliary stress-director curve.

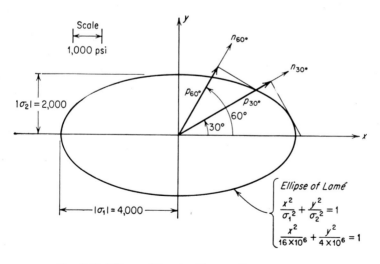

FIG. 7.18. Ellipse of Lamé. Tangent-line construction.

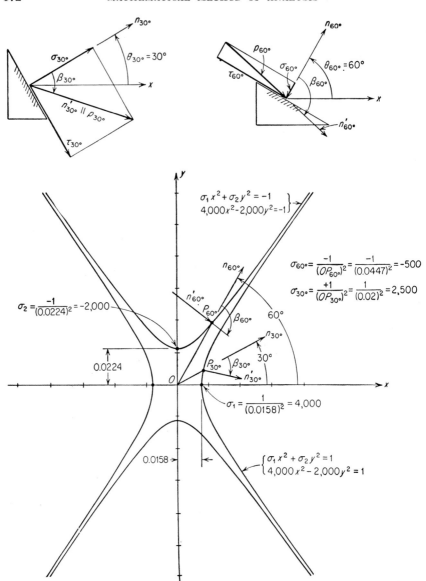

FIG. 7.19. Stress quadric of Cauchy.

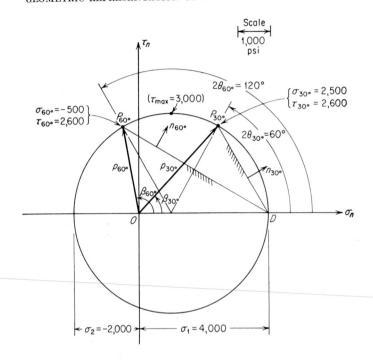

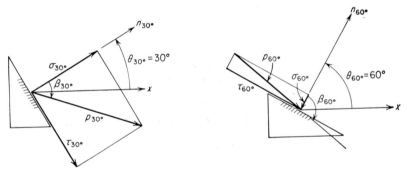

FIG. 7.20. Mohr's circle for stresses: use of the "pole."

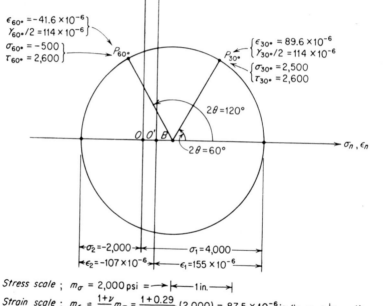

Stress scale ; $m_\sigma = 2,000\,\text{psi} = \longrightarrow|\!\longleftarrow 1\,\text{in.}\longrightarrow|$

Strain scale ; $m_\epsilon = \dfrac{1+\nu}{E}\,m_\sigma = \dfrac{1+0.29}{29.5\times10^6}(2,000) = 87.5\times10^{-6}\,\text{in./in.} = \longrightarrow|\!\longleftarrow 1\,\text{in.}\longrightarrow|$

$$\dfrac{OB}{O'B} = \dfrac{1+\nu}{1-\nu} = \dfrac{1.29}{0.71} = 1.82$$

Fig. 7.21. Mohr's circles for stresses and strains: method of coincident circles.

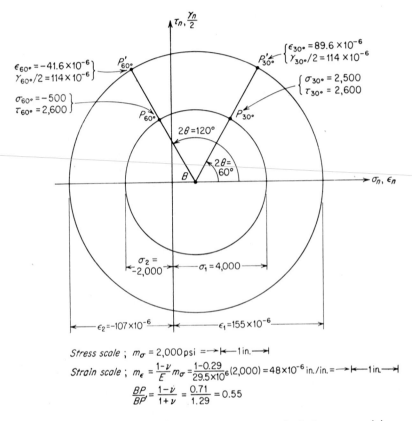

$$\text{Stress scale} \; ; \; m_\sigma = 2{,}000 \, \text{psi} =\!\!\rightarrow\!\!\mid\!\!\leftarrow\!\! 1 \, \text{in.} \rightarrow\!\mid$$

$$\text{Strain scale} \; ; \; m_\epsilon = \frac{1-\nu}{E} m_\sigma = \frac{1-0.29}{29.5 \times 10^6} (2{,}000) = 48 \times 10^{-6} \, \text{in./in.} =\!\!\rightarrow\!\!\mid\!\!\leftarrow\!\! 1 \, \text{in.} \rightarrow\!\mid$$

$$\frac{BP}{BP'} = \frac{1-\nu}{1+\nu} = \frac{0.71}{1.29} = 0.55$$

Fig. 7.22. Mohr's circles for stresses and strains: method of common-origin.

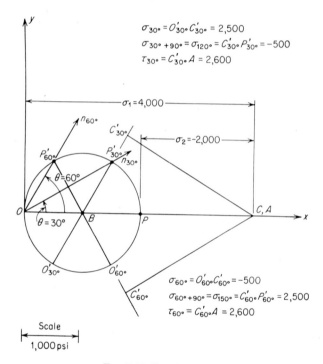

$\sigma_{30°} = O'_{30°} C'_{30°} = 2,500$

$\sigma_{30°+90°} = \sigma_{120°} = C'_{30°} P'_{30°} = -500$

$\tau_{30°} = C'_{30°} A = 2,600$

$\sigma_{60°} = O'_{60°} C'_{60°} = -500$

$\sigma_{60°+90°} = \sigma_{150°} = C'_{60°} P'_{60°} = 2,500$

$\tau_{60°} = C'_{60°} A = 2,600$

Scale

1,000 psi

FIG. 7.23. Dyadic circle.

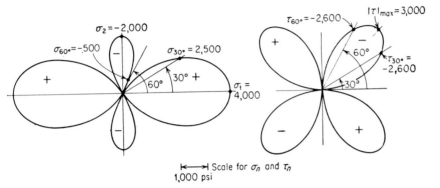

Scale for σ_n and τ_n
1,000 psi

(a) Normal stress σ_n.

(b) Shear stress τ_n using sign convention for Eqs. (7.12).

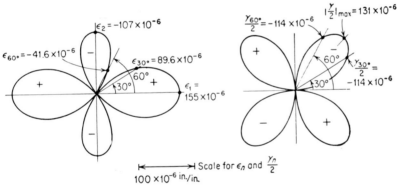

Scale for ϵ_n and $\dfrac{\gamma_n}{2}$
100 ×10^{-6} in./in.

(c) Normal strain ϵ_n.

(d) Shear strain $\gamma_n/2$ using sign convention that $\gamma_n/2$ is positive when the right angle between the two lines inclined at θ and $\theta + 90°$ decreases in going from the unstrained to the strained state.

FIG. 7.24. Polar method of representation of stresses and strains.

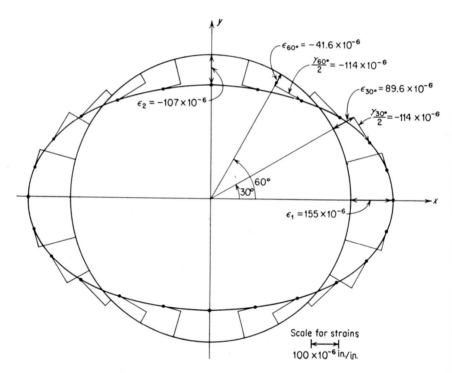

$\epsilon_{60°} = -41.6 \times 10^{-6}$

$\dfrac{\gamma_{60°}}{2} = -114 \times 10^{-6}$

$\epsilon_{30°} = 89.6 \times 10^{-6}$

$\dfrac{\gamma_{30°}}{2} = -114 \times 10^{-6}$

$\epsilon_2 = -107 \times 10^{-6}$

$\epsilon_1 = 155 \times 10^{-6}$

60°

30°

Scale for strains

100×10^{-6} in./in.

FIG. 7.25. Polar method of representation using unit circle as reference.

CHAPTER 8

PROPERTIES OF SPECIAL FAMILIES OF CURVES

We shall deal in this chapter with the properties of some loci, or curves, whose points satisfy certain specified conditions. Although this analysis will be limited here to the plane problem, it may be generalized to the three-dimensional problem.

8.1. Definitions of Various Special Families of Curves. In a plane problem, the magnitude of the algebraically larger principal stress in general varies from point to point. Given a specific value, say, 100 psi, there may exist a number of points at which the algebraically larger principal stresses are equal to this value. The locus of these points, or the curve joining these points, is called a σ_1 isobar of parameter 100 psi. When the parameter takes a different value, say, 90 psi, there will be another set of points at which the algebraically larger principal stresses are equal to 90 psi. The locus of these points, or the curve joining these points, is called a σ_1 isobar of parameter 90 psi. By varying the parameter, a group of curves can be obtained which is called a family of curves. The family of curves each of which joins points having the same values of the algebraically larger principal stress σ_1 is called the σ_1 isobars.

Similarly, the family of curves each of which connects points at which there are equal values of σ_2, $\sigma_1 + \sigma_2$, $\sigma_1 - \sigma_2$, ϵ_1, and ϵ_2 are called the σ_2 isobars, isopachics, isochromatics, ϵ_1 isotenics, and ϵ_2 isotenics respectively. Those curves connecting points at which the principal directions of stress (or strain) are the same are called isoclinics. The families of curves the tangents to which represent the principal directions at the points of tangency are called isostatics, or principal stress trajectories. The families of curves the tangents to which represent the directions of the maximum shear stresses at the points of tangency are called maximum shear trajectories. Besides the characteristics by which these families of curves are defined, there are additional properties which are useful in the interpretation and construction of these curves.

8.2. Isoclinics. It has been shown in Sec. 1.9 that at each point in a two-dimensional stress system there exist in general two mutually perpendicular principal directions. Equations (1.20c) to (1.20e) provide the means for determining these directions. Along an arbitrary curve

179

PQ, these principal directions will vary from point to point (Fig. 8.1). The curve NQ which joins points having parallel principal directions is called an isoclinic. The word isoclinic is from the Greek "iso," meaning "equal," and the Greek "klinein," meaning "incline." The common angle of inclination θ, measured counterclockwise from the positive direction of the x axis to these parallel principal directions, is called the parameter of the isoclinic. Either one of the two mutually perpendicular principal directions may be used in the determination of the parameter θ. There are five useful properties of isoclinics, which will be stated and proved below.

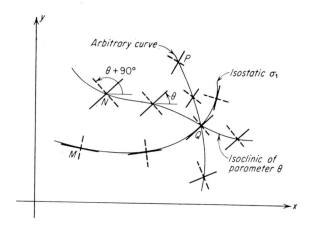

FIG. 8.1. Example of isoclinic and isostatic lines. On all points of the isoclinic the inclination of one of the principal stresses is the same. At all points of the isostatic the principal direction is tangent to the curve.

1. An isoclinic of parameter θ is identical to an isoclinic of parameter $\theta \pm \pi/2$, but not to one of parameter $\pi/2 - \theta$, unless $\theta = n\pi/4$, n being an integer.

By definition, an isoclinic of parameter θ will join those points having one principal direction at an angle θ with the x axis. The other principal direction, being perpendicular to the first one, will make an angle of $\theta + \pi/2$ with the x axis, as shown at point N (Fig. 8.1). All the points on the isoclinic of parameter θ will therefore have another principal direction at an angle of $\theta + \pi/2$ with the x axis. By definition, the isoclinic of parameter $\theta + \pi/2$ joins only those points which have one principal direction at an angle of $\theta + \pi/2$ with the x axis. The isoclinic of parameter $\theta + \pi/2$ and the isoclinic of parameter θ therefore join the same set of points and must be identical. The same proof can be applied to the isoclinic of parameter $\theta - \pi/2$. Unless θ is equal to 0, $\pm\pi/4$, $\pm2\pi/4$,

$\pm 3\pi/4, \ldots$, neither of the two principal directions of the points on the isoclinic of parameter θ will be at an angle of $\pi/2 - \theta$ with the x axis. These points will not lie on the isoclinic of parameter $\pi/2 - \theta$. Thus the isoclinic of parameter θ and the isoclinic of parameter $\pi/2 - \theta$ are not the same.

2. Where an isoclinic intersects a boundary free from shear stresses, its parameter is given by the inclination of the boundary at the point of intersection. The parameter of isoclinics is therefore self-indicative at a free boundary.

At the points on a boundary free of shear stresses (Fig. 8.2), it follows from the definition of principal directions that one of these is tangential

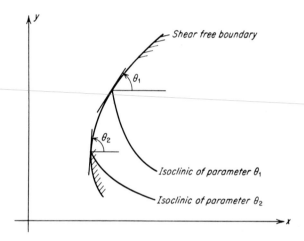

FIG. 8.2. Intersection of an isoclinic with a shear-free boundary. The parameter of the isoclinic is given by the inclination of the boundary at the point of intersection.

to the boundary. Therefore, at the point of intersection of an isoclinic with a boundary free of shear stresses, the inclination of the boundary must give the parameter of the isoclinic.

3. A straight boundary free from shear stress is an isoclinic. A rectangular boundary free from shear stress is a single isoclinic.

From property 2, we have seen that each point on a boundary free from shear stress belongs to an isoclinic whose parameter is equal to the inclination of the boundary. For a curved boundary, the inclination of the boundary changes from point to point, and the points on the boundary will belong to isoclinics of different parameters. At a straight boundary (Fig. 8.3), the inclination of the boundary is constant, and the points on the boundary will belong to isoclinics of the same parameter. In other words, the points on a straight boundary free from shear stress belong to a single isoclinic whose parameter is given by the inclination of the boundary. At a rectangular boundary the points belong to two isoclinics of parameter θ and $\theta + \pi/2$. By property 1, these two isoclinics are one and the same. Thus a rectangular boundary belongs to a single isoclinic.

4. Only one isoclinic can pass through any given point which is not an isotropic point. Two isoclinics never cross each other except at isotropic points.

In a plane problem, an isotropic point is defined as a point at which the two principal stresses are equal. By Eq. (7.6), it is seen that the shear

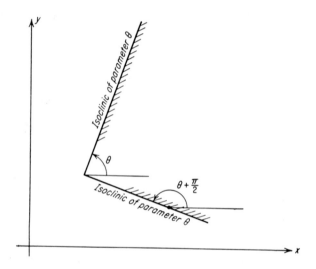

Fig. 8.3. A rectangular shear-free boundary belongs to a single isoclinic.

stress on any plane passing through this point is zero. Since the principal direction is defined as the direction normal to the plane where the shear stresses vanish, any direction at an isotropic point is a principal direction. Therefore the isotropic point can belong to isoclinics of any parameter. Hence isoclinics of different parameters can intersect each other at isotropic points. At any point which is not an isotropic point, there are two and only two principal directions and these are perpendicular to each other. This follows from the two-dimensional counterpart of the discussion of Sec. 1.9. These principal directions have clearly defined angles of inclination θ. Each such point will definitely belong to the isoclinic of parameter θ or $\theta \pm \pi/2$. It cannot belong to two isoclinics. Thus only one isoclinic can pass through any given point which is not an isotropic point, and two isoclinics can never cross each other except at isotropic points.

5. If a body contains an axis of symmetry and the loads are symmetrically distributed with regard to this axis, then the axis of symmetry is an isoclinic.

The body shown in Fig. 8.4 contains an axis of symmetry MN. The loads are also symmetrically distributed with regard to MN. If we divide the body into two halves along the line MN and call F and F' the shear forces exerted on the right half by the left half and on the left half by the right half, respectively, by Newton's third law, the action F and the reaction F' must be equal and must act in opposite directions. Because of symmetry, however, F and F' must be equal and must act in the same direction. The only possible way out of this contradiction is for both F and F' to vanish. In other words, the shear stress is zero along the plane MN. At any point on the axis of symmetry MN, one of the principal

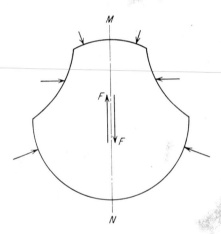

FIG. 8.4. In a symmetrical body symmetrically loaded the axis of symmetry is an isostatic as well as an isoclinic of parameter equal to the inclination of the axis.

directions is therefore along MN. All the points on MN have parallel principal directions and will lie on the isoclinic of parameter equal to the inclination of MN.

Isoclinics can be obtained experimentally using photoelasticity. This method will be explained later in a contemplated volume on photoelasticity. An example of an isoclinic of 0° parameter in a plate with a central circular hole and under uniform tension is shown in Fig. 8.5.

8.3. Isostatics. Isostatics were introduced in Sec. 1.15. Their definition will be repeated here. Referring to Fig. 8.1, the curve MQ, which is everywhere tangent to the principal directions, is called an isostatic. Sometimes the term "principal stress trajectory" or simply "stress trajectory" is used in reference to the same curve. Since at each point there are two mutually perpendicular principal directions, two mutually perpendicular isostatics will pass through each point and the system of isostatics will consist of a system of two orthogonal families of curves. There are several useful properties of isostatics. These will be stated and proved below.

1. Isostatics form a system of two orthogonal families of curves. All the stresses tangent to one family are the algebraically larger principal stresses, and those tangent to the other family are the algebraically smaller principal stresses. It follows that if the direction of the larger

Fig. 8.5. Isoclinic, or locus of points, having the same principal directions (0° and 90° in respect to the vertical axis). The pattern has been obtained photoelastically from a plastic plate, with a hole in the center, loaded vertically under uniform tension.

principal stress is known at one point in the body, then an inspection of the isostatics will give the signs of all tangential stresses on a free boundary.

Let the two orthogonal families of curves be called u and v curves (Fig. 8.6). Let the two principal stresses be called σ_u and σ_v. The value of $\sigma_u - \sigma_v$ will be equal to zero only at isotropic points such as point I. Along any arbitrary line ABC, the value of $\sigma_u - \sigma_v$ will vary continuously from point to point. If this value is positive at A and negative at C, then somewhere along the line ABC there must be an isotropic point where the value is equal to zero. Conversely, if the line ABC is chosen such that it contains no isotropic point, then the signs of $\sigma_u - \sigma_v$ must be the same for

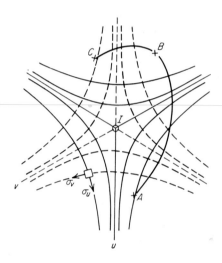

FIG. 8.6. Example of isostatics around an isotropic point.

all points along this line. Usually any two points in a body can be connected by a line not passing through the few isolated isotropic points. Hence $\sigma_u - \sigma_v$ must have the same sign throughout the entire body; in other words, σ_u will be everywhere larger or everywhere smaller than σ_v throughout the entire body. In this book, we use σ_1 and σ_2 to denote the algebraically larger and smaller principal stresses, respectively. We shall use σ_u and σ_v to denote the two principal stresses when we want no restrictions to be imposed on the relative magnitudes of these stresses. In other words, $\sigma_1 - \sigma_2$ is always larger than or equal to zero, while $\sigma_u - \sigma_v$ can be larger than or equal to zero in one case while in another case it can be less than or equal to zero. Graphically, the σ_1 isostatic will be represented by solid curves and the σ_2 isostatic will be represented by dotted curves.

2. Given a point P on an isostatic S_u (Fig. 8.7). Among the three conditions

(a) The isoclinic PQ cuts the isostatic S_u at a right angle at P,

(b) The radius of curvature of the isostatic S_v orthogonal to the given isostatic S_u is infinite at P, and

(c) The principal stress σ_u tangent to the given isostatic S_u is maximum or minimum at P,

we have the following relations:

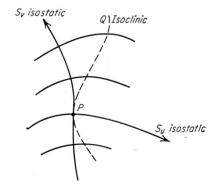

FIG. 8.7. Example of an isoclinic cutting an isostatic at a right angle.

If condition a is true, then conditions b and c must both be true. If condition b is true, then conditions a and c must both be true. If condition c is true, then conditions a and b are both true, if the point P is not an isotropic point. The above relations are also applicable to a boundary free of shear stress since the latter is an isostatic.

If we call ψ and $\psi + \Delta\psi$ the angles which the isostatic S_u makes with the isoclinics of parameters θ and $\theta + \Delta\theta$, respectively (Fig. 8.8), then

$$\cot (\psi + \Delta\psi) = \frac{\Delta S_u}{\Delta S_v}$$

Let ΔS_v approach zero; then both $\Delta\psi$ and ΔS_u approach zero and the ratio $\Delta S_u/\Delta S_v$ approaches dS_u/dS_v. In the limit, we therefore have

$$\cot \psi = \frac{dS_u}{dS_v} \tag{8.1}$$

We recall that in the chapter on stresses (Sec. 1.15) we derived Eqs. (1.47), called the Lamé-Maxwell equations:

$$\frac{\partial\sigma_u}{\partial S_u} = -\frac{\sigma_u - \sigma_v}{\rho_v}$$

$$\frac{\partial\sigma_v}{\partial S_v} = -\frac{\sigma_u - \sigma_v}{\rho_u} \tag{8.2}$$

where

$$\frac{1}{\rho_u} = \frac{\partial \theta}{\partial S_u}$$ (8.3)

$$\frac{1}{\rho_v} = \frac{\partial \theta}{\partial S_v}$$

In Fig. 8.8, if the change in θ is noted, as a point moves along S_u and S_v from the isoclinic θ to the isoclinic $\theta + \Delta\theta$, it is evident that

$$\Delta\theta_v = -\Delta\theta_u$$

From Eqs. (8.3) it can be seen that

$$\Delta S_u = \Delta\theta_u \rho_u$$

$$\Delta S_v = \Delta\theta_v \rho_v$$

and so

$$\frac{\Delta S_u}{\Delta S_v} = -\frac{\rho_u}{\rho_v}$$

This equality holds as ΔS_u and ΔS_v approach zero, and from Eq. (8.1)

$$\cot \psi = -\frac{\rho_u}{\rho_v}$$

If, as in Fig. 8.7, $\psi = 90°$, $\cot \psi = 0$, and except for the special case of $\rho_u = 0$ (an isotropic point),

$$\rho_v = \infty$$

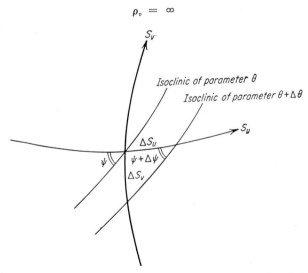

FIG. 8.8. Sketch showing the intersection of an isoclinic and an isostatic.

and from Eqs. (8.2)

$$\frac{\partial \sigma_u}{\partial S_u} = 0$$

Hence σ_u is a maximum or minimum at P.

Next, if ρ_v is infinite at P (Fig. 8.7), then, by Eqs. (8.2), $\partial \sigma_u / \partial S_u$ vanishes or σ_u is a maximum or minimum at P. Also, by Eqs. (8.3), $\partial \theta / \partial S_v$ vanishes, and the isostatic S_v at P must coincide with the isoclinic at P since only along the isoclinic can there be no change in the value of θ. The isoclinic therefore cuts the isostatic S_u at a right angle.

Next, if σ_u is a maximum or minimum at P, then $\partial \sigma_u / \partial S_u$ vanishes. If the point P is not an isotropic point so that $\sigma_u - \sigma_v$ does not vanish, then, by Eqs. (8.2), ρ_v must be infinite. By Eqs. (8.3), $\partial \theta / \partial S_v$ must vanish, and the isoclinic PQ will cut the isostatic S_u at a right angle.

3. Near a convex free boundary, the sign of the radial stress is opposite to that of the tangential stress; near a concave free boundary, these signs are the same.

The free boundary is always an isostatic and the stress perpendicular to the boundary is zero at the boundary. The Lamé-Maxwell equations (8.2) may be applied, keeping in mind two implicit conventions: (1) the sign of ρ is determined as shown in Fig. 1.12; and (2) u and v follow the usual xy coordinate relationship, i.e., at any point the positive direction v is 90° counterclockwise to the positive u direction. Fig. 8.9 shows that for a convex surface the signs of σ_u and σ_v near the boundary are opposite. A like development in Fig. 8.10 shows that for a concave surface the signs of the principal stresses near the boundary agree. In both figures the physical property has been shown for either sign of the radius of curvature following consistently the sign convention.

4. The radial gradient of the radial stress vanishes at (a) an isotropic point on a curved boundary free of shear stresses and (b) any point on a straight boundary free of shear stresses.

Since a shear-free boundary is an isostatic, the radial gradients of the radial stress (Figs. 8.9 and 8.10) are given by

$$\frac{\partial \sigma_u}{\partial S_u} = -\frac{\sigma_u - \sigma_v}{\rho_v}$$

At an isotropic point, $\sigma_u - \sigma_v$ vanishes; along a straight boundary, ρ_v becomes infinite. In either case $\partial \sigma_u / \partial S_u$ vanishes.

5. If a body contains an axis of symmetry and the loads are symmetrically distributed with regard to this axis, then the principal stresses along an isostatic normal to it are either maximum or minimum at every point on this axis of symmetry.

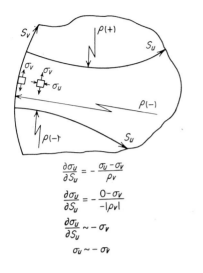

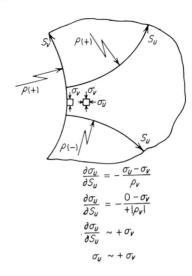

$$\frac{\partial \sigma_u}{\partial S_u} = -\frac{\sigma_u - \sigma_v}{\rho_v}$$

$$\frac{\partial \sigma_u}{\partial S_u} = -\frac{0 - \sigma_v}{-|\rho_v|}$$

$$\frac{\partial \sigma_u}{\partial S_u} \sim -\sigma_v$$

$$\sigma_u \sim -\sigma_v$$

$$\frac{\partial \sigma_u}{\partial S_u} = -\frac{\sigma_u - \sigma_v}{\rho_v}$$

$$\frac{\partial \sigma_u}{\partial S_u} = -\frac{0 - \sigma_v}{+|\rho_v|}$$

$$\frac{\partial \sigma_u}{\partial S_u} \sim +\sigma_v$$

$$\sigma_u \sim +\sigma_v$$

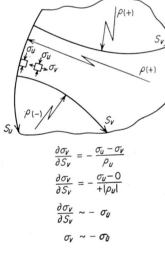

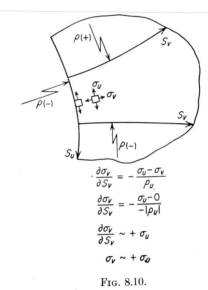

$$\frac{\partial \sigma_v}{\partial S_v} = -\frac{\sigma_u - \sigma_v}{\rho_u}$$

$$\frac{\partial \sigma_v}{\partial S_v} = -\frac{\sigma_u - 0}{+|\rho_u|}$$

$$\frac{\partial \sigma_v}{\partial S_v} \sim -\sigma_u$$

$$\sigma_v \sim -\sigma_u$$

$$\frac{\partial \sigma_v}{\partial S_v} = -\frac{\sigma_u - \sigma_v}{\rho_u}$$

$$\frac{\partial \sigma_v}{\partial S_v} = -\frac{\sigma_u - 0}{-|\rho_u|}$$

$$\frac{\partial \sigma_v}{\partial S_v} \sim +\sigma_u$$

$$\sigma_v \sim +\sigma_u$$

Fig. 8.9.   Fig. 8.10.

FIGS. 8.9 and 8.10. Near a convex free boundary σ_u and σ_v have opposite signs. Near a concave free boundary σ_u and σ_v have the same sign. The sign of ρ is determined by the convention in Fig. 1.12. (The development does not depend on the sign of ρ for the isostatic perpendicular to the free boundary. The positive direction of S_v is always chosen 90° counterclockwise to the positive direction of S_u.)

When the loads are symmetrically distributed with regard to an axis of symmetry of a body (Fig. 8.4), this axis of symmetry is both an isostatic and an isoclinic. By property 2, the principal stresses along an isostatic normal to this axis are therefore either maximum or minimum all along this axis.

6. The distances from a free boundary to a nearby isostatic are inversely proportional to the tangential stresses on the boundary.

The tangential stresses at P, Q, R, ... (Fig. 8.11) are always inversely proportional to the lengths of PP', QQ', RR', ... This property was first pointed out by Neuber, and a simple proof of it using curvilinear coordinates is given in a paper by one of the authors.†

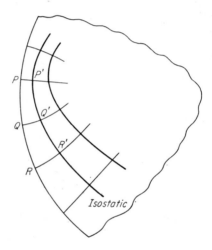

Fig. 8.11. An isostatic near a free boundary.

Isostatics can be obtained experimentally by means of brittle coatings. Several examples are shown in the chapter where brittle coatings are described. Figure 8.12 is a photograph of an aluminum ring under diametral compression showing a complete family of isostatics. It can be observed that the free boundaries belong to one or the other of the isostatic families. Figure 8.13 is a photograph of an aluminum curved bar subjected to a pure-bending moment. The fine crack lines are isostatics, while the heavier lines are isoentatics (see Sec. 8.9).

8.4. Isotropic Points. In a plane problem, an isotropic point is defined as a point at which the two principal stresses are equal. These points are sometimes called singular points. At an isotropic point, the state of stress

---

†A. J. Durrelli, Determination of Stresses on Free Boundaries by Means of Isostatics, *Proc. 15th Semiannual Eastern Photoelasticity Conf.*, June, 1942, p. 32.

is therefore hydrostatic, and isoclinics of different parameters can intersect each other. Around an isotropic point, not on a boundary, isostatics are of two types. In the first type (Fig. 8.14), every isostatic goes around the isotropic point and intersects every one of the isostatics of the other family. This type will be called the interlocking type. The second type (Figs. 8.6 and 8.15) has a number of asymptotes and will be called the asymptotic type. If we construct the isoclinics from the isostatics of the interlocking type (Fig. 8.16), it will be seen that the parameter of the isoclinics passing

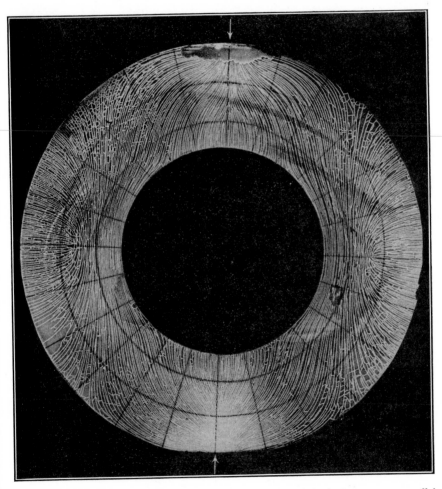

FIG. 8.12. Isostatics, or principal stress trajectories. Principal stresses are parallel and perpendicular to the thin lines on the brittle coating. Two singular points of the interlocking type can be seen on the horizontal axis. Four singular points of the mixed type can be seen on each of the boundaries.

through the isotropic point increases in a counterclockwise direction. If we construct the isoclinics from the isostatics of the asymptotic type (Fig. 8.17), it will be seen that the parameter increases in a clockwise direction. This property is sometimes useful in the construction of isostatics from isoclinics around an isotropic point.

The position and the type of singular points can well be determined experimentally, using brittle coatings. On the horizontal axis of the ring

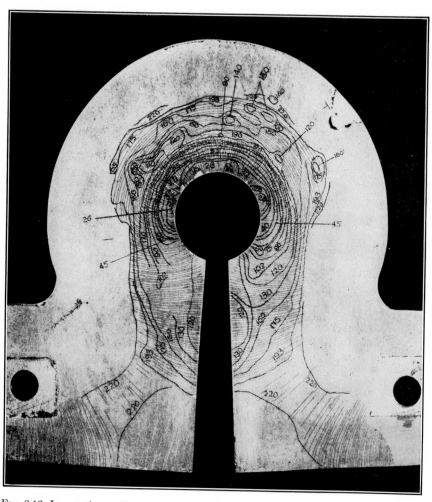

FIG. 8.13. Isoentatics, or lines connecting the ends of the cracks (isostatics), in a brittle-coating test. They have been scribed on the coating, and the figures next to them correspond to the moment that is necessary to apply to the curved beam to bring the crack to that point.

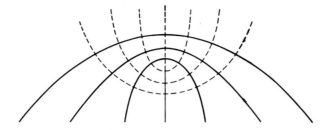

FIG. 8.14. Isostatics around an isotropic point: the interlocking type.

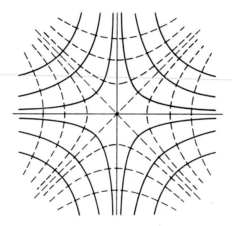

FIG. 8.15. Isostatics around an isotropic point: the asymptotic type.

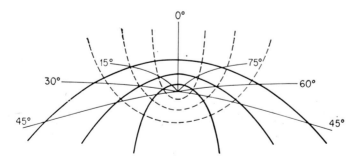

FIG. 8.16. Isoclinics corresponding to the isostatics of the interlocking type. **Here** the parameter of the isoclinics increases in the counterclockwise direction.

shown in Fig. 8.12, two singular points of the interlocking type can be seen. On each of the boundaries four singular points of mixed character can be found.

8.5. Isochromatics. Isochromatics are loci of points of equal maximum shear. The word means "equal color," because photoelastic fringes of the same color correspond to points where the value of the maximum shear is the same.

At the free boundaries, the isochromatic pattern gives directly the value of the principal stress.

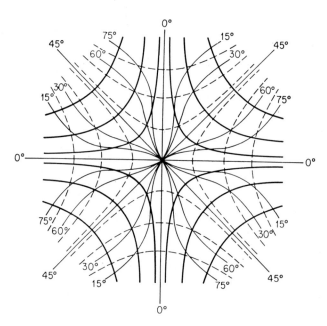

FIG. 8.17. Isoclinics corresponding to the isostatics of the asymptotic type. Here the parameter of the isoclinics increases in the clockwise direction.

An example of isochromatics obtained experimentally by photoelasticity is shown in Fig. 8.18. These show the distribution of maximum shear stresses in the contact region between a disk and a bar. The disk is loaded under compression by the bar.

8.6. Isopachics. These are loci of points of equal sum of principal stresses. The word means "equal thickness," since, in the two-dimensional plane-stress problem, points of equal thickness are points where

FIG. 8.18. Isochromatics, or loci of points of equal maximum shear, obtained photo-elastically.

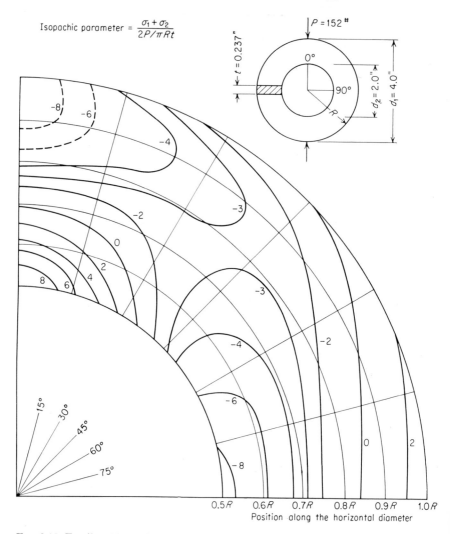

FIG. 8.19. Family of isopachic curves for a ring subjected to a concentrated diametral load. (These lines have been obtained from point-per-point measurements of thickness changes using a Leitz optical comparator.)

the sum of the principal stresses is the same. This is evident from the stress-strain relation,

$$\epsilon_3 = -\frac{\nu}{E}(\sigma_1 + \sigma_2)$$

In these two-dimensional problems, isopachics and isochromatics coincide with the isobars at the free boundaries, giving the values of the principal stresses.

Figure 8.19 is an example of isostatics obtained experimentally by one of the authors.† The changes in thickness of the ring were measured at each point using an optical comparator manufactured by Leitz.

8.7. Isobars. The word isobar meant originally "equal pressure" and is used to denote equal principal stress. There are two sets of isobars, each corresponding to one of the principal stresses.

Isobars can be constructed graphically from isochromatics and isopachics, as shown later (Sec. 8.10).

8.8. Isotenics. Isotenics are loci of points of equal principal strain. As in the case of isobars, there are two sets of curves, each corresponding to one of the principal strains.

The word isotenic means "equal strain" and is introduced here to identify the above sets of curves. The reader should carefully observe the difference between isotenics and isoentatics discussed below.

8.9. Isoentatics. The isoentatics are defined as the lines connecting the ends of the cracks of brittle coatings. When originally introduced, the word was meant to denote "equal stretch" or "equal strain"; however, better knowledge of brittle coatings' failure showed that brittle coatings do not crack according to the maximum-principal-strain law, and the lines connecting the ends of the cracks have a complicated relationship with the state of strain in the specimen under the coating. The word isoentatic, therefore, ceases to denote the curve of equal principal strain. It is still retained to denote the locus of the ends of the cracks of brittle coatings.

An example of isoentatics obtained using Stresscoat is shown in Fig. 8.13. As will be explained in the chapter dealing with brittle coatings, there are several kinds of isoentatics, since they can be produced by direct load or by relaxation; they can encircle first cracks or second cracks; and they can be produced with or without refrigeration of the coating.

8.10. Construction of Isobars from Isopachics and Isochromatics. Let a set of four isopachics (Fig. 8.20) be

$$\sigma_1 + \sigma_2 = m - 1, m, m + 1, m + 2$$

Let a set of five isochromatics be

$$\sigma_1 - \sigma_2 = n - 2, n - 1, n, n + 1, n + 2$$

where m and n are integers. Then, at point A, where the first isopachic intersects the fourth isochromatic, we have

---

† A. J. Durelli and W. F. Riley, Use of Creep to Determine the Sum of the Principal Stresses in Two-Dimensional Problems, *Proc. Soc. Exptl. Stress Anal.*, vol. 14, no. 2, pp. 109–116, 1957.

$$\sigma_1 + \sigma_2 = m - 1$$

$$\sigma_1 - \sigma_2 = n + 1$$

Solving,

$$\sigma_1 = \frac{m + n}{2}$$

$$\sigma_2 = \frac{m - n - 2}{2}$$

At point B, where the second isopachic intersects the third isochromatic, we have

$$\sigma_1 + \sigma_2 = m$$

$$\sigma_1 - \sigma_2 = n$$

or

$$\sigma_1 = \frac{m + n}{2}$$

$$\sigma_2 = \frac{m - n}{2}$$

Evidently σ_1 will have the value $(m + n)/2$ wherever the isopachic of order $m - s$ intersects the isochromatic of order $n + s$, s being any integer.

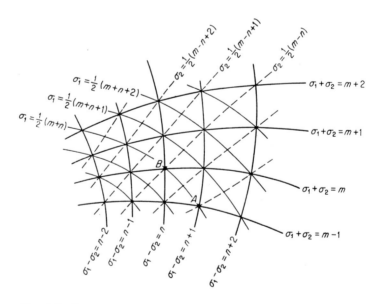

Fig. 8.20. Construction of isobars from isopachics and isochromatics.

The lines of equal σ_1, or the σ_1 isobar, are therefore obtained by taking successive intersections of isopachics and isochromatics, the parameters of the isopachics going up one at a time, those of the isochromatics going down one at a time, or conversely.

On the other hand, σ_2 will have the value $(m - n)/2$ wherever the isopachic of order $m + s$ intersects the isochromatic of order $n + s$, s being any integer. The lines of equal σ_2, or the σ_2 isobar, are therefore obtained by taking successive intersections of isopachics and isochromatics, the parameters of both isopachics and isochromatics going up or down together, one at a time. Figure 8.20 shows this construction, where the σ_1 isobar and the σ_2 isobar are represented by solid and dotted lines, respectively.

8.11. Construction of Isostatics from Isoclinics.
The construction of

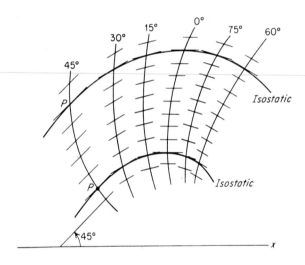

Fig. 8.21. Basic method of construction of isostatics from isoclinics.

isostatics from isoclinics is identical to the graphical solution of a first-order differential equation. The basic method is shown in Fig. 8.21. On each isoclinic, a series of short parallel lines is drawn with the common inclination equal to the parameter of the isoclinic. Starting from any given point P, a smooth curve is sketched by eye so that it is everywhere tangent to these short parallel lines. This gives one isostatic. Continuing this procedure, we can readily obtain the family of isostatics. Generally, the above procedure gives satisfactory results.

In Fig. 8.22 the curved segment P_1P_2 of the isostatic S_u is assumed to be a circular arc so that the inclination of the chord P_1P_2 is the average of the inclinations of the tangents at P_1 and P_2. This leads to a method

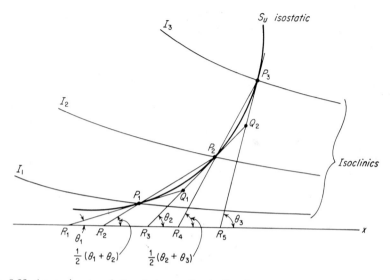

Fig. 8.22. Approximate relation between the inclinations of the chord P_1P_2 and the tangents at P_1 and P_2.

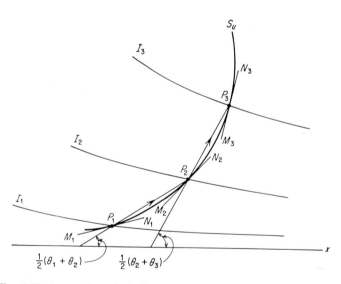

Fig. 8.23. A second method of construction of isostatics from isoclinics.

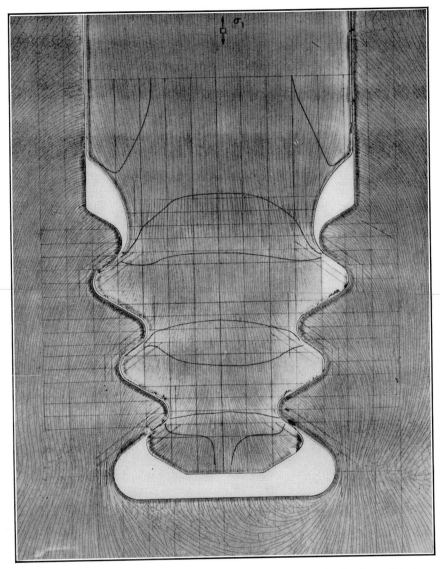

FIG. 8.24. Isostatics of σ_1 family in a dovetail joint. Curves of inflection points have been drawn on the male part of the joints. Principal stress σ_2 goes through a minimum or a maximum at points on these curves.

of construction of isostatics shown in Fig. 8.23. Through any point P_1 on the isoclinic I_1 of parameter θ_1, draw a line making an angle of $\frac{1}{2}(\theta_1 + \theta_2)$ with the x axis, and produce this line until it intersects the isoclinic I_2 of parameter θ_2 at P_2. Through P_2 draw a line making an angle of $\frac{1}{2}(\theta_2 + \theta_3)$

with the x axis, and produce this line until it intersects the isoclinic I_3 of parameter θ_3 at P_3. The isostatic S_u is then obtained by passing a smooth curve through the points P_1, P_2, and P_3. More accuracy can be obtained if we add the lines M_1N_1, M_2N_2, M_2N_3 at P_1, P_2, and P_3, making angles of θ_1, θ_2, θ_3 with the x axis, respectively, and draw the isostatic to pass through P_1, P_2, and P_3 as well as to be tangent to the lines M_1N_1, M_2N_2, and M_3N_3.

8.12. Curves of Inflection Points. These curves are the loci of points at which the principal stresses assume maximum or minimum values.

It is obvious from observation of Eqs. (8.2) that, if the two principal stresses are not equal and one of the principal stresses has a minimum or maximum value, the radius of the isostatic parallel to the other principal stress must be infinite. Now the radius of an isostatic is infinite when the isostatic passes through an inflection point; therefore, curves connecting inflection points of an isostatic family are the loci of points at which the principal stress parallel to the other family of isostatics assumes maximum or minimum values. Figure 8.24 shows the σ_1 family of isostatics in a dovetail joint. These have been experimentally determined, using brittle coatings. On the male part of the joint the curves of inflection points have been drawn.

CHAPTER 9

APPLICATION TO TWO-DIMENSIONAL PROBLEMS

9.1. Elastic Solution of a Thin Plate of Infinite Width with a Circular Hole under Unidimensional Load. Figure 9.1 represents a thin plate of infinite width and length which has a circular hole at its center. The plate is submitted to a uniform tension of magnitude σ_{aG} in the x direction. Polar coordinates will be used. For thin plates, the generalized plane-stress solution is a good approximation of the true solution and will be the solution which we seek. Where body forces vanish, the generalized plane-stress solution has the same stresses as the primary plane-strain solution except for σ_z. Hence the problem is solved if we can find a certain stress function ϕ which satisfies Eq. (6.39) and whose corresponding stresses as computed by Eqs. (6.38) satisfy these boundary conditions:

$$\sigma_r = \tau_{r\theta} = 0 \qquad \text{at } r = a$$

$$\sigma_x = \sigma_{aG} \qquad \sigma_y = 0 \qquad \tau_{xy} = 0 \qquad \text{at } r = \infty$$

or, by Eq. (6.30), $\hfill (9.1)$

$$\sigma_r = \sigma_{aG} \cos^2 \theta \qquad \sigma_\theta = \sigma_{aG} \sin^2 \theta$$

$$\tau_{r\theta} = -\sigma_{aG} \sin \theta \cos \theta \qquad \text{at } r = \infty$$

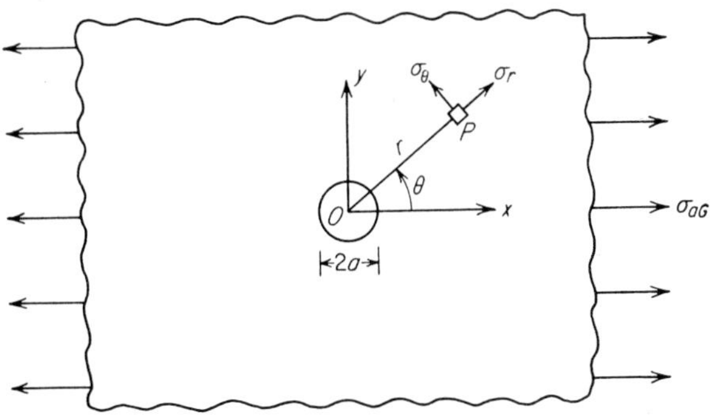

FIG. 9.1. Thin infinite plate with a circular hole under unidimensional tension.

The determination of Airy's function will again be made by some sort of educated guess. Let

$$\phi = Ar^2 + B \ln r + f(r) \cos 2\theta$$

Substituting this into Eq. (6.39), we have

$$\left(\frac{d^2}{dr^2} + \frac{1}{r}\frac{d}{dr} - \frac{4}{r^2}\right)\left(\frac{d^2f}{dr^2} + \frac{1}{r}\frac{df}{dr} - \frac{4f}{r^2}\right) = 0$$

From Eqs. (6.43) the general solution of this ordinary differential equation is

$$f(r) = Cr^2 + Dr^4 + \frac{E}{r^2} + F$$

The stress function is therefore

$$\phi = Ar^2 + B \ln r + \left(Cr^2 + Dr^4 + \frac{E}{r^2} + F\right)\cos 2\theta$$

and the corresponding stress components, from Eqs. (6.38), are

$$\sigma_r = 2A + \frac{B}{r^2} - \left(2C + \frac{6E}{r^4} + \frac{4F}{r^2}\right)\cos 2\theta$$

$$\sigma_\theta = 2A - \frac{B}{r^2} + \left(2C + 12Dr^2 + \frac{6E}{r^4}\right)\cos 2\theta \qquad (9.2)$$

$$\tau_{r\theta} = \left(2C + 6Dr^2 - \frac{6E}{r^4} - \frac{2F}{r^2}\right)\sin 2\theta$$

The constants of integration are now to be determined from the boundary conditions. At $r = a$, $\sigma_r = 0$, so that we have

$$2A + \frac{B}{a^2} = 0$$

$$2C + \frac{6E}{a^4} + \frac{4F}{a^2} = 0$$

The other boundary conditions in Eqs. (9.1) give

$$2C + 6Da^2 - \frac{6E}{a^4} - \frac{2F}{a^2} = 0$$

$$2A + 2C = 0$$

$$-4C = \sigma_{aG}$$

$$D = 0$$

Solving these equations, we have

$$A = \frac{\sigma_{aG}}{4}$$

$$B = -\frac{a^2}{2}\sigma_{aG}$$

$$C = -\frac{\sigma_{aG}}{4}$$

$$D = 0$$

$$E = -\frac{a^4}{4}\sigma_{aG}$$

$$F = \frac{a^2}{2}\sigma_{aG}$$

Substituting these values of constants into Eqs. (9.2), we obtain the following generalized plane solution for a thin plate of infinite width with a hole under tension:[†]

$$\sigma_r = \frac{\sigma_{aG}}{2}\left(1 - \frac{a^2}{r^2}\right) + \frac{\sigma_{aG}}{2}\left(1 - \frac{4a^2}{r^2} + \frac{3a^4}{r^4}\right)\cos 2\theta$$

$$\sigma_\theta = \frac{\sigma_{aG}}{2}\left(1 + \frac{a^2}{r^2}\right) - \frac{\sigma_{aG}}{2}\left(1 + \frac{3a^4}{r^4}\right)\cos 2\theta \qquad (9.3)$$

$$\tau_{r\theta} = -\frac{\sigma_{aG}}{2}\left(1 + \frac{2a^2}{r^2} - \frac{3a^4}{r^4}\right)\sin 2\theta$$

The stresses in the third direction of this generalized plane-stress solution are taken from Eq. (6.28),

$$\sigma_z = \tau_{zx} = \tau_{zy} = 0$$

Here the body is multiply connected, but the resultant of the loads on the exterior boundary of the plate vanishes. Hence the compatibility equation assures a continuous displacement field, and the above is the correct generalized plane-stress condition.

At the edge of the hole, $r = a$, and we have

$$\sigma_\theta = \sigma_{aG}(1 - 2\cos 2\theta) \qquad \sigma_r = \tau_{r\theta} = 0$$

At $\theta = \pi/2$ or $3\pi/2$, we have $\sigma_\theta = 3\sigma_{aG}$, three times the uniform stress applied at the ends of the plate. At $\theta = 0$ or π, we have $\sigma_\theta = -\sigma_{aG}$, a compressive stress equal in magnitude to the applied tensile stress.

[†]This solution was due to G. Kirsch; see *Z. Ver. deut. Ing.*, vol. 42, 1898.

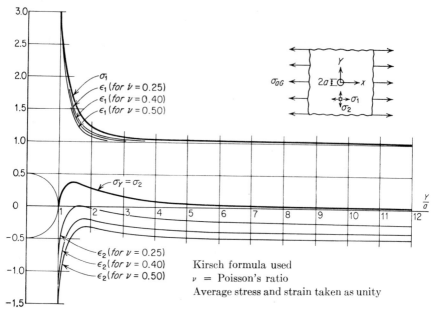

FIG. 9.2. Distribution of stresses and strains on the transversal axis of an infinite plate with a circular hole under a unidimensional load.

For the cross section of the plate through the center of the hole and perpendicular to the x axis, $\theta = \pi/2$, and we have

$$\sigma_\theta = \frac{\sigma_{aG}}{2} \left(2 + \frac{a^2}{r^2} + \frac{3a^4}{r^4} \right) \qquad (9.4)$$

For any values of r large compared with a, the last two terms in Eq. (9.4) become small compared with the first term and $\sigma_\theta = \sigma_{aG}$. The disturbance on the hole is therefore of a localized character. The stress distribution on the transversal axis and at the circular boundary, as well as the isostatics, isoclinics, isotenics, and isobars in the whole field, are shown in Figs. 9.2 to 9.10. Both stresses and strains are presented in dimensionless form.

9.2. Stress Concentration around a Circular Hole in an Infinite Plate of Arbitrary Thickness. For a plate of arbitrary thickness, the primary plane-stress or plane-strain solution must be superimposed on the solution of the corresponding residual problem to obtain the true solution. The residual problem for the case of an infinite plate with a circular hole has been treated by Sternberg and Sadowsky.† Their results indicate that,

† E. Sternberg and M. Sadowsky, Three-dimensional Solution for the Stress Concentration around a Circular Hole in a Plate of Arbitrary Thickness, *J. Appl. Mechanics,* vol. 16, pp. 27–38, March, 1949.

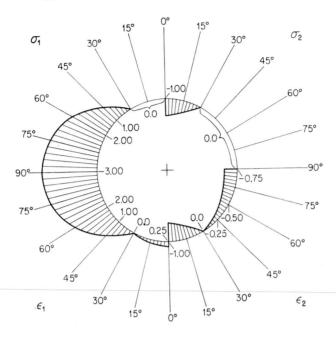

FIG. 9.3. Distribution of stresses and strains at the circular boundary of an infinite plate, with a circular hole, under a unidimensional load. (Kirsch's solution.) $\nu = 0.25$.

under a uniaxial load, the tangential stress σ_θ at the root of the hole is still the maximum stress (Fig. 9.11). However, this σ_θ is not constant along the thickness of the plate. Its value at or near the two end faces of the plate is slightly less than three times the intensity of the load σ_{aG}. Its value in the interior of the plate is slightly more than three times the load. Regardless of the thickness ratio t/D, the values of the largest and smallest σ_θ are never more than 103 per cent or less than 90 per cent of the value, three times the load, given by Kirsch's solution. In engineering applications the stress-concentration factor of 3 can therefore be assumed to be valid for plates of any thickness.

9.3. Elastic Solution of a Thin Plate of Finite Width with a Circular Hole under Unidimensional Load. Figure 9.12 shows a thin plate of infinite length but of finite width W, with a circular hole of diameter $D = 2a$ at its center. The plate is submitted to a uniform tension of magnitude σ_{aG} in the direction of its length. As in the preceding example, this problem is also a plane problem and is solved if we can find a certain Airy's stress function ϕ which satisfies Eq. (6.39) and whose stresses as computed from Eqs. (6.38) satisfy these boundary conditions:

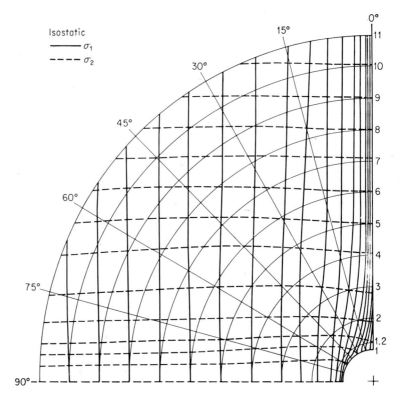

Fig. 9.4. Isostatics in an infinite plate with a circular hole, under a unidimensional load. (Kirsch's solution.)

$$\sigma_r = \tau_{r\theta} = 0 \qquad\qquad \text{at } r = a$$

$$\sigma_r = \sigma_{aG} \qquad \sigma_y = \tau_{xy} = 0 \qquad \text{at } x = \infty$$

$$\sigma_y = \tau_{xy} = 0 \qquad\qquad \text{at } y = \pm W/2$$

Despite a great deal of guessing and reguessing, no stress function composed of a finite number of elementary functions has been found to satisfy the above conditions. The alternative is then to search for a satisfactory stress function composed of an infinite number of elementary functions, i.e., a stress function in the form of an infinite series. To do this, the method of successive corrections will be used. In this method, a function satisfying Eq. (6.39) is chosen which gives stresses satisfying the boundary conditions at one portion of the boundary, say, boundary A, and violating the boundary conditions at the rest of the boundary, say, boundary B. A second function satisfying Eq. (6.39) is then introduced which gives stresses that will correct the discrepancy at boundary B.

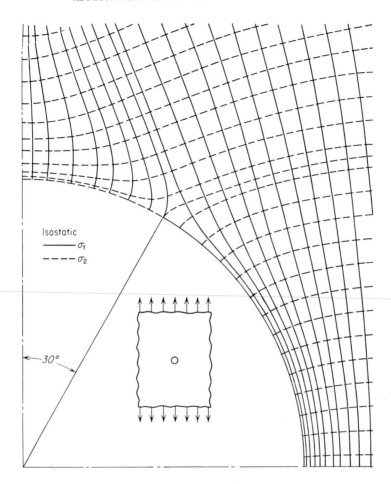

Fig. 9.5. Isostatics around a circular hole in an infinite plate under a unidimensional uniformly distributed load—detail. (Kirsch's solution.)

This second function, however, gives stresses that will disturb the already satisfied conditions at boundary A. This disturbance is removed by introducing a third function satisfying Eq. (6.39). The conditions at boundary B are now again violated through the presence of the stresses given by this third function. A fourth function is introduced to correct this discrepancy, and so on. By properly choosing these series of functions, it is sometimes possible to make the magnitudes of the discrepancies grow smaller and smaller, approaching zero as a limit. In this way, an Airy's stress function in the form of an infinite series is obtained which satisfies Eq. (6.39) and all the boundary conditions. Obviously the stresses ob-

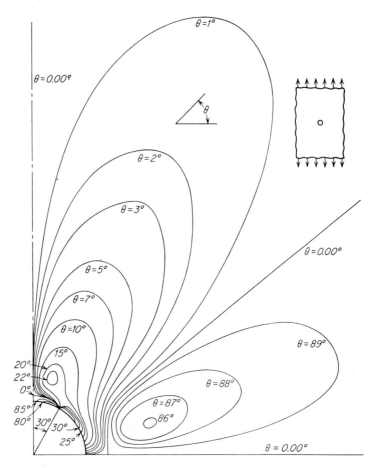

Fig. 9.6. Isoclinics around a circular hole in an infinite plate under a uniaxial uniformly distributed load. (Kirsch's solution.) A photograph of the zero inoclinic is shown in Fig. 8.5.

tained from this Airy's function will also be in the form of an infinite series. Where the rate of convergence is fast, only a few terms in the series need be taken to attain the required degree of accuracy. By this method a solution of the above problem in the form of an infinite series was obtained by Howland.† The convergence of the series is slow for the cases where D/W, the ratio of the diameter of hole to the width of plate, is larger than one-half. Hence, the solution is useful only for the cases where $D/W \leq \frac{1}{2}$.

†R. C. J. Howland, On the Stresses in the Neighborhood of a Circular Hole in a Strip under Tension, *Trans. Roy. Soc. (London)*, vol. A229, pp. 49–86, 1929–1930.

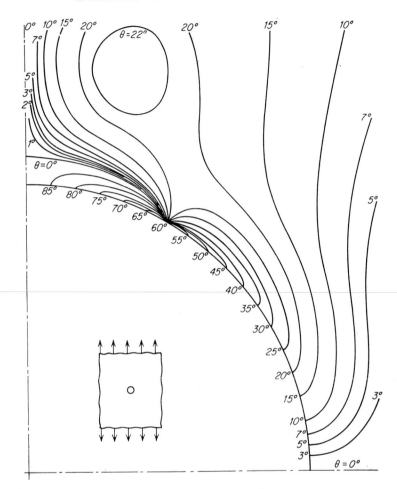

Fɪɢ. 9.7. Isoclinics around a circular hole in an infinite plate under a unidimensional load—detail. (Kirsch's solution.)

The distribution of stresses for the case of a plate having a width equal to twelve times the diameter of the hole is plotted and compared to Kirsch's solution for the infinite plate in Figs. 9.13 and 9.14.†

The graphs in Fig. 9.15 give a stress concentration factor at $r = a$, $\theta = \pi/2$, $3\pi/2$ for all values of D/W. The factors for D/W equal to or less than 0.5 were taken from Howland's paper, and the factors for D/W

†The application of Howland's approach to this particular plate geometry was conducted by E. Saleme (unpublished).

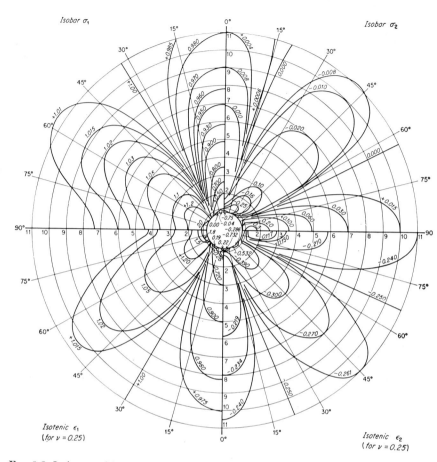

FIG. 9.8. Isobars and isotenics in a thin infinite plate with a circular hole, under a uni-dimensional load. (Kirsch's solution.)

larger than 0.5 were taken from the photoelastic results obtained by Wahl and Beeuwkes.†

9.4. Elastic Solution of a Semi-infinite Plate Acted Upon by a Concentrated Load. *a. Load Normal to the Plate Edge.* The elasticity problem of a concentrated load acting normal to the edge of a thin plate of large expanse will next be considered. The problem is illustrated in Fig. 9.16; and, in accordance with the plane problem as defined in Sec. 6.1, the load is assumed to be a line load uniformly distributed across the thickness t (i.e., invariant with respect to z). The symbol F will be used to denote the intensity of the load in, say, pounds per unit thickness. It is convenient

†A. M. Wahl and R. Beeuwkes, Stress Concentration Produced by Holes and Notches, *Trans. ASME*, pp. 617–623, August, 1934.

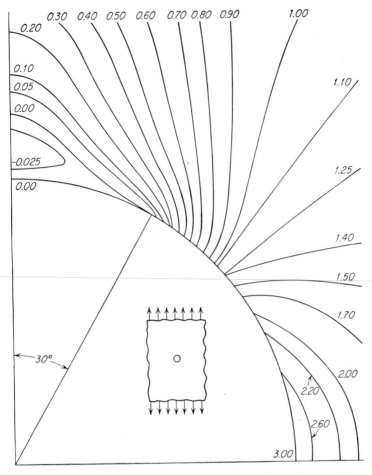

FIG. 9.9. Isobars σ_1 around a circular hole in an infinite plate under a unidimensional load—detail. (Kirsch's solution.)

again to use polar coordinates, and both these and the rectangular coordinates of a general point P in the plate are shown.

A generalized plane-stress solution is sought here, and hence the problem is reduced to that of finding a stress function ϕ which satisfies Eq. (6.39) and whose corresponding stresses are computed from Eqs. (6.38). As it is not within the scope of this text to illustrate how one might be logically motivated toward the solution of these elasticity problems, the inverse approach is again used here, i.e., a ϕ function will be merely stated, and then it will be shown that it generates the correct stress field.

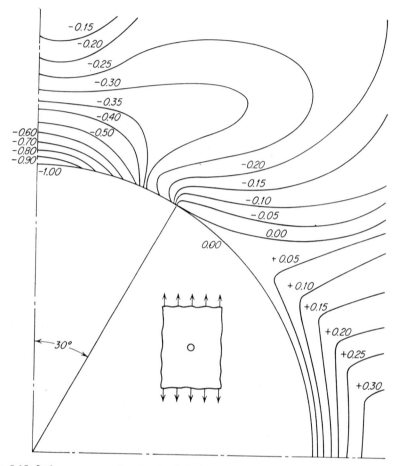

FIG. 9.10. Isobars σ_2, around a circular hole in an infinite plate under a unidimensional load—detail. (Kirsch's solution.)

The boundary conditions are

$$\sigma_\theta = \tau_{r\theta} = 0 \qquad \text{at } \theta = 0, \pi \ (r > 0)$$

$$\sigma_r = \sigma_\theta = \tau_{r\theta} = 0 \qquad \text{at } r = \infty$$

(9.5a)

To express the load F mathematically as a boundary condition on the stresses, consider any semicircle of radius r with center at the origin. If this is removed from the plate and considered as a free body, the resultant of the stresses acting on its cut boundary must be a force of magni-

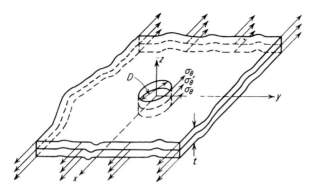

Fig. 9.11. Infinite plate with a circular hole, under uniaxial load. The maximum stress at the top face and the bottom face of the plate, σ_θ, is less than the maximum stress in the interior of the plate, σ_θ'.

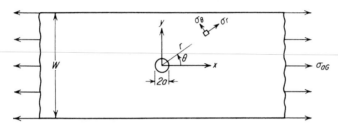

Fig. 9.12. Thin finite plate with a circular hole, under unidimensional load.

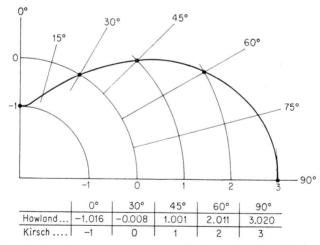

	0°	30°	45°	60°	90°
Howland...	−1.016	−0.008	1.001	2.011	3.020
Kirsch	−1	0	1	2	3

Fig. 9.13. Distribution of tangential stress at the boundary of a circular hole in a plate under a unidimensional uniformly distributed load. Howland's solution for the finite plate (width of plate equals twelve times diameter of hole) shown in solid curve. Kirsch's solution for the infinite plate shown in dots.

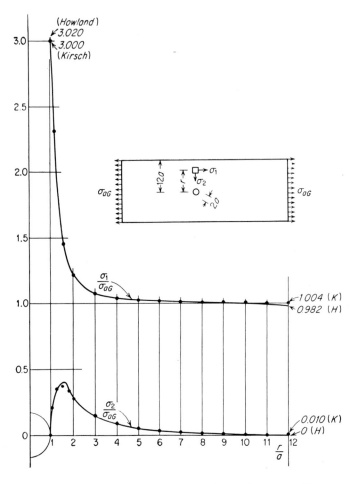

Fig. 9.14. Distribution of stress on the transversal axis of a plate with a circular hole, under a unidimensional uniformly distributed load. Howland's solution for the finite plate (width of plate equals twelve times diameter of hole) shown in solid curve. Kirsch's solution for the infinite plate shown in dots.

tude F acting in the negative y direction along the y axis. This is expressed by saying that, for all values of $r > 0$,

$$\int_0^\pi p_{ny} r \, d\theta = -F \qquad \int_0^\pi p_{nx} r \, d\theta = 0$$

These become, using Eqs. (1.5) and (6.31),

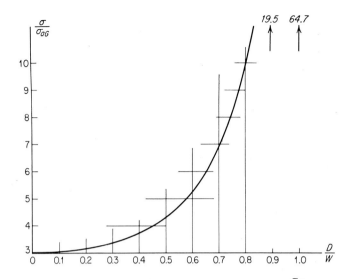

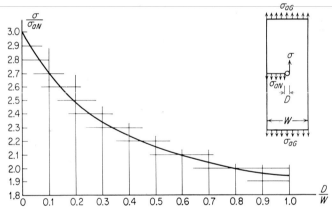

Fig. 9.15. Stress-concentration factors for a finite plate with circular hole, under a unidimensional uniformly distributed load. (Howland and Wahl-Beeuwkes results.)

$$\int_0^\pi (\sigma_r \sin\theta + \tau_{r\theta} \cos\theta) r \, d\theta = -F$$

$$(9.5b)$$

$$\int_0^\pi (\sigma_r \cos\theta - \tau_{r\theta} \sin\theta) r \, d\theta = 0$$

The condition of equilibrum of this semicircle with respect to moments is clearly satisfied because of the symmetry about the y axis.

Now consider the stress function,

$$\phi = \frac{F}{\pi} r\theta \cos\theta \qquad (9.6)$$

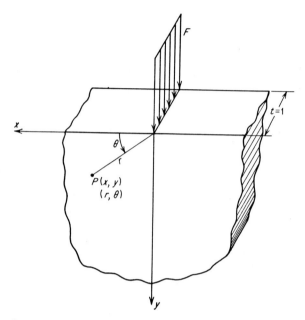

Fig. 9.16. Concentrated normal load acting on the edge of a semi-infinite plate.

It can be verified by substitution that this satisfies Eq. (6.39). There-fore, this does represent a stress field that satisfies equilibrium and com-patibility, and it remains only to be shown that the boundary conditions (9.5) are satisfied. By Eqs. (6.38), the stresses are found to be

$$\sigma_r = -\frac{2F}{\pi} \frac{\sin \theta}{r}$$

$$\sigma_\theta = \tau_{r\theta} = 0$$

(9.7)

These clearly satisfy the boundary conditions (9.5a). The boundary conditions (9.5b), are also satisfied, for

$$\int_0^\pi -\frac{2F}{\pi} \frac{\sin^2 \theta}{r} r \, d\theta = -\frac{2F}{\pi} \int_0^\pi \sin^2 \theta \, d\theta = -F$$

$$\int_0^\pi -\frac{2F}{\pi} \frac{\sin \theta \cos \theta}{r} r \, d\theta = 0$$

Hence the solution (9.7) is the required one.

Using Eqs. (6.31), it is possible to determine the cartesian components of stress from the components in polar coordinates as given by Eqs. (9.7). The calculation gives

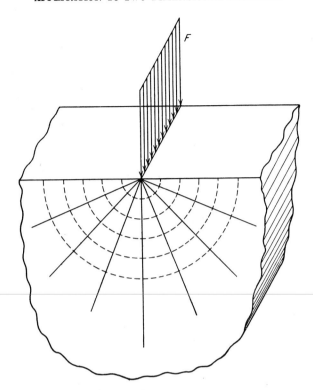

Fig. 9.17. Stress distribution in a semi-infinite plate subjected to a concentrated normal load. Isostatics. The solid lines represent the σ_r (or σ_2) family, and the broken lines represent the σ_θ (or σ_1) family. Compare this with the experimentally determined isostatics in Fig. 9.18.

$$\sigma_x = -\frac{2F}{\pi} \frac{x^2 y}{(x^2 + y^2)^2}$$

$$\sigma_y = -\frac{2F}{\pi} \frac{y^3}{(x^2 + y^2)^2} \tag{9.8}$$

$$\tau_{xy} = -\frac{2F}{\pi} \frac{xy^2}{(x^2 + y^2)^2}$$

These stresses become infinite as r approaches zero, but this sort of discontinuity is to be expected because the load has been mathematically supposed to be acting over an infinitely small area at the origin. If strains and displacements were calculated from these stresses, it would be seen that they also would become infinite as the origin is approached. But large displacements are not tolerated in linear elasticity theory (cf. Sec. 2.4); so the solution obtained here is not valid in the immediate neighbor-

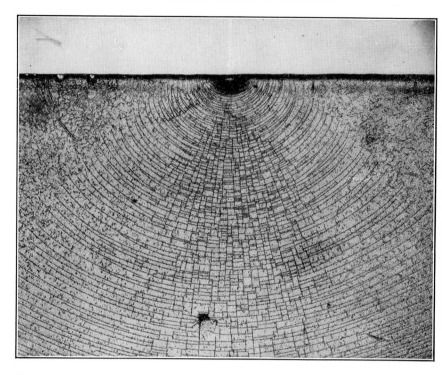

Fig. 9.18. Stress distribution in a rectangular plate subjected to a concentrated normal load. The isostatics have been obtained on a 3-in. by 1-in. by 0.25-in. bakelite plate by means of a brittle coating. The load was applied by means of a $\frac{5}{16}$ in.-diameter steel cylinder. Compare this with the theoretically determined isostatics in Fig. 9.17.

hood of the point of application of the load. In this neighborhood, a more detailed analysis is required which takes into account the geometry and elasticity of the object producing the load F.†

Referring back to Eqs. (9.7), it is observed that, since the shear stress $\tau_{r\theta}$ is zero, the stresses σ_r and σ_θ are principal, the former acting in the radial direction and the latter acting in the tangential direction. It follows that the isostatics, or principal stress trajectories, consist of the radial lines $\theta = $ const and the semicircles $r = $ const. These are shown in Fig. 9.17. They have also been experimentally determined using the brittle-coating technique (Fig. 9.18).

Recalling that isochromatics are loci of points of equal maximum shear

†Elasticity problems of this type have been solved by H. Herz and others. See S. Timoshenko and J. N. Goodier, "Theory of Elasticity," 2d ed., pp. 372ff., McGraw-Hill Book Company, Inc., New York, 1951.

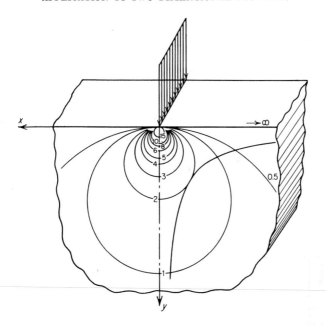

FIG. 9.19. Stress distribution in a semi-infinite plate subjected to a concentrated normal load. Since one of the principal stresses σ_θ is always zero, these lines are at the same time isochromatics, isobars, and isopachics. The figure shows also the values of σ_r along the axis.

(Sec. 8.5), the equation of the family of isochromatics corresponding to the stress field for this problem will be derived from Eqs. (9.7).

The maximum shear stress at any point was shown by Eqs. (3.13) to be equal to one-half the difference of the maximum and minimum principal stresses at the point. The principal stresses are given directly by Eqs. (9.7), and hence†

$$\tau_{max} = \frac{\sigma_r - \sigma_\theta}{2} = \frac{F}{\pi} \frac{\sin \theta}{r}$$

This is the maximum shear stress acting in the xy plane. A shear stress which is just as large acts at 45° to the xy plane, namely, $\tau = (\sigma_r - \sigma_z)/2$, but this is of no concern with regard to isochromatics in a plane-stress field such as this.

In terms of cartesian coordinates, the above becomes

$$\tau_{max} = \frac{F}{\pi} \frac{y}{x^2 + y^2}$$

†The plus or minus sign is immaterial.

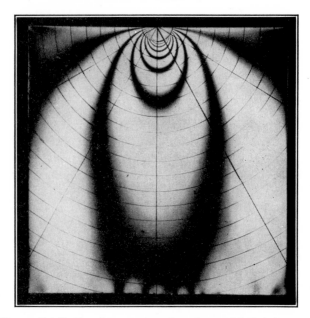

Fig. 9.20a. Stress distribution in a rectangular plate subjected to a concentrated normal load. These isochromatics were obtained photoelastically in a CR-39 model loaded by means of a steel cylinder. Compare this with the isochromatics theoretically determined in Fig. 9.19.

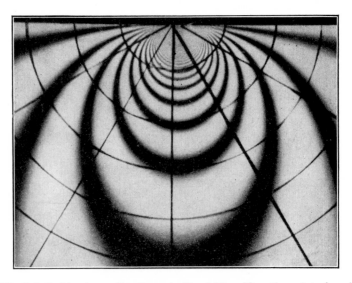

Fig. 9.20b. Detail of isochromatics shown in Fig. 9.20a. Near the point of application of the concentrated load the isochromatics take the shape of circles, tangent to the boundary at that point, as predicted theoretically in Fig. 9.19.

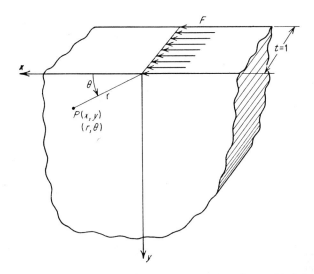

Fɪɢ. 9.21. Concentrated shear load acting on the edge of a semi-infinite plate.

and, after a little algebraic manipulation, it can be transformed to the equation of a family of circles,

$$x^2 + \left(y - \frac{F}{2\pi\tau_{\max}} \right)^2 = \left(\frac{F}{2\pi\tau_{\max}} \right)^2 \tag{9.9}$$

These are shown in Fig. 9.19. Along each curve of the family, $\tau_{\max}$ has the same value. The same family of isochromatics obtained experimentally is shown in Fig. 9.20. Here they are circular near the load but become elongated owing to the presence of the vertical free boundaries.

Since $\sigma_\theta = 0$, the stress σ_r will have the same value along any one of these curves; hence Eq. (9.9) also represents the family of isobars (see Sec. 8.7) and of isopachics (see Sec. 8.6).

b. Load Parallel to the Plate Edge. When a concentrated shear load acts parallel to the plate edge, say, in the positive x direction as illustrated in Fig. 9.21, the stress function has the form

$$\phi = -\frac{F}{\pi} r\theta \sin \theta \tag{9.10}$$

This can again be verified to be a solution of Eq. (6.39); and the stresses, by Eqs. (6.38), are

$$\sigma_r = -\frac{2F}{\pi} \frac{\cos \theta}{r} \tag{9.11}$$

$$\sigma_\theta = \tau_{r\theta} = 0$$

or, in cartesian coordinates, using the transformation equations (6.31)

$$\sigma_x = -\frac{2F}{\pi} \frac{x^3}{(x^2 + y^2)^2}$$

$$\sigma_y = -\frac{2F}{\pi} \frac{xy^2}{(x^2 + y^2)^2} \qquad (9.12)$$

$$\tau_{xy} = -\frac{2F}{\pi} \frac{x^2 y}{(x^2 + y^2)^2}$$

The boundary conditions for this problem take the form:

$$\sigma_\theta = \tau_{r\theta} = 0 \qquad \text{at } \theta = 0, \pi \quad (r > 0)$$

$$\sigma_r = \sigma_\theta = \tau_{r\theta} = 0 \qquad \text{at } r = \infty$$

$$\left. \int_0^\pi p_{ny} r \, d\theta = 0 \qquad \int_0^\pi p_{nx} r \, d\theta = -F \atop \int_0^\pi \tau_{r\theta} r \, r \, d\theta = 0 \right\} (r > 0) \qquad (9.13a)$$

The last three equations again express the equilibrium of a semicircular free body with center at the origin. The very last equation states that the moment of the forces acting on the free body is zero about the origin. Converting these to terms of polar-stress components by Eqs. (1.5) and (6.31),

$$\int_0^\pi (\sigma_r \sin \theta + \tau_{r\theta} \cos \theta) r \, d\theta = 0$$

$$\int_0^\pi (\sigma_r \cos \theta - \tau_{r\theta} \sin \theta) r \, d\theta = -F \qquad (9.13b)$$

$$\int_0^\pi \tau_{r\theta} r^2 \, d\theta = 0$$

The stress field [Eqs. (9.11)] clearly satisfies the boundary conditions (9.13a). Substituting this stress field into the conditions (9.13b),

$$\int_0^\pi -\frac{2F}{\pi} \frac{\cos \theta \sin \theta}{r} r \, d\theta = 0$$

$$\int_0^\pi -\frac{2F}{\pi} \frac{\cos^2 \theta}{r} r \, d\theta = -\frac{2F}{\pi} \int_0^\pi \cos^2 \theta \, d\theta = -F$$

$$\int_0^\pi \tau_{r\theta} r^2 \, d\theta = 0$$

and these are therefore also satisfied.

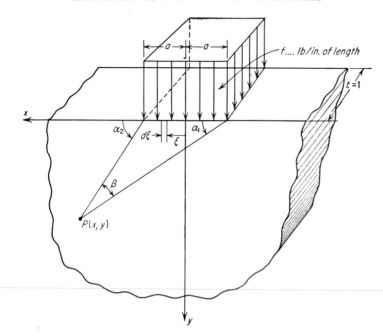

Fig. 9.22. Uniform-normal-load distribution acting on the edge of a semi-infinite plate.

9.5. Elastic Solution of a Semi-infinite Plate Acted Upon by a Distributed Load along Its Edge. *a. Normal Load Uniformly Distributed over a Finite Portion of the Plate Edge.* The solution for the case of any load distribution along the edge of a semi-infinite plate can be obtained using the results of Sec. 9.4 for the concentrated normal and shear loads. The method of doing this will be illustrated here for the case of a uniform normal-load distribution acting over a finite length as pictured in Fig. 9.22.

For the small concentrated normal load $f\, d\xi$ acting at $x = \xi$, the solution (9.8) previously obtained gives the stress field

$$d\sigma_x = -\frac{2f\, d\xi}{\pi}\frac{(x - \xi)^2 y}{[(x - \xi)^2 + y^2]^2}$$

$$d\sigma_y = -\frac{2f\, d\xi}{\pi}\frac{y^3}{[(x - \xi)^2 + y^2]^2}$$

$$d\tau_{xy} = -\frac{2f\, d\xi}{\pi}\frac{(x - \xi)y^2}{[(x - \xi)^2 + y^2]^2}$$

By the principle of superposition, the stress field corresponding to the entire load distribution from $x = -a$ to $+a$ is obtained by summing these incremental stress fields over the entire interval; thus

$$\sigma_x = -\frac{2f}{\pi} \int_{-a}^{a} \frac{(x - \xi)^2 y}{[(x - \xi)^2 + y^2]^2} \, d\xi$$

$$\sigma_y = -\frac{2f}{\pi} \int_{-a}^{a} \frac{y^3}{[(x - \xi)^2 + y^2]^2} \, d\xi$$

$$\tau_{xy} = -\frac{2f}{\pi} \int_{-a}^{a} \frac{(x - \xi)y^2}{[(x - \xi)^2 + y^2]^2} \, d\xi$$

Carrying out the integration, the desired solution for the stresses is found.

$$\sigma_x = -\frac{f}{\pi} \left\{ \arctan \frac{y}{x - a} - \arctan \frac{y}{x + a} \right.$$

$$\left. + \frac{2ay(x^2 - y^2 - a^2)}{[(x + a)^2 + y^2][(x - a)^2 + y^2]} \right\}$$

$$\sigma_y = -\frac{f}{\pi} \left\{ \arctan \frac{y}{x - a} - \arctan \frac{y}{x + a} \right. \qquad (9.14)$$

$$\left. - \frac{2ay(x^2 - y^2 - a^2)}{[(x + a)^2 + y^2][(x - a)^2 + y^2]} \right\}$$

$$\tau_{xy} = -\frac{f}{\pi} \frac{4axy^2}{[(x + a)^2 + y^2][(x - a)^2 + y^2]}$$

Some algebraic manipulation will show that these stresses can also be represented in the following form,

$$\sigma_x = -\frac{f}{\pi} \left[\alpha_2 - \alpha_1 + \frac{1}{2} (\sin 2\alpha_2 - \sin 2\alpha_1) \right]$$

$$\sigma_y = -\frac{f}{\pi} \left[\alpha_2 - \alpha_1 - \frac{1}{2} (\sin 2\alpha_2 - \sin 2\alpha_1) \right] \qquad (9.15)$$

$$\tau_{xy} = +\frac{f}{2\pi} (\cos 2\alpha_2 - \cos 2\alpha_1)$$

where α_1 and α_2 are the angles shown in Fig. 9.22.

It is interesting to note that directly under the load and along the edge, where $\alpha_1 = 0$ and $\alpha_2 = \pi$, the stresses, from Eqs. (9.15), are $\sigma_x = \sigma_y = -f$, $\tau_{xy} = 0$. Along the unloaded portions of the edge, all three stress components are zero. There is thus a finite jump in the stresses σ_x and σ_y along the corners of the loading zone.

It is easy to obtain an equation from which the isostatics may be drawn. This is done by substituting the stress field [Eqs. (9.15)] into Eq. (7.15), which gives the tangent of twice the angle, θ_P, that one of the principal

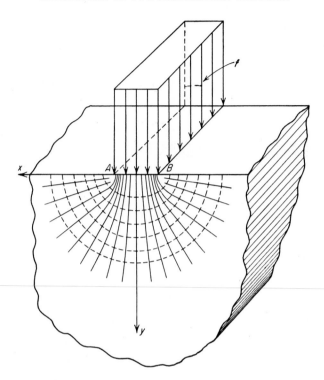

Fig. 9.23. Stress distribution in a semi-infinite plate subjected to a uniform normal load on the edge. Isostatics. The solid lines represent the σ_2 family and the dotted lines represent the σ_1 family.

directions makes with the x axis. The result is

$$\tan 2\theta_P = \frac{\cos 2\alpha_2 - \cos 2\alpha_1}{\sin 2\alpha_2 - \sin 2\alpha_1} \tag{9.16}$$

The isostatics are shown in Fig. 9.23. The method of plotting these curves from Eq. (9.16) is to construct a direction field by drawing at each point $P(\alpha_1,\alpha_2)$ two small perpendicular line segments inclined at the angles θ_P and $\theta_P + 90°$ from the x axis as given by the above equation. These represent the principal directions at each point, and the isostatics can then be sketched in by drawing curves tangent everywhere to these line segments. An experimental brittle-coating test exhibiting one of these families of isostatics is shown in Fig. 9.24.

The principal stresses can be expressed in a simple form by introducing the angle $\beta = \alpha_2 - \alpha_1$. This is seen to be the angle subtending the two rays extending from the point $P(x,y)$ to the corners of the loading zone (Fig. 9.22). Substituting Eqs. (9.15) into Eq. (7.14) and writing the

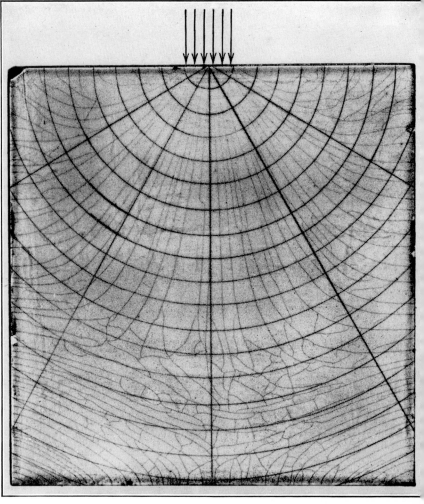

Fig. 9.24. Stress distribution on a square plate subjected to a uniform normal load on the edge. Isostatics experimentally determined using a brittle coating.

results in terms of β, the principal stresses are found, after some algebra, to be

$$\sigma_1, \sigma_2 = -\frac{f}{\pi}(\beta \mp \sin \beta) \qquad (9.17)$$

The sum of the two principal stresses at every point is thus

$$\sigma_1 + \sigma_2 = -\frac{2f}{\pi}\beta \qquad (9.18)$$

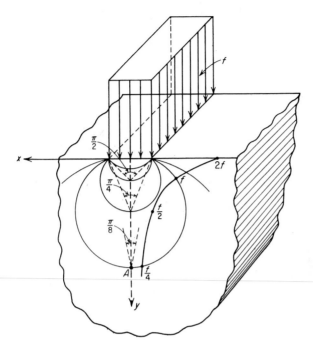

Fɪɢ. 9.25. Stress distribution in a semi-infinite plate subjected to a uniform normal load on the edge. Isopachics and values of the sum of the principal stress along the y axis.

and their difference is

$$\sigma_1 - \sigma_2 = \frac{2f}{\pi} \sin \beta \tag{9.19}$$

Loci of points at which the sum of the principal stresses are equal (i.e., isopachics) are shown in Fig. 9.25. At all points on any one of these curves, the angle β has the constant value $\beta = -(\pi/2f)(\sigma_1 + \sigma_2)$. Corresponding to the circle passing through point A, it has the value $\pi/8$ as indicated, and thus

$$\sigma_1 + \sigma_2 = -\frac{2f}{\pi}\left(\frac{\pi}{8}\right) = -\frac{f}{4}$$

at all points on this circle.

Figures 9.26 shows the isochromatics of the stress field as obtained from Eq. (9.19). At all points on any one of these curves, the angle β has the constant value

$$\beta = \arcsin\left[\frac{2f}{\pi}(\sigma_1 - \sigma_2)\right]$$

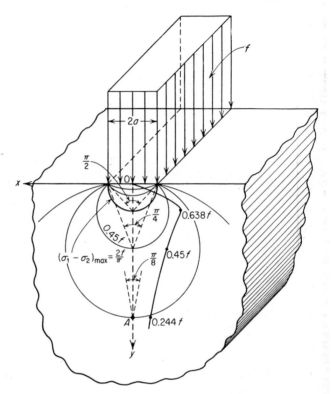

FIG. 9.26. Stress distribution in a semi-infinite plate subjected to a uniform normal load on the edge. Isochromatics. These are the loci of points at which the difference of the principal stresses is constant. Compare this with the photoelastically determined isochromatics in Fig. 9.27.

Again, corresponding to the circle passing through point A, it has the value $\pi/8$; and $\sigma_1 - \sigma_2 = (2f/\pi) \sin (\pi/8) = 0.244f$ is the parameter of the isochromatic circle passing through A.

The results of a photoelastic test of a bakelite model loaded in a manner which simulates the loading of this case very closely is given in Fig. 9.27.

Finally, the isobars σ_1 and σ_2 are plotted in Fig. 9.28. Using Eq. (9.17), the values of σ_1 and σ_2 on the circular isobar passing through point A are

$$\sigma_1, \sigma_2 = -\frac{f}{\pi} \left(\frac{\pi}{8} \mp \sin \frac{\pi}{8} \right) = -0.003f \text{ and } -0.247f$$

respectively.

b. Shear Load Uniformly Distributed over a Finite Portion of the Plate Edge. This case is depicted in Fig. 9.29. An approach, analogous to that used above for the uniform normal load, can be used here. The resulting stress field is given by

$$\sigma_x = -\frac{f}{\pi}\left\{\ln\frac{(x+a)^2+y^2}{(x-a)^2+y^2} - \frac{4axy^2}{[(x+a)^2+y^2][(x-a)^2+y^2]}\right\}$$

$$\sigma_y = -\frac{f}{\pi}\left\{\frac{4axy^2}{[(x+a)^2+y^2][(x-a)^2+y^2]}\right\}$$
(9.20)

$$\tau_{xy} = -\frac{f}{\pi}\left\{\arctan\frac{y}{x-a} - \arctan\frac{y}{x+a}\right.$$

$$\left. + \frac{2ay(x^2-y^2-a^2)}{[(x+a)^2+y^2][(x-a)^2+y^2]}\right\}$$

Fig. 9.27. Isochromatics in a bakelite model (3.94 in. by 7.98 in.) loaded on a small zone of the boundary. The ratio of the loaded zone to the total width is 0.05. Compare this photoelastic pattern with the theoretically determined loci of equal maximum shear in Fig. 9.26.

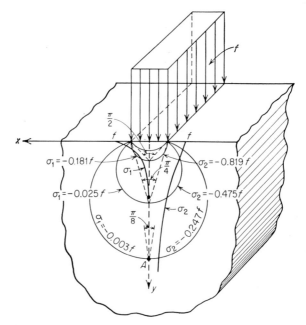

Fig. 9.28. Stress distribution in a semi-infinite plate subjected to a uniform normal load on the edge.   Isobars σ_1 and σ_2 and values of the principal stresses along the y axis.   Both are compression.

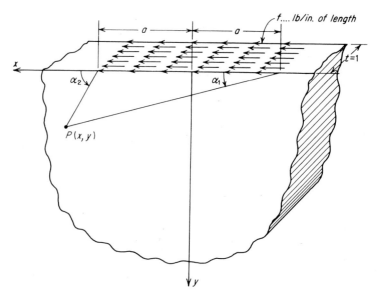

Fig. 9.29. Uniform-shear-load distribution acting on the edge of a semi-infinite plate.

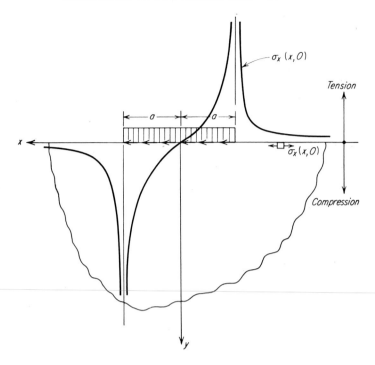

Fig. 9.30. Stress σ_x acting along edge of semi-infinite plate under uniform-shear-load distribution.

or in terms of the angles α_1 and α_2

$$\sigma_x = -\frac{f}{\pi}\left[2\ln\frac{\sin\alpha_2}{\sin\alpha_1} + \frac{1}{2}\left(\cos 2\alpha_2 - \cos 2\alpha_1\right)\right]$$

$$\sigma_y = +\frac{f}{2\pi}\left(\cos 2\alpha_2 - \cos 2\alpha_1\right) \tag{9.21}$$

$$\tau_{xy} = -\frac{f}{\pi}\left[\alpha_2 - \alpha_1 + \frac{1}{2}\left(\sin 2\alpha_2 - \sin 2\alpha_1\right)\right]$$

A plot of the stress $\sigma_x(x,0)$ is given in Fig. 9.30; and it is seen that this stress becomes infinite at the points where the shear abruptly begins and ends. The infinite tensile and compressive stresses parallel to the boundary will occur (theoretically) whenever there is a finite jump in the intensity of an applied shear load. Note that, as mentioned in Sec. 9.5a, this does not happen in the case of a finite jump in a distributed normal load.

9.6. Elastic Solution of a Long Thick-walled Cylinder Subjected to a Uniform Pressure on Inner and Outer Surfaces. The results developed in Sec. 6.12 will be used in the solution of this problem. If the geometry and loading of the cylinder are as shown in Fig. 9.31, the boundary conditions are

$$\sigma_r = -p \qquad \tau_{r\theta} = 0 \qquad \text{at } r = a$$
$$\sigma_r = -q \qquad \tau_{r\theta} = 0 \qquad \text{at } r = b \tag{9.22}$$

The stress function of ϕ^0 [see Eqs. (6.45)] will be shown to be the correct solution to the problem. The fact that ϕ^0 gives stresses which are independent of θ, just as the boundary stresses are, is a good indication that the function is the correct one.

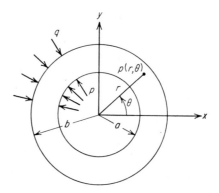

Fig. 9.31. Thick-walled cylinder with inner radius a and outer radius b subjected to the uniform pressures p and q on the inner and outer surfaces respectively.

By observing u_θ of Eqs. (6.45) it is evident that d_0 must vanish for u_θ to be single-valued for all θ. Hence the polar components of stress reduce to

$$\sigma_r = \frac{b_0}{r^2} + 2c_0$$

$$\sigma_\theta = -\frac{b_0}{r^2} + 2c_0 \tag{9.23}$$

$$\tau_{r\theta} = 0$$

The two constants b_0 and c_0 must be determined before the solution is obtained. Substituting Eqs. (9.22) into Eqs. (9.23) and solving for the constants,

$$b_0 = \frac{a^2 b^2 (q - p)}{b^2 - a^2}$$

$$c_0 = \frac{a^2 p - b^2 q}{2(b^2 - a^2)}$$

Substituting these values into Eqs. (9.23), the complete solution is

$$\sigma_r = \frac{(q - p)a^2b^2}{b^2 - a^2}\frac{1}{r^2} + \frac{pa^2 - qb^2}{b^2 - a^2}$$

$$\sigma_\theta = -\frac{(q - p)a^2b^2}{b^2 - a^2}\frac{1}{r^2} + \frac{pa^2 - qb^2}{b^2 - a^2} \quad (9.24)$$

$$\tau_{r\theta} = 0$$

It is interesting to note that $\sigma_r + \sigma_\theta = 2(pa^2 - qb^2)/(b^2 - a^2) = \text{const}$ at any point in the cylinder. Since $\epsilon_z = \nu(\sigma_r + \sigma_\theta)$, the cylinder will undergo a uniform extension or contraction in the direction of the axis of the cylinder and the cross sections perpendicular to the axis remain plane after deformation.

Consider a special case often encountered in practice where the external pressure is zero. In this instance Eqs. (9.24) reduce to

$$\sigma_r = \frac{a^2p}{b^2 - a^2}\left(1 - \frac{b^2}{r^2}\right)$$

$$\sigma_\theta = \frac{a^2p}{b^2 - a^2}\left(1 + \frac{b^2}{r^2}\right) \quad (9.25)$$

$$\tau_{r\theta} = 0$$

From Eqs. (3.13)

$$\tau_{\max} = \tfrac{1}{2}(\sigma_r - \sigma_\theta) = \frac{a^2b^2p}{b^2 - a^2}\frac{1}{r^2} \quad (9.26)$$

Recalling that the isochromatics are lines along which $\tau_{\max}$ is a constant, it is clear by Eq. (9.26) that the isochromatics for a section of a thick-walled cylinder are circular. This is shown in Fig. 9.32 where the photograph is that of an isochromatic pattern for a ring under internal pressure. Also shown in this figure is a comparison between the experimental and theoretical determination of $\tau_{\max}$ as a function of r.

From Eqs. (9.25) or Fig. 9.32 it is evident that σ_r is a compressive stress at $r = a$ and tends to zero as a increases to b. Further, σ_θ is a tensile stress at all points in the body and is a maximum at the inner boundary, where

$$\sigma_{\theta,\max} = p\frac{b^2 + a^2}{b^2 - a^2} \quad (9.27)$$

As b becomes very large, $\sigma_{\theta,\max}$ approaches p and it is evident that the results agree with the results from the solution of the problem of the circular hole in the infinite plate loaded under uniform pressure.

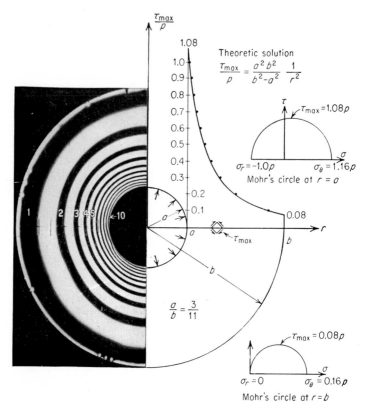

FIG. 9.32. Isochromatic pattern of a ring under a uniform internal pressure. The dots on the graph represent the maximum shear stresses along the radius calculated from isochromatics and the solid line represents the theoretic solution.

PART 2

INTRODUCTION TO THE USE
OF EXPERIMENTAL-STRESS-ANALYSIS METHODS

Three chapters have been assembled in this part, which are somewhat extraneous to the continuous development of a treatise on stress analysis. The three of them are developed independently from theory of elasticity and call on new concepts. They are indispensable however for the correct planning of experimental stress analyses and for the correct interpretation of the results obtained from these analyses.

In some books the presentation of this kind of material is relegated to appendixes. It is believed, however, that it is more logical to look at these new concepts as something which should be learned prior to going into the actual experimental stress analysis rather than something that should be consulted only by specialists. It seems to be in the nature of things that planning of tests and model similitude should be investigated before tests are conducted and models made.

It is also hoped that the effort to apply statistical concepts to mechanical problems will prove fruitful not only in the working out of stress analysis problems, but also in some other phases of applied mechanics.

CHAPTER 10

FUNDAMENTAL CONCEPTS IN STRAIN MEASUREMENTS

10.1. Introduction. It has been shown in the chapter dealing with the theory of stress that a state of stress at a point in a body is defined by the value of the three principal stresses and their directions at that point. Only in a very few instances is the state of stress the same at all points in a stressed body. In these cases, the state of stress is called uniform, or homogeneous. An example of the homogeneous state of stress is the central part of a tensile specimen or a column under axial compression. In general, the state of stress changes from point to point, and stress analysis is the method by which the state of stress at every point can be determined.

The determination of the state of stress at every point is also known as the determination of the stress distribution, in other words, the share of stresses taken by each point, or put a third way, the variation of stresses as a function of position in the body and as a function of direction at each position.

The objective of this determination may be only scientific, or fundamental, i.e., for the sake of knowledge. Or it may be applied to make machine parts and structures lighter and stronger by changing their shapes or by allowing the selection of materials better suited to withstand the kind of stresses determined by the analysis (tension or compression, steady or alternate, rate of application, etc.).

The analysis of the stresses can be conducted theoretically, using mathematics as a tool. Several chapters in the science of mechanics have been developed to follow this approach: the theory of elasticity, of structures, of vibrations, of plasticity, etc. In the first part of this book, an introduction has been presented to the theory of elasticity. The analysis of the stresses also can be conducted experimentally, taking advantage of some physical properties of materials that relate measured quantities to the state of stress. The following chapters of this book will deal with several experimental methods.

The oldest stress-analysis method was probably a simplified theoretical approach. Since the beginning, the theories of stresses and strains were developed by use of Hooke's relationship; therefore, it was logical that the first experimental-stress-analysis method would use the deformation of bodies as an indication of the stress. Rulers and mechanical strain gages were the first tools used to measure these deformations. Quite old, also, is the method of using rubber models to increase the elastic deformation and obtain a more accurate measurement of the deformations and, hence, of the distribution of stresses.

In the early nineteenth century, Navier and Lamé gave thought to the elastic equations, and Brewster established some of the fundamental facts in photoelasticity. For many years, however, the theoretical developments in stress-distribution determinations were far ahead of the experimental developments. When, in 1898, Kirsch solved theoretically the problem of the distribution of stresses around a circular hole in an infinite plate under a uniformly distributed load, the experimental techniques to measure strains were very crude and the knowledge of photoelasticity previously developed was all but forgotten. Soon, however, fundamental developments in experimental analyses were to change the field.

Mesnager in 1913 and Coker at about the same time made an engineering tool out of photoelasticity. Preuss in 1912 built extremely sensitive mechanical strain gages capable of determining elongations on very short base lengths (0.7 mm), and Leon in 1921 conducted quantitative determinations on rubber models. Experimental methods developed then at an increasing rate, and the question of which approach to follow to the solution of a stress-analysis problem first arose. However, the criteria of application of the methods at that time were simple and rather intuitive, since the field of application of each method (theory, mechanical gages, rubber models) was small; the number of possible applications was also small, and the possibilities of approaching the solution of a problem using more than one method were very few.

In the last twenty years, stress-analysis methods have grown in number; their field of application became considerably larger, and many instances of overlapping of these fields made necessary the development of criteria to decide what method to use in each particular case. Besides the three methods mentioned above, electrical strain gages became very popular, mainly those of the bonded-wire resistance type. Inductance and capacitance gages also came to be used in many cases. Acoustic strain gages and brittle coatings were developed at about the same time and found several applications, the former mainly in Europe, the latter mainly in the United States. In the meantime, the old mechanical strain gages were refined and combined with optical systems, attaining a great degree of precision. Recently the pneumatic strain gage was added to the list. Finally X rays were used by many investigators, relating the spacing between atoms to the state of stress.

At the time these experimental tools came to be well known and frequently used, new theoretical tools were developed, such as the iteration and relaxation methods, which are now widely employed. Several analogies between stress equations and the equations representing other physical phenomena were found, thereby allowing the use of new experimental techniques to find stresses.

In the chapters that will follow in the development of this book, criteria for the use of some of the most important methods of experimental stress analysis will be established, and an attempt will be made to evaluate their accuracy and their field of application. These criteria for the use of several methods are necessarily influenced by the experience and background of the persons using them. Thus, the considerations in this book cannot be taken as the only answers to the problem, but rather as guides when decisions have to be made. They are the result of the particular experience of several scientists and engineers working in stress analysis at the Armour Research Foundation.

10.2. Base Length. Before describing in detail the use of experimental-stress-analysis methods, some fundamental concepts should be explained and discussed. The first of these concepts is base length.

No experimental method can give the state of stress at a mathematical dimensionless point. The measurement of the physical property which is related to stress always takes place on a finite volume, and the computed stress is the average of the stresses in that volume. In most cases, one dimension predominates and is called the base length.

For mechanical strain gages, base length is the distance between the two knives, or needle tips, whose change in distance is related to the stress (Fig. 10.1a). For wire electrical-resistance strain gages, base length is the length of one of the loops of the wire whose change in ohmic resistance is related to stress (Fig. 10.1b and e), and, in X rays, it is the distance between atoms. In the grid method, base length is the distance between the lines of the grid (Fig. 10.1d), and, in magnetic strain gages, it is the distance between the supports of the two movable parts, as in Fig. 10.1f.

In photoelasticity, base length has a rather different meaning. In this case, it can be said that base length is the thickness of the plate through which the light passes (Fig. 10.1c). Some of the following considerations cannot be applied directly to this definition.

The shorter the base length, the more accurate will be the determination to the actual state of stress at a point, provided the instrument has enough sensitivity. A long base length of measurement may miss the peak of stress (Fig. 10.2). The larger the gradient of stresses, the shorter the base length should be. In uniform states of stresses, the base length of the

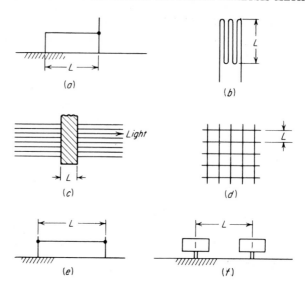

FIG. 10.1. Base length L is the distance over which the measurement is averaged. (a) Mechanical strain gage. (b) Wire electrical-resistance strain gage, bonded. (c) Photoelasticity. (d) Grids. (e) Acoustic strain gage and unbonded wire electrical-resistance strain gage. (f) Magnetic strain gage.

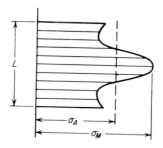

FIG. 10.2. A strain gage with base length L measures an average physical property related to the stress σ_A.

gage is immaterial except that the use of the longest allowable gage will increase the sensitivity and in some cases the precision of the measurement.

10.3. Deformation Sensitivity. The sensitivity of an instrument is defined as the smallest value of the measured quantity that can be read on the scale. Deformation sensitivity (DS) is the sensitivity of an instrument that measures changes in lengths. A good ruler, with 50 divisions to the inch, observed by the bare eye, has a sensitivity of about 0.01 in., since a trained bare eye can usually estimate one-half of the smallest division.

Most strain gages magnify the change in distance. The smallest reading on the scale d divided by the multiplication m of the instrument gives the smallest deformation the instrument can read, or deformation sensitivity.

$$DS = \frac{d}{m} \qquad (10.1)$$

In instruments using the bare eye to read the scale, d is of the order of hundredths of an inch.

Sensitivity should not be confused with reproducibility or with accuracy. Strain gages can be made very sensitive by increasing multiplication (for instance, the needle of a dial gage can be made much longer, or an extra gear could be introduced in the multiplying system without difficulty). However, friction, lost motion, inertia of parts, flexibility of parts, electronic noise, etc., become more and more influential as the magnification increases, and an extremely sensitive instrument may not be accurate.

10.4. Strain Sensitivity. When measured deformations are referred to the base length, i.e., converted to unit deformations (strain), the sensitivity of the measuring instrument is called the strain sensitivity (SS). Thus, the relationship between strain sensitivity and base length can be established. For example, if the base length is 1 in., the deformation sensitivity and the strain sensitivity are given by the same number. If the base length is not 1 in., the deformation sensitivity should be divided by the base length L to obtain the strain sensitivity.

$$SS = \frac{DS}{L} = \frac{d}{mL} \qquad (10.2)$$

The ruler mentioned above has a deformation sensitivity

$$DS = \frac{d}{m} = \frac{0.01}{1} = 0.01 \text{ in.}$$

If the base length over which the change in length is measured is 100 in., the smallest strain that can be read with the ruler is 0.0001, which is the strain sensitivity of the instrument, for this base length, i.e.,

$$SS = \frac{DS}{L} = \frac{0.01}{100} = 0.0001$$

The value 0.0001 may be a good strain sensitivity in the case of concrete or wood columns under axial loading. When gradients of stresses are present, more refined strain gages are necessary. The mechanical strain gage made by Huggenberger has a scale on which it is possible to read 0.01 in. The multiplication of the instrument, however, is about 1,200;

thus, this minimum possible scale reading corresponds to about 0.000008 in. of measured deformation. This is the deformation sensitivity of this strain gage. The distance between the knives of the instrument can be 0.5 in., 1 in., or longer. On a base length of 0.5 in., the strain sensitivity of the instrument is 0.000016; on a 10-in. base length, it is 0.0000008.

Table 10.1 gives the values of the strain sensitivity of several common strain gages for several base lengths. The reader should look at this table as a source of general information only to help him decide which of the several available strain gages may be the best suited to approach the solution of a specific problem. The necessary knowledge of the construction and use of these gages should be obtained from other chapters of this book or from other sources of information.

In bonded-wire electrical-resistance strain gages, the strain sensitivity is sometimes kept constant for different base lengths, because the total length of the wire (and its ohmic resistance) is kept constant by increasing the number of loops (Fig. 10.1b) as the base length decreases. The common instruments of this type, with electronic magnification, have a strain sensitivity of about 0.000005.

When failure is used as an index of stresses (for instance, in brittle coatings), strain sensitivity is defined as the minimum strain required to crack the material. In this case, the term "strain sensitivity" has a different meaning.

10.5. Reproducibility. The exact value of a quantity is well defined when theoretical tools are used. In that sense, we can say that the stress concentration produced by a circular hole in an infinite plate under a uniform loading is 3. Experimentally, no measurement obtained with a sensitive enough instrument reproduces itself when repeated a large enough number of times. The repetition of the measurement, however, allows estimates of the true value of the quantity and of the error in the determination.

Under certain conditions of constant temperature, humidity, speed of loading, etc., the measurements of some of the physical properties used in stress analysis, like birefringence or ohmic resistance, reproduce to very close values. The measurements of other properties, such as the load necessary to fracture a material, reproduce less closely.

10.6. Precision of Measurements. It can be shown that the most probable value of a quantity to be experimentally determined is the arithmetic mean $\bar{X}$ of many measurements X taken of that quantity.

$$\bar{X} = \sum X/N \qquad (10.3)$$

where N = number of measurements.

As the number of measurements increases, the arithmetic mean value

approaches the true value, and if the number of measurements is large
enough, this most probable value of the quantity can be called for practical
purposes the "true" value of that quantity. The differences between this
true value and the value of each measurement are called deviations and
are expressed by x.

$$x = X - \bar{X} \tag{10.4}$$

The degree of precision of an experimental determination can be judged
by the so-called estimate of the "standard deviation of a single observation," which is given by the formula

$$\sigma = \sqrt{\frac{\sum (X - \bar{X})^2}{N - 1}} \tag{10.5}$$

Another index of the precision is the "standard deviation of the mean,"
or "standard error of the mean," which is given by

$$\sigma_{\bar{X}} = \sqrt{\frac{\sum x^2}{N(N - 1)}} \tag{10.6}$$

The standard deviation of a single observation is often referred to the
arithmetic mean. The ratio of the two on a percentage basis is called the
coefficient of variation,

$$V = 100 \frac{\sigma}{\bar{X}} \tag{10.7}$$

The smaller the deviations from the mean and the larger the number of
the measurements, the smaller will be the coefficient of variation of a
determination and the higher the degree of precision.

The idea of precision therefore is related to the reproducibility of the
measurement of the physical quantity. For a determination of the degree
of precision of experimental stress analysis, the measurements should be
repeated several times and the results evaluated statistically, using some
indices such as those shown above. More will be said about the statistical
phases of indices of precision and of accuracy in the next chapter.

10.7. Accuracy. The accuracy of experimental-stress-analysis determinations often means the same as their degree of precision and can be
measured percentagewise by the coefficient of variation [Eq. (10.7)].

The accuracy of experimental measurements can also be expressed by
means of the "probable-error" concept. The probable error of a single
observation is given by

$$p = 0.6745\sigma = 0.6745 \sqrt{\frac{\sum x^2}{N - 1}} \tag{10.8}$$

TABLE 10.1. CHARACTERISTICS

Gage category	Type	Deformation-sensitivity, in.	Multiplication	Strain 1/16-in. base	1/8-in. base	1/4-in. base	1/2-in. base	1-in. base
	Photoelasticity (bakelite 61-893 in standard polariscope)	....	....	....	0.00002	0.00001	0.000005	....
	Brittle coating (Stresscoat)	....	....	....	....	....	....	0.0003
Mechanical	Micrometer Dial gage (0.0001)	0.0001	70	....	0.0008	0.0004	0.0002	0.0001
	(Standard Co.)	0.0001[b]	800	....	....	....	....	0.0001
	Ruler	0.01	1	....	....	....	....	0.01
	Huggenberger (type A)	0.000008	1,200	Not available			0.000016	0.000008
	Porter-Lipp	0.00003	300	Not available			....	0.00003
	Scratch gage (deForest)	0.0001	......	Not available			....	....
	Berry	0.000002[b]	4,000	Not available			....	....
	Whittemore	0.0001[b]	800	Not available			....	....
	C.E.J. (Mikrokator)	0.000005	......	Not available	0.00004	Not available	....	....
Optical	Interferometer, lateral extensometer (Vose)	0.000002	1	....	0.000016	0.000008	0.000004	0.000002
	Tuckerman	0.000004	2,500	Not available		0.000016	0.000008	0.000004
	Preuss	0.0000015	64,000	0.00005[d]	....	....	....	....
		0.000003	32,000	....	0.00002	....	....	....
	Martens	0.000005	1,000[e]	Not available		....	....	....
	Interferometric polariscope (Favre)	....	....	....	....	....	0.000002	0.000001
Electrical	SR-4 (Baldwin indicator)	0.000005	4,000	0.000005[f]	0.000005[f]	0.000005[f]	0.000005[f]	0.000005[f]
	Unbonded electric wire strain gage (Statham G1)	0.000003	......	Not available			....	....
	Linear variable differential transformer	0.00005[h]	......	Not available			....	0.00005
	G.E. magnetic	0.000003	3,000	Not available			....	....
Grid	Grids on rubber	0.0001	......	....	0.0008	0.0004	0.0002	0.0001
	Photogrids (J. A. Miller)	0.000005	......	0.005[k]				
				0.00008	0.00004	0.00002	0.00001	0.000005
	Acoustic strain gage (Telemac)	0.000013[l]	800[l]	Not available			....	....
	Pneumatic (De Leiris)	0.000001	7,000[n]	....	....	....	....	0.000001
	Photoelectric (General Motors)	0.000001	30,000	0.000016	0.000008	0.000004	....	....

[a] Typical yield strain of material.
[b] One-fifth of the 0.0001-in. division is readable, but in general not reliable.
[c] With resetting.
[d] Base length 0.028 in.
[e] Variable. Used only on tensile and compressive specimens.
[f] Strain sensitivity does not vary with base length since the total length of the gage wires is the same for the different gage lengths.

246

Sensitivity				Range, in.	Whole-field information	Point per point determinations	Dynamic determinations
2-in. base	8-in. base	10-in. base	100-in. base				
....	....	....	....	0.010^a	✓	....	✓
....	....	....	....	....	✓	....	✓
0.00005	0.000012	0.00001	....	1.0	....	✓	
0.00005	0.000012	0.00001	0.000001	0.021	....	✓	
0.005	0.00125	0.001	0.0001	....	....	✓	
		Extension bars up to					
0.000004	0.000001	40 in. available		0.008^c	....	✓	
....	Not available			0.008^c	....	✓	
0.00005	Not available			0.25	....	✓	✓
0.00001	0.0000025	....	....	0.004	....	✓	
0.00005	....	0.00001	....	0.024	....	✓	
0.000002	0.0000006	0.0000005	....	0.0005	....	✓	
....	....	....	....	Unlimited in usual applications	....	✓	
0.000002	....	....	....	0.02	....	✓	
....	....	....	....	....	....	✓	
0.000002	0.000001	0.0000005	....	....	....	✓	
....	....	....	....	....	....	✓	
....	....	....	....	0.01^g	....	✓	✓
0.0000015	....	....	....	0.003	....	✓	✓
0.00002	0.000006	0.000005	....	0.005	....	✓	✓
0.0000015^i	....	....	....	0.01	....	✓	✓
....	....	....	....	0.4^j	✓		
....	....	....	....	0.4^j	✓		
0.000002^l	0.000005^m	....	....	0.013^l 0.04^m	....	✓	✓
Not available				....	....	✓	
Not available				....	....	✓	

[a]Post yield gages are claimed to have a range of 0.1 in.
[h]Models with larger deformation sensitivity have larger ranges.
[i]Base length $2\frac{1}{4}$-in.
[j]With common microscope-micrometer. Range can be much larger using gage blocks.
[k]Base length 0.01 in.
[l]Base length 141.4 mm.
[m]Base length 200 mm.
[n]Models with higher magnification and shorter base lengths have also been built.

The probable error of the mean of several measurements N is given by

$$p_0 = 0.6745\sigma_{\bar{x}} = 0.6745 \sqrt{\frac{\sum x^2}{N(N-1)}} \qquad (10.9)$$

The probable error of a single observation is that deviation from the mean in respect to which the deviation of a new measurement of the quantity has the same probability of being larger or smaller.

The idea of accuracy, however, goes beyond the concept of precision. An instrument may reproduce readings with a high degree of precision and have a systematic error, such as the effect on a wire resistance strain gage produced by a change in temperature which is not balanced by a dummy gage or the change in the magnification of a mechanical strain gage due to the wearing of the knives.

As another example, in experimental stress analysis, it is a common procedure to study stress distributions by use of models. A measurement can be very precise in the model and yet not be very accurate in respect to the prototype if the model is not built or loaded in correct similitude with the prototype.

Errors can therefore be classified as systematic, affecting generally the results with the same sign, and accidental, which usually are positive and negative in respect to the true value of the measured quantity. Systematic errors can often be eliminated by calibration of the instrument or by conducting the test under different conditions of loading or of temperature. Only accidental errors can be studied statistically and can be evaluated by some of the indices of precision mentioned above.

It is common practice in many papers to record the accuracy by means of a percentage figure. This is meaningless unless the basis of the per cent is stated. Five per cent error in the measurement of a maximum strain of 0.001 may be realistic since it means that the absolute error is 50 μin./in. In the same specimen there usually are also reported measurements of small strains to which the same per cent accuracy is understood to apply. In general a 0.00005 strain cannot be measured with an error of 5 per cent. Probably the error is even larger than the 50 μin./in. present in the measurement of the maximum strain. This is a 100 per cent error of the measurement at that point.

Most of the time in experimental-stress-analysis work only an estimate of accuracy can be made, based on previous experience and on similar cases. The accuracy of experimental determinations is a function of the degree of control of numerous variables having an influence on the properties used to measure strains (temperature, humidity, loading rate, time, etc.). The accuracy also depends on many technical procedures (model preparation, jig manufacturing, etc.) and on the knowledge of the influence of the uncontrolled variables on the measured quantity. Generally it is impossible to determine exactly the accuracy of a measurement.

10.8. Range. Range is another important concept that should be considered before the selection of a stress-analysis method is made. The range of an instrument is the maximum quantity it can measure. In general, the more sensitive the instrument, the smaller its range. Ranges of some of the common strain gages are also given in Table 10.1. Some mechanical strain gages can be reset. This operation increases their range. The range of photoelastic materials obviously is their yield strain.

10.9. Point per Point and Whole-field Determinations. Experimental-stress-analysis methods have to be appraised from the point of view of the scope of the required information. Some methods give a picture of the stress distribution over a whole field of stresses. Some other methods require point per point determinations, and the whole picture can be obtained only after the accumulation of a large number of individual results. Mechanical, optical, and electrical strain gages are in the latter category. Photoelasticity and brittle coatings are in the former.

It may happen that the results obtained from a single strain gage (mainly of the electrical type) are wrong, sometimes in a systematic way, and the detection of the error is difficult without a knowledge of the distribution of the strains in the neighborhood of the point where that gage has been applied. In whole-field determinations, this difficulty is overcome.

10.10. Operator's Skill. No experimental method gives results which are independent of the operator. Sensitivity values given in Table 10.1 are only approximate and depend on the operator's skill. Systematic errors depend on the operator's skill to an even larger degree. The accuracy of electrical-strain-gage determinations is a function of how well the gage has been cemented to the specimen; how well the soldering of the leads has been realized; how well the changes in temperature are accounted for; etc. The accuracy of a mechanical strain gage depends on how skillfully the gage has been mounted. In photoelasticity, model machining, focusing, and photographing require special training.

It often happens that the selection of a suitable stress-analysis method for a particular problem is based not on the nature of the problem and the merits of the method only but also on the availability of the personnel to use the method.

CHAPTER 11

STATISTICAL METHODS AND THEIR
APPLICATION TO EXPERIMENTAL STRESS ANALYSIS

11.1. Introduction. The science of statistics is essentially a branch of applied mathematics and may be regarded as mathematics applied to the evaluation of experimental data. Since the turn of the century the methods of statistics have infiltrated one branch of science after another until they now hold important positions in all fields. Of particular interest are their applications in the field of experimental stress analysis. There are a number of excellent textbooks dealing with statistical methods, but none of these has dealt directly with problems frequently encountered in the evaluation of stress-analysis data.

The use of statistical tests has many important advantages, among which should be mentioned the possibility of planning experiments whether under laboratory, factory, or field conditions, to provide the most reliable and valid information with the least expenditure of time and energy. Statistical tools are particularly effective in the determination of factors responsible for variability, for they permit the evaluation of the influence of a combination of variables as well as the determination of independent and interrelated effects between the variables. Lastly, statistical methods give indices of precision to tests of scientific hypothesis and to results obtained from recording instruments.

The scope of this chapter will be limited to the discussion of some of the fundamental aspects of statistics such as representation of data, difference between two means, analysis of variance, and regression and correlation analysis. Appropriate examples which not only show the mechanics of the various methods illustrated but also show the application of statistical methods to the failure of brittle materials have been carefully selected. The objective of the chapter is only to introduce statistical methods, and as a result many simplifications have been made. A list of references which show in much more detail the methods discussed has been included at the end of the chapter.

11.2. Representation of Data. A large number of data are often collected by the experimental analyst, and in many cases the data will have an appreciable degree of variation. It is advantageous to reduce these

250

numerous data by replacing them with fewer and more comprehensible quantities provided the reduction does not distort the true significance of the data. Statistically this is possible by using basic measures of central tendency and of variability.

In order to arrange statistical data in a form suitable for immediate and accurate interpretation, it is often necessary to group the data into appropriate classes. One of the most convenient ways of grouping data is the construction of a histogram. A histogram is a bar graph that shows the frequency of occurrence of a measurement within a certain interval. An example of histographic representation of data is illustrated in Fig. 11.1. In this figure the results of a test conducted to calibrate a particular brittle coating are shown. In the calibration process 65 measure-

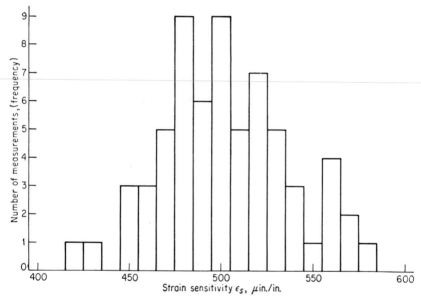

Fig. 11.1. Histogram representing the results of a brittle-coating calibration test.

ments of the strain sensitivity of the coating were taken. The values obtained for the strain sensitivity varied from 415 to 585 μin./in. The range of 170 μin./in. was divided into 17 equal intervals 10 μin./in. in width. The number of measurements occurring in each interval was determined and plotted as a function of the strain sensitivity. The prime advantage of a histographic representation of data is that it gives an over-all view of the variation in a set of data. It indicates whether the data have a central tendency or whether they are spread more or less uniformly over the entire range of variation. It also indicates where the concentrations are located if any occur.

11.3. Measures of Central Tendency. In some problems a general picture of the distribution of the measured values is all that is necessary, and in these cases the construction of a histogram is sufficient. In many problems, however, it is desirable to have numerical measurements of the characteristics of the distribution. One such characteristic is the central tendency of the data (the measure of the center of the distribution). There are three commonly used measures of central tendency, viz., the arithmetic mean, the median, and the mode. Of these three concepts, the arithmetic mean is the most commonly used and will be the only one considered here. The arithmetic mean is defined as

$$\bar{X} = \frac{1}{N} \sum_{i=1}^{N} X_i \tag{11.1}$$

where $\bar{X}$ = arithmetic mean
X_i = ith value of quantity being measured
N = total number of measurements

In practice it is possible to take only a relatively small number of measurements, and hence the true value of the mean, m, is not usually known. However, the arithmetic mean $\bar{X}$ of the sample is an estimate of the true mean m and will tend to approach nearer and nearer to m as N increases.

The arithmetic mean possesses the following mathematical property:†

$$\sum_i (X_i - \bar{X}) = 0 \tag{11.2}$$

This property can be proved in the manner shown below:

$$\sum_i (X_i - \bar{X}) = \sum_i X_i - \sum_i \bar{X} = \sum_i X_i - N\bar{X}$$

$$= \sum_i X_i - N\left(\frac{1}{N} \sum_i X_i\right) = 0$$

When the sample size N is large and the measurements X_i are given to several significant figures, the calculation of the mean can be shortened by employing a method of coding the data. The essential feature of the coding method is to carry out the calculation with reference to a conveniently selected origin, then to adjust the answer so obtained to refer the mean to the original origin and express it in original units. The data may be coded by letting

$$u_i = \frac{X_i - a}{c} \tag{11.3}$$

where a and c are chosen to give as simple an expression as possible of u_i.

†Henceforth $\sum_i \equiv \sum_{i=1}^{N}$.

The arithmetic mean $\bar{X}$ can be computed from the coded mean $\bar{u}$ by employing

$$\bar{X} = c\bar{u} + a \tag{11.4}$$

This relation is determined in the following manner:

$$\bar{u} = \frac{1}{N} \sum_i u_i = \frac{1}{N} \sum_i \frac{X_i - a}{c}$$

$$= \frac{1}{c} \left[\frac{\sum_i X_i}{N} - \frac{\sum_i a}{N} \right]$$

But

$$\frac{\sum a}{N} = a$$

Hence

$$\bar{u} = \frac{1}{c} (\bar{X} - a)$$

$$\bar{X} = c\bar{u} + a$$

11.4. Measures of Variability. Another characteristic of a distribution which is useful to determine is the variability, or spread, in the data. There are three commonly used measures of variability, viz., the average, or mean, deviation; the range; and the standard deviation. Of these three measures, the range is the simplest and easiest to compute, and the standard deviation is the most useful.

The mean deviation is defined as $\sum_i |X_i - \bar{X}|/N$. It will not be used in this chapter.

The range is defined as the difference between the highest and the lowest value of a set of data as shown below,

$$L = X_H - X_L \tag{11.5}$$

where L = range
X_H = highest value measured
X_L = lowest value measured

For small samples the range is a relatively sensitive measure of general variability, but in large samples the range is not as good a measure as the standard deviation.

The standard deviation is defined as

$$\sigma_X = \left[\frac{1}{n} \sum_i (X_i - m)^2 \right]^{\frac{1}{2}} \tag{11.6}$$

where σ_X = standard deviation of variable X
n = a large number of measurements

Usually 30 or more is considered a large number of measurements.

The use of σ to represent the standard deviation in stress-analysis applications has one disadvantage in that σ is also used to represent stresses. However, since σ is used almost universally to represent standard deviation, it is believed that its substitution by another symbol may bring more difficulty than that encountered in differentiating between stresses and standard deviations. It is hoped that the reader will realize the difference by the nature of the problem.

Variance, v_X, another quantity frequently used in statistics, is defined as the square of the standard deviation,

$$v_X = \sigma_X^2 \qquad (11.7)$$

Just as the arithmetic mean $\bar{X}$ is used as an estimate of the true mean m, so for practical considerations an estimate of the standard deviation must be obtained. This estimate of the standard deviation can be obtained by substituting $\bar{X}$ in Eq. (11.6) for m. The value thus obtained for σ_X would always be smaller than if the true mean m were used, because $\sum_i (X_i - m)^2 > \sum_i (X_i - \bar{X})^2$, unless by coincidence $\bar{X} = m$.† This substitution therefore introduces a bias which may be of considerable importance for small samples. To correct for this bias, a compensating substitution $n = N - 1$ is made, and the corrected estimate of the standard deviation becomes

$$S_X = \left[\frac{1}{N-1} \sum_i (X_i - \bar{X})^2 \right]^{\frac{1}{2}} \qquad (11.8)$$

As the number of measurements N increases, the value obtained for S_X approaches the true value of the standard deviation σ_X.

Frequently in discussions concerning the estimate of the standard deviation the word estimate is dropped, and σ is used in place of S. To

$$† \sum_i (X_i - \bar{X})^2 = \sum_i [(X_i - m) + (m - \bar{X})]^2$$

$$= \sum_i [(X_i - m)^2 + 2(X_i - m)(m - \bar{X}) + (m - \bar{X})^2]$$

$$= \sum_i (X_i - m)^2 + 2(m - \bar{X}) \sum_i (X_i - m) + N(m - \bar{X})^2$$

$$= \sum_i (X_i - m)^2 + 2(m - \bar{X})\left(N \frac{\sum_i X_i}{N} - \sum_i m \right) + N(m - \bar{X})^2$$

$$= \sum_i (X_i - m)^2 - 2N(m - \bar{X})^2 + N(m - \bar{X})^2$$

$$= \sum_i (X_i - m)^2 - N(m - \bar{X})^2$$

Hence

$$\sum_i (X_i - m)^2 > \sum_i (X_i - \bar{X})^2$$

avoid confusion, it should be kept in mind that Eq. 11.8 is used to determine the estimate of the standard deviation for small samples whether the quantity obtained is called σ or S. For larger samples ($N > 30$) the difference between σ and S is small enough to be neglected, and the symbol used is not important. This explains the symbols used in Eqs. (10.5), (10.6), and (10.7).

The numerator of Eq. (11.8), $\sum_i (X_i - \bar{X})^2$, is known as the reduced sum of squares, and will be symbolized by

$$[x^2] = \sum_i (X_i - \bar{X})^2 \tag{11.9}$$

which is the sum of the squares of deviations from the mean.

For ease in computation, $[x^2]$ can be written in a different form,

$$[x^2] = \sum_i (X_i - \bar{X})^2 = \sum_i (X_i^2 - 2X_i\bar{X} + \bar{X}^2)$$

$$= \sum_i X_i^2 - 2\bar{X} \sum_i X_i + N\bar{X}^2$$

By Eq. (11.1) this becomes

$$[x^2] = \sum_i X_i^2 - N\bar{X}^2 \tag{11.10a}$$

or

$$[x^2] = \sum_i X_i^2 - \frac{1}{N} \left(\sum_i X_i \right)^2 \tag{11.10b}$$

The use of Eq. (11.10b) eliminates the need for a large number of subtractions, and if a modern calculating machine is available, the quantities $\sum_i X_i^2$ and $\sum_i X_i$ can be readily obtained. A further aid to computation is possible by coding the data as was done in the case of the arithmetic mean. The measurements can be coded by use of Eq. (11.3), and the computations can be carried out for $[u^2]$. Then $[x^2]$ can be determined from $[u^2]$ by using the following expression:

$$[x^2] = c^2[u^2] \tag{11.11}$$

This relation is derived in the following manner: From Eq. (11.10b)

$$[u^2] = \sum_i u_i^2 - \frac{1}{N} \left(\sum_i u_i \right)^2$$

$$= \sum_i \left(\frac{X_i - a}{c} \right)^2 - \frac{1}{N} \left(\sum_i \frac{X_i - a}{c} \right)^2$$

By expanding,

$$c^2[u^2] = \sum_i X_i^2 - 2a \sum_i X_i + \sum_i a^2$$

$$- \frac{1}{N} [(\sum_i X_i)^2 - 2 \sum_i X_i \sum_i a + (\sum_i a)^2]$$

$$= \sum_i X_i^2 - \frac{1}{N} (\sum_i X_i)^2$$

And by Eq. (11.10b)

$$[x^2] = c^2[u^2]$$

11.5. Example of Mean and Standard-deviation Determination. An example illustrating the methods used to calculate the mean and the standard deviation is afforded by considering the results of a test which was conducted to calibrate the brittle coating known commercially as Stresscoat. Eight specimens coated with the brittle coating were tested, and the strain sensitivity of each was recorded. The values obtained were designated by the symbol X. The first step in the calculation was to code the data. This was accomplished by employing Eq. (11.3) and setting $a = 800$ and $c = 10$. Table 11.1 shows this computation:

TABLE 11.1. COMPUTATION TABLE FOR THE STRESSCOAT CALIBRATION

Strain sensitivity X, μin./in.	Coded strain sensitivity u	u^2
890	9	81
890	9	81
800	0	0
880	8	64
900	10	100
850	5	25
780	−2	4
850	5	25
	$\sum_i u_i = 44$	$\sum_i u_i^2 = 380$

The mean of the coded strain sensitivity is calculated from Eq. (11.1).

$$\bar{u} = \frac{1}{N} \sum_i u_i = \frac{1}{8} \times 44 = 5.5$$

The reduced sum of squares of the coded strain sensitivity is found from Eq. (11.10b).

$$[u^2] = \sum_i u_i^2 - \frac{1}{N} (\sum_i u_i)^2 = 380 - \frac{1}{8} \times 44^2 = 138$$

To decode these results, use is made of Eqs. (11.4) and (11.11).

$$\bar{X} = c\bar{u} + a = 10 \times 5.5 + 800 = 855$$

is the estimated mean strain sensitivity of the brittle coating.

$$[x^2] = c^2[u^2] = 10^2 \times 138 = 13,800$$

The estimate of the standard deviation of the measurements is obtained by Eqs. (11.8) and (11.9).

$$S_x = \left(\frac{1}{N-1} [x^2]\right)^{\frac{1}{2}} = \left(\frac{1}{7} \times 13,800\right)^{\frac{1}{2}} = 44.4 \ \mu\text{in./in.}$$

An important point to note at this time is that the estimated mean $\bar{X}$ is a variable quantity in the same manner as the individual measurements X. Repeated sets of measurements would give varying values of $\bar{X}$ just as repeated individual tests give varying values of X. The standard deviation and variance of the measurements of $\bar{X}$ are, respectively,

$$\sigma_{\bar{X}} = \frac{1}{\sqrt{N}} \sigma_x \tag{11.12}$$

(This relation is often called the standard error of the mean.)

$$v_{\bar{X}} = \frac{1}{N} v_x \tag{11.13}$$

Similarly, the sum or difference of two or more variable quantities is itself a variable quantity. Assuming that the quantities in question are independent (i.e., no interaction between the quantities), the standard deviation and variance of the sum or difference of two variables are given by

$$\sigma_{X+Y} = \sigma_{X-Y} = (\sigma_X^2 + \sigma_Y^2)^{\frac{1}{2}} \tag{11.14}$$

$$v_{X+Y} = v_{X-Y} = v_X + v_Y \tag{11.15}$$

11.6. Construction of a Frequency-distribution Curve and Its Use in the Analysis of Data. It was mentioned previously in Sec. 11.2 that a bar graph known as a histogram could be used to show the frequency of occurrence of a measurement within a certain interval. In the general case, as the number of measurements is increased, the width of the intervals used in the construction of the histogram may be reduced. As the number of measurements approaches infinity, the interval width approaches zero and the histographic representation approaches a smooth curve known as a frequency curve. Many problems in analysis arise where it is necessary to employ quantities which are derived from the shape of this curve.

However, in common practice, the number of measurements which are usually taken is insufficient to establish accurately the true frequency curve. In view of this difficulty, the frequency curve is usually assumed to be equivalent to the normal, or Gaussian, curve.

A discussion of the derivation of the Gaussian distribution is beyond the scope of this chapter; however, the application of this frequency distribution to the solution of problems arising in experimental work will be shown. The Gaussian distribution can be expressed mathematically as

$$\overline{Y} = \frac{1}{\sigma_X \sqrt{2\pi}}\, e^{-\frac{1}{2}((X-m)/\sigma_X)^2} \tag{11.16}$$

where $\overline{Y}$ is the frequency with which a variable X will occur if the population from which it was drawn has a mean m and a standard deviation σ_X.

Some properties of a Gaussian distribution for a population with a mean of zero and a standard deviation of 1 are illustrated in Fig. 11.2. In this figure it can be seen that 95 per cent of the measurements of X will be within the ± 1.96 limit and 98 per cent will be within the ± 2.33 limit.

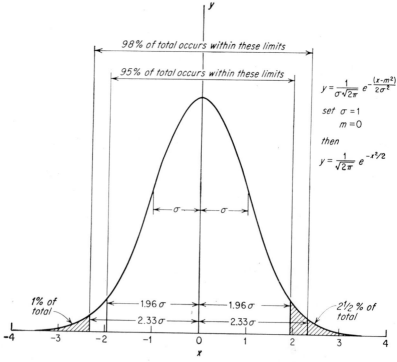

FIG. 11.2. Gaussian distribution for a population with a mean of 0 and a standard deviation of 1.

The Gaussian distribution for a population with a mean of zero, a standard deviation of 1, and a total area of 1 is of particular importance, for both the ordinates and the areas under the curve have been tabulated

TABLE 11.2. PROPERTIES OF THE GAUSSIAN DISTRIBUTION WITH A MEAN OF ZERO, A STANDARD DEVIATION OF 1, AND A TOTAL AREA OF 1 †

Abscissa X_t	Ordinate of frequency-distribution curve Y_t	Area to left of successive ordinates of the frequency-distribution curve A
0.00	0.3989	0.5000
0.05	0.3984	0.5199
0.10	0.3970	0.5398
0.15	0.3945	0.5596
0.20	0.3910	0.5793
0.25	0.3867	0.5987
0.30	0.3814	0.6179
0.35	0.3752	0.6368
0.40	0.3683	0.6554
0.45	0.3605	0.6736
0.50	0.3521	0.6915
0.55	0.3429	0.7088
0.60	0.3332	0.7257
0.65	0.3230	0.7422
0.70	0.3123	0.7580
0.75	0.3011	0.7734
0.80	0.2897	0.7881
0.85	0.2780	0.8023
0.90	0.2661	0.8159
0.95	0.2541	0.8289
1.00	0.2420	0.8413
1.10	0.2179	0.8643
1.20	0.1942	0.8849
1.30	0.1714	0.9032
1.40	0.1497	0.9192
1.50	0.1295	0.9332
1.60	0.1109	0.9452
1.70	0.0940	0.9554
1.80	0.0790	0.9641

Note: The values of Y_t are the same for both positive and negative X_t since the distribution is symmetrical about $X_t = 0$. The values of A must be subtracted from 1 when X_t is negative.

†A. M. Mood, "Introduction to the Theory of Statistics," p. 422, McGraw-Hill Book Company, Inc., New York, 1950.

TABLE 11.2—(Continued)

Abscissa X_t	Ordinate of frequency-distribution curve Y_t	Area to left of successive ordinates of the frequency-distribution curve A
1.90	0.0656	0.9713
2.00	0.0540	0.9772
2.10	0.0440	0.9821
2.20	0.0355	0.9861
2.30	0.0283	0.9893
2.40	0.0224	0.9918
2.50	0.0175	0.9938
2.60	0.0136	0.9953
2.70	0.0104	0.9965
2.80	0.0079	0.9974
2.90	0.0060	0.9981
3.00	0.0044	0.9987
3.10	0.0033	0.9990
3.20	0.0024	0.9993
3.30	0.0017	0.9995
3.40	0.0012	0.9997
3.50	0.0009	0.9998

as a function of X, as is shown in Table 11.2. The values shown in this table may be adjusted to fit the mean, the standard deviation, and the area of any particular sample in question. As an example of fitting a Gaussian curve to experimental data, consider the 65 measurements in the histogram shown in Fig. 11.1. From Eqs. (11.1) and (11.8) the mean and standard deviation were calculated as 502.5 and 34.3 μin./in., respectively. The areas under the histogram, which is the sum of the heights of the columns (the total number of measurements taken) times the interval width, are $65 \times 10 = 650$.

To fit the Gaussian curve to the histogram from the values shown in Table 11.2, it is necessary to adjust the tabulated values X_t and Y_t in the following manner,

$$X = \sigma_X X_t + \bar{X} \tag{11.17}$$

$$Y = \frac{Y_t A_0}{\sigma_X} \tag{11.18}$$

where X, Y = abscissa and ordinate of Gaussian distribution, respectively
X_t, Y_t = tabular values given for abscissa and ordinate, respectively
A_0 = area under histogram
$\bar{X}, \sigma_X$ = estimates of mean and standard deviations, respectively.

Let us consider the line in Table 11.2 which reads $X_t = 0.75$ and $Y_t = 0.3011$. Adjusting these values to fit the mean and standard deviation of the data represented in Fig. 11.1, one obtains, using Eqs. 11.17 and 11.18,

$$X = 34.3 \times 0.75 + 502.5 = 25.7 + 502.5 = 528.2$$

$$Y = \frac{0.3011 \times 650}{34.3} = 5.71$$

Since the Gaussian curve is symmetrical about the mean, the value of 5.71 for the ordinate y may be plotted at both,

$$X = 502.5 \pm 25.7 = 528.2 \text{ and } 476.8$$

By repeating calculations such as this one, it was possible to fit the Gaussian curve which is shown superimposed on the histogram in Fig. 11.3.

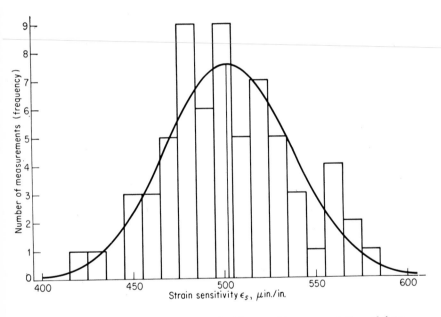

FIG. 11.3. Gaussian curve fitted to the histographic representation of data.

The area under the Gaussian curve is important because it provides a means of predicting the relative frequency of the variates lying within the interval between any two values of X. This fact may be expressed as

$$f(X_1, X_2) = A(X_1, X_2) \tag{11.19a}$$

$$F(X_1, X_2) = A(X_1, X_2)N \tag{11.19b}$$

where $f(X_1,X_2)$ = relative frequency of occurrence of variate between X_1 and X_2

$F(X_1,X_2)$ = absolute frequency of occurrence of the variate between X_1 and X_2

$A(X_1,X_2)$ = area under Gaussian curve between X_1 and X_2

N = number of measurements being considered

The last column in Table 11.2 gives the area under the Gaussian distribution to the left of successive ordinates of the frequency-distribution curve, or in another manner $A(-\infty,X)$. Consider now the line in Table 11.2 which reads $X_t = 0.75$ and $A = 0.7734$, and apply this to the interpretation of the data in Fig. 11.1. By using Eq. (11.19b) and recalling that $X = 528.2$, one obtains

$$F(-\infty,528.2) = 0.7734 \times 65 = 50.2$$

This means that 50.2 out of the 65 measurements of the brittle-coating strain sensitivity were less than 528.2 μin./in. The number of measurements occurring between the limits of $X = \bar{X} \pm \sigma$ will be determined for this group of data as a further example of the relationship between the frequency of the variates and the area under the Gaussian curve. From Eq. (11.17) the values of X_t for $X = \bar{X} \pm \sigma$ are ± 1. Using Eq. (11.19b) and the values of A from Table 11.2, one obtains

$$F(-\infty,1) = A(-\infty,1)N = 0.8413N$$

$$F(-\infty,-1) = A\dagger(-\infty,-1)N = (1 - 0.8413)N$$

$$F(-1,1) = F(-\infty,1) - F(-\infty,-1) = 0.6826 \times 65 = 44.4$$

Hence, it can be concluded that 44.4 out of 65 measurements taken will lie within the interval defined by $X = \bar{X} + \sigma = 536.8$ μin./in. and $X = \bar{X} - \sigma = 468.2$ μin./in. This is about 68 per cent of the measurements, which compares favorably with the 71 per cent which actually occurs.

It is interesting at this point to consider the application of this distribution to the evaluation of results obtained from a brittle-coating test. Suppose a test specimen had been coated along with the 65 calibration strips just considered. When the coating on the specimen failed during loading, the best estimate of the strain indicated by the coating would be the value of the arithmetic mean determined from the calibration strips.‡ It is important, however, to know how reliable is this estimate of the strain. For the case under consideration the strain at the first crack in the speci-

---

†Note when using Table 11.2 that the values of A must be subtracted from 1 when X_t is negative.

‡In this case the influence of biaxial stresses, and the gradient of stresses on the failure of the coating, has been neglected.

men as indicated by the coating will be between 502.5 ± 34.3 about 68 per cent of the time, as was shown in the example considered above. It can also be shown that the strain as indicated by the coating will be between 502.5 ± 68.6 about 95 per cent of the time. Use of the methods just outlined permits a more precise evaluation of the brittle-coating data and gives an estimate of the reliability of the brittle-coating analysis.

Tests have been developed which indicate any significant variation of a frequency distribution from that described by the Gaussian curve. These tests have not been described here; however, they can be found in many texts on statistics.†

Several other frequency distributions exist, viz., Poisson's, the binomial, the hypergeometric, and the Student, or t, distribution. Only the last of these will be discussed here since it is the most applicable of those listed, although the others should not be considered unimportant.

11.7. Test of Difference between Two Means. Frequently encountered in experimental stress analysis is the problem of determining whether an observed difference between the means of two series of results is attributable to random variation or whether it is significant. In most cases the number of measurements recorded are limited in number; hence the test for the difference between the means must not be limited by the requirement of a large sample. To this end, use will be made of the Student, or t, distribution, which takes into account sampling errors and permits a rigorous test of significance.

The t distribution was developed by W. S. Gossett. It was devised to take sampling fluctuations into account by setting up the ratio of the difference between the sampling mean and the population mean to its estimated standard deviation. This ratio was called t and is expressed as

$$t = \frac{(\bar{X} - m)(N)^{\frac{1}{2}}}{S} \tag{11.20}$$

If a number of samples are drawn it is found that t has a symmetric, bell-shaped, but nonnormal distribution with a distribution function of the form

$$Y = C\left(1 + \frac{t^2}{q}\right)^{-(q+1)/2} \tag{11.21}$$

where C = const depending on q
$q = N - 1$, the number of degrees of freedom

The concept of degrees of freedom is not easily defined; yet it holds an important role in many forms of statistical analysis. In general it is the

†See Ref. 1, pp. 412–421.

number of individuals or groups being compared minus the number of constraints on the system.

The appearance of the t curve is very much like the Gaussian curve, and in fact as N increases, the t curve approaches the Gaussian curve in the limit.

The essentials of the method to test whether the difference between two means is significant are the following: (1) Make a hypothesis that $\bar{X}_1 - \bar{X}_2 = 0$, and (2) estimate the probability of obtaining a value of the difference due to random variation equal to or greater than the actual difference. If this probability is small, the hypothesis is not acceptable and it can be concluded that the difference between the means $\bar{X}_1$ and $\bar{X}_2$ is significant.

In practice a set of values (Table 11.3) have been developed which allow comparison of the experimental results with the t distribution in making the test of significance. This can be accomplished by computing t_0, a measure of the actual difference between the two means related to the t distribution, and comparing it with t_α, a value taken from the table.

The following computations enable one to determine t_0. A close approximation of S^2 is given by

$$S^2 = \frac{\sum(X_1 - \bar{X}_1)^2 + \sum(X_2 - \bar{X}_2)^2}{N_1 + N_2 - 2}$$

which simplifies as a result of Eq. (11.9) to

$$S^2 = \frac{[x_1^2] + [x_2^2]}{N_1 + N_2 - 2} \tag{11.22}$$

It can be shown that

$$t_0 = \frac{\bar{X}_1 - X_2}{\sqrt{S^2(1/N_1 + 1/N_2)}} \tag{11.23}$$

If $|t_0| > t_\alpha$, then the hypothesis can be rejected and it can be concluded that there exists a significant difference between the means $\bar{X}_1$ and $\bar{X}_2$. The value used for t_α depends on two factors, viz., the size of the sample and the level of significance of the test. Two levels of 5 per cent and 1 per cent are commonly used in testing the means. The 5 per cent level means that the probability of a random variation being taken for a significant difference is only 5 per cent. If the 5 per cent level indicates a significant difference between the two means, it is generally considered that the evidence is strong of a real difference between them. However, if the 1 per cent level is used, it is reasonably certain that an actual difference exists. In using the 1 per cent level one is almost certain that an actual difference does exist; however, in using such a strong test real differences will often be attributed to random variation.

TABLE 11.3. VALUES OF t_α †

De- grees of free- dom	Probability of exceeding a given value of $\pm t$ (Sum of the shaded areas) α								
n	.5	.4	.3	.2	.1	.05	.02	.01	.001
1	1.000	1.376	1.963	3.078	6.314	12.706	31.821	63.657	636.619
2	.816	1.061	1.386	1.886	2.920	4.303	6.965	9.925	31.598
3	.765	.978	1.250	1.638	2.353	3.182	4.541	5.841	12.941
4	.741	.941	1.190	1.533	2.132	2.776	3.747	4.604	8.610
5	.727	.920	1.156	1.476	2.015	2.571	3.365	4.032	6.859
6	.718	.906	1.134	1.440	1.943	2.447	3.143	3.707	5.959
7	.711	.896	1.119	1.415	1.895	2.365	2.998	3.499	5.405
8	.706	.889	1.108	1.397	1.860	2.306	2.896	3.355	5.041
9	.703	.883	1.100	1.383	1.833	2.262	2.821	3.250	4.781
10	.700	.879	1.093	1.372	1.812	2.228	2.764	3.169	4.587
11	.697	.876	1.088	1.363	1.796	2.201	2.718	3.106	4.437
12	.695	.873	1.083	1.356	1.782	2.179	2.681	3.055	4.318
13	.694	.870	1.079	1.350	1.771	2.160	2.650	3.012	4.221
14	.692	.868	1.076	1.345	1.761	2.145	2.624	2.977	4.140
15	.691	.866	1.074	1.341	1.753	2.131	2.602	2.947	4.073
16	.690	.865	1.071	1.337	1.746	2.120	2.583	2.921	4.015
17	.689	.863	1.069	1.333	1.740	2.110	2.567	2.898	3.965
18	.688	.862	1.067	1.330	1.734	2.101	2.552	2.878	3.922
19	.688	.861	1.066	1.328	1.729	2.093	2.539	2.861	3.883
20	.687	.860	1.064	1.325	1.725	2.086	2.528	2.845	3.850
21	.686	.859	1.063	1.323	1.721	2.080	2.518	2.831	3.819
22	.686	.858	1.061	1.321	1.717	2.074	2.508	2.819	3.792
23	.685	.858	1.060	1.319	1.714	2.069	2.500	2.807	3.767
24	.685	.857	1.059	1.318	1.711	2.064	2.492	2.797	3.745
25	.684	.856	1.058	1.316	1.708	2.060	2.485	2.787	3.725
26	.684	.856	1.058	1.315	1.706	2.056	2.479	2.779	3.707
27	.684	.855	1.057	1.314	1.703	2.052	2.473	2.771	3.690
28	.683	.855	1.056	1.313	1.701	2.048	2.467	2.763	3.674
29	.683	.854	1.055	1.311	1.699	2.045	2.462	2.756	3.659
30	.683	.854	1.055	1.310	1.697	2.042	2.457	2.750	3.646
40	.681	.851	1.050	1.303	1.684	2.021	2.423	2.704	3.551
60	.679	.848	1.046	1.296	1.671	2.000	2.390	2.660	3.460
120	.677	.845	1.041	1.289	1.658	1.980	2.358	2.617	3.373
∞	.674	.842	1.036	1.282	1.645	1.960	2.326	2.576	3.291

†Reprinted from Table III, Distribution of t, in R. A. Fisher and F. Yates, "Statistical Tables for Biological, Medical, and Agricultural Research," Oliver & Boyd, Ltd. Edinburgh and London, 1948.

Consider as an example the problem of determining whether there exists a difference in the flexural strength of plaster mortar beams cut from the top and bottom of a slab of plaster mortar. Let the quantities X_1 and X_2 refer to the flexural strength of the top and bottom beams, respectively. The data obtained in the tests conducted on the beams are given in Table 11.4.

TABLE 11.4. DATA OBTAINED BY TESTING PLASTER MORTAR BEAMS

X_1	u_1	u_1^2	X_2	u_2	u_2^2
427	27	729	452	52	2,704
458	58	3,364	508	108	11,664
432	32	1,024	426	26	676
425	25	625	383	−17	289
392	−8	64	521	121	14,641
403	3	9	496	96	9,216
434	34	1,156			
455	55	3,025			
	$\sum = 226$	$\sum = 9{,}996$		$\sum = 386$	$\sum = 39{,}190$

$N_1 = 8 \qquad N_2 = 6 \qquad a = 400$

From Eqs. (11.1) and (11.4)

$$\bar{u}_1 = \frac{226}{8} = 28.25 \qquad \bar{X}_1 = 400 + 28 = 428$$

$$\bar{u}_2 = \frac{386}{6} = 64.33 \qquad \bar{X}_2 = 400 + 64 = 464$$

From Eqs. (11.10) and (11.11)

$$[x_1^2] = [u_1^2] = 9{,}996 - \frac{226^2}{8} = 3{,}611$$

$$[x_2^2] = [u_2^2] = 39{,}190 - \frac{386^2}{6} = 14{,}357$$

From Eq. 11.22

$$S^2 = \frac{3{,}611 + 14{,}357}{8 + 6 - 2} = 1{,}497$$

$$S = 38.6$$

From Eq. 11.23

$$t_0 = \frac{428 - 464}{38.6 \ \sqrt{\frac{1}{8} + \frac{1}{6}}} = -1.73$$

Referring to Table 11.3 and reading across the line for $n = N_1 + N_2 - 2 = 12$, one obtains for t_α at various levels of significance the following:

$$t_{0.01} = 3.055$$
$$t_{0.05} = 2.179$$
$$t_{0.10} = 1.782$$
$$t_{0.20} = 1.356$$

The test for a significant difference in the means is

$$| t_0 | > t_\alpha$$

Hence it can be concluded that at the 1, 5, and 10 per cent levels the difference in the means was caused by chance variation. At about the 11 per cent level, it can be stated that the difference in the means of the flexural strength of the beams is real, although the risk of an error in this conclusion is 11 per cent.

11.8. Confidence Limits. In experimental work the mean and the standard deviation of the universe from which measurements are taken are not usually known. The best estimate of the mean is $\bar{X}$; however, it is frequently desirable to determine an interval about $\bar{X}$ which will have a high probability of containing the true mean m. This interval is known as a confidence interval. Its limits may be calculated from Eq. (11.20),

$$m = \bar{X} \pm \frac{tS}{\sqrt{N}} \tag{11.24}$$

The width of the interval obviously depends upon t, which is a function of the degree of confidence one wishes to place in the estimate. If t is taken at the 5 per cent level of significance, the true mean will fall within the confidence interval 95 per cent of the time.

Consider again the example where eight Stresscoat specimens were tested (see Table 11.1). For this group of data the estimated mean and standard deviation were calculated as 855 and 44.4 μin./in., respectively. To determine the interval in which m will fall 95 per cent of the time if the samplings were repeated under the same conditions, Eq. (11.24) should be used. Hence

$$m = 855 \pm \frac{2.365 \times 44.4}{\sqrt{8}} = 855 \pm 37$$

or $\qquad 818 < m < 892$

In other words, if eight more measurements were repeated, the probability that the estimated mean obtained from these samples would lie between 818 and 892 μin./in. is 95 per cent.

11.9. Analysis of Variance. The analysis-of-variance method, which was developed primarily by Fisher, provides a means to analyze the variation which occurs in a group of experimental determinations. In general, this variation is a result of the combined influence of a number of different factors. Some factors, which are known to be the cause of the variation, are called assignable causes; however, as is often the case, there exist other factors, which cannot be segregated and which are called chance causes. The fundamental problem to which the analysis-of-variance method is applied is the determination of the contributing factors of variation in a group of experimental determinations. The simplest case of the analysis-of-variance method will be introduced here by means of an example.

Consider the data shown in Table 11.5, where eight determinations of the strain sensitivity of Stresscoat are given for five different curing temperatures. In this simple case the possible variations between the eight determinations of the strain sensitivity will be disregarded, and only the variation due to curing temperature will be considered. The method, however, is not limited to the consideration of only one source of variation, for it can be extended to cover two, three, to N factors if so desired. In general the higher-order analyses are longer and more complex, but

TABLE 11.5. STRAIN SENSITIVITY OF STRESSCOAT AS A FUNCTION OF
CURING TEMPERATURE

		Curing temp, °F					
		82	95	106	116	135	
i \ j		1	2	3	4	5(k)	
Strain sensitivity (10^{-5} in./in.)	1	79	73	49	47	43	
	2	84	77	51	48	36	
	3	74	74	58	40	34	
	4	85	74	65	45	35	
	5	92	78	57	49	35	
	6	98	87	60	43	43	
	7	77	73	57	42	34	
	8(r)	79	73	63	47	40	Totals
$\sum X$		668	609	460	361	300	2,398
$\sum X^2$		56,236	46,521	26,658	16,361	11,356	157,132
$(\sum X)^2$		446,224	370,881	211,600	130,321	90,000	1,249,026
$\bar{X}$		83.5	76.1	57.5	45.1	37.5	$\bar{\bar{X}} = 59.95$

the principles are essentially the same as those employed in a simple analysis of variance.

Specifically the problem to be answered is: What is the probability that the observed differences in the mean values of the strain sensitivity for the five curing temperatures might have arisen through random sampling errors? It may be noted that this objective is similar to the t tests just discussed; in fact the simplest case of analysis of variance (one factor with two replications) yields the same result as the t test. The scope of the application of the t test is, however, far more limited than that of the analysis-of-variance method.

Use of the analysis-of-variance method requires the computation of three sums of squares, viz., the total sum of squares, the column sum of squares, and the residual sum of squares. These quantities may be computed in the following manner:

1. The total sum of squares is defined as the sum of squares of the deviations of the 40 measurements of strain sensitivity from the grand mean.

$$A = \sum_i^r \sum_j^k (X_{ij} - \bar{\bar{X}})^2 = \sum_i^r \sum_j^k X_{ij}^2 - \frac{1}{N} (\sum_i^r \sum_j^k X_{ij})^2 \qquad (11.25)$$

where $\bar{\bar{X}}$ = grand mean

N = total number of measurements

i, j = subscripts referring to rows and columns, respectively

r = number of measurements in each column

k = number of columns

The total sum of squares can be calculated from the data in Table 11.5 in the following manner:

$$A = 157{,}132 - \tfrac{1}{40} \times 2{,}398^2 = 13{,}372$$

2. The sum of squares between columns is defined as the sum of squared deviations of the column means from the grand mean weighed by the number of measurements in each column

$$B = r \sum_i^k (\bar{X}_j - \bar{\bar{X}})^2$$

$$= \frac{1}{r} \sum_j^k (\sum_i^r X_{ij})^2 - \frac{1}{N} (\sum_i^r \sum_j^k X_{ij})^2 \qquad (11.26)$$

Referring again to the sums at the bottom of Table 11.5, the sum of squares between the columns can be calculated as:

$$B = \tfrac{1}{8} \times 1{,}249{,}026 - \tfrac{1}{40} \times 2{,}398^2 = 12{,}368$$

3. The sum of squares within the columns is frequently called the residual sum of squares. It is defined as the sum of the squared deviation

of this individual measurements in each column from the mean of the given column summed for all the columns.

$$C = \sum_{j}^{k} [\sum_{i}^{r} X_{ij}^2 - \frac{1}{r} (\sum_{i}^{r} X_{ij})^2]$$

which by proper transformation can be converted to

$$C = \sum_{i}^{r} \sum_{j}^{k} X_{ij}^2 - \frac{1}{r} \sum_{j}^{k} (\sum_{i}^{r} X_{ij})^2 \qquad (11.27)$$

By Eqs. (11.25) to (11.27) it is clear that

$$A = B + C \qquad (11.28)$$

Equation (11.28) can be used to calculate the residual sum of squares; however, it is advisable to use this relationship as a check on the independent calculation of A, B, and C.

Referring to the sums at the bottom of Table 11.5, the residual sum of squares can be calculated as

$$C = 157{,}132 - \frac{1{,}249{,}026}{8} = 1{,}004$$

Using Eq. (11.28), the values obtained for A, B, and C can be checked.

$$13{,}372 = 12{,}368 + 1{,}004 = 13{,}372$$

The respective sums of squares are recorded in an analysis-of-variance table, as illustrated in Table 11.6. The values under the column headed

TABLE 11.6. ANALYSIS-OF-VARIANCE TABLE FOR THE STRAIN SENSITIVITY OF STRESSCOAT CURED AT FIVE DIFFERENT TEMPERATURES

Source of variation	Sum of squares	Degrees of freedom	Mean square	F_0
Curing temp (columns)....	$B = 12{,}368$	$k - 1 = 4$	$B/(k - 1) = 3{,}092$	107
Experimental error (residual)...............	$C = 1{,}004$	$N - k = 35$	$C/(N - k) = 28.7$	
Total...............	$A = 13{,}372$	$N - 1 = 39$		

Mean Square are obtained by dividing the sum of squares in each row by the corresponding number of degrees of freedom. The value for F_0 may be obtained from the ratio of the mean square for the columns over the mean square for the residual, or

$$F_0 = \frac{B(N - k)}{C(k - 1)} \qquad (11.29)$$

The test to determine whether the observed differences in the mean values of the strain sensitivity for the five curing temperatures are significant is accomplished by comparing F_0 with F_α in much the same manner t_0 was compared with t_α in the t test. The term F_α is obtained from a table† listing the values of the F distribution. The values of F_α depend on two factors: (1) the value of α (the level of significance of the test) and (2) the number of degrees of freedom of both the column and residual sources of variation. It can be concluded that the difference is significant if

$$F_0 > F_\alpha \qquad (11.30)$$

For the example being considered, $F_{0.01} = 3.98$; hence, since $107 \gg 3.98$, it can be concluded with practically no uncertainty that the curing temperature does influence the coating strain sensitivity.

The example just described shows how the analysis of variance of an obviously simple case can be conducted. For more complicated analyses the reader is referred to the usual texts on statistics, in particular to Fisher.[3]·‡

11.10. Regression and Correlation Analysis. In experimental analysis the situation often occurs where one dependent variable is a function of one or more independent variables. In such situations it is sometimes desirable to determine the influence of the independent variables on the dependent variable. This determination, whether it be a curve or an equation, can best be made by employing statistical methods. The proper statistical method to use depends upon the nature of the problem. If the dependent variable is a function of only one independent variable, it is usually advisable to fit a curve statistically to the data. If the dependent variable is a function of two or more independent variables, a multiple regression analysis is required to obtain the relating equation.

a. Curve Fitting. To statistically fit a curve to experimental data, one must first decide upon what type of curve may best fit the trend of the data. By plotting the dependent vs. the independent variable, the selection of the type of curve necessary is usually apparent. One simple but often effective method of fitting this curve is to sketch it in so that it appears to divide the points into two groups of approximately the same number of points at approximately the same distance from the curve. A more rigorous approach to fit the curve is to employ the method of least squares to determine the constants of the equation expressing the curve.

---

†This table is too long to include in this chapter, but it can be found in the appendix of most texts on statistics. (See Reference 1, pp. 618-623.)

‡Superior numerals in the text correspond to the numbered references at the end of the chapter.

Consider first the problem of fitting a straight line to a set of data using the method of least squares. Let

$$X_{1r} = a + bX_2 \tag{11.31}$$

where X_{1r} = estimate of dependent variable X_1

X_2 = independent variable

a, b = constants of the equation of a straight line

From Eq. (11.31) the sum of squares of the difference between the dependent variable and the independent variable can be expressed as

$$\sum (X_1 - X_{1r})^2 = \sum (X_1 - a - bX_2)^2$$

The method of least squares requires that a and b be determined so that $\sum (X_1 - X_{1r})^2$ is a minimum. Hence

$$\frac{\partial \sum (X_1 - a - bX_2)^2}{\partial a} = 2 \sum (X_1 - a - bX_2)(-1) = 0$$

$$\frac{\partial \sum (X_1 - a - bX_2)^2}{\partial b} = 2 \sum (X_1 - a - bX_2)(-X_2) = 0$$

From the above relations it follows that the least-square equations for determining a and b are

$$Na + b \sum X_2 = \sum X_1$$
$$a \sum X_2 + b \sum X_2^2 = \sum X_1 X_2 \tag{11.32}$$

When all points lie on a straight line and there is no scatter, there is perfect or linear correlation between the two variables. However, when there exists some scatter about the line, it is possible to employ a coefficient of correlation to measure the relative amount of variation in the dependent variable that is explained by the independent variable. The coefficient of correlation in this case is given below:

$$R^2 = 1 - \frac{N-1}{N-2} \left(\frac{[X_1^2] - b_2[X_1 X_2]}{[X_1^2]} \right)$$

where

$$[X_1 X_2] = \sum X_1 X_2 - \frac{1}{N} \sum X_1 \sum X_2$$

When the value obtained for R^2 is relatively large, say 0.8 to 0.9 (80 to 90 per cent of the variance has been accounted for by the independent variable), the estimate of the dependent variable is usually accurate. For a more thorough coverage of this concept see Ref. 1.

If the data to which the curve is to be fitted are not linear in form, a quadratic equation is frequently employed to represent the form of the curve

$$X_{1r} = a + bX_2 + cX_2^2 \qquad (11.33)$$

The least-squares equations for determining a, b, and c can be derived in the same manner as previously. The derivation leads to the three following equations:

$$Na + b \sum X_2 + c \sum X_2^2 = \sum X_1$$

$$a \sum X_2 + b \sum X_2^2 + c \sum X_2^3 = \sum X_1 X_2 \qquad (11.34)$$

$$a \sum X_2^2 + b \sum X_2^3 + c \sum X_2^4 = \sum X_1 X_2^2$$

The procedure just outlined can be illustrated using the data previously employed in the analysis-of-variance example. Letting X_1 denote the strain sensitivity of the coating and X_2 denote the curing temperature, it is convenient to determine the type of curve by plotting the data (see Fig. 11.4). From this figure it can be seen that the plotted data do not fall along a straight line and that a quadratic equation will fit the points better. However, for this example both the straight-line and the quadratic expressions were used in order to show the improvement of the quadratic over the straight-line representation of the data.

The calculation of the constants occurring in the straight-line and quadratic representation was performed by employing Eqs. (11.32) and (11.34), respectively. The numerical values necessary in these equations were computed from the data in Table 11.5 and are shown below.

$$\sum X_1 = 2,398 \qquad \sum X_2^2 = 469,328 \qquad \sum X_1 X_2 = 243,767$$

$$\sum X_2 = 4,272 \qquad \sum X_2^3 = 52,968,240 \qquad \sum X_1 X_2^2 = 25,481,533$$

$$\sum X_2^4 = 6,129,000,469$$

Substitution of some of these values in Eq. (11.32) gives for the straight-line representation

$$\left. \begin{array}{l} 40a + \quad 4{,}272b = \quad 2{,}398 \\ 4{,}272a + 469{,}328b = 243{,}767 \end{array} \right\} \; a = 160.7, \; b = -0.943$$

and by Eq. (11.31) the straight-line representation is:

$$X_{1r} = 160.7 - 0.943X_2$$

which has been plotted in Fig. 11.4.

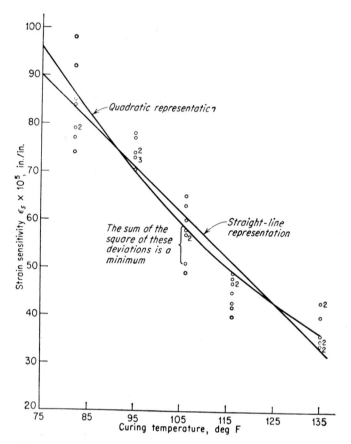

FIG. 11.4. Example of fitting a curve to brittle-coating data. The small circles represent the data, and the small numbers are used when two or three points coincide.

Substitution of numerical values in Eq. (11.34) gives for the quadratic representation

$$
\begin{aligned}
40a + \quad 4{,}272b + \quad\quad 469{,}328c &= \quad\quad 2{,}398 \\
4{,}272a + \quad 469{,}328b + \quad\quad 52{,}968{,}240c &= \quad\quad 243{,}767 \\
469{,}328a + 52{,}968{,}240b + 6{,}129{,}000{,}464c &= 25{,}481{,}533
\end{aligned}
\quad
\begin{aligned}
&a = 247, \\
&b = -2.57, \\
&c = 0.00749
\end{aligned}
$$

and by Eq. (11.33) the quadratic is

$$
X_{1r} = 247 - 2.57X_2 + 0.00749X_2^2
$$

which has been plotted in Fig. 11.4. Examination of this figure shows that the quadratic representation more closely fits the data than the straight-line representation. It would be possible to improve the quadratic curve by considering a cubic or even a higher-order polynomial. The disadvantage in using the higher-order polynomials is the amount of calculation involved in determining the constants.

b. Multiple Regression Analysis. If one encounters a situation where instead of having only one independent variable there exist several independent variables, it is possible to express the value of the dependent variable in terms of the several independent variables by means of an equation. This is accomplished by use of a multiple regression analysis, which is dealt with in this section.

Let the multiple regression equation for expressing the dependent variable in terms of the independent variable be represented as

$$X_{1r} = a + b_2 X_2 + b_3 X_3 + \cdots + b_k X_k \qquad (11.35)$$

where

$\qquad X_{1r}$ = estimate of dependent variable X_1

$\quad X_2, X_3, \ldots, X_k$ = independent variables

$\quad a, b_2, b_3, \ldots, b_k$ = constants of regression equation, called regression coefficients.

To determine these coefficients, equations are derived by employing the method of least squares, as was the case in the previous section. This method of derivation is based on the fact that $\sum (X_1 - X_{1r})^2$ is a minimum. Hence, by this relation and Eq. (11.35) one finds

$$\sum (X_1 - X_{1r})^2 = (X_1 - a - b_2 X_2 - b_3 X_3 - \cdots - b_k X_k)^2 = \Delta^2$$

For $\sum (X_1 - X_{1r})^2$ to be a minimum, it follows that

$$\frac{\partial \Delta^2}{\partial a} = 2[\sum (X_1 - a - b_2 X_2 - b_3 X_3 - \cdots - b_k X_k)(-1)] = 0$$

$$\frac{\partial \Delta^2}{\partial b_2} = 2[\sum (X_1 - a - b_2 X_2 - b_3 X_3 - \cdots - b_k X_k)(-X_2)] = 0$$

$$\frac{\partial \Delta^2}{\partial b_k} = 2[\sum (X_1 - a - b_2 X_2 - b_3 X_3 - \cdots - b_k X_k)(-X_k)] = 0$$

These relations lead to the following set of equations, which may be solved for $a, b_2, \ldots, b_k$:

$$Na + b_2 \sum X_2 + b_3 \sum X_3 + \cdots + b_k \sum X_k = \sum X_1$$

$$a \sum X_2 + b_2 \sum X_2^2 + b_3 \sum X_2 X_3 + \cdots + b_k \sum X_2 X_k = \sum X_1 X_2$$

$$a \sum X_3 + b_2 \sum X_2 X_3 + b_3 \sum X_3^2 + \cdots + b_k \sum X_3 X_k = \sum X_1 X_3 \qquad (11.36)$$

$$\cdots \cdots \cdots \cdots \cdots \cdots \cdots \cdots \cdots \cdots \cdots$$

$$a \sum X_k + b_2 \sum X_2 X_k + b_3 \sum X_3 X_k + \cdots + b_k \sum X_k^2 = \sum X_1 X_k$$

The set of equations shown above can be solved for the regression coefficients by using substitution, elimination, determinants, or the Doolittle system, depending upon the number of variables involved and the training of the computer.

It is possible to measure the reliability with which the regression equation predicts the dependent variable. This is done by computing what is referred to as the standard error of the estimate from the following relationship,

$$S_e = \left(\frac{[x_1^2] - b_2[x_1x_2] - b_3[x_1x_3] - \cdots - b_k[x_1x_k]}{N - k} \right)^{\frac{1}{2}}$$ (11.37)

where

$$[x_1^2] = \sum X_1^2 - \frac{1}{N} (\sum X_1)^2$$ (11.38)

$$[x_1x_k] = \sum X_1X_k - \frac{1}{N} (\sum X_1)(\sum X_k)$$

The value obtained for the standard error of the estimate from Eqs. (11.37) and (11.38) is an unbiased estimate of the variance of X_{1r} about X_1. This indicates that about two-thirds of the time the value predicted by the regression equation will be within $\pm S_e$ of the true measure of the dependent variable.

In regression analysis the correlation coefficient (discussed in part a) is again used to show the degree of association between the dependent and independent variables. When more than one variable is considered, the correlation coefficient is called a multiple correlation coefficient and has the more general form shown below:

$$R^2 = 1 - \frac{N - 1}{N - k} \left(\frac{[x_1^2] - b_2[x_1x_2] - b_3[x_1x_3] - \cdots - b_k[x_1x_k]}{[x_1^2]} \right)$$ (11.39)

The theory of regression just discussed was limited to an analysis of linear, noninteracting, independent variables; however, it can be extended to include cases where the regression equations would have higher-order and cross-product terms, or both. If the nonlinear terms enter into the equation in an additive manner, they can be taken into account simply as an extra variable and the equations for the regression coefficients can be derived in the manner previously discussed. The only difficulty in the analysis is the solution of the set of Eqs. (11.36) for the regression coefficients. If the number of independent variables considered is 5 and each contains 1 nonlinear term, then it is necessary to solve an 11 × 11 set of simultaneous equations.

References

1. Duncan, A. J.: "Quality Control and Industrial Statistics," Richard D. Irwin, Inc., Homewood, Ill., 1952.

2. Ezekiel, M.: "Methods of Correlation Analysis," John Wiley & Sons, Inc., New York, 1941.
3. Fisher, R. A.: "Statistical Methods for Research Workers," Oliver & Boyd, Ltd., Edinburgh and London, 1950.
4. Johnson, P. O.: "Statistical Methods in Research," Prentice-Hall, Inc., Englewood Cliffs, New Jersey, 1949.
5. Mode, E. B.: "Elements of Statistics," Prentice-Hall, Inc., Englewood Cliffs, New Jersey, 1949.
6. Mood, A. M.: "Introduction to The Theory of Statistics," McGraw-Hill Book Company, Inc., New York, 1950.
7. Tippett, L. H. C.: "The Methods of Statistics," Williams & Norgate, Ltd., London, 1941.
8. Wright, P. J. F.: "Statistical Methods in Concrete Research," Cement and Concrete Association, London, March, 1954.

CHAPTER 12

DIMENSIONAL ANALYSIS

12.1. Introduction. This chapter can be developed in an autonomous way without using the methods of analysis introduced in the theory of elasticity. It is also true that, although dimensional analysis will help in a better understanding of some problems in theory of elasticity, the latter can be completely developed without using any of the dimensional-analysis approaches. As a matter of fact, the organized approach to dimensional analysis is very recent, whereas the theory of elasticity is an old science. In stress analysis, the main application of dimensional analysis will be found in the design of models.

A knowledge of dimensional analysis is necessary for the proper design of models and the correct interpretation of the test results obtained from them.

12.2. Dimensions of Physical Quantities. In mechanics, the fundamental dimensions are usually taken as mass, length, and time, denoted, respectively, by M, L, and T. The dimensions of other physical quantities follow from their definitions or from physical laws. For example, the dimension of velocity, LT^{-1}, follows from its definition, quotient of length by time. Acceleration is defined as the quotient of velocity by time and has the dimension LT^{-2}. From Newton's law, force equals the product of mass and acceleration; it follows that force has the dimension MLT^{-2}. The dimensions of various physical quantities commonly encountered in mechanics are given in Table 12.1. Note that strain, angle, and Poisson's ratio are dimensionless.

12.3. Dimensionless Products. Given the five variables, length l, area A, strain ϵ, force F, and modulus of elasticity E, it may be observed that there are an infinite number of products of powers of these five variables. Examples are $\mu_1 = l^2 A^3 F^2 E$, $\mu_2 = A^2 \epsilon^{\frac{1}{2}}$, $\mu_3 = A l^{-2}$, $\mu_4 = F^{-1}EA$. Here the exponents may be either an integer or a fraction, and positive, zero, or negative. The dimensions of products of powers are calculated by replacing each variable by its corresponding dimensions and computing the resulting exponents of M, L, and T. Thus we replace l by $[L]$, A by $[L]^2$, ϵ by $[1]$, F by $[MLT^{-2}]$, E by $[ML^{-1}T^{-2}]$ and obtain

TABLE 12.1. DIMENSIONS OF ENTITIES

Length, l..$[L]$
Area, A...$[L^2]$
Volume, V...$[L^3]$
Time, t...$[T]$
Force, F, P.......................................$[MLT^{-2}]$
Mass, m...$[M]$
Specific weight, γ...............................$[ML^{-2}T^{-2}]$
Mass density, ρ..................................$[ML^{-3}]$
Angle, θ, ϕ, etc..............................$[1]$
Pressure and stress, p, σ......................$[ML^{-1}T^{-2}]$
Velocity, v..$[LT^{-1}]$
Acceleration, a....................................$[LT^{-2}]$
Angular velocity, ω.............................$[T^{-1}]$
Angular acceleration, α..........................$[T^{-2}]$
Energy, work, T, W...............................$[ML^2T^{-2}]$
Momentum, $\mathfrak{M}$.............................$[MLT^{-1}]$
Power, P..$[ML^2T^{-3}]$
Moment of a force, M..............................$[ML^2T^{-2}]$
Moment of inertia of an area, I....................$[L^4]$
Moment of inertia of a mass, I.....................$[ML^2]$
Modulus of elasticity, E...........................$[ML^{-1}T^{-2}]$
Strain, ϵ.......................................$[1]$
Poisson's ratio, ν.................................$[1]$

Dimension of $\mu_1 = [L]^2[L^2]^3[MLT^{-2}]^2[ML^{-1}T^{-2}] = [M^3L^9T^{-6}]$

Dimension of $\mu_2 = [L^2]^2[1^2]^{\frac{1}{2}} = [L^4]$

Dimension of $\mu_3 = [L^2][L]^{-2} = 1$

Dimension of $\mu_4 = [MLT^{-2}]^{-1}[ML^{-1}T^{-2}][L^2] = 1$

In general, the dimensions of a product of powers

$$\mu = l^{k_1}A^{k_2}\epsilon^{k_3}F^{k_4}E^{k_5}$$

will be

$$[L]^{k_1}[L^2]^{k_2}[1]^{k_3}[MLT^{-2}]^{k_4}[ML^{-1}T^{-2}]^{k_5}$$

or

$$[M]^{k_4+k_5}[L]^{k_1+2k_2+k_4-k_5}[T]^{-2k_4-2k_5}$$

Products of powers like μ_3 and μ_4, whose exponents of M, L, and T all vanish, are called dimensionless products of powers. Evidently the product μ will be dimensionless if and only if the exponents k_1, k_2, k_3, k_4, and k_5 satisfy all three of the following equations:

$$k_4 + k_5 = 0$$
$$k_1 + 2k_2 + k_4 - k_5 = 0 \qquad (12.1)$$
$$-2k_4 - 2k_5 = 0$$

There are an infinite number of combinations of the exponents k_1, k_2, k_3, k_4, and k_5 which satisfy the above condition so that the number of dimensionless products of powers which can be formed out of the five variables l, A, ϵ, F, and E is infinite. Examples are $\pi_1 = Al^{-2}$, $\pi_2 = F^{-1}El^2$, $\pi_3 = F^{-1}EA$, $\pi_4 = A^2l^{-4}$, and $\pi_5 = \epsilon^{-1}$. Here π denotes a dimensionless product of powers and has no connection whatsoever with the value 3.1416. In this chapter, μ will denote a product of powers of variables, whether dimensionless or not. The use of π will be reserved to designate a dimensionless product of powers of variables, and the shortened term *dimensionless product* will be used for this.

Forming some products of powers of the dimensionless products, it can be noticed that

$$\pi_3 = \pi_1\pi_2$$

$$\pi_4 = \pi_1^2$$

so that π_3 and π_4 can be expressed as products of powers of π_1 and π_2. This suggests the following definition:

A set of *independent* dimensionless products of given variables is one in which none of these products can be expressed as a product of powers of other dimensionless products in the set. Here again, the exponents of the powers may be integers or fractions, positive, zero, or negative.

For example, π_1 and π_2 form a set of independent dimensionless products, π_2 and π_3 form another set of independent dimensionless products, π_2, π_3, and π_5 form still another set of independent dimensionless products, and many more sets of independent dimensionless products can be formed out of the infinite number of dimensionless products. Evidently if, in a set of dimensionless products, only one of them contains a particular variable, then this dimensionless product will be an independent one. The simplest way to construct a set of independent dimensionless products is therefore to make one variable appear exclusively in one dimensionless product, another variable to appear exclusively in another dimensionless product, etc.

For example, in the set of independent dimensionless products composed of π_1, π_3, and π_5, l appears exclusively in π_1, F appears exclusively in π_3, and ϵ appears exclusively in π_5.

12.4. Matrices and Determinants. Dimensional analysis is based on a theorem demonstrated first by Buckingham and known sometimes as the π *theorem*. To understand this theorem, some knowledge is required of the elementary properties of matrices. These will be given below.

A rectangular array of numbers is called a matrix. If the number of columns equals the number of rows, the matrix is called a square matrix, of order n. If there are n rows and m columns ($n \neq m$), the matrix is said to be of order $n \times m$. Associated with every square matrix of order

n is a number called the determinant of order n. The determinants obtained after crossing out certain rows or columns or both from a matrix are called the "determinants of the matrix." Tables 12.2 and 12.3 give an example of a matrix and one of its third-order determinants

TABLE 12.2. EXAMPLE OF A MATRIX

a_1	a_2	a_3	a_4
b_1	b_2	b_3	b_4
c_1	c_2	c_3	c_4

TABLE 12.3. A THIRD-ORDER DETERMINANT OF THE MATRIX OF TABLE 12.2

$$\begin{vmatrix} a_1 & a_3 & a_4 \\ b_1 & b_3 & b_4 \\ c_1 & c_3 & c_4 \end{vmatrix}$$

Determinants can be evaluated by the methods commonly used in algebra. For example, the value of the determinant of Table 12.3 is $a_1 b_3 c_4 + a_3 b_4 c_1 + a_4 b_1 c_3 - a_1 b_4 c_3 - a_3 b_1 c_4 - a_4 b_3 c_1$. It occasionally happens that all determinants above a certain order taken from a matrix have the value zero. The following definition is employed in algebra:

If a matrix contains a nonzero determinant of order r, and if all determinants of order greater than r that the matrix contains have the value zero, the rank of the matrix is said to be r.

12.5. Complete Set of Dimensionless Products. The concept of a complete set of dimensionless products is essential in dimensional analysis. The following is the definition of a complete set of dimensionless products:

A set of dimensionless products of given variables is *complete* if each product in the set is independent of the others in the set, and every dimensionless product of the variables is a product of powers of dimensionless products in the set. In other words, a complete set of dimensionless products is a set of independent dimensionless products with the additional property that every possible dimensionless product of the variables may be expressed as a product of powers of the dimensionless products in the set. For example, π_1 and π_2 have been shown to be independent of each other and form a set of independent dimensionless products. Also, π_3 and π_4 have been shown to be expressible as products of powers of π_1 and π_2. Now if it can be shown furthermore that any dimensionless product $\pi = l^{k_1} A^{k_2} \epsilon^{k_3} F^{k_4} E^{k_5}$ is expressible as a product of powers of π_1 and π_2, then π_1 and π_2 will form a complete set. Similarly π_2 and π_3 will form a complete set if they meet the above conditions for a complete set.

After dealing with the previous example the general case will be discussed next. Let us consider the n variables whose dimensions are given in Table 12.4. The rectangular array of numbers a_i, b_i, c_i giving the

TABLE 12.4. A DIMENSIONAL MATRIX

	x_1	x_2	$\cdots$	x_n
M	a_1	a_2	$\cdots$	a_n
L	b_1	b_2	$\cdots$	b_n
T	c_1	c_2	$\cdots$	c_n

dimensions of the variables x_1, x_2, $\ldots$, x_n corresponding to the fundamental units in the first column is called the dimensional matrix of these variables. Evidently the product $x_1^{k_1} x_2^{k_2} \cdots x_n^{k_n}$ will be dimensionless if and only if the exponents k_1, k_2, $\ldots$, k_n satisfy all three of the following equations:

$$a_1 k_1 + a_2 k_2 + \cdots + a_n k_n = 0$$

$$b_1 k_1 + b_2 k_2 + \cdots + b_n k_n = 0 \qquad (12.2)$$

$$c_1 k_1 + c_2 k_2 + \cdots + c_n k_n = 0$$

By the theory of algebra it can be shown† that (1) Eqs. (12.2) possess exactly $n - r$ linearly independent solutions in which r is the rank of the dimensional matrix given in Table 12.4 and (2) any solution $(k_1, k_2, \cdots , k_n)$ is a linear combination of these $n - r$ linearly independent solutions. Since each solution $(k_1, k_2, \cdots , k_n)$ represents a dimensionless product, property (1) is equivalent to stating that these $n - r$ dimensionless products are independent of each other and property (2) is equivalent to stating that all other dimensionless products may be expressed as a product of powers of these $n - r$ dimensionless products. Hence the following important theorem on dimensional analysis:

The number of dimensionless products in a complete set is equal to the total number of variables minus the rank of their dimensional matrix.

It should be pointed out that there is an infinite number of complete sets. By accumulating any $n - r$ independent dimensionless products, a complete set is obtained.

Returning to the example given earlier in this chapter, we have the five variables l, A, ϵ, F, and E. Their dimensions are given in Table 12.5.

TABLE 12.5. THE DIMENSIONAL MATRIX OF THE FIVE
VARIABLES l, A, ϵ, F, AND E

	l	A	ϵ	F	E
M	0	0	0	1	1
L	1	2	0	1	-1
T	0	0	0	-2	-2

†See any standard text on theory of equations, for instance, L. W. Griffiths, "Introduction to the Theory of Equations," chap. 7, John Wiley & Sons, Inc., New York, 1947.

It can be shown by evaluation that all determinants of the third order taken from the matrix of Table 12.5 are zero and at least one of the second-order determinants is not zero. Therefore the rank of the dimensional matrix is 2. Hence there are only $5 - 2$, or 3, dimensionless products in the complete set. Accordingly, $\pi_1 = Al^{-2}$, $\pi_2 = F^{-1}El^2$, $\pi_5 = \epsilon^{-1}$ constitutes a complete set of dimensionless products of the variables l, A, ϵ, F, and E. It should be noted that any three independent dimensionless products here will form a complete set.

12.6. Dimensional Homogeneity. An equation will be said to be dimensionally homogeneous if the form of the equation does not depend on the units of measurement. For example, the equation of the falling body ($h = \frac{1}{2}gt^2$) is valid whether length is measured in feet, meters, or inches and whether time is measured in hours, years, or seconds, provided g is measured in the same units of length and time as h and t. Therefore, by definition, the equation is dimensionally homogeneous. If the value $g = 32.2$ ft/sec^2 is substituted in the equation, there results $h = 16.1t^2$. This equation applies only if length is measured in feet and time is measured in seconds and is not dimensionally homogeneous.

The application of dimensional analysis to physical problems is based on the hypothesis that the solution of physical problems is always expressible by means of a dimensionally homogeneous equation in terms of specified variables. This hypothesis is justified by the fact that the fundamental equations of mechanics are dimensionally homogeneous and that relationships that may be deduced from these equations are consequently dimensionally homogeneous.

We quote, without proof, a fundamental theorem on dimensional analysis called Buckingham's theorem:†

If an equation is dimensionally homogeneous, it can be reduced to a relationship among a complete set of dimensionless products.

12.7. Elastic Structures Statically Loaded. All the above applies to any physical phenomenon. In the following, an application will be developed to the case of statically loaded elastic structures. The material of the structure can be completely defined by the modulus of elasticity E and Poisson's ratio ν as shown in the chapter on the theory of elasticity. The geometry of the structure can be defined by one length l and the ratios r_1, r_1', r_1'', ... of all other lengths to l. The loads can be divided into five categories.

1. Concentrated loads acting on a point can be specified by one of them, P, and the ratios r_2, r_2', r_2'', ... of the others to P. P will have the dimension of a force.

---

†For the proof of this theorem, see Henry L. Langhaar, "Dimensional Analysis and Theory of Models," chap. 4, John Wiley & Sons, Inc., New York, 1951.

2. Loads distributed on a line can be specified by one of them, Q, and the ratios r_3, r_3', r_3'', ... of all others to Q. Q will have the dimension of a force per unit length.

3. Loads distributed on a surface can be specified by one of them, R, and the ratios r_4, r_4', r_4'', ... of all others to R. R will have the dimension of a force per unit area.

4. Loads distributed in a volume can be specified by one of them, S, and the ratios r_5, r_5', r_5'', ... of all others to S. S will have the dimension of a force per unit volume. Body forces such as the dead weight of structures and seismic loads belong to this category.

5. Prescribed boundary displacements can be specified by one of them, U, and the ratios r_6, r_6', r_6'', ... of all others to U. U will have the dimension of a length.

The directions of the loads can be specified by θ, θ', θ'', ... The formula for the stress at a point whose coordinates are x, y, z, will be

$$\sigma = f_1(x,y,z,E,\nu;l,r_1,r_1',\cdots;P,r_2,r_2',\cdots;Q,r_3,r_3'\cdots;R,r_4,r_4',\cdots;$$
$$S,r_5,r_5',\cdots;U,r_6,r_6',\cdots;\theta,\theta',\theta'',\cdots) \tag{12.3}$$

assuming isotropy and homogeneity and Hooke's law. The dimensional matrix of the above variables is

TABLE 12.6. DIMENSIONAL MATRIX OF VARIABLES OF ELASTIC STRUCTURES

	σ	x	y	z	E	ν	l	P	Q	R	S	U
M	1	0	0	0	1	0	0	1	1	1	1	0
L	-1	1	1	1	-1	0	1	1	0	-1	-2	1
T	-2	0	0	0	-2	0	0	-2	-2	-2	-2	0

r_1	r_1'	...	r_2	r_2'	...	r_3	r_3'	...	r_4	r_4'	...	r_5	r_5'	...	r_6	r_6'	...	θ	θ'	...
0	0	...	0	0	...	0	0	...	0	0	...	0	0	...	0	0	...	0	0	...
0	0	...	0	0	...	0	0	...	0	0	...	0	0	...	0	0	...	0	0	...
0	0	...	0	0	...	0	0	...	0	0	...	0	0	...	0	0	...	0	0	...

Since all the third-order determinants taken from the above matrix are zero, and at least one of the second-order determinants is not zero, the rank of the matrix is 2. The number of independent dimensionless products necessary to form a complete set of dimensionless products is therefore two less than the number of variables. The following constitutes a complete set of dimensionless products:

$$\frac{\sigma}{E}, \frac{x}{l}, \frac{y}{l}, \frac{z}{l}, \nu, \frac{P}{El^2}, \frac{Q}{El}, \frac{R}{E}, \frac{Sl}{E}, \frac{U}{l}, r_1, r_1', \cdots,$$

$$r_2, r_2', \cdots, r_3, r_3', \cdots, r_4, r_4', \cdots, r_5, r_5', \cdots, r_6, r_6', \cdots, \theta, \theta', \cdots$$

By Buckingham's theorem, Eq. (12.3) is reducible to the following form:

$$\frac{\sigma}{E} = f_2\left(\frac{x}{l}, \frac{y}{l}, \frac{z}{l}, \nu, \frac{P}{El^2}, \frac{Q}{El}, \frac{R}{E}, \frac{Sl}{E}, \frac{U}{l},\right.$$

$$r_1, r_1', \cdots ; r_2, r_2', \cdots ; r_3, r_3', \cdots ;$$

$$\left. r_4, r_4', \cdots ; r_5, r_5', \cdots ; r_6, r_6', \cdots ; \theta, \theta', \cdots \right) \qquad (12.4)$$

In experimental stress analysis, it is often impracticable to perform tests on the real structure or prototype. In such cases, a model of the real structure is built, usually at a reduced scale and often of a different material. Tests are performed on the model, and the stresses and strains in the model are determined. The stresses and strains in the real structure can then be obtained if the relations between the stresses and strains in the model and the prototype are known. This relation can be established by dimensional analysis and will now be shown. Equation (12.4) is applied to both model and prototype. Although the form of the function f_2 is unknown, it is the same for both. If we make a model such that the numerical values of all the dimensionless products x/l, y/l, z/l, ν, ... at the right-hand side of Eq. (12.4) are equal to those of the prototype, respectively, then the numerical value of σ/E for the model will also be equal to that of the prototype. If the subscript m is used for the model and p for the prototype, then

$$\frac{\sigma_p}{E_p} = \frac{\sigma_m}{E_m}$$

or

$$\sigma_p = \frac{E_p}{E_m} \sigma_m$$

The true stress at any point x, y, z in the prototype would then be equal to the stress at the similarly situated point in the model multiplied by the ratio between the modulus of elasticity of prototype to that of model.

Making x/l, y/l, z/l the same for both model and prototype means that the stress is to be taken at similarly situated points in the model and prototype. Making r_1, r_1', ... the same for both model and prototype means geometric similarity for the model and prototype. Making r_2, r_2', ... ; r_3, r_3', ... ; r_4, r_4', ... ; r_5, r_5', ... ; r_6, r_6', ... ; θ, θ', ... the same means similarity of load distribution. If the stresses do depend on ν, then the model material should have the same Poisson's ratio as the prototype. Making P/El^2, Q/El, R/E, Sl/E, U/l the same for both means

$$\frac{P_m}{P_p} = \frac{E_m}{E_p}\left(\frac{l_m}{l_p}\right)^2$$

$$\frac{Q_m}{Q_p} = \frac{E_m}{E_p}\frac{l_m}{l_p}$$

$$\frac{R_m}{R_p} = \frac{E_m}{E_p}$$

$$\frac{S_m}{S_p} = \frac{E_m}{E_p}\frac{l_p}{l_m}$$

$$\frac{U_m}{U_p} = \frac{l_m}{l_p}$$

The loads must therefore be scaled down according to these rules.

Similar analyses can be carried out for the displacement w and the strain ϵ at any point x, y, z, of the structure. Thus

$$\frac{w}{l} = f_3\left(\frac{x}{l},\frac{y}{l},\frac{z}{l},\nu,\frac{P}{El^2},\ldots\right)$$

$$\epsilon = f_4\left(\frac{x}{l},\frac{y}{l},\frac{z}{l},\nu,\frac{P}{El^2},\ldots\right)$$

For a model which has all its values of x/l, y/l, z/l, ν, P/El^2, . . . equal to that of the prototype,

$$\frac{w_m}{w_p} = \frac{l_m}{l_p}$$

$$\epsilon_m = \epsilon_p$$

The deformations have not been assumed small. The above applies to all structures made of materials obeying Hooke's law and stressed below its proportional limit. Very flexible steel springs, thin plates transversely loaded to large deflection, and other structures where the stresses, strains, displacements, and redundant reactions are in general not proportional to the loads can therefore also be analyzed by the above procedure.

12.8. Linear Structures. From the theory of elasticity, we know that, for stiff structures where the deformations do not affect the action of the loads, the stresses, strains, displacements, and redundant reactions are always linear functions of the loads. This knowledge makes the following simplification of Eq. (12.4) possible:

$$\frac{\sigma}{E} = \frac{P}{El^2}\, g_1\!\left(\frac{x}{l},\frac{y}{l},\frac{z}{l},\nu,r_1,r_1',\ldots,r_2,r_2',\ldots,\theta,\theta',\ldots\right)$$

$$+ \frac{Q}{El}\, g_2\!\left(\frac{x}{l},\frac{y}{l},\frac{z}{l},\nu,r_1,r_1',\ldots,r_2,r_2',\ldots,\theta,\theta',\ldots\right)$$

$$+ \frac{R}{E}\, g_3\!\left(\frac{x}{l},\frac{y}{l},\frac{z}{l},\nu,r_1,r_1',\ldots,r_2,r_2',\ldots,\theta,\theta',\ldots\right) \qquad (12.5)$$

$$+ \frac{Sl}{E}\, g_4\!\left(\frac{x}{l},\frac{y}{l},\frac{z}{l},\nu,r_1,r_1',\ldots,r_2,r_2',\ldots,\theta,\theta',\ldots\right)$$

$$+ \frac{U}{l}\, g_5\!\left(\frac{x}{l},\frac{y}{l},\frac{z}{l},\nu,r_1,r_1',\ldots,r_2,r_2',\ldots,\theta,\theta',\ldots\right)$$

Similar expressions exist for w/l and ϵ. If we make $x/l,\ y/l,\ z/l,\ \nu,\ r_1,\ r_1',\ \ldots,$ $r_2, r_2', \ldots, r_3, r_3', \ldots, r_4, r_4', \ldots, r_5, r_5', \ldots, r_6, r_6', \ldots, \theta, \theta', \ldots$ the same for model and prototype, then

$$\frac{\sigma}{E} = C_1\frac{P}{El^2} + C_2\frac{Q}{El} + C_3\frac{R}{E} + C_4\frac{Sl}{E} + C_5\frac{U}{l}$$

where the constants $C_1, C_2, \ldots, C_5$ are independent of the loads $P, Q, R, S,$ U and are the same for model and prototype. By running five separate tests on the model, each test using only one among the five types of loads P, Q, R, S, U, the values of these constants $C_1, C_2, \ldots, C_5$ can be determined for any point whose stress is required.

Similar constants for the strain ϵ and displacement w/l can be determined in the same manner. This reasoning will be applied to two concrete cases in the following examples.

Example 1. Let us consider a thick plate with a hole (Fig. 12.1), under a uniformly distributed load R_p at its two ends. Let the modulus of elasticity and Poisson's ratio of the material of the plate be E_p and ν_p, respectively. The problem is to design a model to study the stress distribution of this thick plate.

By Eq. (12.5), the stresses σ_p in the prototype at any point A_p whose coordinates are x, y, z are given by

$$\frac{\sigma_p}{E_p} = \frac{R_p}{E_p}\, g_3\!\left(\frac{x}{l},\frac{y}{l},\frac{z}{l},\nu,r_1,r_1',r_1''\right)$$

(12.6)

or

$$\sigma_p = R_p g_3\!\left(\frac{x}{l},\frac{y}{l},\frac{z}{l},\nu,r_1,r_1',r_1''\right)$$

Consider a model which is geometrically similar to the prototype so

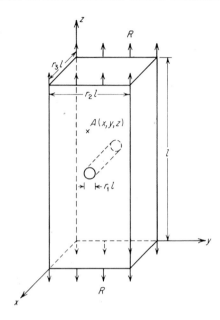

FIG. 12.1. Thick plate with a hole, under a uniformly distributed load.

that r_1, r_1', r_1'' are the same for the model and prototype.   Let the model be made of a material having the same Poisson's ratio as that of the prototype.   Under a uniformly distributed load R_m, the stresses in the model at a similarly situated point A_m will be given by

$$\sigma_m = R_m g_3 \left(\frac{x}{l}, \frac{y}{l}, \frac{z}{l}, \nu, r_1, r_1', r_1'' \right) \tag{12.7}$$

where g_3 will have the same value as in Eq. (12.6).

Equation (12.6) is divided by Eq. (12.7) to obtain

$$\frac{\sigma_p}{\sigma_m} = \frac{R_p}{R_m} \tag{12.8}$$

The stresses in the prototype and in the geometrically similar model at similarly situated points are therefore in the same proportion as the intensity of the uniformly distributed load.   The materials of the prototype and the model must have the same Poisson's ratio but not necessarily the same modulus of elasticity.   The length scale factor of the model does not appear in Eq. (12.8), so that the model can be made one-tenth or five times as large as the prototype and Eq. (12.8) still holds.

If the plate is thin, from the theory of elasticity we have the additional knowledge that the plane-stress solution is applicable.   This means that for this case both the thickness of the plate and Poisson's ratio will not enter the solution for stresses. For such a prototype the model must be geometrically similar to the prototype in the direction of its width and length. It can be a thin plate of any thickness which is small compared with the diameter of the hole, made of any elastic material. The relation between the stresses in the model and the prototype will still be given by Eq. (12.8). Here again, the length scale factor of the model does not enter Eq. (12.8). The model can be half or twice the size of the prototype and Eq. (12.8) always holds.

Example 2. Let us consider a thick cylinder with an eccentric hole, loaded as shown in Fig. 12.2. By Eq. (12.5) the stresses σ_p at any point A_p whose coordinates are x, y, z are given by

$$\frac{\sigma_p}{E_p} = \frac{P_p}{E_p l_p^2}\, g_1\!\left(\frac{x}{l},\frac{y}{l},\frac{z}{l},\nu,r_1,r_1',r_1''\right) + \frac{R_p}{E_p}\, g_3\!\left(\frac{x}{l},\frac{y}{l},\frac{z}{l},\nu,r_1,r_1',r_1''\right) \qquad (12.9)$$

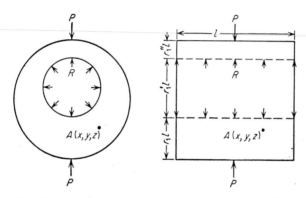

FIG. 12.2. Cylinder under internal pressure and a concentrated diametral load.

Construct a model geometrically similar to the given cylinder, and made of a material whose Poisson's ratio is the same as that of the prototype. Then, at a similarly located point A_m in the model, the stresses under similarly distributed loads P_m and R_m will be

$$\frac{\sigma_m}{E_m} = \frac{P_m}{E_m l_m^2}\, g_1\!\left(\frac{x}{l},\frac{y}{l},\frac{z}{l},\nu,r_1,r_1',r_1''\right) + \frac{R_m}{E_m}\, g_3\!\left(\frac{x}{l},\frac{y}{l},\frac{z}{l},\nu,r_1,r_1',r_1''\right) \qquad (12.10)$$

where g_1 and g_3 have the same values as in Eq. (12.9).

To get σ_p from the observed σ_m in the model, either one of the two following methods can be used.

Method 1. The principle of superposition will be used. The portion of the stress $(\sigma_p)_1$ due to P_p alone will be determined separately from the portion of the stress $(\sigma_p)_2$ due to R_p alone. Then the true stress σ_p due to P_p and R_p will be obtained as the sum of $(\sigma_p)_1$ and $(\sigma_p)_2$. Two separate tests must therefore be conducted, one employing P_m only on the model, and the other employing R_m only on the model. The values of $(\sigma_p)_1$ and $(\sigma_p)_2$ are obtained from these two tests separately by the method shown in Example 1.

Method 2. The ratio of P/l^2 to R will be made the same in model as in prototype, so that

$$\frac{P_p}{l_p^2} = R_p \frac{P_m}{R_m l_m^2} \tag{12.11}$$

By Eqs. (12.9), (12.11),

$$\sigma_p = \frac{P_p}{l_p^2} g_1 + R_p g_3$$

$$= R_p \frac{P_m}{R_m l_m^2} g_1 + R_p g_3 \tag{12.12}$$

$$= \frac{R_p}{R_m} \left[\frac{P_m}{l_m^2} g_1 + R_m g_3 \right]$$

Therefore by Eqs. (12.10) and (12.12),

$$\sigma_p = \frac{R_p}{R_m} \sigma_m \tag{12.13}$$

Given any combination of P_p and R_p, it is sufficient to load the specimen in such a way that Eq. (12.11) is fulfilled, and the stresses in the prototype σ_p can be calculated from the observed stress σ_m in the model. In this method only one test needs to be conducted. But the stresses obtained will be only those corresponding to the given combination of P_p and R_p. To obtain the stresses of a different combination of P_p and R_p, a second test must be performed in a similar manner. After the stresses corresponding to any two different combinations of P_p and R_p are obtained, the stresses due to a load of P_p or R_p alone can be computed by solving two simultaneous equations. The stresses corresponding to any other combinations of P_p and R_p can then be obtained by superposition.

It should be pointed out that no restrictions are imposed on the value of the modulus of elasticity E_m of the material of the model. The stresses are independent of the modulus of elasticity. The strains in the prototype ϵ_p are always calculated from the stresses and will of course depend on E_p.

12.9. Composite Structures. Where the structure is composed of two or more materials whose moduli of elasticity and Poisson's ratios are $E, E_1, E_2, \ldots$; $\nu, \nu_1, \nu_2, \ldots$ respectively, the additional dimensionless products $E_1/E, E_2/E, \ldots$; $\nu, \nu_1, \nu_2, \ldots$ would appear, and these must be the same for model and prototype. Often Poisson's ratio does not affect appreciably the stresses sought and can therefore be omitted. For example, the model of a reinforced-concrete structure may be made of materials having the same ratio of moduli as between steel and concrete but with Poisson's ratios different from steel and concrete.

12.10. Application of the Method to a Specific Stress-analysis Problem. Suppose it is desired to determine experimentally stresses and strains set up by shock waves impinging upon obstructions embedded in a wave-propagating medium. Since full-scale tests are expensive, the possibility of experimentally studying the problem by means of scaled-down models might be considered. For example, the stresses could be determined photoelastically, and a purely optical approach might be used to obtain displacements and hence strains. By means of the methods of dimensional analysis discussed in this chapter, the feasibility of using such experimental methods to study this problem will be investigated. It is cautioned, however, that this discussion should be looked upon as only an example illustrating the use of the methods of this chapter; and while a set of scale laws are derived which must necessarily be adhered to in conducting the experiment, there is no reason to believe that these laws represent a sufficient set of conditions to be met. For a new problem such as this which is gone into for the first time, a simplified approach is useful as a preliminary feasibility study; but it may be found that additional variables over the ones selected have influence on the problem.

The variables involved in specifying the phenomena are contained in some function

$$\tau = F(x,y,z,E,E_0,\epsilon,\nu,\nu_0,\rho,\rho_0 t; l,r_1,r_1',\ldots;P,r_2,r_2',\ldots;$$

$$Q,r_3,r_3',\ldots;R,r_4,r_4',\ldots;S,r_5,r_5',\ldots;U,r_6,r_6',\ldots;\theta,\theta',\theta'',\ldots) \qquad (12.14)$$

which gives the stress at the point x, y, z. Symbols which appear here and were not present in the previous examples are those arising from the dynamic nature of the problem, viz., mass density ρ and time t. The terms E_0, ν_0, ρ_0 refer to to the obstructions, while E, ϵ, ν, ρ refer to the wave-transmitting medium. The remainder of the variables apply throughout both.

The following simplification and assumptions are made: By the introduction of E and ν it is implicitly assumed that the phenomenon occurs entirely within the elastic range. This is not quite true in the case of many photoelastic materials. In most plastics, for example, the modulus of elasticity E has been found to vary with strain rate. If this effect is very pronounced, the problem becomes much more complicated. It will nevertheless be supposed in this illustrative example that E and ν are constants and that this approximation will lead to sufficiently accurate results.

It will be further assumed that no damping occurs, i.e., that there is no wave attenuation resulting from internal friction, or, as it is often called, "hysteresis damping." Damping is present to some extent in all materials, but in this example it will be neglected.

Isotropy and homogeneity are, of course, also assumed. The terms S, r_5, r_5', $\cdots$ can be excluded if body forces are neglected. In many applications, obstructions can be considered to be acted upon by a plane-strain shock wave (i.e., one for which the strain perpendicular to the direction of its travel is zero). This suggests using for the model wave-transmitting medium a slab of photoelastic material (see Fig. 12.3). Knowing the stress-time shape of the shock wave approaching the obstructions, a simulated stress- (or displacement-) time wave can be applied to one end of the model

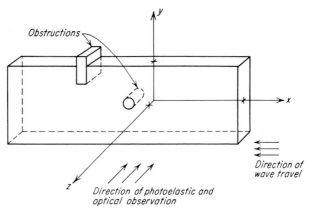

FIG. 12.3. Possible laboratory method for determining stresses around and displacements of obstructions partially or fully embedded in an elastic medium.

medium, and the resulting stresses and displacements around the obstructions can be determined by photoelasticity and optical techniques as schematically indicated in the figure. By so formulating the problem, the variables P, r_2, r_2', ... ; Q, r_3, r_3', ... ; R, r_4, r_4', ... ; r_6, r_6', ... θ, θ', θ'', ... can be omitted in Eq. (12.14), leaving simply the displacement $U = U(t)$, which represents the plane motion of particles in the medium immediately in front of the obstruction. Equation (12.14) thus simplifies to

$$\sigma = F[x,y,z,E,E_0,\epsilon,\nu,\nu_0,\rho,\rho_0;t;l,r_1,r_1',...;U(t)] \qquad (12.15)$$

Examination of the dimensional matrix of these variables will show that at least one third-order determinant is not zero†, so that the rank of the

†One nonzero determinant is that corresponding to the three variables σ, ρ, t; that is,

$$\begin{vmatrix} 1 & 1 & 0 \\ -1 & -3 & 0 \\ -2 & 0 & 1 \end{vmatrix} = -2$$

matrix is 3. The number of independent dimensionless products necessary to form a complete set of dimensionless products is therefore three less than the number of variables. One of the ways of writing the complete set is

$$\frac{\sigma}{E\epsilon}, \frac{x}{l}, \frac{y}{l}, \frac{z}{l}, \frac{E_0}{E}, \epsilon, \nu, \nu_0, \frac{\rho l^2}{Et^2}, \frac{\rho_0}{\rho}, r_1, r_1', \ldots, \frac{U}{l\epsilon} \qquad (12.16)$$

If the value of each of these groups is made the same for the model and prototype, then, by Buckingham's theorem, the law [Eq. (12.15)] governing the phenomena will hold for both. Making x/l, y/l, z/l, r_1, r_1', ... equal for both means that the model will be geometrically similar to the prototype and that the stresses occurring in the model will occur in the prototype at geometrically similar locations. Using subscripts m and p to denote model and prototype, respectively, and introducing the scale factors

$$K_\sigma = \frac{\sigma_p}{\sigma_m} \qquad K_E = \frac{E_p}{E_m} \qquad K_\epsilon = \frac{\epsilon_p}{\epsilon_m}$$

the condition of equality between model and prototype of the first dimensionless product can be written

$$K_\sigma = K_E K_\epsilon$$

This can be done for all the dimensionless groups, with the results

$$K_\sigma = K_E K_\epsilon \qquad K_E = K_{E_0} \qquad K_\epsilon = 1 \qquad K_\nu = K_{\nu_0} = 1$$
$$K_\rho K_l^2 = K_E K_t^2 \qquad K_\rho = K_{\rho_0} \qquad K_U = K_l K_\epsilon$$

If the test is kept within the linear range of elasticity, the requirement $K_\epsilon = 1$ need not be met. This is because a deviation from this requirement corresponds only to an equal deviation in K_σ and K_U, which in turn merely implies a higher or lower stress and displacement level.

The requirement that $K_\nu = K_{\nu_0} = 1$ means that Poisson's ratio for both model and prototype obstruction and wave-transmitting medium must be equal. Quite probably it will not be possible to adhere to the requirement, and it must be neglected.

A final simplification: if E_0 is much larger than E (that is, the obstructions can be assumed to be rigid compared with the wave-transmitting medium), E_0 can be dropped from the analysis. The final set of scale-law equations is then

$$K_\sigma = K_E K_\epsilon \qquad (12.17a)$$

$$K_\rho K_l^2 = K_E K_t^2 \qquad (12.17b)$$

$$K_\rho = K_{\rho_0} \qquad (12.17c)$$

$$K_\nu = K_l K_\epsilon \qquad (12.17d)$$

$$K_\epsilon = \text{arbitrary but below elastic limit} \qquad (12.17e)$$

There are many possible ways of combining the variables to obtain a complete set of dimensionless products such as given in (12.16); however, the one chosen leads to a form of Eqs. (12.17) which admits a direct physical interpretation. Thus, Eq. (12.17a) is representative of the stress-strain relations [see Eqs. (4.17)], and Eq. (12.17b) corresponds to the wave equation in mechanics.† The third equation simply states that the ratio of densities of obstruction to wave-propagating medium must be the same for both model and prototype, and Eq. (12.17d) expresses the strain-displacement relations of the theory of elasticity [Eqs. (2.11) and (2.13)]. Other scale factors can be derived from those in Eq. (12.17), viz.:

Wave-velocity scale factor $\quad = K_l/K_t$ $\qquad$ (12.18a)

Wave-acceleration scale factor $\quad = K_l/K_t^2$ $\qquad$ (12.18b)

Particle velocity scale factor $\quad = K_U/K_t = K_l K_\epsilon/K_t$ $\qquad$ (12.18c)

Particle acceleration scale factor $= K_U/K_t^2 = K_l K_\epsilon/K_t^2$ $\qquad$ (12.18d)

The basic design equation for setting up the experiment is Eq. (12.17b). To illustrate, suppose the values

$$E_p = 55{,}000 \text{ psi}$$

$$\rho_p = 90 \text{ lb/ft}^3$$

are assumed for soil; and

$$E_m = 18 \text{ psi}$$

$$\rho_m = 62 \text{ lb/ft}^3$$

are taken for the chosen photoelastic model material; then by Eq. (12.17b)

$$\frac{K_l}{K_t} = \sqrt{\frac{55{,}000/18}{90/62}} \cong 46$$

This means that, for a wave traveling 1,700 fps in the soil, the model wave velocity will be 1,700/46 = 37 fps. The above also establishes the ratio of the scales for length and time. If a convenient length scale is 150, the time scale will be approximately 3. The acceleration scale will correspondingly be, by Eq. (12.18b),

$$\frac{K_l}{K_t^2} = \frac{150}{9} = 16.7$$

From Eqs. (12.18c), (12.18d), particle velocities and accelerations will, on the other hand, be $K_l K_\epsilon/K_t = 46K_\epsilon$ and $K_l K_\epsilon/K_t^2 = 16.7K_\epsilon$, respectively, which indicates that these are proportional to the strain scale factor, whatever its value is chosen to be.

†A simplified form of which is, for example, that the velocity v of a wave propagating in a long slender elastic bar having density ρ and modulus of E is expressed by: $v = \sqrt{E/\rho}$.

12.11. Structural Similarity. If the fundamental equations governing the phenomena are known, the scale-factor laws may be derived directly from these equations without utilizing the methods of dimensional analysis. Thus in the example mentioned in Sec. 12.10 we might expect that the stress-strain relations, the strain-displacement relations, and the wave equations of mechanics are known to apply. By writing these equations in their most general form for both the model and the prototype, and introducing the scale factors, Eqs. (12.17) will result directly.

In order that the reader may understand these concepts, he is advised to pursue the following simple examples which illustrate the use of structural similarity in the derivation of the basic scale-factor laws in each particular problem.

Straight Member under Axial Load. One of the simplest problems which may be solved by the principles of structural similarity is that of a straight tension member under a unidimensional uniformly distributed axial load. Such a member of rectangular cross section is shown in Fig. 12.4. Here

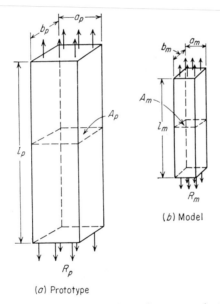

FIG. 12.4. Geometric similarity between model and prototype in the case of a straight bar under a unidimensional state of stress.

it may seem that the dimensions of a geometrically similar model are given by $l_m = \lambda l_p$, $a_m = \lambda a_p$, and $b_m = \lambda b_p$, where λ is a given constant factor. The cross-sectional area of the prototype is given by

$$A_p = a_p \times b_p \tag{12.19}$$

The area in the model will be given by

$$A_m = \lambda^2 \times A_p \tag{12.20}$$

Similarly it is seen that

$$V_m = \lambda^3 \times V_p \tag{12.21}$$

where V_m and V_p represent the volumes of the model and prototype respectively.

If the stresses are defined as total force across any cross section divided by cross-sectional area, i.e., $\sigma_p = R_p/A_p$ and $\sigma_m = R_m/A_m$, it may be seen, using Eq. (12.20), that

$$\sigma_m = \frac{R_m}{\lambda^2 A_p} \tag{12.22}$$

If the requirement that the stresses in the model and in the prototype be the same is to be satisfied, it is necessary that the load on the model satisfy the relation

$$R_m = \lambda^2 R_p \tag{12.23}$$

If the requirement that the load on the model and on the prototype be the same is to be satisfied, it is necessary that the stress in the model satisfy the following relation:

$$\sigma_m = \frac{\sigma_p}{\lambda^2} \tag{12.24}$$

At this point it may be observed that the elastic constants E and ν do not influence the scaling laws of either the model stresses or model loads. Assuming that the elastic constants of the mode and the prototype are different, it is necessary that the scale-factor laws for the model strains contain one of these constants, viz., Young's modulus, E. Thus, we have

$$\epsilon_p = \frac{\sigma_p}{E_p} = \frac{R_p}{A_p E_p} \tag{12.25}$$

$$\epsilon_m = \frac{\sigma_m}{E_m} = \frac{R_m}{\lambda^2 A_p E_m} \tag{12.26}$$

From (12.26) it is easily seen that the requirement that the strains in the model and in the prototype be the same implies either that $E_m = E_p$ and $R_m = \lambda^2 R_p$ or that $E_m \neq E_p$ and

$$R_m = \frac{\lambda^2 E_m}{E_p} R_p \tag{12.27}$$

The requirement that the loads on the model and on the prototype be the same implies that

$$\epsilon_m = \frac{E_p}{\lambda^2 E_m} \epsilon_p \tag{12.28}$$

It should be observed from Eq. (12.22) that, regardless of the geometric shape of the cross section, if $A_m = A_p/K$,

$$\sigma_m = K\sigma_p \tag{12.29}$$

provided that the loads are the same. It should also be pointed out that Eqs. (12.25) and (12.26), relating the strains in the model to the strains in the prototype, will be valid regardless of the shape of the cross section. That is, if

$$A_m = \lambda^2 A_p$$

whatever the shape of A_m and A_p, the strains in the model will still be related to the strains in the prototype and Eqs. (12.27) and (12.28) will still be valid. Another important result shown by these considerations is that the modulus of elasticity may be determined from specimens of any cross section.

The total displacement of any specimen is given by

$$\Delta l = l\epsilon \tag{12.30}$$

Thus the total displacements in the model and in the prototype are given respectively as

$$\Delta l_m = l_m \epsilon_m \tag{12.31}$$

$$\Delta l_p = l_p \epsilon_p \tag{12.32}$$

Substituting (12.26) into (12.31), we obtain

$$\Delta l_m = \frac{R_m l_m}{\lambda^2 A_p E_m} \tag{12.33}$$

If $\Delta l_p = \Delta l_m$, then it follows from (12.32) and (12.33) that

$$\frac{R_p}{E_p} = \frac{l_m}{\lambda^2 l_p} \frac{R_m}{E_m} \tag{12.34}$$

Then Eq. (12.34) must be the scale-factor law relating the model loads and modulus of elasticity to the prototype loads and modulus of elasticity when it is desired that displacements in the model and in the prototype be the same. It can be seen from (12.34) that if $E_m = E_p$, then

$$R_m = \lambda^2 R_p l_p/l_m \tag{12.35}$$

If, on the other hand, the loads on the model and prototype are the same, i.e., $R_m = R_p$, then it follows from (12.25), (12.26), (12.31), and (12.32) that the scale-factor law relating the total displacement and modulus of elasticity of the model to the total displacement and modulus of elasticity of the prototype is given by

$$\Delta l_m = \frac{l_m}{l_p} \frac{E_p}{\lambda^2 E_m} \Delta l_p \tag{12.36}$$

Uniformly Loaded, Simply Supported Beam. The second example of interest is the problem of the uniformly loaded, simply supported beam. Figure 12.5 illustrates such a beam. If it were desirable to study the mechanical behavior of such a beam by means of a model, it would be

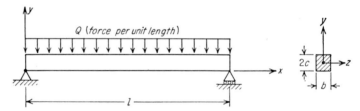

Fig. 12.5. Simply supported beam under uniformly distributed load.

necessary to determine the scale-factor laws relating the deflections and stresses in such a model to the stresses and deflections in the prototype.

The length, depth, and width of the model are assumed to be given respectively as $l_m = \lambda l_p$, $2c_m = 2\lambda c_p$, and $b_m = \lambda b_p$. The coordinate system is defined in Fig. 12.5. If we define a value C as

$$C = \frac{I}{c} \tag{12.37}$$

where I is the moment of inertia of the cross section of any beam and $2c$ is the depth of that beam, then we have from the properties of geometrical similarity that

$$I_m = \lambda^4 I_p \tag{12.38}$$
$$C_m = \lambda^3 C_p \tag{12.39}$$

From elementary strength of materials the deflection at any point on this beam, the elastic moment, and the longitudinal normal stress are given respectively by:

$$y = \frac{Qx}{24EI} (-l^3 + 2lx^2 - x^3) \tag{12.40a}$$

$$M = \frac{Qx}{2} (l - x) \tag{12.40b}$$

$$\sigma = \frac{M}{C} = \frac{Qx}{2C} (l - x) \tag{12.40c}$$

Substituting into Eqs. (12.40) the geometrical dimensions and constants of the prototype and model, we arrive at the relations

$$y_p = \frac{Q_p x_p}{24 E_p I_p} (-l_p^3 + 2l_p x_p^2 - x_p^3) \tag{12.41a}$$

$$y_m = \frac{Q_m x_m}{24 E_m I_m} (-l_m^3 + 2l_m x_m^2 - x_m^3) \tag{12.41b}$$

$$M_p = \frac{Q_p x_p}{2} (l_p - x_p) \tag{12.41c}$$

$$M_m = \frac{Q_m x_m}{2} (l_m - x_m) \tag{12.41d}$$

$$\sigma_p = \frac{M_p}{C_p} = \frac{Q_p x_p}{2C_p} (l_p - x_p) \tag{12.41e}$$

$$\sigma_m = \frac{M_m}{C_m} = \frac{Q_m x_m}{2C_m} (l_m - x_m) \tag{12.41f}$$

Substituting the geometrical dimensions of the model in terms of the geometrical dimensions of the prototype into Eq. (12.41b), (12.41d), and (1241f) and using the relations (12.41a), (12.41c), and (12.41e), we get

$$y_m = \frac{Q_m}{Q_p} \frac{E_p}{E_m} y_p \tag{12.42a}$$

$$M_m = \frac{Q_m}{Q_p} \lambda^2 M_p \tag{12.42b}$$

$$\sigma_m = \frac{Q_m}{Q_p} \frac{\sigma_p}{\lambda} \tag{12.42c}$$

From Eqs. (12.42) we see that, if $E_m = E_p$ and $Q_m = Q_p$, the deflections of the model and prototype are the same. It should be pointed out at this time that because Q_m and Q_p are defined as loads per unit length, if the length is doubled the total load will be doubled but the deflections will remain the same.

It is observed from Eqs. (12.41) and (12.42) that if $\sigma_m = \sigma_p$, the resulting scale factor laws will be

$$Q_m = \lambda Q_p \tag{12.43a}$$

$$M_m = \lambda^3 M_p \tag{12.43b}$$

$$y_m = \lambda \frac{E_p}{E_m} y_p \tag{12.43c}$$

Cantilever Beam under Concentrated Load. Another example similar to the last one is the problem of the cantilever beam under a concentrated end load. Fig. 12.6 shows such a beam of length l under load P. The maximum deflection y_{max} is found from elementary strength theory considerations to be given by:

$$y_{max} = \frac{Pl^3}{3EI} \qquad (12.44)$$

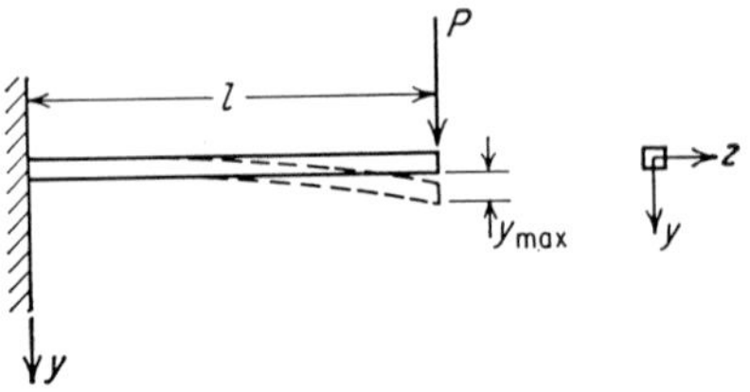

FIG. 12.6. Cantilever beam under concentrated load at the end.

If a model were constructed geometrically similar to the prototype, its length would be given as $l_m = \lambda l_p$ and the moment of inertia I_m would be given as $I_m = \lambda^4 I_p$. As is easily seen, the equations for the maximum deflection in the prototype and model are then given respectively as

$$y_{p\ max} = \frac{P_p l_p^3}{3E_p I_p} \qquad (12.45a)$$

$$y_{m\ max} = \frac{P_m l_m^3}{3E_m I_m} \qquad (12.45b)$$

By substituting into (12.45b) the geometrical dimensions of the model in terms of those of the prototype, we obtain the scale-factor law for the maximum deflections,

$$y_{m\ max} = \frac{P_m}{P_p} \frac{E_p}{E_m} \frac{(y_{p\ max})}{\lambda} \qquad (12.46)$$

From Eq. (12.46) it can be seen that one way to have $y_{m\ max} = y_{p\ max}$ is to make $E_p = E_m$ and $P_m = \lambda P_p$.

Thus if we construct a model whose dimensions are, say, one-half of those of the prototype and which is made of the same material, and load them in a manner such that $P_m = \frac{1}{2}P_p$, we will observe that the bar AB as shown in Fig. 12.7 will remain horizontal after deflection of the two cantilever beams (See Fig. 12.7).

Heavy Beam Simply Supported. The last example is the problem of the simply supported beam under its own weight. Fig. 12.8 illustrates this beam in its undeflected and deflected positions. Although this beam may be considered for structural purposes as a special case of the simply supported beam under a uniform load, it is also of interest to obtain scale-

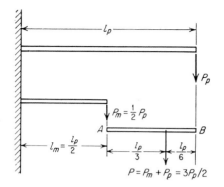

$$y_{m\,\text{max}} = y_{p\,\text{max}} \ \textit{if} \ E_p = E_m \ \textit{and} \ P_m = \lambda P_p$$

Fig. 12.7. Cantilever beams assembly applying the scaling law $y_{m\,\text{max}} = \dfrac{P_m}{P_p}\dfrac{E_p}{E_m}\dfrac{y_{p\,\text{max}}}{\lambda}$. The bar AB should remain horizontal if $E_p = E_m$ and $P_m = \lambda P_p$.

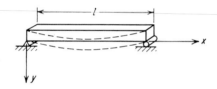

Fig. 12.8. Simply supported beam under its own weight.

factor laws relating the densities and other physical constants of the model to the corresponding quantities in the prototype. Let γ_m and γ_p be the densities of the model and the prototype respectively.

From Eq. (12.43a) and the fact that

$$Q_m = \gamma_m A_m = \gamma_m(\lambda^2 A_p)$$

we conclude that to have $y_m = y_p$, the scale-factor law relating the density of the model to the density of the prototype must be given by

$$\gamma_m = \frac{E_m}{\lambda^2 E_p}\gamma_p \tag{12.47}$$

If $E_m = E_p$, the scale-factor law reduces to

$$\gamma_m = \frac{1}{\lambda^2}\gamma_p \tag{12.47a}$$

If it were desirable to have $\sigma_m = \sigma_p$, then the scale-factor law relating the densities is given by

$$\gamma_m = \frac{1}{\lambda}\gamma_p \tag{12.48}$$

and as a result the relation between the deflections is given by

$$y_m = \lambda \frac{E_p}{E_m} y_p \qquad (12.49)$$

If the models were made of the same material, then it is easily seen that the scale-factor laws for the stresses, deflections, and moments would be given respectively by

$$\sigma_m = \lambda \sigma_p \qquad (12.50a)$$

$$y_m = \lambda^2 y_p \qquad (12.50b)$$

$$M_m = \lambda^4 M_p \qquad (12.50c)$$

Use of Two Scale Factors. Sometimes it becomes convenient to have two factors: one (call it λ) for the longitudinal dimensions, and the second (call it η) for transversal dimensions. Thus the dimensions and mechanical constants of a beam might be $l_m = \lambda l_p$, $x_m = \lambda x_p$, $A_m = \eta^2 A_p$, $I_m = \eta^4 I_p$, $C_m = \eta^3 C_p$. In the first example above for the simply supported beam under uniform loading the equation relating the deflections becomes, using these quantities,

$$y_m = \frac{Q_m \lambda^4 x_p}{24 E_m \eta^4 I_p} (-l_p^3 + 2l_p x_p^2 - x_p^3) \qquad (12.51)$$

It is obvious that the equation relating the bending moments is identical to Eq. (12.42b). However, the equation relating the stresses becomes

$$\sigma_m = \frac{Q_m}{Q_p} \frac{\lambda^2}{\eta^3} \sigma_p \qquad (12.52)$$

Therefore the scale-factor law relating the loads necessary to make $\sigma_p = \sigma_m$ is given by

$$Q_m = \frac{\eta^3}{\lambda^2} Q_p \qquad (12.53)$$

The scale-factor law relating the deflections is then given by

$$y_m = \frac{E_p}{E_m} \frac{\lambda^2}{\eta} y_p \qquad (12.54)$$

PART 3

GRID METHODS

CHAPTER 13

GRID METHODS

13.1. Introduction. The first simple idea that comes to mind for the detection of surface strains in a model is to put a grid on its surface and observe the distortions of the grid as the load is put on. For rectangular grids, if the initial and final spacing of the grid lines as well as the change in length of one of the diagonals of the elementary squares are measured, the principal strains and principal directions can be calculated easily by the rosette formula. For other types of grid geometries, for instance, polar grids, similar measurements can be made and the strains determined. There are various methods of putting the grid on the specimen and of measuring the distortion of the grid under load. The methods of putting on the grid will be discussed first.

13.2. Methods of Putting on Grids. *a. Hand Scratching.* For plates made of relatively soft, transparent materials like plastics, grid lines can be hand-scratched on the front face by a sharp razor blade guided by a straightedge. For these thin scratches to show, the light source should come from behind the specimen. The scratches will then appear as thin, dark lines against a light background. Filling the scratches with ink will also increase the contrast. This method is the simplest and the least expensive, but the grid lines cannot be spaced with precision.

Circular scratches can be obtained by using a compass with a sharpened point. The scratches obtained in this way, however, are not so thin as those obtained using razor blades.

b. Machine Scribing. Grid lines can be scratched on the surface of the model by machine scribing. The lines obtained are well defined and evenly spaced.

c. Ink Drawing. For rubber models which cannot take scratches, the grid lines may be drawn in ink by hand. In measuring the spacing between two lines, the centers of these lines must be estimated. Since the error of this estimate increases with increasing thickness of the lines, the accuracy of this method will be higher with thin lines. An alternative is to try to draw relatively thick lines but with sharply defined edges. Measurements are then made from the edges rather than from the center of the lines.

Grid lines can also be drawn in ink on transparent plastics to study

305

large deformations. An example of ink lines drawn on a Lucite sheet, to study its formability properties, is shown in Fig. 13.1. Using vacuum, a sphere was produced in the center of the sheet, and the amount of permanent strain introduced was determined by comparing the grid on the spherical part to the grid on the undeformed sheet.

d. Rubber Threads. For soft porous materials, thin rubber threads of about 0.008 in. in diameter can be firmly glued on the specimen by latex. The threads have a very low modulus of elasticity so that their effect on the rigidity of the specimen is negligible. Because threads are manufactured by the extrusion process, they have uniform thickness and straight sides.

e. Photogrid. A fine grid can be printed on the surface of the model by photographic means. The surface is first cleaned and lightly roughened by rubbing with fine pumice. It is then coated with a thin layer of high-contrast light-sensitive emulsion. Many types of emulsions are satisfactory for this work, for instance, those used by Brewer and Glassco† or by Miller.‡ Generally four or five thin layers are sprayed at about 1-min intervals to allow the layers to dry. The model should be kept out of the light between sprayings and under subdued light during sprayings. Provision should often be made for fume removal. After drying, a master negative is placed in close contact with the model. Exposure to an intensive light source is made. To secure maximum clarity of the lines, a vacuum printing frame is preferred. The development of the exposed emulsion then follows the procedure set down for the particular emulsion used.

To make the master negative, a plate glass is first coated with wax. A fine grid is ruled on the plate glass. These lines are etched and filled with lead sulfide. The master negative is then obtained from the master grid by contact printing. In this way master negatives of 100 lines per inch with a maximum of ±1 per cent deviation from the nominal spacing of 0.01 in. may be obtained. This deviation becomes negligible only for large strains involving 50 per cent or more elongation or shortening. For such cases, measurements need be made only on the spacings under maximum load, and no measurements are made on the initial spacings under zero load, because the nominal spacing can be taken as the initial spacings.

An example of a photogrid on an aluminum sheet is shown on Fig. 13.2.

f. Embedded Rubber Threads. The grid method can also be used in conjunction with soft transparent plastics. For this application the grid network is constructed of thin rubber threads which are fastened to

†G. A. Brewer, and R. B. Glassco, Determination of Strain Distribution by the Photogrid Process, *J. Aeronaut. Sci.*, vol. 9, no. 1, pp. 1–7, November, 1941.

‡J. A. Miller, Improved Photogrid Techniques for Determination of Strain over Short Gage Lengths, *Proc. Soc. Exptl. Stress Anal.*, vol. 10, no. 1, pp. 29–34, 1952.

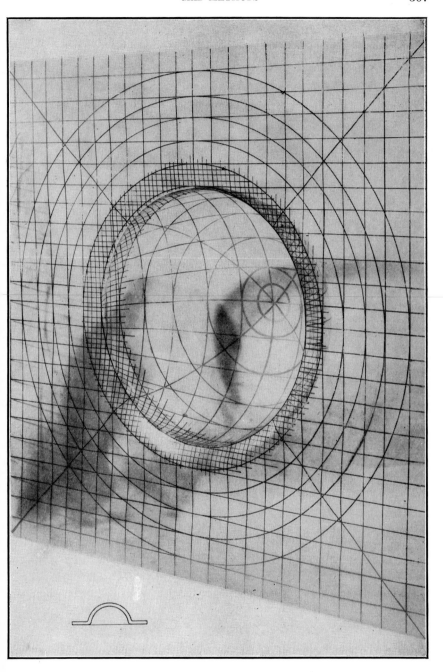

FIG. 13.1. Grid lines drawn in ink used to study formability properties of transparent plastics. The sketch shows a central cross section.

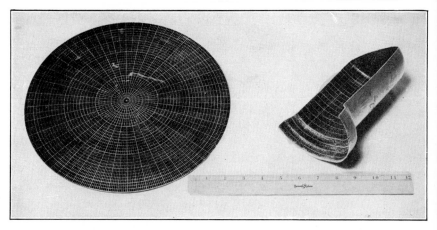

Fig. 13.2 Photogrid applied to the surface of an aluminum Alclad 24-S0 sheet. The photograph at right shows the distortion produced by forming. (Brewer and Glassco.)

the edges of a mold. The soft plastic is then cast around the network. The properties and the manufacturing details of a typical soft material used can be found elsewhere.† In this manner, the grid can be located at any desired position in the model. In cases where the grid is cemented to the surface of the model, the light transmitted through the model is distorted somewhat, since the latex emulsion builds up around the threads, and the light rays are refracted by this uneven surface. When the grid is embedded in the model this difficulty is not encountered. Fig. 13.3a shows a photograph of a mold with the rubber thread grid in place prior to pouring. As can be seen from this photograph, the grid can be placed at any desired distance from the surface of the model, and the grid lines can be easily spaced at intervals as close as $\frac{1}{16}$ in. Fig. 13.3b shows a cured sheet of the plastic with the embedded grid in place. Fig. 13.3c shows a typical model machined from a sheet of the material. Sheets of the material can be cast in any desired size and thickness.

This method can be used in three-dimensional, dynamic, and plastic deformation studies.

13.3. Methods of Measurement of Grids. There are two common methods for the measurement of the distortions of the grid lines.

1. For strains that remain after the load is removed, a micrometer microscope can be used to measure the spacings of the grid lines directly on the specimen both before and after the loading, or only after the loading if the original spacing is accurately known. For elastic strains the dis-

---

† A. J. Durelli and W. F. Riley, Developments in the Grid Method of Experimental Stress Analysis, *Proc. Soc. Exptl. Stress Anal.*, vol. 14, no. 2, pp. 91-100, 1957.

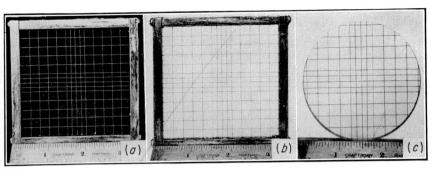

FIG. 13.3. A series of photographs showing various stages in the preparation of a photo-elastic model with an embedded grid. (a) A mold with the rubber thread grid in place prior to casting. (b) A sheet of cured plastic with the embedded grid. (c) A model machined from the sheet.

tortions of the grid will be gone after the load is removed so that this method cannot be used. If the strains at only a few points are needed, measurements directly on the specimen can be made by the microscope while the load is on. Where a large number of measurements is to be made, these measurements become difficult to conduct and the method given below may be used.

2. Two pictures of the specimens are taken, one at zero load and the other at maximum load. These will furnish a permanent record of the distortion of the grid, which can later be examined at ease. Measurements on the spacings of grid lines are made on these two pictures instead of on the specimen. Two important sources of error in this method must be carefully guarded against. First, photographic paper usually shrinks with time. Measurements on the same print on different days often show discrepancies of the order of the strains due to the stresses. Glass plates, though more expensive, are therefore preferred. Second, often owing to slack motions in loading mechanisms, the specimen may move a little during the loading process. Since the camera is usually unaffected by the loading, there will be a relative motion between specimen and camera caused by the loading. The component of this relative motion in the plane of the specimen does not change the distance between the specimen and camera so that the size of the image formed on the plate will not be changed. But the component in the direction of the camera will change the size of the image and often cause a serious error in the computed strain. For instance, let P_1Q_1 represent an object placed at a distance d from the center of the lens (Fig. 13.4). Let $P'Q_1'$ be its image formed on the photographic plate at a distance d' away from the center of the lens. Let the object be displaced to its new position P_2Q_2 without

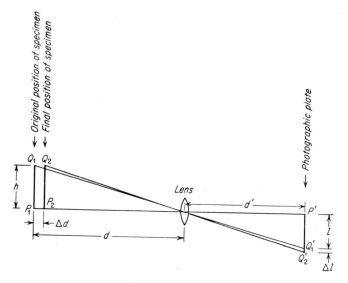

F_IG. 13.4. Error introduced in photographic strain measurements due to movement of specimen.

changing its length. Then the new image will be represented by $P'Q'_2$. Using the properties of similar triangles, we have

$$\frac{l}{d'} = \frac{h}{d} \tag{13.1}$$

$$\frac{l + \Delta l}{d'} = \frac{h}{d - \Delta d} \tag{13.2}$$

Taking the difference of the above two equations, we have

$$\frac{\Delta l}{d'} = \frac{h}{d} \frac{\Delta d}{d - \Delta d} \tag{13.3}$$

By Eqs. (13.1) and (13.3) we obtain the apparent strain ϵ_{ap} due to the movement of the specimen,

$$\epsilon_{ap} = \frac{\Delta l}{l} = \frac{\Delta d}{d - \Delta d} \tag{13.4}$$

At each point in the specimen this apparent strain is the same in all directions; hence it is a hydrostatic strain. In general, the amount of displacement in the direction of the camera may be different at different points so that this hydrostatic strain may vary from point to point in the specimen and is not necessarily homogeneous. An idea of the magnitude of the error involved in experiments using flexible loading mechanisms having slack motions can be obtained from this numerical example. Let $d = 10$ in. and $\Delta d = 0.01$ in.; then, by Eq. (13.4), $\epsilon_{ap} = 0.001$, which may be larger than the strains caused by the loading. Such small movements of the specimen will not throw the image out of focus so that the presence of the error cannot be detected through inspection of the image to check whether it becomes blurred or not. Since the slack motion of most loading mechanisms will have taken place by the time a small load is on, it is advisable to use a fraction of the maximum load, say, one-fifth, as the initial load, to take two pictures, one at this load and one at the maximum load, and to measure the change of strain due to the increase of load. Where portions of the specimen have zero or known strains under load, these can be used to compute the motion of the specimen. Usually the hydrostatic apparent strain does not vary appreciably from point to point so that it can be taken as the same for all points and a single correction applied to all the measured strains.

13.4. Determination of Stress Concentrations by Fischer's Method. Suppose we have a number of points A_0, A_1, ... , A_n on a straight line parallel to the X axis (Fig. 13.5). Let X_0, X_1, ... , X_n be the X coordinates of these points before the body undergoes deformation. After deformation,

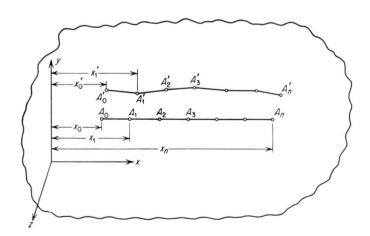

Fig. 13.5. Fischer's method of determination of stress concentrations. After deformation, $A_0 A_n$ is displaced to $A_0' A_n'$.

suppose these points move to their new positions A_0', A_1', ... , A_n'. Let X_0', X_1', ... , X_n' be the X coordinates of these new positions. By definition, the displacements in the X direction, denoted by u, are $X_0' - X_0$, $X_1' - X_1$, ... , $X_n' - X_n$ for the points A_0, A_1, ... , A_n, respectively. If we plot these displacements against the X coordinates of the undeformed positions of the points, we obtain a number of points a_0, a_1, ..., a_n (Fig. 13.6). If we pass a smooth curve through these points, then the slope of the curve, du/dx, will give the strain in the X direction, ϵ_x. This method of plotting the ux curve and obtaining ϵ_x from its slope was due to Fischer.[†] It has several advantages over the usual method of calculating the strains. (1) A point which deviates excessively from the smooth curve can be

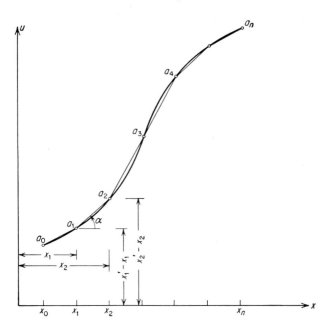

Fig. 13.6. Fischer's method of determination of stress concentrations. The slope of the curve at each point gives the strain at that point.

discovered immediately from a glance at this ux curve. Measurements on this point can be carefully checked again to detect a probable mistake, or, if that is not possible, the point is discarded. (2) In the usual method, the average strain in the interval A_1A_2 is computed by the formula $\epsilon_x = \Delta l/l$ or

$$\epsilon_x = \frac{(x_2' - x_1') - (x_2 - x_1)}{x_2 - x_1}$$

This corresponds to the slope $\tan \alpha$ of the chord a_1a_2 in Fig. 13.6. Similarly the average strain in the interval A_0A_1 is given by the usual method as the slope of the chord a_0a_1. The strain ϵ_x at A_1 is then taken as the mean

[†] G. Fischer, "Versuche uber die Wirkung von Kerben an elastische beanspruchten Biegestaben," dissertation T. H. Aachen, 1932, VDI Verlag G.m.b.h., Düsseldorf, 1932.

slope of the chords a_0a_1 and a_1a_2. This mean is close to the slope of the tangent at a_1, so that here the accuracy of the usual method, though not so good as Fischer's method, is almost as good. At or near a stress concentration (for instance, A_3), however, the average of the two slopes of the chords a_2a_3 and a_3a_4 is much lower than the slope of the tangent through a_3. The ordinary method therefore misses the peak strain, whereas Fischer's method does not. For the determination of stress concentration, Fischer's method is therefore always preferred.

13.5. Determination of the Distribution of Stresses in a Plate with a Circular Hole, under Unidimensional Load by the Rubber-model Method. The problem of the hole in a plate under tension was investigated by the rubber-model method. A rubber sheet 36 in. in length, 12 in. in width, and $\frac{1}{4}$ in. in thickness was used (Fig. 13.7). A circular hole 1 in. in diam-

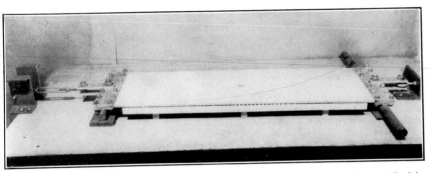

FIG. 13.7. Test setup for rubber sheet (36 by 12 by $\frac{1}{4}$ in. with a 1-in. hole stretched in its plane). The grid is drawn with India ink. The sheet rests on ball bearings to decrease friction.

eter was drilled in its center, and a constant deformation was applied to the sheet by means of a turnbuckle. When the sheet was hung vertically, it was found that the dead weight of the loading jig and rubber sheet produced enough strains to distort the circular hole. To avoid this, the sheet was therefore placed in a horizontal position. To avoid friction, the sheet was supported on ball bearings, as shown in Fig. 13.8. On the rubber sheet, a fine grid was drawn with India ink (Fig. 13.9). Both polar and cartesian-coordinate systems were used. The distance between lines varied from 1/32 to $\frac{1}{2}$ in.

Photographs of the sheet were taken for a small initial load and for increasing amounts of load. The camera setup is shown in Fig. 13.10. The photograph of the grid at about 10 per cent longitudinal deformation is shown in Fig. 13.11. Photographic plates and not films were used.

The first obvious feature of the photographs is that the drawn circles become ellipses after deformation. The circle on the longitudinal axis

FIG. 13.8. Ball bearings used to support the rubber sheet loaded horizontally.

of the sheet away from the hole and the two ends elongates longitudinally and contracts transversely. With the micrometer microscope, it is easy to measure on the two photographic plates the lengths of the longitudinal and transversal diameter before and after deformation. Dividing the change in length by the original length, the two principal strains are obtained. The ratio between them is Poisson's ratio, since the transversal stress is negligible there.

It is also obvious that, although the directions of the axes of the ellipse on the longitudinal axis of the plate remain longitudinal and transversal, the axes of the other ellipses shifted. The directions of these axes are the directions of the principal strains and stresses.

Superimposing the original circle on the deformed ellipse, as shown in Fig. 13.11, the strains in all directions become apparent. These strains are proportional to the distance between the circle and ellipse. (The circles should be small for this to be true.)

The hole in the plate becomes elliptical; its axes coincide with the axis of the plate. In the polar-coordinate system radial lines diverge prominently at the boundary near the transversal axis and converge at the boundary near the longitudinal axis, making it easy to understand the two fundamental facts produced by the hole:

1. There is an extra elongation at the boundary on the transversal axis (stress-concentration phenomenon).

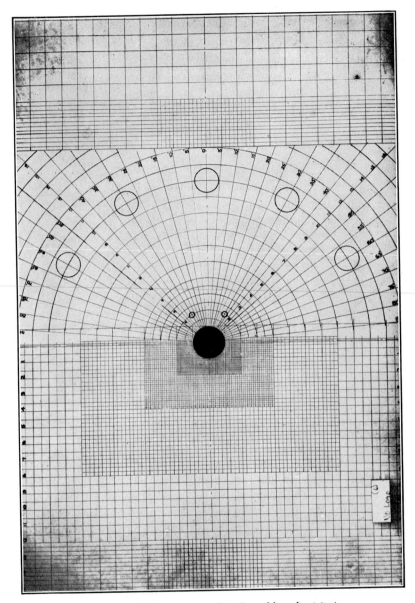

FIG. 13.9. Grid system used in the rubber-sheet test.

2. There is a contraction at the boundary on the longitudinal axis. Since at free boundaries the state of stress is unidimensional, this contraction demonstrates the existence of a compressive stress.

The longitudinal and transversal strains on the transversal axis through

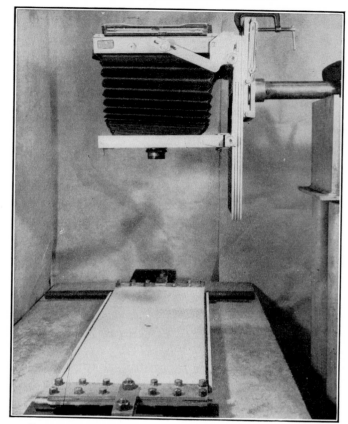

FIG. 13.10. Camera arrangement in the rubber-sheet test.

the center of the hole are obtained by micrometer-microscope measurements on the two photographs, one at a small initial load and the other at about 10 per cent longitudinal deformation. Fischer's method was used. The uniform longitudinal strain at the portion of the plate midway between the hole and the clamped ends is also measured. These measured strains are translated into stresses by the stress-strain relations. The ratios of the stresses on the transversal axis to the stress in the uniform field are computed, plotted, and compared with Howland's theoretical values (Fig. 13.12). The agreement is fair. It was found that the stress-strain relationship for the particular rubber used (Hevea natural rubber 28.5%, fillers 56.3%, vulcanizer 8.6%, sulfur 3.1%, oils 3.5%) is practically straight for strains not larger than 10 per cent. The modulus of elasticity was therefore assumed to be constant. Its value did not enter the final result because only the stress ratios, not stresses, were calculated. Poisson's ratio of the rubber was assumed to be 0.32 in the computations. A point ($r = 2.12a$; $\theta = 28°17'$) was arbitrarily selected for the determina-

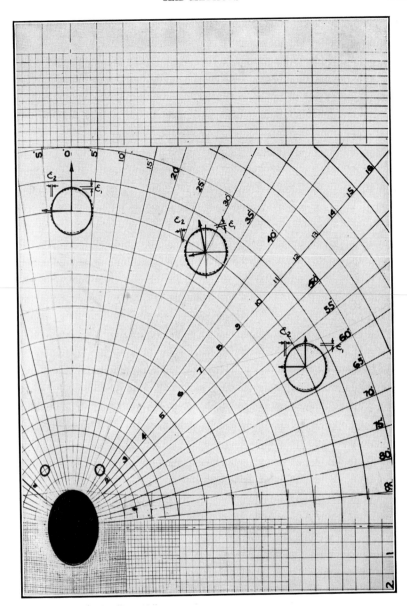

FIG. 13.11. Rubber sheet under about 10 per cent elongation.

tion of stresses from measured strains. Three strains were measured (longitudinally, transversally, and at 45°), and the principal stresses and principal directions were calculated by the rosette formula and the stress-strain relations (Fig. 13.13). Here also, the check with values obtained by Kirsch's formula is fair.

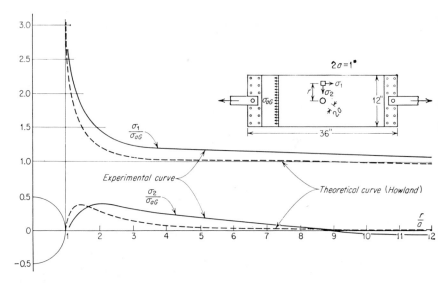

Fɪɢ. 13.12. Distribution of stress on the transversal axis of a plate with a circular hole, under a unidimensional uniformly distributed load. (Comparison of theory and rubber-model measurements.) Poisson's ratio of rubber is taken as 0.32.

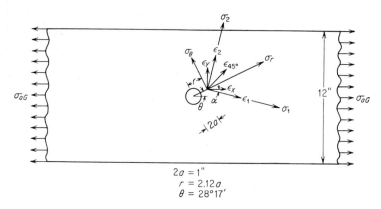

$2a = 1''$
$r = 2.12a$
$\theta = 28°17'$

	Theoretical value (Kirsch)	Experimental value
σ_1	$0.924\sigma_{aG}$	$0.938\sigma_{aG}$
σ_2	$-0.168\sigma_{aG}$	$-0.190\sigma_{aG}$
α	$12°20'$	$13°10'$

Fɪɢ. 13.13. Theoretical and experimental determination of stress and strain at any point on a plate with a circular hole, under unidimensional uniformly distributed load.

13.6. Determination of the Stress-Strain Relations of a Rubberlike Material. The rubber-thread method was used to determine the stress-strain relations of a rocket propellant. The thread used has a diameter of 0.008 in., and was glued on the specimen by latex. A series of motion pictures were taken on the specimen as it was loaed to failure.

Measurements were made on these pictures by means of a comparator and the stress-strain curve plotted. Owing to the large deformations involved, true stress and natural strain were used. Figure 13.14 shows pictures of the specimen before loading, during loading, and after failure. The straight rubber threads become wavy under loading. This strongly indicates that the material is not homogeneous.

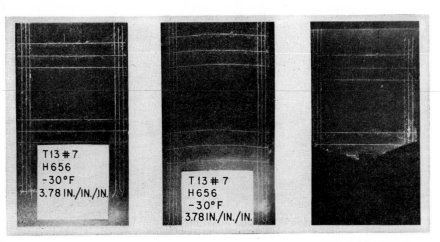

FIG. 13.14. Rubber-thread grid cemented to a rubberlike-material, tensile specimen. The photograph at the left shows the unloaded specimen. The photograph at the right shows the specimen after failure. The photograph in the middle shows nonhomogeneous strain produced by heterogeneity in the material.

13.7. Grids for Point Location. Sometimes in experimental stress analysis, in particular in connection with photoelasticity and the brittle-coating method, it is found convenient to have a grid on the specimen to help in the location of points. When the specimens are of complicated shape, this is often a necessity. The grids are then used, not to measure strains, but to allow a precise location of the points where strains or stresses are determined, and they often coincide with a coordinated system, either cartesian or polar. For photoelastic applications these grids are often scribed on the surface of the plastic specimen. For brittle-coating applications the grids are usually drawn with Dykem Steel Blue. An example of grids on brittle-coating specimens is shown in Figs. 17.2 and 17.3 of the chapter on applications of brittle coating. An example of grids on photoelastic specimens is shown in Fig. 13.15.

Fig. 13.15. Grid scribed on a photoelastic specimen to allow a precise location of the points where stresses are determined. The grid lines were scratched on a plastic model by means of a sharp-point steel scriber.

13.8. Determination of the Distribution of Strains in a Disk under Diametral Compression. To use the embedded-rubber-thread technique, a sheet of plastic was molded about a grid of rubber threads, and then cured for two days. A disk was then machined from the sheet and placed in a loading frame. Since the plastic had photoelastic properties the disk and loading frame were placed in a field of circularly polarized light. Fringe patterns and the grid network were photographed simultaneously. These data are illustrated in Fig. 13.16, which shows (*a*) a light-field photograph before the load was applied, (*b*) a loaded photograph of grid distor-

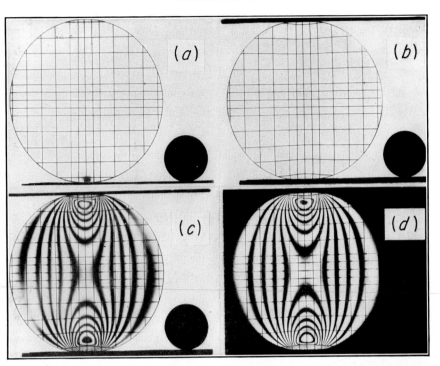

Fig. 13.16. A series of photographs showing complete photoelastic and grid displacement data. (*a*) A light-field photograph before the load was applied. The fringe at the point of support is due to the dead weight of the disk. (*b*) A photograph of the grid displacements after the load was applied with the polariscope elements removed. (*c*) A photograph of the light-field isochromatics and grid displacements. (*d*) A photograph of the dark-field isochromatics and grid displacements. The black circles in (*a*), (*b*), and (*c*) are a reference sphere used to compensate for film shrinkage. Data obtained from the grids are sufficient to solve the elastic problem.

tions only, (*c*) light-field isochromatics and grid distortions, and (*d*) dark-field isochromatics and grid distortions. Only Figs. 13.16*a* and *b* are needed for the grid analysis. These two photographs give all values of strain and by use of E and ν all values of stress. However Figs. 13.16*c* and *d* will be used for comparison.

An enlarged view of the isochromatic pattern and the grid distortions in the neighborhood of the load are shown in Fig. 13.17.

A fixed reference should always be placed in the field of the photographs to compensate for possible errors which could be introduced by film shrinkage. In this study a small sphere was used, as seen in Fig. 13.16.

The photographs of the disk were taken on a diffused-light polariscope, and both a measuring microscope and an optical comparator were used to make the grid measurements. It is believed that the optical measurements of grid displacements are accurate to $\pm$ 0.0002 in.

Fig. 13.17. An enlarged view of the photoelastic isochromatics and grid displacements in the neighborhood of the point of application of the load.

In order to compare the photoelastic results with the strain measurements determined from the grid displacements, the following relationship was derived. From the plane-stress equations in Exercise 6.3,

$$\epsilon_1 = \frac{1}{E}(\sigma_1 - \nu\sigma_2) \qquad \epsilon_2 = \frac{1}{E}(\sigma_2 - \nu\sigma_1)$$

The difference in principal strain is then found to be

$$\epsilon_1 - \epsilon_2 = \frac{1 + \nu}{E}(\sigma_1 - \sigma_2)$$

The ratio of principal stress difference to principal strain difference is thus a constant.

$$\frac{\sigma_1 - \sigma_2}{\epsilon_1 - \epsilon_2} = \frac{E}{1 + \nu}$$

The difference in principal stress was computed for the horizontal and vertical diameters of the disk using the photoelastic isochromatics and the fringe value for the material of 0.54 psi in./fringe. The two principal strains were determined for the two diameters from the grid displacements by Fischer's method. The strain difference was then computed and plotted. The results of these calculations are presented in the form of the curves shown in Figs. 13.18 and 13.19. A comparison between the photoelastic and grid network results is shown in Tables 13.1 and 13.2.

TABLE 13.1. HORIZONTAL DIAMETER

Position	$\sigma_1 - \sigma_2$ psi	$\epsilon_1 - \epsilon_2$	$\dfrac{\sigma_1 - \sigma_2}{\epsilon_1 - \epsilon_2}$ psi
0.1D	3.26	0.0053	612†
0.2D	7.80	0.0183	426
0.3D	13.40	0.0320	419
0.4D	18.55	0.0433	427
0.5D	20.55	0.0490	419

TABLE 13.2. VERTICAL DIAMETER

Position	$\sigma_1 - \sigma_2$ psi	$\epsilon_1 - \epsilon_2$	$\dfrac{\sigma_1 - \sigma_2}{\epsilon_1 - \epsilon_2}$ psi
0.1D	39.70	0.090	441
0.2D	29.80	0.069	429
0.3D	24.60	0.058	424
0.4D	21.60	0.052	415
0.5D	20.55	0.049	419

†Not used for the statistical measures.

From the data of Tables 13.1 and 13.2, statistical measures of the quantity $\dfrac{\sigma_1 - \sigma_2}{\epsilon_1 - \epsilon_2}$ were calculated as indicated below:

a. Mean = 424.3
b. Standard deviation = 7.76
c. Coefficient of variation = 1.83

The results presented in Tables 13.1 and 13.2 show that the strain measurements correlate very well with the photoelastic results. Except in the region of very low strains near the boundary of the disk and in the region of high strain gradient near the point of application of the load,

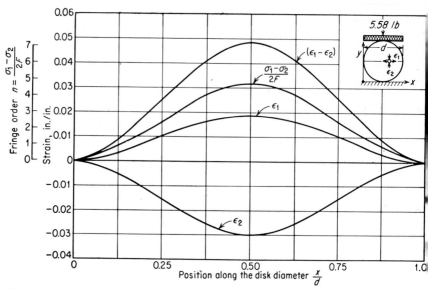

Fig. 13.18. Photoelastic and grid measurement results for the horizontal diameter of the disk.

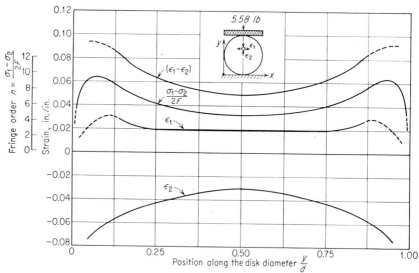

Fig. 13.19. Photoelastic and grid measurement results for the vertical diameter of the disk.

the coefficient of variation is less than 2.00. The value of $E/(1 + \nu)$ computed independently was found to be 420. This compares favorably with the mean of the disk results, 424.3.

In addition to the comparisons of Tables 13.1 and 13.2, a static equilibrium check was conducted by determining the distributions of σ_y across the horizontal diameter from the measured strains and the elastic constants of the material. The total normal force across the diameter checked to within 2.5 per cent of the applied load.

The usefulness of the method is limited to cases in which large deformations of the plastic do not produce appreciable changes in the boundary conditions. It is obvious in Fig. 13.17 that the distribution of stress at the zone of contact is very different from the corresponding distribution produced by a load concentrated at a point. This limitation is also encountered in other methods of stress analysis such as the "freezing" technique in three-dimensional photoelasticity.

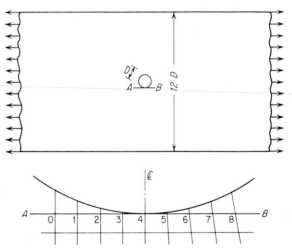

Points on the longitudinal grid line tangent to the hole	Distance measured from point O, in.	
	Plate not loaded	Plate loaded
0	0	0
1	0.018	0.027
2	0.034	0.053
3	0.057	0.089
4	0.073	0.116
5	0.098	0.158
6	0.111	0.181
7	0.136	0.222
8	0.162	0.261

Fig. 13.20. Use of Fischer's method to determine the stress concentration at the boundary of a hole.

EXERCISE

Determine the average strains in the eight intervals on the line AB (Fig. 13.20). From these average strains compute the strains at the seven interior points 1, 2, ... , 7. Determine the strains at these seven interior points again by Fischer's method, and calculate the per cent difference between the results obtained from these two methods. Determine the strains a third time using Fischer's method; however, in addition, take advantage of the symmetry in respect to the transversal axis.

PART 4

BRITTLE-COATING METHODS

CHAPTER 14

GENERAL BACKGROUND OF BRITTLE COATINGS

14.1. Principle of the Method. The principles on which the brittle-coating method are based are: (1) the adhesion of a layer of a specially prepared coating to the specimen or component to be stress analyzed; (2) the failure of this coating when the state of stress in the specimen reaches a certain critical value. The coating is deposited on the surface of the specimen either in liquid form and hardens by evaporation or in solid form and is melted by heating. Some coatings have to be cured at high temperatures. Some other coatings such as Stresscoat can harden by evaporation at room temperature but are sometimes cured at moderately high temperatures to improve their properties.

The strains produced in the specimens to be stress-analyzed are transmitted to the layer of the coating because of the adhesion between coating and specimen. These strains develop a state of stress in the coating. However, since the coating modulus of elasticity and Poisson's ratio are appreciably different from those in the specimen, a mathematical computation has to be developed to determine the state of stress in the coating as a function of the state of stress in the specimen and, conversely, to give the right interpretation to the information obtained from the coating failure.

Most coatings develop residual stresses when they harden, since in general they shrink when they reach a solid state. These residual stresses play a very important part in coating behavior. If the stresses are tensile, the larger they are, the smaller will be the necessary added stress to crack the coatings. It is likely that cracks stay open after the load removal because of the presence of tensile residual stresses and that compressive residual stresses are responsible for the closing up of the cracks.

It should also be pointed out that coatings (which are often made of natural resins) have a much larger coefficient of thermal expansion than the metals to which they adhere. This introduces several problems of thermal stresses which have to be carefully analyzed.

14.2. History of Brittle Coatings' Use in Stress Analysis. Brittle coating is a layer of specially prepared coating which can crack in response to the surface strains of its base material. The crack occurs normal to the maximum tensile stress on the surface unless the maximum and

329

minimum stresses are of close values. Also, in general, it is possible to determine by a simple calibration device the threshold strain, or minimum strain, necessary to start a crack.

With the above information it is possible to obtain the over-all picture of the stress distribution over the surface of a complex machine part or structure and if necessary to plan for further strain measurements by using strain gages at selected points of interest. Since the direction of the crack coincides with the direction of a principal stress, it is possible to determine the state of stress at a point by using only two strain gages instead of three.[†]

The accuracy of strain measurements in stress-concentrated areas depends on the gage length of the strain gage. Brittle coatings have in effect a very short gage length and are therefore ideal for measuring strain at the stress-concentration points.

The principle of brittle coatings was known many years ago when strain patterns were observed on mill scale on hot-rolled steel which was stressed to the point where appreciable plastic flow occurred. Some qualitative analyses based on this strain pattern were also made, but the wide application of this principle was prevented by the poor surface adhesion of mill scale, which resulted in flaking as well as cracking. Another disadvantage was that this strain pattern could not be observed in the elastic region which is of most interest in many cases. Further attempts were made to find the strain pattern at a lower strain level by using whitewash, without much success owing to the erratic behavior of whitewash on polished surfaces.

The earliest practical form of brittle coating for strain measurements was developed by Dietrich and Lehr[1] of Germany in 1932. Their coating, consisting of a special lacquer with an approximate range of strain sensitivity[‡] of 0.0002 to 0.0009, was successfully used for the studies of stress concentrations and for the determination of the principal stress directions in connecting rods and in pistons by the Maybach firm in Germany. The actual strain measurements were made by special mechanical strain gages of short gage length.[2] Similar researches on brittle-coating materials were conducted by Portevin and Cymboliste[3] of France in 1934, using natural and synthetic resins and various solvents. The difficulty encountered in this pioneer work was that the coatings did not possess

---

[†]This is easily seen by reference to the Mohr's-circle construction for strains (Fig. 7.8). If two gages are oriented in the two perpendicular principal directions, the strains ϵ_1 and ϵ_2 are found, thereby completely defining the circle.

[‡]The term *strain sensitivity* as used in connection with brittle coatings is defined as the minimum strain that will crack the coating under a unidimensional state of stress.

any defined strain sensitivity, which made quantitative analysis very difficult.

A more systematic approach to the studies on compositions and characteristics of brittle coating materials was made by G. Ellis[4] at the Massachusetts Institute of Technology in 1937. A series of brittle coatings were further developed by Ellis with A. V. De Forest and F. B. Stern[5] and were made available commercially under the name Stresscoat by the Magnaflux Corporation in 1941. Since then, Stresscoat has been widely used in the United States, and numerous articles on the properties of Stresscoat and its various applications have been published.

About the same time, B. P. Haigh[6] of Great Britain was experimenting with plumber's resin on structural steel in order to observe the presence of Lüders' lines in plastically yielded steel. Powdered plumber's resin was sprinkled on the specimen to cover the surface uniformly and then melted by the flame of a blowtorch. The disadvantage of this coating was that it did not show strain patterns in the elastic region, but it was successfully applied later by J. S. Blair[7] to determine the occurrence of yielding.

R. F. Tylecote[8,9] conducted a research on brittle-coating material in order to discover a coating which would have the sensitivity of Stresscoat but would also be less affected by temperature and humidity. He found that varnish No. 108 of Pinchin, Johnson and Company was the best available material other than Stresscoat. When heat-treated at 167°F for 16 hr, this varnish had a strain sensitivity of 0.0015. This is rather high; e.g., if used on steel, a unidimensional stress of $E \times \epsilon = 30 \times 10^6 \times 0.0015 = 45,000$ psi would be required to crack the coating. N. R. Goncharov[10] of Russia used a solution of alcoholic amyl acetate (100 cc), rosin (50 g), and celluloid (5 g), which was painted on the specimen and dried at a temperature of 140° to 176°F for 20 to 30 min. A second coating was applied, and the specimen was kept at the same temperature for another 30 to 40 min. Heat-treatment in this case was considered necessary to remove the brush marks, and if possible the specimen was to be preheated to a temperature not lower than 212°F prior to the application of coating. The coating had a strain sensitivity of 0.001 to 0.002.

14.3. Present Developments. The most widely used brittle coating is Stresscoat. The operational details and properties of this coating are described in another chapter. Stresscoat consists of 150 to 300 parts by weight of carbon disulfide, 100 parts by weight of a resinlike product, and $\frac{1}{2}$ to 30 parts by weight of a plasticizer.[11] The plasticizer is added to control the strain sensitivity of the coating. Since this strain sensitivity is a function of the environmental temperature and humidity at the time of the test, the amount of plasticizer to be added is in general dependent on the humidity and temperature. Unplasticized coatings will tend to "craze,"† but, on the other hand, excessive plasticizer is likely to lower the residual tensile stress to the extent that cracks once formed will close upon the release of the strain which caused the crack formation. Strain sensitivities of Stresscoat run from 0.0003 to 0.0030.

Magnaflux Corporation states that the minute bubbles formed during the process of spraying Stresscoat have the effect of making the crack pattern more regular and dependable.[12] It has generally been found that, for liquid brittle coatings, the spraying method gives the most uniform thickness of coating in comparison with other methods, such as dipping and painting. The method of spraying is used in other countries besides the United States.

Rockey[13] of England experimented on resin-based lacquers (No. 1 and No. 108) which are available commercially. He found that, when heat-treated from 158 to 239°F for 24 hr, these lacquers had a strain sensitivity of 0.0003 to 0.0004. The coatings when cooled did not appear to be very sensitive to changes of room temperature and humidity. These characteristics are considered advantageous since elaborate temperature and humidity control is not necessary for precise work. Other experimental details of the technique and the applications, such as the use of aluminum undercoating to obtain a reflecting surface and the use of calibration strips by the cantilever-beam method, are similar to those for Stresscoat.

Salmon[14] of France developed two forms of brittle-coating materials which were later made available by G. Jarre-Departement Laboratorie in Paris. The first consists of 4 parts of rosin and 1 part of dammar gum. This mixture is prepared for use either in a powder form or cast in stick form. The surface of the part to be tested is polished, cleaned, degreased, and heated by means of a blowtorch or a bunsen burner. The powder is then sprinkled on or the stick is rubbed on the surface while the part is still hot. The strain sensitivity of this coating is said to be about 0.00001. This is the most sensitive coating available so far, but precise results cannot be obtained because of unavoidable irregularities involved in applying the coating. The second form of brittle coating is liquid and consists of synthetic resin disolved in trichloroethylene or benzene. This liquid lacquer is applied by a special electric spray gun, and the specimen is heat-treated at a temperature ranging from 104 to 212°F for 1 to 20 hr. The oven temperature and drying time are predetermined by means of a chart and vary with the testing temperature and sensitivity. The coating has an average strain sensitivity of 0.0005.

Salmon states that the sensitivity of the coating varies with the material

---

†This term is used to denote the random formation of cracks caused primarily by thermal stresses set up in a coating because of a temperature gradient or a different thermal coefficient of expansion of coating and coated specimen, or both.

on which the coating is applied. It is said that the sensitivity is 25 to 30 per cent lower for steel than for aluminum. For this reason, it is recommended that the test pieces for calibrations must be of the same material as the specimen. This large variation in sensitivity with different specimen materials can be attributed to the high temperature to which Salmon's coated specimens were heat-treated. During the cooling the different thermal-expansion coefficients of different specimen materials may have a large effect on the residual stress in the coating and therefore on its sensitivity. An interesting development of this French brittle coating is the technique used to increase the visibility of the cracks. A coating of cellulose is applied before the brittle coating to increase the surface reflection of the specimen and eliminate the tedious work of polishing its surface. Another technique used by Salmon to make the cracks visible on the surface of wood and cement is to glue a sheet of silver foil (0.02 mm thick) to the surface.

Taira[16] of Japan developed a brittle coating the composition of which is a phenol resin and titanic white dissolved in a mixture of benzene, toluene, and xylene. The strain sensitivity ranges from 0.00027 to 0.0025 depending on the ratios of the mixture and the drying condition. Taira claims that the crack density of this brittle coating is a function of $\sigma_1 - \nu\sigma_2$, where ν is the Poisson's ratio of the coating. In some two-dimensional problems this allows the solution of the Laplace equation for $\sigma_1 + \sigma_2$ with the aid of numerical methods like the relaxation method. The two equations enable one to solve for σ_1 and σ_2 for every point on the surface of the specimen.

Nakahara,[17] also of Japan, used a brittle coating with a high portion of plasticizer to measure the plastic strain in a drawn blank of copper and aluminum. The strain sensitivity of this coating ranged from 0.005 to 0.03. For calibration, the coating was sprayed on thin aluminum strips. The strips were then wrapped around an involute surface where the known radius of curvature at every point on the surface defined the strain on the strip.

Some early applications of brittle-coating analysis were made in Germany by H. Kayser and A. Herzog.[18,19]

The discussion of these two sections is summarized with more details as to the coating compositions in Table 14.1.

Table 14.1. Various Brittle-Coating Materials

Authorities cited by numbers in Bibliography	Composition			Strain sensitivity	Remarks
	Resin	Solvent	Plasticizer		
Dietrich[1]	Special lacquer	......	......	0.0002–0.0009	
Cymboliste and Portevin[3]	Copals (Manilla, Zanzibar, Congo, Madagascar, sandarac) Phenols (bakelite, rosins, etc.), treated	Alcohol (ethyl, methyl, butyl, amyl) Ether (acetate amyl, acetate butyl, ethyl-glycol) Hydrocarbons (toluene, xylene)			
Haigh[6]	Plumber's resin				
Tylecote[8,9]	Lacquer No. 108 (Pinchin, Johnson & Co., London)	......	......	......	Melted by flame
Rockey[13]	Lacquer No. 1 and No. 108 (Pinchin, Johnson & Co., London)	......	......	0.0003–0.0004	

334

Goncharov[10]	50 g rosin and 5 g celluloid	100 cc alcoholic amyl acetate			
	Alberto 50% Rosin 50% Iditol 50% Rosin and iditol 50%	Xylene 50% Methyl alcohol 50% Methyl alcohol 50% Methyl alcohol 50%	Add paraffin 1-5% to decrease brittleness	0.001-0.002	Painted by brush
Stresscoat[11]	Rosin and 6% zinc oxide 6% limed rosin 15% calcium acetated rosin	Carbon disulfide Methylene dichloride 1,2-cis-dichloroethylene	Dibutylphthalate Normal butylstearate Normal butylstearate	0.0003-0.0030	Sprayed
Salmon[14]	Rosin 4 parts and dammar gum 1 part	......	......	0.00001	Solid form
	Synthetic resin	Benzene, alcohol, trichloroethylene			
Guyot[15]	Rosin 300 g	Acetone 1 liter	Tricresylphosphate 10 cc	0.0005	Sprayed
	Rosin 300 g	Acetone 1 liter	Tricresylphosphate 3 cc	0.00005	Sprayed
Taira[16]	Phenol resin, titanic white and nitrocellulose	Benzene, toluene, xylene	......	0.00027-0.0025	Sprayed
Nakahara and Murota[17]	Limed rosin, titanic white, phenol resin	Benzene, toluene, xylene	Dibutylphthalate	0.005-0.03	Sprayed

REFERENCES

1. Dietrich, O., and E. Lehr: Das Dehnungslinienverfahren, *Z. des Ver. deut. Ing.*, vol. 76, pp. 973–982, 1932.
2. Lehr, E.: "Spannungsverteilung in Konstruktionselementen," VDI Verlag G.m.b.H., Düsseldorf, 1934.
3. Cymboliste, M., and A. Portevin: Procédé d'étude de la distribution des efforts élastiques dans les pièces métalliques, *Rev. mét.*, vol. 31, pp. 147–158, 1934.
4. Ellis, G.: "Strain Indicating Lacquers," master's thesis, Massachusetts Institute of Technology, Department of Aeronautical Engineering.
5. De Forest, A. V., G. Ellis, and F. B. Stern: Brittle Coating for Quantitative Strain Measurements, *J. Appl. Mech.*, vol. 9, no. 4, pp. A184–188, 1942.
6. Haigh, B. P.: Electric Welding as an Integral Part of Structural Design, *Trans. N.E.C.I.E.S.*, vol. 56, pp. 43–82, 1939.
7. Blair, J. S.: The Use of Plumber's Resin to Determine the Occurrence of Yield, *Proc. Inst. Mech. Engrs. (London)*, vol. 161, p. 176, 1949.
8. Tylecote, R. F.: Examination of Stress Distribution in Spot Welded Joints in Light Alloys by Means of the Brittle Lacquer Process, *Trans. Inst. Welding*, vol. 5, no. 3, p. 120, 1942.
9. Tylecote, R. F.: The Brittle Lacquer Method for Estimating the Stress Distribution in Welded and Riveted Joints, *Sheet Metal Ind.*, vol. 23, pp. 2194–7, 1946.
10. Goncharov, N. R.: The Brittle Lacquer Method of Determining Stresses, "Stress Determination in Machine Parts by Means of Tensometers and Lacquers (Leningrad-Moscow)," 1946.   Abstracted by G. S. Smith, *Metallurgia*, pp. 290–292, April, 1948.
11. Ellis, G.: "Resinous Composition for Determining the Strain Concentration in Rigid Articles," U.S. Patent 2,428,559, Oct. 7, 1947.
12. Magnaflux Corporation: "Principles of Stresscoat, A Manual for Use with the Brittle Coating Stress Analysis Method," 1955.
13. Rockey, K. C.: Stress Analysis Using the Brittle Lacquer Process, *Trans. Inst. Marine Engrs.*, vol. 63, no. 3, pp. 43–54, 1951.
14. Salmon, B.: L'Analyse des constraintes par la méthode des vernis craquelants, *Tech. et sci. aéronaut.*, no. 13, 1950.
15. Guyot, H.: Un nouveau vernis craquelant, le vernis émail, *Recherche aéronaut.*, no. 17, pp. 37–44, 1950.
16. Taira, S., T. Nishimura, and H. Maeda: Strain Determination by Brittle Coating, *Tech. Repts. Eng. Research Inst., Kyoto Univ.*, vol. 3, no. 1, December, 1953.
17. Nakahara, I., and T. Murota: Drawnability of a Blank with Hole, Strain Determination by Brittle Coating, *Japan Soc. Mech. Engrs.*, November, 1954.
18. Kayser, H., and A. Herzog: Uber das Zusammenwirken von Nietverbindung und Schweissnaht, *Der Stahlbau*, vol. 7, no. 15, pp. 113–115, 1934.
19. Kayser, H., and A. Herzog: Die Untersuchung zweiachsig beanspruchter Konstruktions-glieder mit Hilfe des Reisslackverfahrens, *Die Baulechnik*, vol. 14, no. 23, pp. 310–316, May 29, 1936.

CHAPTER 15

STRESSES AND STRAINS IN BRITTLE COATINGS

15.1. Introduction. In this chapter an analysis will be conducted to determine the state of stress in the coating as a function of the state of stress in the specimen. It is obvious that, if the elastic constants of the coating and the specimen were the same, the same state of stress would be found on the common layer of the coating and the specimen. Since these constants are very different, even the sign of the stress in the coating may sometime become the opposite of that in the specimen.

At the time the coating is cured, it develops, in general, residual tensile stresses which will help those produced by the external loading to crack the coating. Sometimes these residual stresses may even be sufficiently high to crack the coating without any external loading. The theoretical analysis conducted in the following paragraphs takes this into account, always assuming that the residual stresses in the coating sprayed on the specimen are the same as the residual stresses in the coating sprayed on the calibration strip. This can be assured by keeping the specimen and the calibration strips together during the curing period.

15.2. State of Stress in the Coating. On the top surface of the coating (Fig. 15.1) there are no external loads, so that the stresses perpendicular to this surface are zero. For the layer immediately below the top surface,

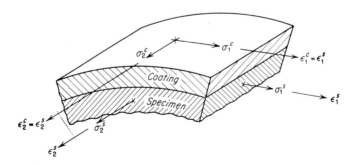

Fig. 15.1. Stresses and strains in the coating and the specimen before any crack is opened.

337

these stresses will be zero, or close to zero. Since the coating is thin, all its layers can be thought of as lying immediately below the top surface. The stresses perpendicular to the coating throughout the depth of the coating are therefore small compared with stresses in other directions. Without appreciable error, we can neglect these stresses and assume a state of plane stress to exist in the coating. Let us also assume perfect adhesion between the coating and the base specimen; the strains in the coating will be then identical to the strains in the specimen, and the principal directions of the strains in the coating will coincide with those of the specimen. Since the principal directions of stresses and strains are the same, the principal directions of the stresses in the coating will also coincide with those of the specimen. The relations between the stresses in the coating and the stresses in the specimen can be derived in the following way. By Hooke's law,

$$E_s \epsilon_1^s = \sigma_1^s - \nu_s \sigma_2^s$$

$$E_s \epsilon_2^s = \sigma_2^s - \nu_s \sigma_1^s$$

$$E_c \epsilon_1^c = \sigma_1^c - \nu_c \sigma_2^c \tag{15.1}$$

$$E_c \epsilon_2^c = \sigma_2^c - \nu_c \sigma_1^c$$

where E_c = modulus of elasticity of the coating
E_s = modulus of elasticity of specimen
ϵ_1^c = principal strain in coating in direction of ϵ_1^s produced by external load
ϵ_1^s = algebraically larger principal strain in specimen
ϵ_2^c = principal strain in coating in direction of ϵ_2^s produced by external load
ϵ_2^s = algebraically smaller principal strain in specimen
ν_c = Poisson's ratio of brittle coating
ν_s = Poisson's ratio of specimen
σ_1^c = principal stress in coating in direction of σ_1^s produced by external load. It is the difference between the total stress and the residual stress
σ_1^s = algebraically larger principal stress in specimen
σ_2^c = principal stress in coating in direction of σ_2^s produced by external load. It is the difference between the total stress and the residual stress
σ_2^s = algebraically smaller principal stress in specimen

The sign convention used is positive ϵ for elongation and positive σ for tension.

Since perfect adhesion between base metal and coating requires that

$$\epsilon_1^c = \epsilon_1^s \tag{15.2}$$

$$\epsilon_2^c = \epsilon_2^s$$

we can solve Eqs. (15.1) and (15.2) to find σ_1^c and σ_2^c in terms of σ_1^s and σ_2^s.

$$\sigma_1^c = \frac{E_c}{E_s(1 - \nu_c^2)} [(1 - \nu_c \nu_s)\sigma_1^s + (\nu_c - \nu_s)\sigma_2^s]$$

$$\sigma_2^c = \frac{E_c}{E_s(1 - \nu_c^2)} [(1 - \nu_c \nu_s)\sigma_2^s + (\nu_c - \nu_s)\sigma_1^s] \tag{15.3}$$

$$\sigma_1^c - \sigma_2^c = \frac{E_c}{E_s} \frac{1 + \nu_s}{1 + \nu_c} (\sigma_1^s - \sigma_2^s)$$

σ_1^s has been defined as the algebraically larger principal stress so that $\sigma_1^s - \sigma_2^s$ is always positive. Since the values of modulus of elasticity and Poisson's ratio are always positive, the third of Eqs. (15.3) shows that $\sigma_1^c - \sigma_2^c$ is always positive. In other words, σ_1^c, which has been defined as the principal stress in the coating in the direction of σ_1^s, is always algebraically larger than σ_2^c.

Equations (15.3) are the basic equations governing the relation between the stresses in the coating and the stresses in the specimen. For the case where $\nu_c = 0.42$, $\nu_s = 0.29$, the graphs of these basic equations are represented in Fig. 15.2. For other values of ν_c and ν_s the graph of the basic equations will take the same general shape.

It is common practice to determine the sensitivity of the brittle coating by means of cantilever calibration strips as shown in Fig. 15.3, which are not necessarily made out of the same material as the specimen. The smaller principal stress in the metal strip, σ_2^s, is zero. If we call A the point on the cantilever calibration strip where the cracks start to appear, then from the first two of Eqs. (15.3), by setting σ_2^s equal to zero, by using the relation $\sigma_1^s = E_s \epsilon_s^d$, and by changing ν_s to ν_a, we obtain

$$\sigma_1^c = \frac{1 - \nu_c \nu_a}{1 - \nu_c^2} E_c \epsilon_s^d \tag{15.4}$$

$$\sigma_2^c = \frac{\nu_c - \nu_a}{1 - \nu_c^2} E_c \epsilon_s^d$$

where ν_a is the Poisson's ratio of the material of the calibration strip and ϵ_s^d is the larger principal strain at A (Fig. 15.3), commonly called the strain sensitivity in direct loading of the brittle coating used.

15.3. Law of Failure of Brittle Coatings. Historically, in the first published paper on the subject, O. Dietrich and E. Lehr assumed that the

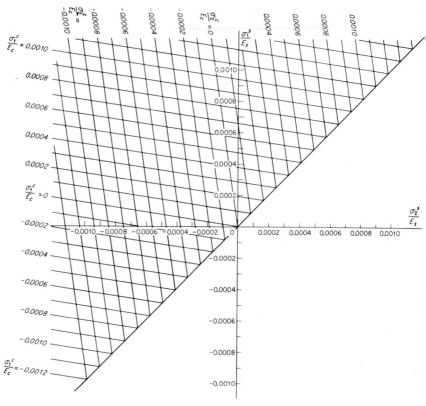

FIG. 15.2. Principal stresses in the coating as a function of the principal stresses in the specimen. $\nu_c = 0.42$, $\nu_s = 0.29$.

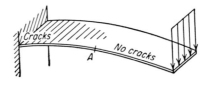

FIG. 15.3. Cantilever calibration strip, used to determine the strain sensitivity of the coating. The deflection at the free end of the strip is known. The strain at A is called the strain sensitivity ϵ_s^d.

brittle coatings they used failed according to the maximum-tensile-strain law. This law states that if, and only if, the larger principal strain reaches a critical value, then cracks perpendicular to the direction of this principal strain will appear. This assumption, however, was not substantiated by

heir experiments. Studies† on Stresscoat soon showed that, in a simple
compression test, the lateral tensile strain ϵ_1^c (Fig. 15.4) may be several
imes larger than the critical tensile strain ϵ_s^d required to crack the coating
Fig. 15.3), and yet no cracks will appear. In fact, no cracks have yet
been reported on Stresscoat in carefully controlled simple compression
ests. This phenomenon proves that the maximum-tensile-strain law is
not suitable for Stresscoat. Recent studies showed that, to completely
lescribe the law of failure of Stresscoat, variables such as manufacturer's

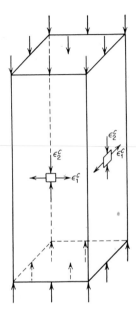

FIG. 15.4. Simple compression on a prismatic column. The lateral tensile strain ϵ_1^c of
the coating is several times larger than the strain sensitivity ϵ_s^d; yet no cracks appear.

coating number, speed of loading, and gradients of principal stresses must
be considered. At present, the influence of these variables on the law of
failure is not well understood. Since the maximum-tensile-stress law of
failure is generally adopted for brittle materials, it seems plausible that
this law should be used as a first approximation of the failure phenomena of
brittle coatings. In our discussion in this chapter, we shall therefore assume
that the brittle coating fails when the maximum tensile stress in the coating
itself reaches a critical value. The simplicity of this law helps in the under-

†A. J. Durelli, and T. N. De Wolf, Law of Failure of Stresscoat, *Proc. Soc. Exptl.
Stress Anal.*, vol. 6, no. 2, pp. 68–83, 1948.
    A. J. Durelli, R. H. Jacobson, and S. Okubo, Further Studies of Some Properties of
Stresscoat, *Proc. Soc. Exptl. Stress Anal.*, vol. 13, no. 1, p. 35, 1955.

standing of the coating-failure phenomenon and in the analysis of the data. Experimental data available at this time indicate that the error introduced by assuming this law would probably not be large in many cases of ordinary application. At the end of this chapter, it is shown how the same approach used here could be applied to other laws of failure when more experimental data prove them to represent more accurately the phenomenon.

15.4. Determination of the Ultimate Strength of the Coating. As the coating changes from the liquid state to the solid state, a hydrostatic tension due to shrinkage will be produced. In some cases, this tension may be larger than the ultimate strength of the coating and may produce random cracks. Random cracks denote cracks oriented at all directions so that there is no preferential direction. The cracks near the center of the plate (Fig. 15.13) are typical random cracks. In most cases, however, the hydrostatic tension is not sufficient to crack the coating. Some time after the coating solidifies, its creep property will relieve some of this hydrostatic tension. When the curing has been done at a temperature higher than room temperature, the coating must be further cooled down to the test temperature. If this cooling takes place suddenly, the induced hydrostatic tension in the coating may again be larger than the ultimate strength and random cracks will appear. In properly conducted tests, however, this cooling is very slow so that a large part of the hydrostatic tension set up by the temperature drop is relieved. Still, an appreciable amount of residual tension denoted by σ_R^c probably remains.

The maximum-tensile-stress law of failure assumes that the coating will crack when the maximum principal stress in the coating is larger than, or equal to, a critical value σ_u, defined as the ultimate strength of the coating. For the calibration strip (Fig. 15.3), if the coating starts to crack at point A, then σ_u must be equal to the sum of the residual stress σ_R^c and the applied stress σ_1^c. Using the first of Eqs. (15.4) to obtain the value of σ_1^c, we have

$$\sigma_u = \frac{1 - \nu_c \nu_a}{1 - \nu_c^2} E_c \epsilon_s^d + \sigma_R^c \tag{15.5}$$

The strain sensitivities ϵ_s^d of Stresscoat No. 1202 and No. 1206 at 76°F and 50 per cent relative humidity as commonly determined on aluminum cantilever calibration strips are approximately 106×10^{-5} and 70×10^{-5}, respectively, according to the chart supplied by the manufacturer. The values of ν_c and E_c at 76°F as determined by Stokey[†] are approximately 0.45 and 215,000 psi for Stresscoat No. 1202 and 0.42 and 285,000 psi for No. 1206, respectively. Using these values and taking ν_a as 0.33, Eq. (15.5) gives the values of $\sigma_u - \sigma_R^c$ as 243 and 209 psi for Stresscoat No. 1202 and No. 1206, respectively.

[†] W. F. Stokey, Elastic and Creep Properties of Stresscoat, *Proc. Soc. Exptl. Stress Anal.*, vol. 10, no. 1, pp. 179–186, 1952.

The strain sensitivity of Stresscoat that is free of any residual stress is estimated by Ellis[†] to be about 350×10^{-5}. Using this value in Eq. (15.5), the ultimate strength of Stresscoat comes out to be of the order of 900 psi. This implies that the residual stress σ_R^c is of the order of 680 psi, in the example above.

The values of E_c given above are for completely dried coating. At the time of test, the outer surface of the coating will generally be completely dried. Since it is the outer layer which fails, the value of E_c for the completely dried coating seems a legitimate one to use in our calculations. The ultimate strength determined above obviously will be the ultimate strength of the outer layer of the Stresscoat.

15.5. Analysis of Brittle-coating Data, Assuming the Maximum-tensile-stress Law of Failure. *a. Cracks Perpendicular to σ_1 by Direct Loading.* Assuming the maximum-tensile-stress law of failure for the Stresscoat, the coating will crack when the value of σ_1^c as calculated from Eqs. (15.3) is larger than, or equal to, $\sigma_u - \sigma_R^c$. Hence, by Eqs. (15.3), cracks perpendicular to σ_1^c will be impending when

$$\frac{E_c}{E_s(1 - \nu_c^2)} \left[(1 - \nu_c\nu_s)\sigma_1^s + (\nu_c - \nu_s)\sigma_2^s \right] = \sigma_u - \sigma_R^c \qquad (15.6)$$

In properly conducted tests, the coating on the calibration strip is cured in the same manner as the coating on the specimen. Hence, the residual stress σ_R^c present in the coating on the calibration strip and in the coating on the specimen may be taken as the same.

We shall define σ_0^d as the minimum σ_1^s required to crack the coating in the direct-loading test when σ_2^s is zero. Then from Eq. (15.6), by substituting σ_0^d for σ_1^s and setting σ_2^s equal to zero, we obtain

$$\frac{E_c}{E_s(1 - \nu_c^2)} (1 - \nu_c\nu_s)\sigma_0^d = \sigma_u - \sigma_R^c$$

or

$$\sigma_0^d = \frac{E_s}{E_c} \frac{1 - \nu_c^2}{1 - \nu_c\nu_s} (\sigma_u - \sigma_R^c) \qquad (15.7)$$

From Eqs. (15.5) and (15.7), we can eliminate $\sigma_u - \sigma_R^c$ and determine the value of σ_0^d,

$$\sigma_0^d = \frac{1 - \nu_c\nu_a}{1 - \nu_c\nu_s} E_s \epsilon_s^d \qquad (15.8)$$

[†]Greer Ellis, Resinous Composition for Determining the Strain Concentration in Rigid Articles, U.S. Patent 2,428,559, Oct. 7, 1947.

Equations (15.5) and (15.8) are to be used for direct loading. For relaxation loading, the technique of which is explained later, the strain at A on the calibration strip shown in Fig. 15.3 will be denoted by ϵ_s^r. Equations (15.5) and (15.8) when applied to relaxation loading will therefore be as follows,

$$\sigma_u = \frac{1 - \nu_c \nu_a}{1 - \nu_c^2} E_c \epsilon_s^r + \sigma_R^c \tag{15.9}$$

$$\sigma_0^r = \frac{1 - \nu_c \nu_a}{1 - \nu_c \nu_s} E_s \epsilon_s^r \tag{15.10}$$

where σ_0^r is the minimum σ_1^s required to crack the coating in the relaxation-loading test.

The Stresscoat used in relaxation loading is assumed to have the same Poisson's ratio as the Stresscoat used in direct loading.

For the special case where the calibration-strip material has the same Poisson's ratio as the test specimen so that $\nu_a = \nu_s$, Eqs. (15.8) and (15.10) reduce to

$$\sigma_0^d = E_s \epsilon_s^d \tag{15.11}$$

$$\sigma_0^r = E_s \epsilon_s^r \tag{15.12}$$

The value of ν_c is in the neighborhood of 0.44. If the calibration strips are of aluminum and the specimen is of steel, so that $\nu_a = 0.33$, $\nu_s = 0.29$, then the ratio $(1 - \nu_c \nu_a)/(1 - \nu_c \nu_s)$ is 0.975. If we use Eqs. (15.11) and (15.12) instead of Eqs. (15.8) and (15.10), there will be an error of $2\frac{1}{2}$ per cent.

Equation (15.6) gives the relation which must exist between the applied stresses σ_1^s and σ_2^s and the ultimate strength σ_u of the coating when cracks are impending. This ultimate strength σ_u is related in Eq. (15.7) to σ_0^d, the minimum uniaxial tensile stress in the specimen required for cracking the coating. By eliminating σ_u from Eqs. (15.6) and (15.7), we obtain the relation which must exist between σ_1^s, σ_2^s, and σ_0^d when a crack in the coating perpendicular to σ_1^s is impending,

$$\frac{\sigma_1^s}{\sigma_0^d} + \frac{\nu_c - \nu_s}{1 - \nu_c \nu_s} \frac{\sigma_2^s}{\sigma_0^d} = 1 \tag{15.13}$$

Equation (15.13) gives the ratio between the uniaxial loading and the biaxial loading for cracking the same coating. It gives us a measure of the effect of the algebraically smaller principal stress σ_2^s on the cracking of the coating perpendicular to the algebraically larger principal stress σ_1^s. For this reason, this equation will be called the biaxiality equation. It states that, whenever the combinations of σ_1^s and σ_2^s are such that the sum of the quantities on the left side of Eq. (15.13) is equal to or larger than unity, then the stress σ_1^c in the coating will be equal to or larger than the maximum stress which the coating can take and cracks perpendicular to τ_1^s will appear. For the special case where σ_2^s vanishes, it follows from the biaxiality equation that σ_1^s has to be equal to σ_0^d for the cracks to appear. This checks with the definition of σ_0^d.

   b. Cracks Perpendicular to σ_2^s by Direct Loading. Immediately after the coating is cracked in the direction perpendicular to σ_1^s, ϵ_1^c becomes less than ϵ_1^s at all points in the coating, except the common layer with the specimen. For any point at the edge of the cracks (point P in Fig. 15.5 and points P_1 and P_2 in Fig. 15.6), both the residual stress σ_R^c and the

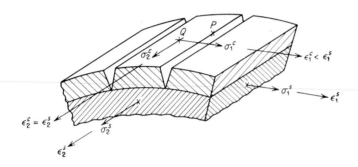

FIG. 15.5. Stresses and strains in the coating and the specimen after the cracks perpendicular to σ_1^s are opened.

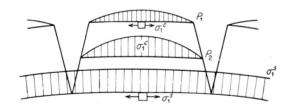

FIG. 15.6. Distribution of σ_1^c after the coating is cracked perpendicular to σ_1^s.

applied stress σ_1^c in the direction of σ_1^s are reduced to zero. For any point not at the edge of the cracks (point Q in Fig. 15.5), these stresses are also reduced, but not necessarily to zero. Further increase of the load may cause the stress in the direction of σ_2^s at some points to reach the ultimate strength σ_u. Cracks perpendicular to σ_2^s will now originate there. At the instant when these secondary cracks are impending, the stresses in the coating at the points where the secondary cracks originate are given by

$$\sigma_1^c = k(\sigma_u - \sigma_R^c)$$

$$\sigma_2^c = \sigma_u - \sigma_R^c$$

$$\epsilon_1^c < \epsilon_1^s \qquad (15.14)$$

$$\epsilon_2^c = \epsilon_2^s$$

so that k is defined as the ratio of σ_1^c to $\sigma_u - \sigma_R^c$ at the instant when the cracks perpendicular to σ_2^s are just going to appear and at the point where these cracks originate. In the above, we have neglected the change of residual stress in the direction of σ_2^s due to the opening up of the cracks perpendicular to σ_1^s. However, this would be taken into account by the experimental determination of k. As explained later, k may not be a constant and may depend on thickness of the coating and other factors.

To obtain the relation between σ_1^s, σ_2^s, and σ_0^d when the cracks perpendicular to σ_2^s are opening up, we proceed as follows: From the second and fourth of Eqs. (15.1) and the first and last of Eqs. (15.14), we obtain

$$\sigma_2^c = k\nu_c(\sigma_u - \sigma_R^c) + \frac{E_c}{E_s}(\sigma_2^s - \nu_s\sigma_1^s) \qquad (15.15)$$

By Eq. (15.15) and the second of Eqs. (15.14), we obtain

$$\frac{E_c}{E_s}(\sigma_2^s - \nu_s\sigma_1^s) = (1 - k\nu_c)(\sigma_u - \sigma_R^c) \qquad (15.16)$$

By Eqs. (15.7) and (15.16), we conclude that cracks perpendicular to σ_2^s will be impending when

$$\frac{1 - \nu_c^2}{(1 - k\nu_c)(1 - \nu_c\nu_s)}\frac{\sigma_2^s}{\sigma_0^d} - \nu_s\frac{1 - \nu_c^2}{(1 - k\nu_c)(1 - \nu_c\nu_s)}\frac{\sigma_1^s}{\sigma_0^d} = 1 \qquad (15.17)$$

Equation (15.17) gives the condition under which additional cracks perpendicular to σ_2^s will be opened after those cracks perpendicular to σ_1^s are already open. It states that, if the combinations of σ_1^s and σ_2^s are such that the sum of the left-side quantities of Eq. (15.17) is equal to or larger than, unity, then the stresses in the coating in the direction of σ_2^s will be equal to, or greater than, the maximum stress which the coating can take and cracks perpendicular to σ_2^s will appear in addition to those perpendicular to σ_1^s which already exist. This equation is applicable only after the coating has been cracked in the direction perpendicular to σ_1^s.

Let the load on a specimen be increased slowly. Call P the load on the specimen when cracks perpendicular to σ_1^s begin to appear. Then the stresses in the specimen σ_1^s and σ_2^s corresponding to the load P must satisfy the biaxiality equation (15.13). After the cracks perpendicular to σ

are opened up, the load on the specimen is increased slowly again. Call αP the load on the specimen when cracks perpendicular to σ_2^s begin to appear. Within the elastic limit of the material of the specimen, stresses in the specimen are always proportional to the load. The principal stresses in the specimen when the external load is αP are therefore $\alpha \sigma_1^s$ and $\alpha \sigma_2^s$. These are the stresses occurring when the second crack is impending and must satisfy Eq. (15.17), in which σ_1^s and σ_2^s are replaced by $\alpha \sigma_1^s$ and $\alpha \sigma_2^s$, respectively,

$$\frac{1 - \nu_c^2}{(1 - k\nu_c)(1 - \nu_c\nu_s)} \frac{\alpha\sigma_2^s}{\sigma_0^d} - \nu_s \frac{1 - \nu_c^2}{(1 - k\nu_c)(1 - \nu_c\nu_s)} \frac{\alpha\sigma_1^s}{\sigma_0^d} = 1 \qquad (15.18)$$

Equations (15.13) and (15.18) can be solved simultaneously to give σ_1^s and σ_2^s,

$$\frac{\sigma_1^s}{\sigma_0^d} = \frac{1 - \nu_c\nu_s}{1 - \nu_s^2}\left(1 - \frac{1 - k\nu_c}{\alpha}\frac{\nu_c - \nu_s}{1 - \nu_c^2}\right)$$

$$\frac{\sigma_2^s}{\sigma_0^d} = \frac{1 - \nu_c\nu_s}{1 - \nu_s^2}\left(\nu_s + \frac{1 - k\nu_c}{\alpha}\frac{1 - \nu_c\nu_s}{1 - \nu_c^2}\right) \qquad (15.19)$$

$$\frac{\sigma_2^s}{\sigma_1^s} = \frac{\nu_s + \dfrac{1 - k\nu_c}{\alpha}\dfrac{1 - \nu_c\nu_s}{1 - \nu_c^2}}{1 - \dfrac{1 - k\nu_c}{\alpha}\dfrac{\nu_c - \nu_s}{1 - \nu_c^2}}$$

where σ_1^s and σ_2^s are the principal stresses corresponding to the load P producing the cracks perpendicular to σ_1^s; α is always larger than unity. σ_0^d is given by Eq. (15.8).

c. *Cracks Produced by Relaxation.* A technique called relaxation loading is often employed in brittle-coating analysis. Here the coating is cured while the maximum load P is maintained on the specimen, so that only a hydrostatic residual stress σ_R^c is present in the coating while the specimen is under load P. When this maximum load P is later completely released, the induced stresses in the brittle coating are identical to those induced by a load of $-P$ on the specimen. Similarly, the stresses induced in the brittle coating due to a partial release of the initial high load P to the final low load $P - \beta P$ will be identical to those caused by a loading of $-\beta P$ in the specimen. In this book, a relaxation load of $-\beta P$ will denote a release of the initial load P to the final load $P - \beta P$. Obviously, the initial load P will be completely released if β is equal to unity.

It should be pointed out that the terms direct loading and relaxation loading are entirely relative. We can call one loading the direct loading and its reversed loading the relaxation loading. We can also call the reversed loading the direct loading and the unreversed loading the relaxation loading. In other words, a direct loading can be any loading. A relaxation loading is a reversed direct loading.

Suppose that a coating of sensitivity ϵ_s^d starts to crack in a direction perpendicular to σ_1^s when the load is P. Then the stresses in the specimen, σ_1^s and σ_2^s, corresponding to the load P must satisfy the biaxiality equation (15.13). This cracked coating is then removed and a new coating of a strain sensitivity ϵ_s^r is applied and cured. Suppose this new coating starts to crack at the same point in a direction perpendicular to the first crack under the relaxation load $-\beta P$. Within the elastic limit of the material of the specimen, stresses in the specimen are proportional to the load so that the stresses in the specimen when the load is $-\beta P$ are $-\beta\sigma_1^s$ and $-\beta\sigma_2^s$. These are the stresses occurring when the second crack is impending and must again satisfy the biaxiality equation (15.13). However, the algebraically larger principal stress is now $-\beta\sigma_2^s$, the algebraically smaller stress is now $-\beta\sigma_1^s$, and the uniaxial load σ_0^r required to crack the coating is now $(1 - \nu_c\nu_a)/(1 - \nu_c\nu_s)E_s\epsilon_s^r$ as given by Eq. (15.10) instead of $(1 - \nu_c\nu_a)/(1 - \nu_c\nu_s)E_s\epsilon_s^d$ as given by Eq. (15.8). We have called σ_1^s, σ_2^s, and σ_0^d the algebraically larger principal stress, the algebraically smaller principal stress, and the minimum uniaxial tensile stress in the specimen required for cracking the coating used in the direct-loading test, so that $-\beta\sigma_2^s$, $-\beta\sigma_1^s$, and $(\epsilon_s^r/\epsilon_s^d)\sigma_0^d$ will be the algebraically larger principal stress, algebraically smaller principal stress, and the minimum uniaxial tensile stress in the specimen required for cracking the coating used in the relaxation-loading test. By substituting these new values of σ_1^s, σ_2^s, and σ_0^d into Eq. (15.13), we obtain

$$\frac{-\beta\epsilon_s^d}{\epsilon_s^r}\frac{\sigma_2^s}{\sigma_0^d} + \frac{\nu_c - \nu_s}{1 - \nu_c\nu_s}\frac{-\beta\epsilon_s^d}{\epsilon_s^r}\frac{\sigma_1^s}{\sigma_0^d} = 1 \qquad (15.20)$$

Equations (15.13) and (15.20) can be solved simultaneously to give

$$\frac{\sigma_1^s}{\sigma_0^d} = \frac{(1 - \nu_c\nu_s)^2}{(1 - \nu_c^2)(1 - \nu_s^2)}\left[1 + \frac{\epsilon_s^r}{\beta\epsilon_s^d}\cdot\frac{\nu_c - \nu_s}{1 - \nu_c\nu_s}\right]$$

$$\frac{\sigma_2^s}{\sigma_0^d} = \frac{-(1 - \nu_c\nu_s)^2}{(1 - \nu_c^2)(1 - \nu_s^2)}\left[\frac{\nu_c - \nu_s}{1 - \nu_c\nu_s} + \frac{\epsilon_s^r}{\beta\epsilon_s^d}\right] \qquad (15.21)$$

$$\beta = \frac{\text{initial high load in relaxation test minus low load in relaxation test producing crack perpendicular to } \sigma_2^s}{\text{direct load } P \text{ producing crack perpendicular to } \sigma_1^s}$$

where σ_1^s, σ_2^s = principal stresses corresponding to direct load P

σ_0^d = minimum uniaxial tensile stress in specimen required to crack coating used in direct loading

σ_0^d is given by Eq. (15.8). β is always larger than zero. The coating used in relaxation loading is assumed to have the same Poisson's ratio as the coating used in direct loading.

15.6. Failure Chart of the Coating, Assuming that the Coating Fails When σ_1^c Reaches the Ultimate Tensile Strength. The failure chart shown in Fig. 15.7 has been drawn to represent in a convenient way the failure phenomenon of the coating for the case where $\nu_c = 0.42$, $\nu_s = 0.33$, and $k = 0.6$. The abscissa and the ordinate are the dimensionless quan-

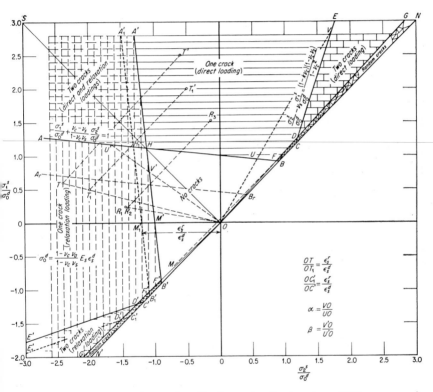

FIG. 15.7. Failure chart for the coating. Maximum-tensile-stress law of failure assumed. Poisson's ratio in specimen $\nu_s = 0.33$, Poisson's ratio in coating $\nu_c = 0.42$, $k = 0.6$, and $\angle$ GON $= 1\frac{1}{2}°$.

tities σ_1^s/σ_0^d and σ_2^s/σ_0^d. In the special case where the material of the cantilever calibration strip has the same Poisson's ratio as the material of the test specimen, these quantities would be simply $\sigma_1^s/E_s\epsilon_s^d$ and $\sigma_2^s/E_s\epsilon_s^d$, respectively. Each point on the chart corresponds to a specific combination of the principal stresses σ_1^s and σ_2^s. By definition σ_1^s is always larger than or equal to σ_2^s; hence all possible combinations of the principal stresses are represented by points confined in the half plane to the upper left of the line $N'N$ where $\sigma_1^s = \sigma_2^s$. The biaxiality equation (15.13) is represented by the straight line AB. This line always intercepts the σ_1^s/σ_0^d axis at unity. Its slope depends on the Poisson's ratios of the coating ν_c and of the specimen ν_s. If ν_c and ν_s are equal, then the slope is equal to zero and the line AB will be a horizontal line. Equation (15.17) is represented by the straight line CDE. The position of this line depends on the values of ν_c, ν_s, and k.

For any combinations of the principal stresses σ_1^s and σ_2^s corresponding to points inside zone $N'BA$, the sum of the quantities on the left side of the biaxiality equation (15.13) is less than unity so that no cracks perpendicular to σ_1^s would open up in the brittle coating. For any combinations of the principal stresses σ_1^s and σ_2^s corresponding to points inside zone ABN, the sum of the quantities on the left side of the biaxiality equation (15.13) is larger than unity so that cracks would open up perpendicular to σ_1^s. For any combinations of the principal stresses σ_1^s and σ_2^s represented by points inside zone ECN, the sum of the quantities on the left side of equation (15.17) is equal to or larger than unity so that additional cracks perpendicular to σ_2^s will appear.

For any values of the principal stresses σ_1^s and σ_2^s represented by points on the line $N'N$, these two principal stresses are equal. By Eqs. (15.3), the two principal stresses in the coating, σ_1^c and σ_2^c, are also equal to each other. The state of stress in both the specimen and the coating is therefore hydrostatic. For those points on the line $N'B$, the sum of the quantities on the left side of the biaxiality equation is less than unity, the stress in the coating σ_1^c, in the direction of σ_1^s, is less than the maximum stress which the coating can take, and no cracks will appear. For those points on the line BN, the above sum is larger than unity so that σ_1^c is larger than the maximum stress which the coating can take. Being equal to σ_1^c, σ_2^c at the same time also exceeds that limiting stress. In fact, since the state of stress is hydrostatic, the stress in any direction is equal to σ_1^c and larger than the limiting stress which the coating can take. Random cracks, i.e., cracks without preferential directions, will therefore appear. Theoretically, random cracks will occur only for the state of stress represented by the points exactly on the line BN. Practically, any state of stress inside a zone $GFBN$ will produce random cracks. It seems reasonable to assume that random cracks will appear when σ_2^s reaches a certain percentage of σ_1^s. Hence, the line FG defining the zone of random cracks can be assumed to be a straight line passing through the origin. The angle which the line FG makes with the line ON should be determined experimentally.

In a relaxation test, the sign of the load is reversed so that all stresses change sign. For instance, if the stresses at a point in a specimen under a direct load P are given as

$$\sigma_x = \quad 3{,}600 \text{ psi}$$
$$\sigma_y = -14{,}400 \text{ psi}$$
$$\tau_{xy} = 0$$

so that

$$\sigma_1^s = \sigma_x = \quad 3{,}600 \text{ psi}$$
$$\sigma_2^s = \sigma_y = -14{,}400 \text{ psi}$$

then the stresses at the same point under a relaxation load $-P$ must be

$$\sigma_1^s = -\sigma_y = 14{,}400 \text{ psi}$$
$$\sigma_2^s = -\sigma_x = -3{,}600 \text{ psi}$$

Evidently the value of σ_1^s due to the relaxation loading $-P$ is always equal to the value of $-\sigma_2^s$ due to the direct loading P, and the value of σ_2^s due to the relaxation loading $-P$ is always equal to the value of $-\sigma_1^s$ due to the direct loading P. If the strain sensitivities of the coatings used in the direct and relaxation loadings are equal so that σ_0^d for the two loadings are also equal, then the stresses due to the loadings P and $-P$ are always represented by two points on the failure chart symmetrically located with respect to the 45° line OS. For instance, if T represents the stresses due to a direct load P, then T' will represent the stresses due to a relaxation load $-P$. Also, if T represents the stresses due to a relaxation load $-P$, then T' will represent the stresses due to a direct load P.

Suppose the stresses at a point under the direct load P correspond to points inside zone $A'B'N'$, where $A'B'$ and AB are symmetrically located with respect to OS; then the stresses at the same point under the relaxation load $-P$ will correspond to points in the zone ABN, and one crack will appear. For this reason, zone $A'B'N'$ is marked "one-crack zone" and covered with dashed lines to indicate that one crack will appear when the load is reversed. Since the zone AHA' lies inside ABN and $A'B'N'$, it is marked "two-crack zone" to indicate that cracks will appear under both the direct load and the relaxation load. In the zone BHB' the points before and after the reversal of load all lie under the line AB; hence, it is marked "no-crack zone" to indicate that no cracks will appear under either the direct load or the relaxation load. Similarly, lines $F'G'$ and $C'E'$ are drawn so that these two lines and the lines FG and CE are symmetrically located with respect to the line OS. Zones $E'D'G'$ and $G'F'B'N'$ will be the zones where two cracks and random cracks, respectively, will appear upon a reversal of load.

Where the strain sensitivities of the coatings used in the direct loading and the relaxation loading are different, the stresses due to direct and relaxation loadings are no longer represented as points symmetrically located with respect to the line OS. For instance, if in the above example we have $\epsilon_s^d = 60 \times 10^{-5}$, $\epsilon_s^r = 72 \times 10^{-5}$, and $E_s = 10 \times 10^6$, then

$$\sigma_0^d = 6{,}000 \text{ psi}$$
$$\sigma_0^r = 7{,}200 \text{ psi}$$

Under the direct load P the stresses are given by

$$\frac{\sigma_1^s}{\sigma_0^d} = \quad 0.60$$

$$\frac{\sigma_2^s}{\sigma_0^d} = -2.40$$

Under the relaxation load $-P$ the stresses are given by

$$\frac{\sigma_1^s}{\sigma_0^r} = \quad 2.00$$

$$\frac{\sigma_2^s}{\sigma_0^r} = -0.50$$

On the failure chart the point T_1', representing the stresses due to the relaxation loading, is obtained from the point T, representing the stresses due to the direct loading, by two displacements. The first is a radial displacement TT_1 toward or away from the origin so that the ratio of OT to OT_1 is the same as the ratio of ϵ_s^r to ϵ_s^d. The second is a reflection T_1T_1' about the line OS. If we draw a line $A_1'M_1'B_1'$ parallel to $A'M'B'$ and with the ratio OM_1'/OM' equal to the ratio $\epsilon_s^r/\epsilon_s^d$, then for any point inside zone $A_1'B_1'N'$ representing the stresses due to a direct loading P the corresponding point representing the stresses due to the relaxation loading $-P$ will lie inside the zone ABN, and one crack will appear. The line of demarcation of the several zones is therefore $A_1'B_1'$ instead of $A'B'$. Similarly, the line of demarcation $C'E'$ also shifts to its new position $C_1'E_1'$ where $C_1'E_1'$ is parallel to $C'E'$ and the ratio OC_1'/OC' is equal to the ratio $\epsilon_s^r/\epsilon_s^d$.

The location of the lines AB and CE depends only on ν_c, ν_s, and k and not on the sensitivity of the coating, because the abscissa and the ordinate represent the ratios of the magnitude of the biaxial stresses necessary to crack the coating to the magnitude of the uniaxial stress necessary to crack the coating. The uniaxial stress is shown by Eq. (15.8) to be directly proportional to both the strain sensitivity of the coating and the modulus of elasticity of the specimen. For different combinations of ν_c, ν_s, and k the lines of demarcation AB and CE, will occupy slightly different positions from those shown in Fig. 15.8. The general shape of those zones of no

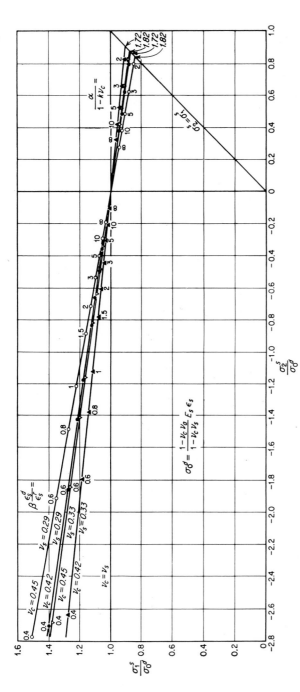

Fig. 15.8. Chart for the determination of both principal stresses, assuming the maximum-tensile-stress law of failure in the coating. Values shown on the portions of curves to the right and to the left of the σ_1^s/σ_0^d axis are those of $\alpha/(1 - kv_c)$ and $\beta(\epsilon_\delta^d/\epsilon_\delta)$, respectively.

crack, one crack, two orthogonal cracks, and random cracks, however, will still be the same. The different positions of the line AB corresponding to four combinations of ν_c and ν_s are shown on a larger scale in Fig. 15.8.

By the use of the failure chart, the prediction of cracks becomes very simple. For example, let the stresses in an aluminum specimen due to a tensile load of 1,000 lb be

$$\sigma_1^s = \quad 15,000 \text{ psi} \qquad \sigma_2^s = \quad 14,700 \text{ psi} \qquad \text{at } Q_1$$

$$\sigma_1^s = \quad 15,000 \text{ psi} \qquad \sigma_2^s = \quad 11,400 \text{ psi} \qquad \text{at } Q_2$$

$$\sigma_1^s = \quad 15,000 \text{ psi} \qquad \sigma_2^s = \quad -3,000 \text{ psi} \qquad \text{at } Q_3$$

$$\sigma_1^s = \quad 15,000 \text{ psi} \qquad \sigma_2^s = \quad -12,000 \text{ psi} \qquad \text{at } Q_4$$

$$\sigma_1^s = \quad -3,000 \text{ psi} \qquad \sigma_2^s = \quad -12,000 \text{ psi} \qquad \text{at } Q_5$$

$$\sigma_1^s = \quad -10,800 \text{ psi} \qquad \sigma_2^s = \quad -12,000 \text{ psi} \qquad \text{at } Q_6$$

$$\sigma_1^s = \quad -11,700 \text{ psi} \qquad \sigma_2^s = \quad -12,000 \text{ psi} \qquad \text{at } Q_7$$

$$\sigma_1^s = \quad 3,000 \text{ psi} \qquad \sigma_2^s = \quad -6,600 \text{ psi} \qquad \text{at } Q_8$$

Let ϵ_s^d as obtained from aluminum strips be 60×10^{-5}. The problem is to predict the presence or absence of cracks at these eight points under the given load and under a completely reversed load applied on a coating of $\epsilon_s^r = 72 \times 10^{-5}$ obtained from aluminum calibration strips. Assume $\nu_c = 0.42$, $\nu_s = 0.33$, $k = 0.6$, and $\angle GON = 1\frac{1}{2}°$.

By Eq. (15.11),

$$\sigma_0^d = 6,000 \text{ psi}$$

$$\text{At } Q_1 \qquad \frac{\sigma_1^s}{\sigma_0^d} = \quad 2.50 \qquad \frac{\sigma_2^s}{\sigma_0^d} = \quad 2.45$$

$$Q_2 \qquad \frac{\sigma_1^s}{\sigma_0^d} = \quad 2.50 \qquad \frac{\sigma_2^s}{\sigma_0^d} = \quad 1.90$$

$$Q_3 \qquad \frac{\sigma_1^s}{\sigma_0^d} = \quad 2.50 \qquad \frac{\sigma_2^s}{\sigma_0^d} = \quad -0.50$$

$$Q_4 \qquad \frac{\sigma_1^s}{\sigma_0^d} = \quad 2.50 \qquad \frac{\sigma_2^s}{\sigma_0^d} = \quad -2.00$$

$$Q_5 \qquad \frac{\sigma_1^s}{\sigma_0^d} = \quad -0.50 \qquad \frac{\sigma_2^s}{\sigma_0^d} = \quad -2.00$$

$$Q_6 \qquad \frac{\sigma_1^s}{\sigma_0^d} = \quad -1.80 \qquad \frac{\sigma_2^s}{\sigma_0^d} = \quad -2.00$$

$$Q_7 \qquad \frac{\sigma_1^s}{\sigma_0^d} = \quad -1.95 \qquad \frac{\sigma_2^s}{\sigma_0^d} = \quad -2.00$$

$$Q_8 \qquad \frac{\sigma_1^s}{\sigma_0^d} = \quad 0.5 \qquad \frac{\sigma_2^s}{\sigma_0^d} = \quad -1.10$$

The stresses at Q_1 correspond to a point inside zone $NBFG$. Hence, random cracks will appear under the tensile load of 1,000 lb, but no cracks will appear in the separate relaxation-load test in which the initial 1,000-lb tensile load is completely removed. The stresses at Q_2 are represented by a point inside zone GDE. Hence, two orthogonal cracks will appear under the 1,000-lb tensile load, but no cracks will appear in the relaxation load of 1,000 lb compression. At Q_3, where stresses belong to zone $EDFHA$, one crack will appear in the direct-load test (1,000-lb tensile load), and none in the relaxation-load test (1,000 lb compression). At Q_4, whose stresses belong to zone $A_1'H_1A$, two cracks will appear, one under the 1,000-lb tensile load and the other under the 1,000-lb compressive load. At Q_5, Q_6, and Q_7, whose stresses correspond to zones $AH_1F_1'D_1'E_1'$, $E_1'D_1'G'$, and $G'F'B'N'$, no cracks will appear under the tensile load of 1,000 lb, but one crack, two cracks, and random cracks will appear, respectively, under the 1,000-lb compressive load. At Q_8, whose stresses correspond to zone BH_1B_1', no cracks will appear either under the 1,000-lb tensile load or under the 1,000-lb compressive load.

15.7. Formula for the Calculation of "Apparent" Stress. The failure chart and all the formulas in this chapter have been derived from the assumption that the brittle coating fails when the maximum tensile stress in the coating reaches the ultimate strength. If, in addition to this, a second assumption is made, viz., that the value of σ_2^s is zero, then the biaxiality equation (15.13) will give $\sigma_1^s = \sigma_0^d$, so that Eq. (15.8) becomes

$$\sigma_1^s = \sigma_0^d = \frac{1 - \nu_c \nu_a}{1 - \nu_c \nu_s} E_s \epsilon_s^d \qquad (15.22)$$

The stress σ_1^s obtained from Eq. (15.22) will be termed "apparent" stress. On the failure chart, this apparent stress is represented as a point on the σ_1^s/σ_0^d axis at which the value of the ordinate is unity. Where r_2^s/σ_0^d is known to be zero or small compared with unity, the apparent stress represents a good estimate of the true stress. The error of this estimate increases as the absolute magnitude of the biaxiality ratio σ_2^s/σ_1^s becomes larger and larger, reaching a value of about 15 per cent when the ratio σ_2^s/σ_1^s is ± 1.

15.8. Coating Cracked in One Direction by a Direct Load and Later Cracked at the Same Point in a Direction Perpendicular to the First One by a Higher Direct Load. We shall consider in more detail the analysis of the data of a coating cracked in two orthogonal directions. In Fig. 15.9, let ABC be the isentatic for the external load P, that is, the loci of the ends of the cracks opened up when the external load is P. Let DEF be the isentatic for the external load $2P$. At this amount of load, cracks perpendicular to σ_2^s also appear. Let the dotted lines GHI and LMN be the isentatics for the second crack for the loads $2P$, $3P$, respectively. Then the stresses at A, B, and C, due to the load P, and the stresses at D, E, and F, under the load $2P$, must correspond to points located on the line AF of Fig. 15.7. The stresses at G, H, and I, due to the load $2P$, and the stresses at L, M, and N, due to the load $3P$, must correspond to points on the line DE of Fig. 15.7. Further, the stresses at the points of intersection O_1, O_2, O_3, and O_4 of solid and dotted isoentatics due to the load P are uniquely determined from Eqs. (15.19) by putting α equal to 3 and by using the known values of ϵ_s^d, E_s, ν_a, ν_c, ν_s, and k. This unique set of principal stresses is represented as point U on the line AF shown in Fig. 15.7. Point U may also be determined graphically by drawing a straight line from the origin O to intersect the two lines AF and DE at U and V so that the ratio of the length OV to the length OU is 3. Similarly the value of α can be estimated for other points such as B in Fig. 15.9 and

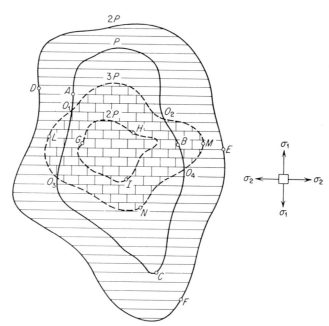

Fig. 15.9. Example of isoentatics for cracks perpendicular to σ_1 (solid line) and for the second cracks perpendicular to σ_2 (broken line).

both principal stresses uniquely determined graphically or by Eqs. (15.19).

The positions of the points on the line AF corresponding to four combinations of ν_c, ν_s, and $\alpha/(1 - k\nu_c)$ are shown on a large scale in Fig. 15.8. For other combinations of ν_c, ν_s, and $\alpha/(1 - k\nu_c)$, the positions of these points can be obtained by interpolation.

To demonstrate the above analysis, we shall solve the following example:

At a certain point A of a steel specimen, cracks in one direction begin to appear when the external load is 1,500 lb. At the same point A, cracks perpendicular to the above-mentioned cracks begin to appear when the load reaches 3,000 lb. The strain sensitivity ϵ_s^d of the coating as obtained from the aluminum cantilever calibration strips is 60×10^{-5}. The value of the following constants are given as

$$\nu_a = 0.33$$

$$\nu_c = 0.44$$

$$\nu_s = 0.29$$

$$E_s = 30 \times 10^6 \text{ psi}$$

$$k = 0.5$$

The two principal stresses are required in the specimen at point A when the external load is 1,000 lb. We shall assume that the brittle coating cracks according to the maximum-tensile-stress law of failure.

To solve the above example, we first calculate the value of σ_0^d by substituting the given values of ν_a, ν_c, ν_s, E_s, and ϵ_s^d in Eq. (15.8),

$$\sigma_0^d = \frac{1 - \nu_c \nu_a}{1 - \nu_c \nu_s} E_s \epsilon_s^d = 17{,}650 \text{ psi}$$

By substituting the given values of ν_c, ν_s, and k into Eqs. (15.19) and noting that $\alpha = 3{,}000/1{,}500 = 2.0$, we have

$$\frac{\sigma_1^s}{\sigma_0^d} = \frac{1 - \nu_c \nu_s}{1 - \nu_s^2}\left(1 - \frac{1 - k\nu_c}{\alpha}\frac{\nu_c - \nu_s}{1 - \nu_c^2}\right) = 0.883$$

$$\frac{\sigma_2^s}{\sigma_0^d} = \frac{1 - \nu_c \nu_s}{1 - \nu_s^2}\left(\nu_s + \frac{1 - k\nu_c}{\alpha}\frac{1 - \nu_c \nu_s}{1 - \nu_c^2}\right) = 0.679$$

or

$$\sigma_1^s = 15{,}600 \text{ psi}$$

$$\sigma_2^s = 12{,}000 \text{ psi}$$

The same analysis can be conducted graphically. In Fig. 15.8 we selected the second line corresponding to $\nu_c = 0.42$ and $\nu_s = 0.29$. On this line we locate the point where $\alpha/(1 - k\nu_c) = 2.56$. The coordinates of this point are 0.90 and 0.68, giving the values of σ_1^s/σ_0^d and σ_2^s/σ_0^d, respectively. From the same figure, for $\nu_c = 0.45$, $\nu_s = 0.29$, $\alpha/(1 - k\nu_c) = 2.56$, we read 0.88 and 0.68 as the values of σ_1^s/σ_0^d and σ_2^s/σ_0^d, respectively. By interpolation, for $\nu_c = 0.44$, $\nu_s = 0.29$, $\alpha/(1 - k\nu_c) = 2.56$, the values of σ_1^s/σ_0^d and σ_2^s/σ_0^d are therefore 0.89 and 0.68, respectively. This checks with 0.88 and 0.68 calculated above. These principal stresses are those in the specimen at point A corresponding to an external load of 1,500 lb. The principal stresses in the specimen at point A corresponding to an external load of 1,000 lb are therefore

$$\sigma_1^s = \frac{1,000}{1,500} \times 15,600 = 10,400 \text{ psi tension}$$

$$\sigma_2^s = \frac{1,000}{1,500} \times 12,000 = 8,000 \text{ psi tension}$$

Since the directions of σ_1^s and σ_2^s are always perpendicular and parallel to the direction of the first crack, respectively, the stresses occurring at point A on the surface of the specimen are solved completely by our Stresscoat test.

15.9. Coating Cracked in One Direction by a Direct Load and Later Cracked at the Same Point in a Direction Perpendicular to the First One by a Relaxation Load. The following is an analysis of the data when a relaxation test is conducted: In Fig. 15.10, let the thick lines ABC and DEF be the isoentatics for the direct loads P and $2P$, respectively. Let the lines GHI and LMN be the isoentatics due to the relaxation loading $-0.3P$ and $-0.6P$, respectively. The relaxation-loading test is run after

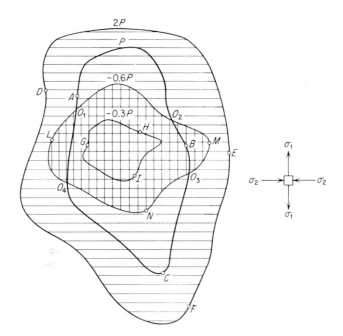

FIG. 15.10. Example of isoentatics due to direct loading (thick line) and due to relaxation loading (thin line).

the coating of the direct-loading test is removed and a new coating is put on the specimen. Again, the stresses at A, B, and C, due to the load P, and the stresses at D, E, and F, due to the load $2P$, must correspond to points located on the line AF of Fig. 15.7. The stresses at G, H, and I, due to the relaxation load $-0.3P$, and the stresses at L, M, and N, due to the relaxation load $-0.6P$, must correspond to points on the line $F'A'$ of Fig. 15.7. Further, the stresses at the points of intersection O_1, O_2, O_3, and O_4, of thick and thin isoentatics, due to the direct load P, are uniquely determined from Eqs. (15.21) by putting $\beta = 0.6$ and by using the known values of ϵ_s^d, ϵ_s^r, E_s, ν_a, ν_c, and ν_s. This unique set of principal stresses is represented as point U' on the line AF shown in Fig. 15.7. Point U' may also be determined graphically by drawing a straight line through the origin O to intersect the two lines AF and $A'F'$ at U' and V' so that the ratio of the length OV' to the length OU' is $\beta(\epsilon_s^d/\epsilon_s^r)$. Similarly, the value of β can be determined for other points such as B in Fig. 15.10 and both principal stresses uniquely determined by Eqs. (15.21). The positions of the points on the line AF corresponding to four combinations of ν_c, ν_s, and $\beta(\epsilon_s^d/\epsilon_s^r)$ are shown on a large scale in Fig. 15.8. For other combinations of ν_c, ν_s, and $\beta(\epsilon_s^d/\epsilon_s^r)$, the positions of these points can be obtained by interpolation.

It should be pointed out that the relaxation-loading test is conducted on an uncracked coating and not on the coating that was already cracked in the direct-loading test. Otherwise the cracks would make ϵ_1^c different from ϵ_1^s so that the above analysis would no longer be valid.

To demonstrate the above analysis, we shall solve the following example:

At a certain point A of a steel specimen, cracks in one direction began to appear when the external load was 1,500 lb. The strain sensitivity ϵ_s^d of the coating as obtained from the aluminum cantilever calibration strips is 60×10^{-5}. This coating was removed, a new coating was applied and cured, while a load of 3,500 lb was maintained on the specimen. On the partial release of the 3,500-lb load to 1,700 lb, cracks perpendicular to those observed in the first test began to appear at the same point A. The strain sensitivity ϵ_s^r of the coating used in the relaxation test as determined by aluminum cantilever calibration strips is 70×10^{-5}. The values of the following constants are given as

$$\nu_a = 0.33$$

$$\nu_c = 0.44$$

$$\nu_s = 0.29$$

$$E_s = 30 \times 10^6 \, \text{psi}$$

The two principal stresses in the specimen are required at point A

when the external load is 1,000 lb. We shall assume that the brittle coating cracks according to the maximum-tensile-stress law of failure.

To solve this example, we first calculate the value of σ_0^d from Eq. (15.8).

$$\sigma_0^d = \frac{1 - \nu_c \nu_a}{1 - \nu_c \nu_s} E_s \epsilon_s^d = 17{,}650 \text{ psi}$$

Next, by Eqs. (15.21), we have

$$\frac{\sigma_1^s}{\sigma_0^d} = \frac{(1 - \nu_c \nu_s)^2}{(1 - \nu_c^2)(1 - \nu_s^2)} \left[1 + \frac{\epsilon_s^r}{\beta \epsilon_s^d} \cdot \frac{\nu_c - \nu_s}{1 - \nu_c \nu_s} \right] = 1.22$$

$$\frac{\sigma_2^s}{\sigma_0^d} = \frac{-(1 - \nu_c \nu_s)^2}{(1 - \nu_c^2)(1 - \nu_s^2)} \left[\frac{\nu_c - \nu_s}{1 - \nu_c \nu_s} + \frac{\epsilon_s^r}{\beta \epsilon_s^d} \right] = -1.20$$

or

$$\sigma_1^s = \quad 21{,}500 \text{ psi}$$

$$\sigma_2^s = -21{,}200 \text{ psi}$$

The same analysis can be conducted graphically. In Fig. 15.8 we select the second line corresponding to $\nu_c = 0.42$ and $\nu_s = 0.29$. On this line we locate the point where $\beta(\epsilon_s^d / \epsilon_s^r) = 1.2 \times (60/70) = 1.03$. The coordinates of this point are 1.16 and -1.16, which are the values of σ_1^s / σ_0^d and σ_2^s / σ_0^d, respectively. From the same figure, for $\nu_c = 0.45$, $\nu_s = 0.29$, $\beta(\epsilon_s^d / \epsilon_s^r) = 1.09$, we read 1.24 and -1.20 as the values of σ_1^s / σ_0^d and σ_2^s / σ_0^d, respectively. By interpolation, for $\nu_c = 0.44$, $\nu_s = 0.29$, $\beta(\epsilon_s^d / \epsilon_s^r) = 1.03$, the values of σ_1^s / σ_0^d and σ_2^s / σ_0^d are therefore 1.21 and -1.19, respectively. This checks well with 1.22 and -1.20 calculated above.

The principal stresses determined above are those in the specimen at point A corresponding to an external load of 1,500 lb. The principal stresses in the specimen at point A corresponding to an external load of 1,000 lb are therefore

$$\sigma_1^s = \frac{1{,}000}{1{,}500} \times 21{,}500 = 14{,}300 \text{ psi tension}$$

$$\sigma_2^s = \frac{1{,}000}{1{,}500} \times (-21{,}200) = -14{,}100 \text{ psi compression}$$

Since the directions of σ_1^s and σ_2^s are perpendicular and parallel to the direction of the first crack, respectively, the surface stresses at point A are solved completely by our coating test.

15.10. Coating Cracked in One Direction by a Direct Load and Not Cracked at the Same Point in a Direction Perpendicular to the First One by the Highest Direct Load and the Highest Relaxation Load. In those cases where cracks perpendicular to σ_1^s are obtained, but no cracks perpendicular to σ_2^s appear under the highest possible direct load and relaxation load corresponding to certain values of $\alpha/(1 - k\nu_c)$ and $\beta(\epsilon_s^d / \epsilon_s^r)$, negative information can still be obtained. The state of stress must correspond to points on the failure line AF between these values of $\alpha/(1 - k\nu_c)$ and $\beta(\epsilon_s^d/\epsilon_s^r)$ corresponding to the highest loads which fail to crack the coating in the direction perpendicular to σ_2^s.

To demonstrate the above, we shall solve the following example:

At a certain point A of a steel specimen, cracks in one direction began to appear when the external load was 1,500 lb. At the same point A, no cracks perpendicular to the above-mentioned cracks appeared at the highest load of 3,500 lb. A separate relaxation test in which the initial load of 3,500 lb was completely released also showed no cracks at A perpendicular to the above-mentioned crack. The strain sensitivities of the coatings used in the direct loading and the relaxation loading as determined on aluminum calibration strips are $\epsilon_s^d = 60 \times 10^{-5}$ and $\epsilon_s^r = 70 \times 10^{-5}$. The values of the following constants are given as:

$$\nu_a = 0.33$$

$$\nu_c = 0.44$$

$$\nu_s = 0.29$$

$$E_s = 30 \times 10^6 \text{ psi}$$

$$k = 0.5$$

The upper limit and the lower limit of both principal stresses at point A are required when the external load is 1,000 lb. We assume that the brittle coating cracks according to the maximum-tensile-stress law of failure.

To solve this problem, we first calculate the value of σ_0^d from Eq. (15.8),

$$\sigma_0^d = \frac{1 - \nu_c\nu_a}{1 - \nu_c\nu_s} E_s\epsilon_s^d = 17,650 \text{ psi}$$

Next, we note that a crack did appear at point A at a load of 1,500 lb. Hence, at that load, the principal stresses at A must correspond to a point located on the line $\nu_c = 0.44$, $\nu_s = 0.29$ in Fig. 15.8. (This line is not shown in Fig. 15.8, but its position can be obtained there by interpolation.) On this line, a point which corresponds to $\alpha/(1 - k\nu_c) = 2.99$ can be located by interpolation. Now for any point which lies to the right of this point, $\alpha/(1 - k\nu_c)$ is less than 2.99 or α is less than 2.33, using our given values, $k = 0.5$ and $\nu_c = 0.44$. A direct load of 2.33 times the load that cracks the coating perpendicular to σ_1^s should therefore produce a crack perpendicular to σ_2^s. Since the 3,500-lb load, which is 2.33 times the 1,500-lb load, did not succeed in cracking the coating perpendicular to σ_2^s, our stresses must be represented by points on the line $\nu_c = 0.44$, $\nu_s = 0.29$ to the left of the point $\alpha/(1 - k\nu_c) = 2.99$. Similarly, any point to the left of the point $\beta(\epsilon_s^d/\epsilon_s^r) = 2.00$ or $\beta = 2.33$ would mean that a crack perpendicular to σ_2^s should be produced by the release of the 3,500-lb load. Since this did not happen in our given data, our stresses must lie to the right of the point $\beta(\epsilon_s^d/\epsilon_s^s) = 2.00$. The upper and lower limits of σ_1^s/σ_0^d and σ_2^s/σ_0^d are therefore the coordinates of the points $\alpha/(1 - k\nu_c) = 2.99$ and $\beta(\epsilon_s^d/\epsilon_s^s) = 2.00$ on the line $\nu_c = 0.44$, $\nu_s = 0.29$, or

$$0.88 < \frac{\sigma_1^s}{\sigma_0^d} < 1.13$$

$$-0.70 < \frac{\sigma_2^s}{\sigma_0^d} < 0.62$$

or: 15,500 psi tension $< \sigma_1^s <$ 20,000 psi tension

$-12,400$ psi compression $< \sigma_2^s <$ 10,900 psi tension

These are the limits of the principal stresses at point A corresponding to an external load of 1,500 lb. The limits of the principal stresses at point A corresponding to an external load of 1,000 lb are therefore obtained by proportion,

10,300 psi tension $< \sigma_1^s <$ 13,300 psi tension

$-8,300$ psi compression $< \sigma_2^s <$ 7,300 psi tension

The best estimate for the values of σ_1^s and σ_2^s will therefore be the mean of the two extremes.

$\sigma_1^s = \tfrac{1}{2}(10,300 + 13,300) = 11,800$ psi $\bigg\}$ under the external load

$\sigma_2^s = \tfrac{1}{2}(-8,300 + 7,300 = -500$ psi $\bigg\}$ of 1,000 psi

The apparent stress calculated from Eq. (15.22) is

$\sigma_1^s = \sigma_0^d = 17,650$ psi   under the external load of 1,500 psi

or $\sigma_1^s = 11,750$ psi   under the external load of 1,000 psi

which is practically equal to the mean, 11,800 psi, obtained above. Hence, for this example, the apparent stress calculated by the simple equation (15.22) represents the best estimate for σ_1^s. This is generally true of the stress σ_1^s at any point where the coating is cracked perpendicular to σ_1^s by a direct load but not cracked perpendicular to σ_2^s by the highest direct load and the highest relaxation load. Similarly, it is also generally true that the apparent-stress formula represents the best estimate for σ_2^s at any point where the coating is cracked perpendicular to σ_2^s by a relaxation load, but not cracked perpendicular to σ_1^s by the highest relaxation load and the highest direct load.

15.11. Determination of the Second Principal Stress by Graphical Integration. When the values of σ_1^s and ρ_1 are known at every point on an isostatic S_2 (Fig. 15.11) and the value of σ_2^s is known at one point on this isostatic, it is possible to determine the value of σ_2^s at any point on this isostatic by integrating the Lamé-Maxwell equations,

$$\sigma_2^s = \int \frac{\sigma_2^s - \sigma_1^s}{\rho_1}\, dS_2$$

If σ_1^s and ρ_1 can be expressed as analytic functions of S_2, the integration may be performed analytically and an analytic expression of σ_2^s in terms of S_2 may be obtained. In experimental stress analysis, however, σ_1^s and ρ_1 usually cannot be expressed as analytic functions of S_2. A graphical integration is therefore necessary to calculate the value of σ_2^s. From brittle-coating data the value of σ_1^s is not determined exactly, but rather an approximation to σ_1^s which was called apparent stress. Using this

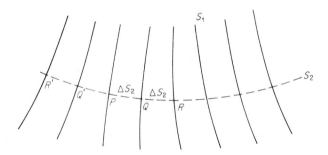

Fig. 15.11. Graphical integration of Lamé-Maxwell equations. Division into a number of equal segments ΔS_2 of an isostatic S_2.

apparent stress, the integration may be performed in the following manner: The isostatic S_2 is first divided into a number of short segments ΔS_2 of equal length (Fig. 15.11). The following quantities are then calculated in the order stated.

1. $(\sigma_2^s - \sigma_1^s)/\rho_1$ at P, the point of known σ_2^s.
2. Change of σ_2^s between P and Q, by the formula

$$\Delta\sigma_2^s = \frac{\sigma_2^s - \sigma_1^s}{\rho_1}\, \Delta S_2$$

where $(\sigma_2^s - \sigma_1^s)/\rho_1$ are those at P.

3. σ_2^s at Q by the relation

$$\sigma_2^s \text{ at } Q = (\sigma_2^s \text{ at } P) + \Delta\sigma_2^s \text{ calculated in (2)}$$

4. Change of σ_2^s between Q and R by the formula

$$\Delta\sigma_2^s = \frac{\sigma_2^s - \sigma_1^s}{\rho_1} \Delta S_2$$

where $(\sigma_2^s - \sigma_1^s)/\rho_1$ are those at Q.

5. σ_2^s at R, by the relation

$$\sigma_2^s \text{ at } R = (\sigma_2^s \text{ at } Q) + \Delta\sigma_2^s \text{ calculated in (4)}$$

The calculations can be continued until the values of σ_2^s at all points to the right of P are obtained. The values of σ_2^s at all points Q', R', ... to the left of P can be calculated in a similar way. If a point is reached at which the value of σ_2^s is known, the value obtained through integration can be checked against this known value and the error distributed along the path of integration.

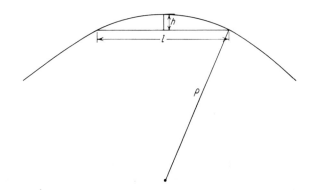

Fig. 15.12. Graphical determination of the radius of curvature of any curve. The radius of curvature ρ is given approximately by $l^2/8h + h/2$.

The radius of curvature ρ_1 can be measured on the curves S_1 by two methods. Where ρ_1 is short, circles of different radii can be drawn on the curve by a compass. The one which fits the curve closest at the point of tangency will give the best estimate of ρ_1. Where ρ_1 is long, the base l and height h of a short segment of the curve can be measured (Fig. 15.12) and ρ_1 calculated from the formula

$$\rho_1 = \frac{l^2}{8h} + \frac{h}{2}$$

This formula is exact for a circular arc and is close for any curve if the base l is taken relatively short.

The value of σ_2^s obtained in the manner prescribed above is not the exact value, since, as was pointed out above, the values used for σ_1^s were only the apparent stresses. The analysis might be further refined by computing an "improved" value of σ_1^s from the apparent stress, the calculated value of σ_2^s, and by use of the failure chart. An iterative procedure could be used to determine σ_1^s and σ_2^s correct to more significant figures.

15.12. Effect of Refrigeration. Generally no cracks can be obtained in a large portion of the surface of the test specimen because even under the highest possible load, which is limited by yielding or failure of the specimen, the stresses in these areas are not large enough to crack the coating. These stresses correspond to points in the no-crack zone ABM of Fig. 15.7. The techniques usually employed to obtain crack patterns in these areas are refrigeration or dye etching, or both.

Refrigeration produces two separate effects. First, it changes the ultimate tensile strength of the coating from σ_u^0 at test temperature t_0 to σ_u^r at the lowered temperature t_r. Second, it induces a hydrostatic tension in the coating. This tension, denoted by σ_H^c, can be computed as follows:

The contraction per unit length of the coating due to the temperature drop from t_0 to t_r is

$$\gamma_c(t_0 - t_r)$$

and the contraction per unit length of the specimen due to the temperature drop from t_0 to t_s is

$$\gamma_s(t_0 - t_s)$$

where γ_c and γ_s are the coefficients of lineal thermal expansion of the coating and the specimen, respectively.

The expansion per unit length of the coating due to the hydrostatic tension σ_H^c at temperature t_r is given by the corresponding hydrostatic strain,

$$(1 - \nu_c) \frac{\sigma_H^c}{E_c^r}$$

where E_c^r is the modulus of elasticity of the brittle coating at temperature t_r.

The contraction of the test specimen due to the hydrostatic compression is negligible.

Assuming perfect adhesion between coating and specimen, we have

$$\gamma_c(t_0 - t_r) - \gamma_s(t_0 - t_s) = (1 - \nu_c) \frac{\sigma_H^c}{E_c^r}$$

or
$$\sigma_H^c = \frac{E_c^r}{1 - \nu_c} [\gamma_c(t_0 - t_r) - \gamma_s(t_0 - t_s)] \qquad (15.23)$$

This relative expansion in the coating produced by refrigeration can be thought of as if it were produced by a hydrostatic tension in the specimen. This fictitious hydrostatic tension in the specimen, σ_H^s, which would induce the same amount of stress in the coating as refrigeration, can be computed by substituting E_c^0 for E_c, σ_H^c for σ_1^c, σ_H^s for both σ_1^s and σ_2^s in the first of Eqs. (15.3),

$$\sigma_H^c = \frac{E_c^0}{E_s(1 - \nu_c^2)} (1 - \nu_c\nu_s + \nu_c - \nu_s)\sigma_H^s$$

$$\text{or} \qquad \sigma_H^s = \frac{E_s}{E_c^0} \frac{1 - \nu_c}{1 - \nu_s} \sigma_H^c$$

(15.24)

where E_c^0 is the modulus of elasticity of the brittle coating at temperature t_0.

Once the constants σ_u^0, σ_u^r, γ_c, γ_s, ν_c, and ν_s are determined for the particular coating and test specimen used, the effect of refrigeration can be evaluated. In the following example, let us assume that the given values are

$$E_c^0 = 2.8 \times 10^5 \,\text{psi}$$

$$E_c^r = 3.0 \times 10^5 \,\text{psi}$$

$$E_s = 30 \times 10^6 \,\text{psi}$$

$$\gamma_c = 60 \times 10^{-6}/°\text{F}$$

$$\gamma_s = 6.3 \times 10^{-6}/°\text{F}$$

$$t_0 = 65°\text{F}$$

$$t_r = 55°\text{F}$$

$$t_s = 65°\text{F}$$

$$\sigma_u^0 = 890 \,\text{psi}$$

$$\sigma_u^r = 910 \,\text{psi}$$

$$\sigma_R^c = 680 \,\text{psi}$$

$$\sigma_1^s = 5,000 \,\text{psi}$$

$$\sigma_2^s = -30,000 \,\text{psi}$$

$$\nu_c = 0.45$$

$$\nu_s = 0.29$$

The prediction of the presence or absence of cracks before and after refrigeration is required. Let us call σ_0^0 the uniaxial tensile stress in the specimen producing failure in the coating at temperature t_0. The analysis can be conducted as follows: By Eq. (15.7)

$$\sigma_0^0 = \frac{E_s}{E_c^0} \frac{1 - \nu_c^2}{1 - \nu_c\nu_s} (\sigma_u^0 - \sigma_R^c) = 20,600 \,\text{psi}$$

Therefore,
$$\frac{\sigma_1^s}{\sigma_0^0} = 0.24$$

$$\frac{\sigma_2^s}{\sigma_0^0} = -1.45$$

This state of stress is represented by point R_1 in Fig. 15.7. Since R_1 is in the no-crack zone, there will be no cracks before refrigeration.

After refrigeration, calling σ_0^r the uniaxial tensile stress in the specimen producing failure at temperature t_r,

$$\sigma_0^r = \frac{E_s}{E_c^r} \frac{1 - \nu_c^2}{1 - \nu_c \nu_s} (\sigma_u^r - \sigma_R^c) = 21{,}100 \text{ psi}$$

so that
$$\frac{\sigma_1^s}{\sigma_0^r} = 0.24$$

$$\frac{\sigma_2^s}{\sigma_0^r} = -1.42$$

This state of stress is represented in Fig. 15.7 by point R_2. The movement of point R_1 to R_2 is due only to the change in ultimate strength of the coating because of the change in temperature. In most cases, this change will probably be small.

The hydrostatic state of stress is computed by Eqs. (15.23) and (15.24)

$$\sigma_H^c = 325 \text{ psi}$$

$$\sigma_H^s = 26{,}900 \text{ psi}$$

$$\frac{\sigma_H}{\sigma_0^r} = 1.28$$

The final state of stress after refrigeration is given by the following:

$$\frac{\sigma_1^s}{\sigma_0^r} = 1.52$$

$$\frac{\sigma_2^s}{\sigma_0^r} = -0.14$$

This final state of stress is represented in Fig. 15.7 by point R_3. Since R_3 is located in the one-crack zone, there will be one crack perpendicular to σ_1 in the coating after refrigeration.

Refrigeration is represented on the failure chart by two separate displacements. The point is first displaced toward or away from the origin until it is at σ_0^0/σ_0^r times its initial distance from the origin. It is then displaced upward to the right along a 45° line until the increase of the ordinate or abscissa is equal to σ_H/σ_0^r. The final location will then dictate whether there will be no crack, one crack, two orthogonal cracks, or random cracks after refrigeration.

The radial displacement represented by the change of σ_0^d computed by the change of $(\sigma_u - \sigma_R^c)/E_c$ is probably always small compared with the displacement along the 45° line due to σ_H^s, as the above example illustrates. In the following discussion, σ_0^0/σ_0^r will therefore be assumed to be unity and refrigeration treated as a single displacement upward to the right along a 45° line.

Returning to the failure chart, let MF be a line parallel to NN'. For any combination of principal stresses represented by points inside the zone $MFBN'$, refrigeration will move them across the line FB into the zone of random cracks. For those represented by the points inside the zone AFM, refrigeration will move them across the line AF representing a crack perpendicular to σ_1. Further refrigeration will move them across the line CE representing the second crack orthogonal to the first. The effect of refrigeration on relaxation loading is similar to that on direct loading, i.e., a displacement upward to the right along a 45° line. From Eqs. (15.23) and (15.24) we have

$$\sigma_H^s = \frac{E_c^r}{E_c^0} \frac{E_s}{1 - \nu_s} [\gamma_c(t_0 - t_r) - \gamma_s(t_0 - t_s)]$$

(15.25)

or

$$\frac{\sigma_H^s}{\sigma_0^d} = \frac{E_c^r}{E_c^0} \frac{E_s}{\sigma_0^d(1 - \nu_s)} [\gamma_c(t_0 - t_r) - \gamma_s(t_0 - t_s)]$$

Refrigeration can therefore be represented on the failure chart as a shift of the line AB to its new position A_rB_r so that A_rB_r is parallel to AB and the distance BB_r is equal to $\sqrt{2}$ times the right-hand quantity of Eq. (15.25). A_rB_rN will now be the zone of no crack, and A_rB_rN' will now be the zone of one or more cracks. The length of the shift, BB_r, of course depends on the degree of refrigeration.

15.13. Experimental Determination of the Location of the Line OG on the Failure Chart. The crack pattern of an aluminum circular plate with clamped edges loaded perpendicular to the plate with a uniformly distributed pressure is shown in Fig. 15.13. An enlarged picture of a portion of the plate is shown in Fig. 15.14. Here the radial stress is never larger than the tangential stress. Their ratio, σ_2^s/σ_1^s, is found by electrical-strain-gage measurements to decrease from unity at the center of the plate to zero at the point P_4 (Fig. 15.13). At the point P_1, where the random cracks border on the preferential radial cracks, σ_2^s/σ_1^s has the value 0.95. Hence, the line OG of the failure chart (Fig. 15.7) makes an angle with the σ_1^s/σ_0^d axis whose tangent is approximately equal to 0.95.

15.14. Experimental Determination of the Value of k. Point P_2 (Fig. 15.13) was cracked first in the radial direction under a uniformly distributed

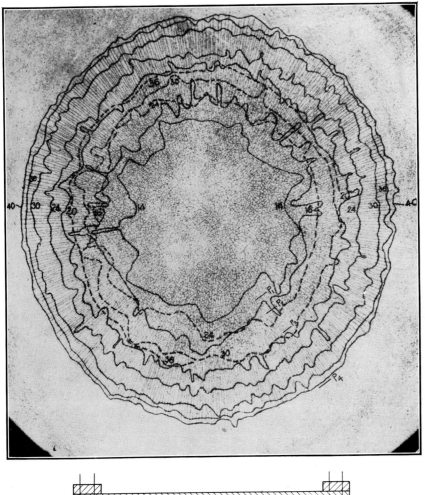

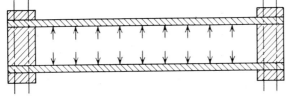

Fig. 15.13. Crack pattern of an aluminum circular plate with clamped edges loaded perpendicular to the plate with a uniformly distributed pressure.

pressure of 16 in. Hg and later in the circumferential direction at a pressure of 24 in. Hg. The ratio σ_2^s/σ_1^s at P_2 found by the electrical-strain-gage data is 0.92. Using this value and putting $\nu_s = \frac{1}{3}$, $\nu_c = 0.42$, $\alpha = 24/16$ into the third of Eqs. (15.19), we obtain the value of k as 0.54. Similarly from the point P_3 in Fig. 15.13 we obtain the value of k as 0.64.   Hence, for the particular coating tested the value of k is probably in the neighborhood of 0.6.

Figure 15.15 shows the crack pattern of an aluminum tube with tapered walls under internal pressure so that the ratio of σ_2^s/σ_1^s at every point on its external surface is $\frac{1}{2}$.   Here the second crack isoentatic (broken line) marked 1,000 psi corresponds to the first crack isoentatic (solid lines) of

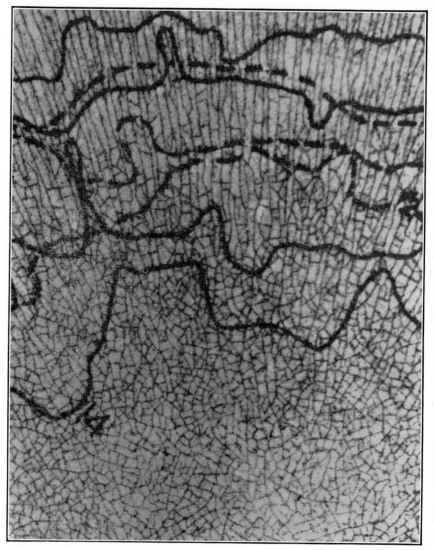

Fig. 15.14. Enlarged picture of a portion of the circular plate shown in Fig. 15.13.

pproximately 220 psi. A point cracked first in the axial direction at a
pressure of 220 psi was therefore cracked again later in the circumferential
direction at a pressure of 1,000 psi. With $\nu_c = 0.42$ for the No. 1206

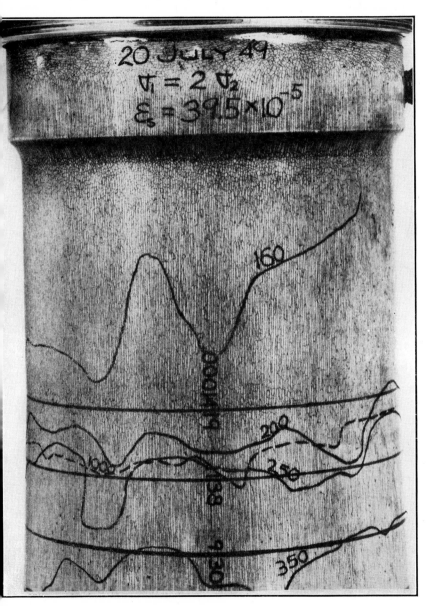

FIG. 15.15. Crack pattern of an aluminum tube with tapered walls under internal
pressure.

Stresscoat used and putting $\nu_s = \frac{1}{3}$, $\alpha = 1,000/220$, and $\sigma_2^s/\sigma_1^s = \frac{1}{2}$, th third of Eqs. (15.19) gives the value of k as 0.74.

The value of k probably is not a constant and depends on many factor such as the ratio of the thickness of the coating to the spacing betweer

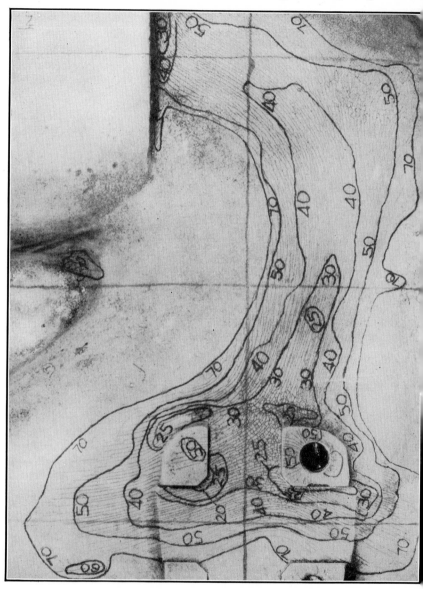

FIG. 15.16. Crack pattern of a pressure vessel. Figures on isoentatics correspond to hundreds of pounds per square inch internal pressure.

djacent cracks perpendicular to σ_1^s and the magnitude and gradient of σ_1^s/σ_0^d. This may explain the discrepancy found in the above determinations f the value of k.

15.15. Formulas and Charts to Be Used in the Analysis of Brittle-oating Data, Assuming Other Laws of Failure. If other laws of failure re assumed, the same procedure as outlined above can be used to derive he formulas and to construct the failure chart. In case the law of failure loes not have an analytic expression, no analytic formulas can be derived ut the failure chart and the values of $\alpha/(1 - k\nu_c)$ and $\beta(\epsilon_s^d/\epsilon_s^r)$ on the ailure curve can still be found graphically.

Exercises

15.1. Calculate the two principal stresses in the coating if the principal stresses in he specimen are 5,000 psi and $-20,000$ psi, respectively. Assume $E_c = 2.8 \times 10^5$ psi, $E_s = 30 \times 10^6$ psi, $\nu_c = 0.42$, $\nu_s = 0.29$. Check your results by using the graph of 'ig. 15.2.

15.2. Using the same values of E_c, E_s, ν_c, and ν_s as given in Exercise 15.1, calculate a) σ_1^c and σ_2^c if $\sigma_1^s = 10,000$ psi, $\sigma_2^s = 0$; (b) σ_1^s and σ_2^s if $\sigma_1^c = 250$ psi, $\sigma_2^c = 0$; (c) σ_1^c nd σ_2^c if $\sigma_1^s = \sigma_2^s = 5,000$ psi.

15.3. Eliminate σ_0^d from Eqs. (15.8) and (15.13) so that the biaxiality equation 15.13) is expressed in terms of ϵ_s^d instead of σ_0^d.

15.4. At a certain point A of an aluminum specimen, cracks in one direction began o appear when the external load was 1,000 lb. At the same point A, cracks perpenlicular to the above-mentioned cracks began to appear when the load reached 3,000 lb. The strain sensitivity ϵ_s^d of the coating as obtained from aluminum cantilever calibration strips is 65×10^{-5}. Given

$$\nu_a = 0.33$$
$$\nu_c = 0.45$$
$$\nu_s = 0.33$$
$$E_s = 10 \times 10^6 \text{ psi}$$
$$k = 0.5$$

Required the two principal stresses in the specimen at point A when the external load is 900 lb. Assume the brittle coating will crack according to the maximum-tensile-stress law of failure.

15.5. At a certain point A of a steel specimen, cracks in one direction began to to appear when the external load was 2,000 lb. The strain sensitivity ϵ_s^d of the coating as obtained from the aluminum cantilever calibration strips is 60×10^{-5}. This coating was removed, a new coating was applied and cured, while a load of 3,000 lb was maintained on the specimen. On the partial release of the 3,000-lb load to 1,200 lb, cracks perpendicular to those observed in the first test began to appear at the same point A. The strain sensitivity ϵ_s^r of the coating used in the relaxation test as determined on aluminum cantilever calibration strips is 55×10^{-5}. Given

$$\nu_a = 0.33$$
$$\nu_c = 0.45$$
$$\nu_s = 0.29$$
$$E_s = 30 \times 10^6 \text{ psi}$$

Required the two principal stresses in the specimen at point A when the external load is 1,900 lb. Assume the brittle coating will crack according to the maximum-tensile-stress law of failure.

15.6. At a certain point A of a steel specimen, cracks in one direction began to appear when the external load was 1,200 lb. At the same point A, no cracks perpendicular to the above-mentioned cracks appeared under the highest load of 3,000 lb. A separate relaxation test in which the initial load of 3,000 lb was completely released also showed no cracks at A. The strain sensitivities of the coatings used in the direct loading and the relaxation loading as determined on aluminum calibration strips are $\epsilon_s^d = 65 \times 10^{-5}$ and $\epsilon_s^r = 75 \times 10^{-5}$. Given

$$\nu_a = 0.33$$
$$\nu_c = 0.45$$
$$\nu_s = 0.29$$
$$E_s = 30 \times 10^6 \text{ psi,}$$
$$k = 0.5$$

Required the upper and lower limits of both principal stresses at A when the external load is 1,000 lb. Assume the brittle coating will crack according to the maximum-tensile-stress law of failure.

15.7. Using the data given in the example of Sec. 15.12, predict whether the coating is going to crack if the value of t_r is 60°F instead of 55°F. Determine the maximum value of t_r which will just crack the coating.

15.8. Give the conditions under which σ_2^s can be determined or closely estimated by means of brittle-coating tests alone.

15.9. In Fig. 15.16, (a) draw the isoentatic for cracks perpendicular to σ_2, for the maximum load of 7,000 psi internal pressure; (b) show zones where σ_1 is very nearly equal σ_2; (c) compute the maximum stress on the coated wall of the steel vessel, assuming $\epsilon_s = 0.0006$.

CHAPTER 16

PROPERTIES OF STRESSCOAT

16.1. Introduction. In this chapter some properties of the brittle coating known on the market under the trade name of Stresscoat, and manufactured by Magnaflux Corporation, will be reviewed. This coating is essentially the only coating in use in the United States at the present time. In spite of several shortcomings such as its toxic and explosive solvent and its sensitivity to temperature changes, it possesses many important advantages with respect to other brittle coatings. For this reason its properties will be dealt with here in some detail.

The objective of the method of stress analysis employing brittle coatings is to determine the state of stress on the surface of a coated specimen. This state of stress is evaluated most of the time by the determination of the amount of load required to crack the coating at specific points on the specimen. There are, however, other characteristics of the coating, which are also related to the state of stress in the specimen, and which can also, in some cases, help in the evaluation of this state of stress. These will be reviewed briefly.

More details on this subject can be found in the paper "Study of Some Properties of Stresscoat," presented before the Society for Experimental Stress Analysis in 1950, and published in the Society's *Proceedings*, vol. 12, no. 2.

16.2. Variables Influencing the Coating Behavior. The following forty variables may influence the final behavior of the coating. They are all listed here to present a complete picture of the phenomenon, although they are not all independent, and although the influence of some of them may be small.

A. Liquid state of Stresscoat
    1. Grade of Stresscoat used (identified by manufacturer's number)
    2. Amount of thinner added
    3. Age of liquid coating
B. Adjustments of spraying unit
    4. Humidity of air used in spraying
    5. Pressure of air
    6. Relative amounts of air and liquid used in gun

C. Application of coating
   7. Distance of gun from surface being sprayed
   8. Speed of spraying traverse
   9. Coating thickness
   10. Direction of spraying
   11. Time elapsed between spray passes

D. Heat-treatment (if used)
   12. Time elapsed between spraying and starting heat-treatment
   13. Rate of temperature increase
   14. Temperature of heat-treatment
   15. Time maximum temperature is maintained
   16. Rate of temperature decrease
   17. Humidity during curing

E. 18. Elastic constants of the coating

F. Testing conditions
   19. Temperature during testing
   20. Humidity during testing
   21. Time elapsed between spraying and testing
   22. Repetition of load
   23. Speed of load application on specimen
   24. Time maximum load is applied
   25. Time interval between increments of load

G. Stress conditions
   26. Gradient of stress perpendicular to crack
   27. Gradient of stress in direction of coating crack
   28. Elastic constants of material under coating
   29. Biaxiality of stresses
   30. Influence of hydrostatic pressure
   31. Triaxiality of stresses
   32. Second principal stress producing cracking
   33. Proximity to free boundaries
   34. Residual stress in the coating

H. Increase in sensitivity
   35. Drop in temperature while load is maintained on coating (refrigerating technique)
   36. Effect of application of etchant
   37. Effect of application of Statiflux penetrant

I. Crack-detection methods
   38. Direct visual observation
   39. Dye etchant
   40. Statiflux penetrant

16.3. Characteristics Used to Evaluate the Coating. Some charac eristics of the behavior of the coating that are influenced by the above ariables are as follows:

1. Strain sensitivity ϵ_s. This is defined as the minimum strain necessary o crack the coating in a unidimensional state of stress (coating sensitivity s defined as the inverse of strain sensitivity). The strain sensitivity is letermined by using a strip $\frac{1}{4}$ in. by 1 in. by 12 in. loaded as a cantilever eam with effective span of 10 in., under a fixed deformation (see sketch n Fig. 16.11 and photograph in Fig. 16.28) and measuring the location of he first crack (FC). The first crack is defined as that crack which sepaates the cracked and uncracked zones of the coating, regardless of its ength.

2. Continuous crack (CC). A continuous crack is defined as the first rack extending from one boundary of the beam to the other boundary.

3. Crazing, or failure by shrinkage and by thermal and humidity effects, vithout loading the specimen.

4. Closing of cracks after unloading.

5. Crack density.

6. Flaking.

These six characteristics are measurable and can be used to evaluate he influence of the 40 variables previously mentioned.

A complete study of Stresscoat properties would be extremely long because the number both of the variables and the characteristics is unusually large.

Some of these variables can be measured, as in the case of temperature, humidity, and time; but some, such as the spraying variables, (7) to (11), are difficult to control and are dependent upon the experience of the operator. The following discussion of the variables will include an evaluation of their influence on the six above-mentioned characteristics whenever the results of past study or experience are available. The fact that the influence of many of these variables has not been determined precisely makes calibration imperative for each test. The evaluation of the characteristics will be done statistically wherever possible, since the dispersion of values often is large. Range of the results and standard deviation (or coefficient of variation) will be mostly used.

16.4. Influence of the Variables on Strain Sensitivity and on the Continuous Crack. 1. *Grade of Stresscoat Used (Identified by Manufacturer's number)*. If the Stresscoat obtained from the factory were uniform, it could be stated that, with all other variables kept constant, the lower the number of the Stresscoat used, the lower the sensitivity obtained (the higher the strain sensitivity). However, inconsistencies in the strain sensitivity of Stresscoat from different batches of the same coating number

are often found so that for this reason calibration is imperative for eac]
test. The Magnaflux instructions† include a family of curves indicatin
the combination of temperature, humidity, and Stresscoat number givin
a strain sensitivity of 0.0008 (Figs. 16.1 and 16.2). According to the sam
instruction book, the strain sensitivity 0.0007 can be obtained using on
number of Stresscoat higher than the one indicated by the figure. Th
strain sensitivity 0.0009 can be obtained by using one number lower
The data shown in the two following diagrams are not consistent, an

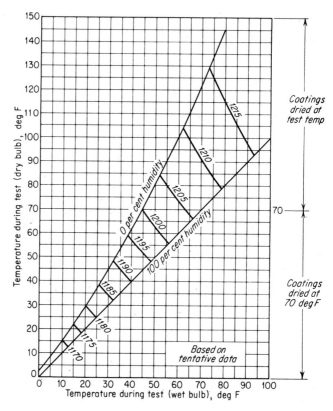

Fig. 16.1. Family of curves recommended by Magnaflux Corporation to obtain 0.0008
strain sensitivity using coatings 1170 to 1215 at different temperatures and humidities.

should be used only as guides to decide what coating number to use. A
better method of predicting the influence of this variable can be found in
Sec. 16.5 when its influence has been evaluated statistically.

2. *Amount of Thinner Added.* Tests made with calibration cantilever

†Magnaflux Corporation, "Principles of Stresscoat," edited by H. N. Staats, Chicago,
Ill., 1955.

strips indicate that the influence of extra thinner (carbon disulfide) on strain sensitivity is particularly critical for small amounts of thinner and more noticeable in the first crack than in the first continuous crack (CC). Figure 16.3 shows the results on a percentage basis.

The conclusion seems to be that not all of the thinner evaporates between the time of spraying and the time of testing, i.e., the curing time. This is

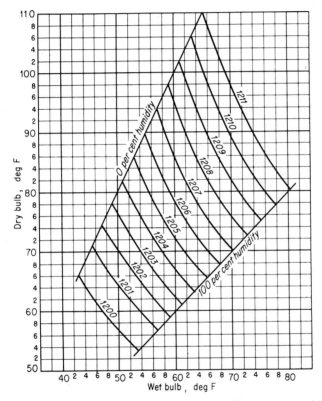

Fig. 16.2. Family of curves recommended by Magnaflux Corporation to obtain 0.0008 strain sensitivity using coatings 1200 to 1211 at different temperatures and humidities.

substantiated by the results of the test shown in Fig. 16.4. It is conceivable that for longer curing times, or higher curing temperatures, larger amounts of thinner would evaporate, and hence the influence of the addition of different amounts of thinner may be smaller. This would in particular be true in the case where high percentages of thinner were employed.

3. *Age of Liquid Coating.* Stresscoat is made from natural resins which are subject to aging. Time has also an influence on the amount of thinner present in the liquid if the container is not perfectly sealed or has been opened several times.

It is believed that the coating is more sensitive when it has been made from an older liquid.

4. *Humidity of Air Used in Spraying.* Large bubbles in the coating may be caused by the water vapor in the spraying air. It is advisable to use a filter in the air system to eliminate any water or oil that may be present.

5. *Pressure of Air.* To eliminate the influence of this variable, the spray-gun air pressure is often standardized at 20 psi. However, when a portable compressor is used without an intermediary tank, the pressure drops when the gun is spraying. A large tank with a pressure regulator should be

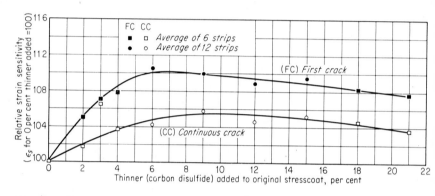

Fig. 16.3. Influence of added thinner on coating sensitivity. Coating 1205 cured and tested at 75°F dry-bulb, 60°F wet-bulb. Age of the liquid, more than 11 months. Curing time, 22 hr.

used to keep the pressure constant. It has been observed that, the greater the pressure, the "dustier" is the appearance of the coating because there is more air to evaporate the solvent in the liquid and consequently some of the resin reaches the surface of the specimen in solid form.

6. *Relative Amounts of Air and Liquid Used in Gun.* This variable can be changed by adjusting the air to liquid controls of the gun. Usually, the standard position of these controls is that which permits a maximum amount of air. The larger the air-to-liquid ratio, the more numerous are the microscopic air bubbles in the coating.

7. *Distance of Gun from Surface Being Sprayed.* Measurements taken during normal spraying have shown that the distance between the spray gun and specimen is usually 3 to 4 in.

Various-shaped surfaces, such as cavities and fillets surrounded by high walls, may cause a dusty coating because of excessive swirling of the spray around an enclosed or partially enclosed space. In this case, dustiness may be corrected by shortening the distance of the gun from the surface.

It is believed that small changes in the distance between the gun and he surface do not influence the strain sensitivity appreciably.

8. *Speed of Spraying Traverse.* Objects of complicated shapes with curves, fillets, and corners usually require changes in speed of spraying raverse. Several measurements of spraying traverse speeds which were made in spraying calibration strips indicated a speed of about 5 ± 1 fps. This variable indirectly affects the strain sensitivity through its influence on the coating thickness, which is discussed under item 9.

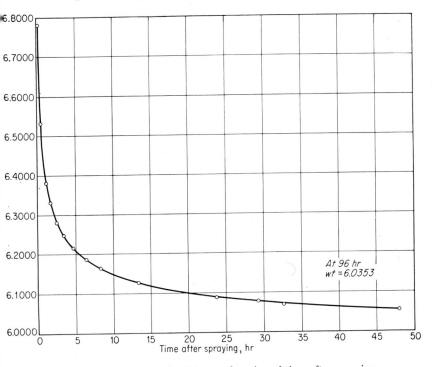

At 96 hr
wt = 6.0353

FIG. 16.4. Loss of carbon disulfide as a function of time after spraying.

9. *Coating Thickness.* *a.* COATING THICKNESS PER GUN PASS. From a series of tests conducted by spraying individual calibration strips in the direction of the length of the strip, and by cross-spraying groups of strips (Fig. 16.9), the coating thickness per pass was found to vary from 0.00022 to 0.0006 in. (Fig. 16.5).

The coating thickness was measured by a Magnegage, which measures the thickness of a nonmagnetic material, such as the brittle coating, when backed by a magnetic material. In most of the studies described here, about one-third of the strips used were made of steel because of its magnetic properties.

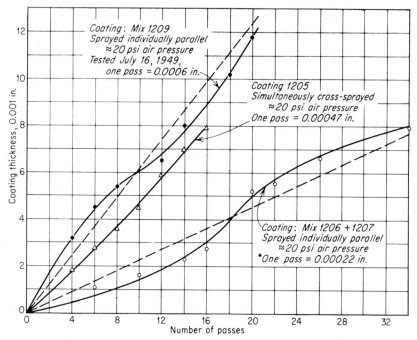

FIG. 16.5. Relationship between number of passes of the gun and thickness of the coating. Distance from the gun to the specimen, 3 to 4 in. Speed of spraying traverse, about 5 ± 1 fps. (Gun reconditioned with new nozzle.)

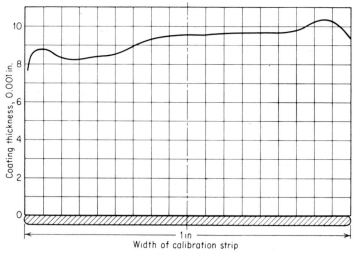

FIG. 16.6. Coating thickness along the width of a calibrating strip. Sprayed individually parallel.

A plot of the thickness measurements obtained across a strip is shown in Fig. 16.6. The increases in thickness observed near the edges may be significant in cases when changes in thickness influence strain sensitivity. Often the maximum stresses to be determined in specimens, using the brittle-coating method, occur at such free boundaries.

Measurements along the length of a strip showed that the maximum variation in the coating thickness was of the order of 0.0005 in. The influence of this variation can be evaluated from the discussion of the results below.

b. INFLUENCE OF COATING THICKNESS ON STRAIN SENSITIVITY (CONSTANT TEMPERATURE). The values of strain sensitivity obtained from calibration strips sprayed to different coating thicknesses are plotted in Fig. 16.7 for two different coating numbers. The results of two tests for Stresscoat 1206.5 are compared with previous tests by De Forest, Ellis, and Stern†

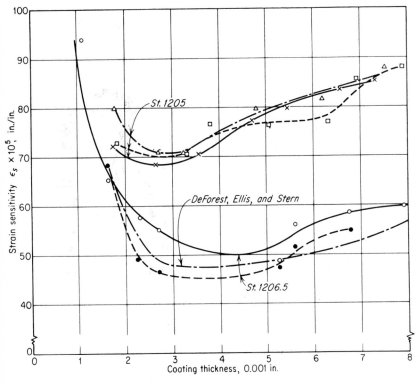

FIG. 16.7. Influence of coating thickness on coating strain sensitivity. Coatings cured at about 75°F and tested approximately 22 hr after spraying.

† A. V. De Forest, G. Ellis, and F. Stern, Brittle Coatings for Quantitative Strain Measurements, *J. Appl. Mech.*, vol. 9, pp. A184–188, December, 1942.

and show that the change in sensitivity is small within certain limits of thickness.

The results of three tests for coating 1205 show a smaller limit of allowable thickness variation for a constant coating sensitivity; so it is very probable that this limit of allowable thickness variation will vary with the different grades of coating used.

An investigation of the effect of heat-treatment for different thicknesses on strain sensitivity also has been made and is discussed in item 14.

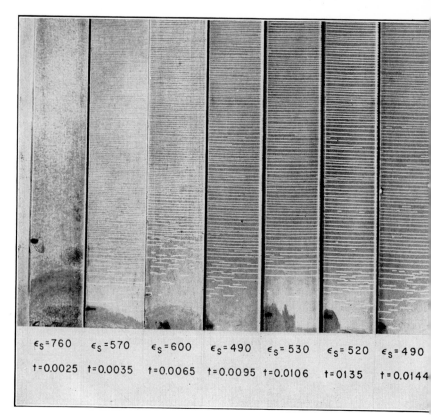

$\epsilon_s = 760$ $\epsilon_s = 570$ $\epsilon_s = 600$ $\epsilon_s = 490$ $\epsilon_s = 530$ $\epsilon_s = 520$ $\epsilon_s = 490$

$t = 0.0025$ $t = 0.0035$ $t = 0.0065$ $t = 0.0095$ $t = 0.0106$ $t = 0135$ $t = 0.0144$

Fig. 16.8a. Appearance of coating and of cracks on strips with varying coating thickness. Statiflux-penetrant method of crack detection.

The appearance of the coating and of the cracks also changes with increased thickness. This is shown in Fig. 16.8a and b.

10. *Comparison between Individually Parallel- and Simultaneously Cross-sprayed Calibration Strips.* To study the effect produced by these two different methods of spraying on the strain sensitivity of the coating and on its first continuous crack, two groups of strips were sprayed to as

nearly the same thickness as possible to minimize the effect of the differences in thickness on coating behavior (see Fig. 16.9). Everything else being kept constant, cross spraying produces a thicker coating for the same number of passes per strip because of the overlapping of the spraying passes, as shown in item 9a. The effect of simultaneous cross spraying also is to produce a less "glossy," or "drier," coating than that of the individu-

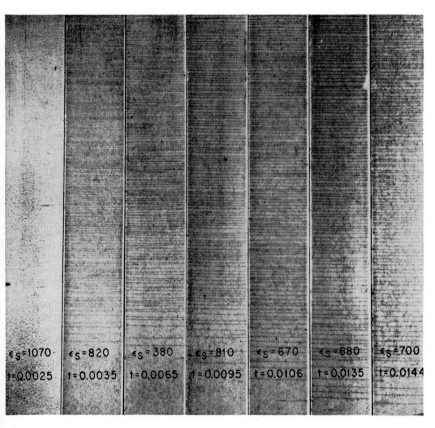

FIG. 16.8b. Appearance of coating and of cracks on strips with varying coating thickness. Dye-etch method of crack detection.

ally parallel-sprayed strips. This seems to be due to the formation of dust on the cross-sprayed strips because of the overlapping. Cross-sprayed strips may crack differently from parallel-sprayed strips in that the first few continuous cracks are sometimes farther apart.

Later in this chapter it is shown how brittle-coating results can be analyzed statistically. The statistical analysis of brittle-coating properties is very important because frequently a large dispersion of values is encountered. Table 16.1 presents statistically the results obtained using the two different methods of spraying.

The data in Table 16.1 show that the strain-sensitivity coefficient of variation and the thickness coefficient of variation are about the same for both methods of spraying. The average strain sensitivity, however,

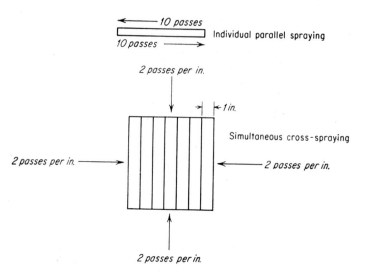

FIG. 16.9. Two different ways of spraying calibrating strips.

TABLE 16.1. COMPARISON OF SIMULTANEOUS CROSS AND PARALLEL SPRAYING

	Individually parallel-sprayed (25 strips)	Simultaneously cross-sprayed (25 strips)
Average strain sensitivity...................	61.4×10^{-5}	68.1×10^{-5}
Standard deviation of strain sensitivity...........	4.27×10^{-5}	4.35×10^{-5}
Coefficient of variation of strain sensitivity, %......	6.95	6.39
Average thickness at points near first crack, 10^{-3} in....	4.98	5.36
Standard deviation of thickness, 10^{-3} in...........	0.353	0.406
Coefficient of variation of thickness, %...........	7.09	7.56

is 10 per cent higher in the case of the simultaneously cross-sprayed strips. This behavior may be explained by the longer time between passes in the simultaneously cross-spraying technique, which increases strain sensitivity, as discussed in the next item. Generally, the increase in thickness per pass is more regular by cross spraying than by individual spraying and is recommended for use.

11. *Time Elapsed between Spray Passes.* In spraying large and complicated objects for testing, it is usually difficult to keep constant the time elapsed between spraying passes. Figure 16.10 summarizes the results obtained from six groups of 10 strips per group when sprayed with 2, 4, 6, 10, 15, and 50 sec between spraying passes.

The results showed a gradual increase in strain sensitivity, with the maximum change occuring up to a time of about 16 or 17 sec between passes; thereafter the increase in strain sensitivity was less, with practically

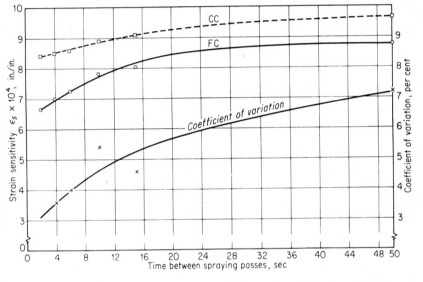

FIG. 16.10. Coating strain sensitivity and coefficient of variation as a function of time between spraying passes.

no change from 30 to 50 sec. The variation of strain sensitivity between the 2- and 50-sec periods indicates an increase of 24 per cent. The coefficient of variation was calculated and also found to increase with the time between spraying passes. The influence of time between spraying passes is less pronounced on the continuous crack. It is advisable to keep the time between spraying passes as constant as possible and not less than 5 sec.

12. *Time Elapsed between Spraying and Starting Heat-treatment.* It was found that the strain sensitivity increased with the time elapsed between spraying and placing the coating into a heating unit. Although the number of strips used in the test conducted to study this point was small, differences in strain sensitivity were sufficiently noticeable. To eliminate the influence of this variable in most cases, the time between spraying and heating is fixed at 5 min.

13. *Rate of Temperature Increase in the Heat-treatment.* As yet, no investigations have been made to study the effect of the rate of temperature increase of the heat-treatment on strain sensitivity.

14. *Maximum Temperature of Heat-treatment.* Heat-treatments were found to have strong influence on strain sensitivity. The coatings studied to determine this influence were cured at a constant temperature for 17 hr, then cooled slowly for 2 hr under forced-air circulation. Next the blower was shut off and the oven opened slightly for another hour of cooling. Finally, the strips were removed and cooled for 2 hr at 75°F dry bulb (DB) and 60°F wet bulb (WB) (the constant-temperature and -humidity conditions of the air-conditioned testing room); hence a total time of 22 hr elapsed between spraying and testing. This cooling technique ensures a fairly low rate of temperature decrease, which in turn lowers the chances of crazing. For comparison purposes some strips were cured without heat-treatment, remaining at 75°F for the entire 22 hr.

No attempt was made to control the humidity in the oven during the curing process. The absolute humidity in the ovens was considered to be fairly constant owing to the fact that the ovens had little leakage and were all within an air-conditioned room.

Since it is almost impossible to obtain coatings of the same thickness, the effect of coating thickness and curing temperature on the strain sensitivity of one coating was studied first. The strips were sprayed with Stresscoat 1205 and cured at temperatures of 75, 79, 82, 95, 106.5, 115, and 135°F for a number of different coating thicknesses. The results obtained from the average of many strips are shown in Fig. 16.11, and the data of this figure, plotted with coating thickness as the parameter, are shown in Fig. 16.12.

The results obtained from the tests conducted to study the influence of heat-treating temperature on coatings of different numbers were corrected to account for the difference in coating thicknesses. The results were adjusted to a standard thickness of 0.0055 in. by the use of curves similar to those in Fig. 16.11. The corrected curves in Fig. 16.13 show the final results.

A few comments are pertinent to these curves. The portions of the curves in Fig. 16.11 for a normal coating thickness of 0.005 to 0.006 in. show a slight increase in strain sensitivity for slight increases in curing temperatures up to a maximum of 82°F. Above this, a rapid decrease in strain sensitivity occurs with increasing curing temperatures. The flatness of the 79 and 82°F curves, as compared with the curves for 106.5°F and greater, indicate that, in curing at the higher temperatures, considerable care must be taken to produce a coating of constant thickness to minimize variations in strain sensitivity.

It is interesting to note in Fig. 16.12 that the strain sensitivity for thin coatings (less than about 0.0035 in.) cured at temperatures up to approximately 107°F is higher than that for the same coatings cured at 75°F. At any given temperature over approximately 90°F, the strain sensitivity increases with decreasing thickness. This fact may be explained by a consideration of moisture effects on the coating.

The explanation of the influence of coating thickness on strain sensitivity

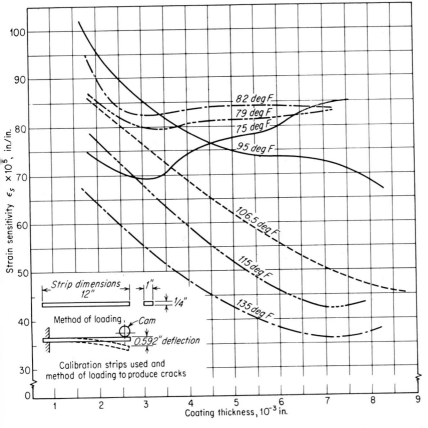

FIG. 16.11. Strain sensitivity of coating 1205 as a function of coating thickness and curing temperature. (Smoothed curves.) Strips were cross-sprayed, cured in air, heat-treated for 17 hr, oven-cooled, and cooled in air. Total elapsed time between spraying and testing was 22 hr.

is very involved. It is believed that one of the most important factors influencing the behavior of the coating is the amount of carbon disulfide and moisture in the coating at the time of the test. The coating thickness has an influence on the amount of carbon disulfide evaporated and on the amount of moisture absorbed and, therefore, appreciably affects the behavior of the coating. A qualitative sketch of the influence of coating thickness on the moisture content of heat-treated coatings is shown in Fig. 16.14. In this figure, it is shown that when the coating is first removed from the oven (time $t = 0$) it is essentially free of moisture. As time progresses, the coating begins to absorb moisture from the atmosphere at its outside surface. The curves in Fig. 16.14a show that after some period

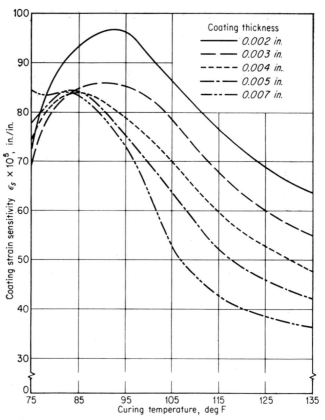

Fig. 16.12. Influence of curing temperature on strain sensitivity of coating 1205 for various thicknesses.

of time, t_1, the moisture content across the coating thickness is near the saturation limit at the outside surface while it is still relatively low at the inside surface. Theoretically, as time goes to infinity, the moisture content across the entire coating thickness approaches the saturation limit. Tests conducted on coating No. 1204 cured at 125°F indicate that the moisture-absorption process was still incomplete even after 48 hr. Possibly this period of moisture absorption could be reduced appreciably ɔy curing in ovens in which a humidity equivalent to that of the testing ɹumidity would be maintained.

The ultimate strain of the coating varies across its thickness in a manner ɹimilar to the moisture content. The increased moisture content at the ɔutside surface tends to increase the ultimate strain of the coating by ɹecreasing its modulus of elasticity. This variation in ultimate strain ʋs. coating thickness is shown as a function of time in Fig. 16.14a. The

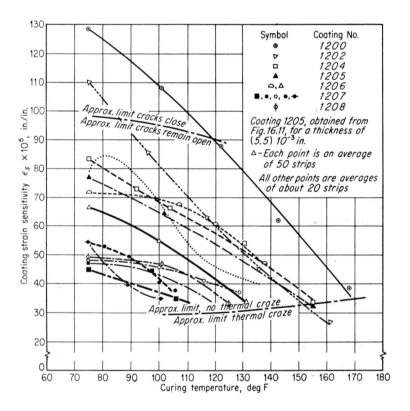

FIG. 16.13. Strain sensitivity as a function of curing temperature corrected for a standard coating thickness (5.5×10^{-3} in.).

results shown in this figure indicate that, if a heat-treated coating were subjected to a tensile stress, the crack would probably begin inside the coating. This contradicts the common belief that the coating cracks always begin at the outside surface.

If a brittle coating is cured at room temperature in a controlled atmosphere, there will be no variation in moisture content across the thickness of the coating; however, the coating thickness in this case will influence the carbon disulfide content of the coating, as is illustrated qualitatively in Fig. 16.14b. This figure shows that upon completion of the application of the coating (time $t = 0$), the carbon disulfide content is uniform across the coating thickness. As time progresses, the coating begins to lose carbon disulfide to the atmosphere at its outside surface. The curves in Fig. 16.14b show that after some time, t_1, the carbon disulfide content is essentially zero at the outside surface, while it is still relatively high at the inside surface. Theoretically, as time goes to infinity, the carbon

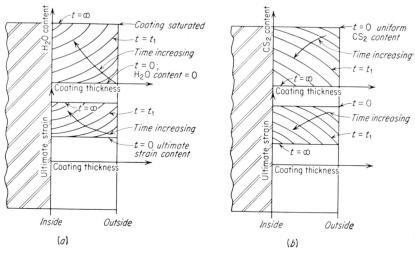

Fig. 16.14. Qualitative sketch of the influence of coating thickness on moisture and carbon disulfide content and the ultimate strain of the coating. (a) Influence of coating thickness on moisture content and ultimate strain of heat-treated coatings. Time measured from the instant the coatings were removed from ovens with 0 per cent relative humidity. (b) Influence of coating thickness on carbon disulfide and ultimate strain of coatings cured at room temperatures. Time measured from the instant of completion of coating application.

disulfide content across the entire coating thickness approaches zero. Tests conducted on coating No. 1206 cured at 75°F indicate that the evaporation of the carbon disulfide was not complete after 96 hours (see Fig. 16.4).

The variation of the carbon disulfide content across the coating thickness results in an accompanying variation of the ultimate strain of the coating across its thickness, as is illustrated in Fig. 16.14b. The decreased carbon disulfide content increases the modulus of elasticity of the coating, thereby decreasing its ultimate strain. For this reason, coatings cured at room temperature will exhibit maximum sensitivity at their outside surface; hence they will begin, as commonly believed, to crack from the outside surface.

The above discussion is not intended to explain completely the influence of the coating thickness on its behavior, but, rather, to point out a few ways in which thickness may influence the strain sensitivities of brittle coatings.

Above a certain minimum curing temperature (Fig. 16.13), the strain sensitivity varies inversely as the curing temperature. This increased brittleness may be due to decreased tensile strength, increased modulus of elasticity, increased residual stress, or any combination of these factors.

The curve corresponding to one of the tests of coating 1205 in Fig. 16.13 was obtained from interpolated data from the curves in Fig. 16.11 giving the strain sensitivities of this coating as a function of thickness. This test shows that for 85°F there is an increase in strain sensitivity over the strain sensitivity obtained at 75°F. This increase is not apparent in any other curve. It should be noted, however, that no values are recorded for 85°F in any of the other curves, and it is therefore possible that the slight increase shown by coating 1205 might also be found in other coatings.

15. *Time Maximum Temperature Is Maintained in the Heat-treatment.* At present no investigations have been made concerning the effect on the coating sensitivity of the time the maximum temperature is maintained. This knowledge is very desirable for the use of Stresscoat in field applications, where the specimens cannot be brought into a laboratory and where time is an important element.

16. *Rate of Temperature Decrease in the Heat-treatment.* A high rate of temperature decrease of the coating is usually desirable to save time. The results obtained from one group of strips, allowed to cool at a slow rate as described in item 14, were compared with the results obtained from another group, allowed to cool at a higher rate by completely opening the top lid of the oven. After 3 hr of cooling within the oven, they were given an additional 2 hr of cooling outside of the ovens to ensure temperature equilibrium. The first noticeable difference was the occurrence of crazing on some of the strips with a high rate of cooling, especially on the steel strips (see Sec. 16.8). No crazing occurred on the slowly cooled strips. Measurements of the strain sensitivities were 46.4×10^{-5} and 45.6×10^{-5}, respectively, for slow and rapid cooling. This difference (about 1.7 per cent) shows nothing significant.

It is believed that even slower rates of cooling, at the end of the cooling-off period, will lower the crazing limit (Fig. 16.13), allowing an increase of the obtainable sensitivity of any particular coating.

17. *Humidity during Curing.* It is known that strain sensitivity varies with the relative humidity during testing (item 20). The initial humidity conditions in the curing oven in all probability also affect the strain sensivity regardless of the relative humidity during testing.

It has been noticed that when specimens are kept at constant temperature in water, and are tested when wet, the strain sensitivity increases appreciably, compared to the strain sensitivity in the air at the same temperature.

The air circulation during drying also seems to be important.

18. *Elastic Constants of the Coating.* So far only one attempt has been made to determine directly the elastic constants of Stresscoat. Stokey† manufactured both evaporated and cast test specimens from Stresscoat. The cast specimens were obtained by allowing a thin layer of Stresscoat to dry on a plate and then scraping up the residue. This residue was melted and cast to the desired shape in molds. The evaporated specimens were hollow tubes and thin strips. The hollow tubes were obtained by spraying the Stresscoat liquid on a gelatin rod. The gelatin was later removed by warming slightly. The small beams were made by dipping strips of tissue paper in Stresscoat. The paper was located at the neutral axis of the beam and made no contribution to the stiffness.

The results published by Stokey were obtained from the dipped Stresscoat specimens and are reproduced in Table 16.2.

The sprayed Stresscoat, because of the presence of many microscopic air bubbles, was found to be less rigid than the dipped Stresscoat. The values obtained for the modulus of rigidity for the sprayed Stresscoat were only 60 per cent of those given in the table.

Although these values seem to be only tentative, they are approximate enough to allow the use of the formulas developed in the previous chapter.

Stokey points out that the outer layers of the coating dry first and have a higher modulus of elasticity. This value, however, corresponds to the values at failure since failure starts at the surface, even if layers inside are not completely dry.

19. *Temperature during Testing.* If all other variables are kept constant, the sensitivity of the coating decreases with an increase in the testing temperature.

Results obtained using Stresscoat 1204 on strips which were kept in water and were tested immediately after being removed from the water are shown in Fig. 16.15. The temperature of the water was allowed to cool slowly from 90 to 71°F. The humidity of the strips obviously was constant, and the temperature was the only variable influencing the strain sensitivity.

Results obtained by De Forest, Ellis, and Stern‡ for a constant absolute humidity corresponding to a water-vapor pressure of 0.37 in. Hg are also shown in the figure.

---

†W. F. Stokey, Elastic and Creep Properties of Stresscoat, *Proc. Soc. Exptl. Stress Anal.*, vol. 10, no. 1, pp. 179–186, 1952.

‡De Forrest, Ellis, and Stern, *op. cit.*, pp. A184–188.

TABLE 16.2. ELASTIC PROPERTIES OF STRESSCOAT†

No. 1206

Drying time, days	Thin-walled tubes	Beams
	Modulus of rigidity, psi	Modulus of elasticity, psi
1	52,000	50,000
3	74,000	103,000
7	97,000	165,000
Maximum	101,000	Greater than 250,000

Specimens made by evaporating Stresscoat

Cast specimens

Beams			Rods
Modulus of elasticity, psi	Poisson's ratio	Calculated modulus of rigidity, psi	Modulus of rigidity, psi
310,000	0.42	109,000	101,000

No. 1202

Specimens made by evaporating Stresscoat

Drying time, days	Thin-walled tubes	Beams
	Modulus of rigidity, psi	Modulus of elasticity, psi
1	30,000	125,000
3	48,000	210,000
7	67,000	250,000
Maximum	73,000	275,000

Cast specimens

Beams			Rods
Modulus of elasticity, psi	Poisson's ratio	Calculated modulus of rigidity, psi	Modulus of rigidity, psi
225,000	0.45	77,500	76,000

†According to Stokey.

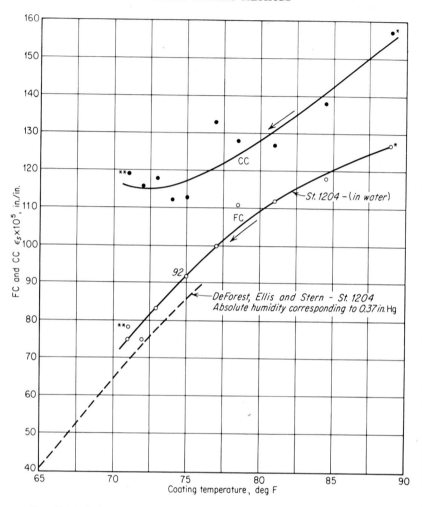

Fig. 16.15. Relationship between testing temperature and strain sensitivity.

20. *Humidity during Testing.* It is possible to understand the influence of changes of humidity on the strain sensitivity of the coating from the following discussion of Fig. 16.16: The strips cured at 130°F were tested periodically after being removed from the heating chamber. The strain sensitivity decreased sharply at the beginning because of the decrease in temperature. A low of ϵ_s = 0.0003 was obtained in about 30 min, after which the strain sensitivity increased. The explanation of this phenomenon is probably the following: After removal from the heating chamber, where the relative humidity is very low, the coating is placed in the room, which has higher humidity, and loses sensitivity because of moisture absorption.

Thirty minutes is about the time when the decrease in strain sensitivity due to the drop in temperature balances the increase in strain sensitivity due to the increase in relative humidity.

According to De Forest, Ellis, and Stern[†], the strain sensitivity varies almost directly as the relative humidity. In their tests the strain sensitivity changed from 100×10^{-5} at 85 per cent relative humidity to 40×10^{-5} at about 22 per cent relative humidity.

21. *Time Elapsed between Spraying and Testing.* The results of tests conducted to study the change in ϵ_s as a function of the period of time between spraying and testing are shown in Fig. 16.17. This coating aged

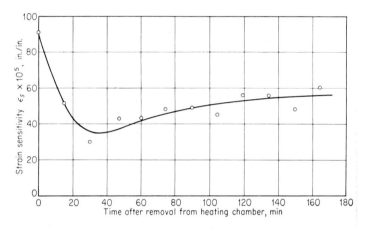

Fig. 16.16. Variation of strain sensitivity with time after heat-treating. (Each point corresponds to values obtained from one strip.) Coating 1204. Maximum curing temperature, about 130°F. Age of coating when the test started, 19 hr.

at a constant temperature of 75°F and at a constant humidity of 40 per cent. The lower number near the points represents the number of strips used to make the average, and the straight vertical segments going through the points represent the standard deviations of the values obtained. The strain sensitivity after reaching a minimum value about 18 hr after spraying increased about 20 per cent in 12 hr and then decreased again. It again started increasing at about 48 hr after spraying. No satisfactory explanation was found for this slight reverse of curvature, and although observed several times, it has been omitted from the curves shown in Fig. 16.17. The dry-bulb temperature was kept constant ±1°F, and the wet-bulb-temperature oscillation was ±0.75°F.

22. *Repetition of Load.* Virgin coatings give larger values of ϵ_s than coatings that have been loaded once or twice previously up to the same

†*Ibid.*

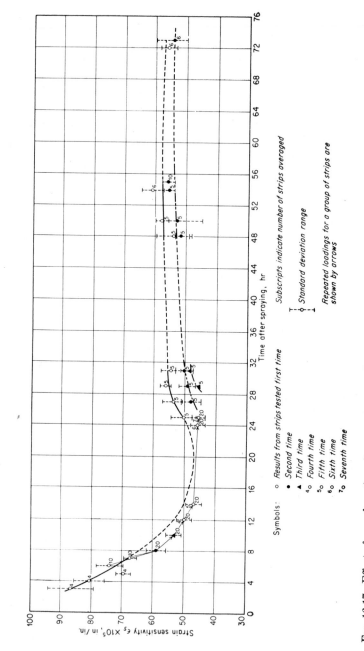

Fig. 16.17. Effect of age of coating after spraying on strain sensitivity. Coating cross-sprayed from four directions; total of eight passes. Cured and aged at $75 \pm 1°F$ dry-bulb; $60 \pm \frac{3}{4}°F$ wet-bulb. Mixture of coatings Nos. 1206 and 1207.

Symbols: o Results from strips tested first time   Subscripts indicate number of strips averaged

 • Second time
 4o Third time   ⊢--⊣ Standard deviation range
 ▲ Fourth time
 5o Fifth time
 6o Sixth time   Repeated loadings for a group of strips are
 7o Seventh time   shown by arrows

398

load. In Fig. 16.17 the upper number near a point represents the number of times the strip has been tested.

In the heat-treated specimens there was, in general, less difference between the strain sensitivity of virgin strips and the strain sensitivity of strips tested two or three times. The lower strain sensitivity which occurs the second time a strip is tested may be due to some invisible cracks made by the first application of the load and accented by the second application of the load.

23. *Speed of Load Application on Specimen.* In spite of its brittleness the coating creeps, and if the load were applied slowly enough, if would

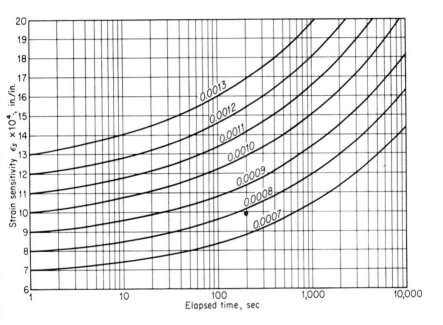

Fig. 16.18. Family of curves in the Magnaflux instruction book, relating strain sensitivity and time required to apply the load at constant speed.

not crack. Magnaflux Corporation recommends the use of the family of curves shown in Fig. 16.18 to account for changes in speed of load application.

24. *Time Maximum Load is Applied.* The load duration on a specimen to be stress-analyzed with brittle coatings may vary in practical applications over a range of time from a few milliseconds to several seconds or even minutes. To study the influence of the load duration on the strain sensitivity, the time range was divided in two parts. The first part dealt with static loading, or load durations of 2 sec or more. The second part

dealt with dynamic loading, in which load durations were about 3 or 4 millisec.

The standard calibrating fixture was employed in the first phase of this study. Using this fixture, it is possible to apply the maximum load to the strip in approximately 1 sec. The results of this study are shown in Fig. 16.19, where strain sensitivity is plotted as a function of time of the loading. This figure indicates that the changes in sensitivity are negligible after 15 sec. It can be concluded therefore that calibration and loading time for static tests should be standardized at 15 sec.

In order to study the properties of the coating under dynamic loading, it was necessary to employ a calibration member which could be subjected to different forms of dynamic loading and in which the maximum strain applied could be varied. To this end, a hollow tapered-wall cylinder as illustrated in Fig. 16.20 was chosen.

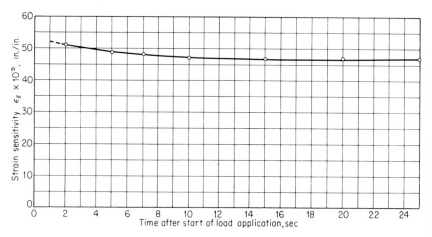

Fig. 16.19. Influence of the time load is applied to specimen. (Each point represents average of 28 strips.) Coating 1206. Curing temperature, 89°F. Total drying time, 23.5 hr. Load applied in 1 sec.

The calibration cylinder was supported rigidly at the upper end and a long guide rod was attached to its lower end. The dynamic load was produced by dropping a tup on a spring anvil carried at the bottom end of the guide rod. The test setup is illustrated in Fig. 16.21. In this figure the electronic equipment used to calibrate the cylinder with electrical strain gages is shown.

A number of tests were conducted to determine the difference in dynamic and static strain sensitivities as a function of the manufacturer's coating number, curing temperature, and coating thickness, using the Statiflux method of crack detection, which will be described in item 40. A typical example of the appearance of the cylinder after the completion of a test is shown in Fig. 16.22.

The results illustrated in Figs. 16.23 to 16.27 are representative of those obtained from a very large series of tests. The effect of coating thickness on static and dynamic strain sensitivities is shown in Figs. 16.23 to 16.25. These curves apply to the following parameters: coating No. 1202 cured at 75, 100, and 125°F, respectively, and tested at about 75°F and 40 per cent relative humidity. The influence of coating numbers and curing temperatures on static and dynamic strain sensitivities is

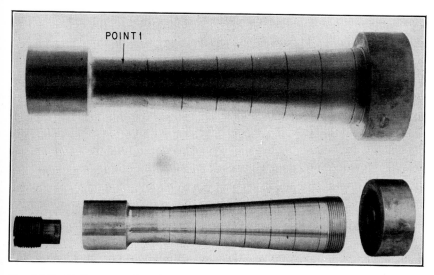

Fig. 16.20. Hollow tapered-wall cylinder used as the calibration member for dynamic studies. Strains are constant at points on each transversal cross section. Strains vary along the longitudinal axis of the cylinder.

shown in Figs. 16.26 and 16.27, respectively. These latter curves are based on a coating thickness of 0.006 in., tested at 75°F and 40 per cent relative humidity.

The data obtained in this series of tests have been evaluated statistically. A method known as linear regression of a multivariate universe has been employed to obtain a linear equation expressing the dynamic strain sensitivity of the brittle coating as a function of coating number, curing temperature, and coating thickness. The description of this method of analysis can be found in Sec. 11.10b. A relation known as a regression equation is shown below and is valid for testing conditions of 75°F and 40 per cent relative humidity and for the form of dynamic loading shown in the figures.

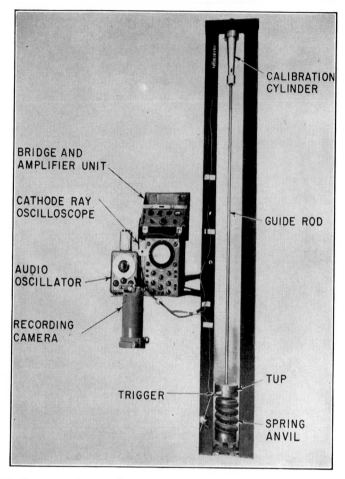

Fig. 16.21. Test setup for recording dynamic strains by use of electrical-resistance-type strain gages.

$$\epsilon_s = 80{,}457 - 65.6 \, (\text{St. No.}) - 3.31 \, (\text{CT}) - 31{,}175 \, (t)$$

where ϵ_s = dynamic strain sensitivity obtained using Statiflux method of crack detection, μin./in.

    St. No. = coating number

    CT = curing temperature, °F

    t = coating thickness, in.

It can be concluded from the results of this research program that, for Stresscoat numbers higher than 1200, an appreciable difference nearly always existed between the static and dynamic strain sensitivities. In general, the strain sensitivity determined dynamically was higher than

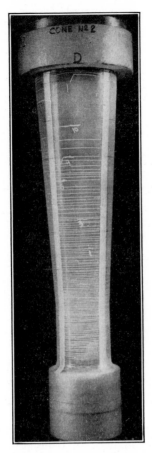

Fig. 16.22. Typical crack formation produced on the calibration cylinder. The numbers shown refer to the values of impact energy necessary to crack the coating up to the levels indicated by the numbers.

that determined statically. This appears to be a contradiction of a previous finding of Ellis and Stern,† for they reported that the coatings react the same way for single impulses of a load of 0.005 sec duration as for 1 sec duration. Unfortunately, Ellis and Stern did not indicate what coating they tested, the temperature of curing, or the thickness of the coating. If these conditions had been given, a comparison would have been possible. Possibly Ellis and Stern based their conclusion on tests which were conducted under particular conditions where dynamic and static strain sensitivities were not appreciably different.

†G. Ellis and F. Stern, Dynamic Stress Analysis with Brittle Coatings, *Proc. Soc. Exptl. Stress Anal.*, vol. 3, no. 1, pp. 102–111, 1945.

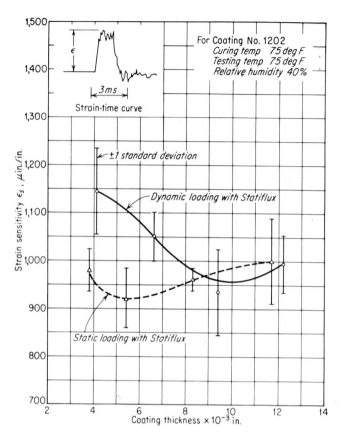

Fig. 16.23. Effect of coating thickness on static and dynamic strain sensitivities, using the Statiflux method of crack detection. The static load was held for 15 sec.

In general, for the range of coatings studied (1200 to 1206), the dynamic strain sensitivities decreased with increasing coating thicknesses up to about 0.0085 in. For thicknesses greater than 0.0085 in., no general trend for dynamic strain sensitivities could be detected. The influence of coating thickness on the static strain sensitivities depends on whether or not the coating has been heat-treated (cured at a temperature higher than room temperature.) For heat-treated coatings, the static strain sensitivities decreased with increasing thicknesses, and, for coatings cured at 75°F, the static strain sensitivities increased with increasing thicknesses. It was found that, for coatings cured at 75°F, the difference between the static and dynamic strain sensitivities decreased as the coating thickness was increased.

25. *Time Interval between Increments of Load.* Tests conducted to

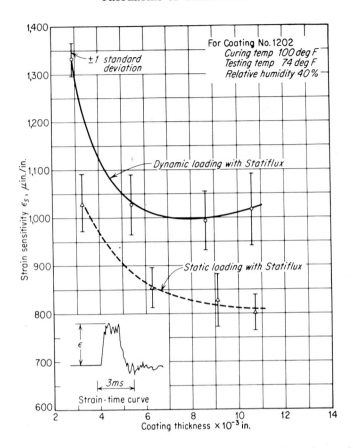

Fɪɢ. 16.24. Effect of coating thickness on static and dynamic strain sensitivities, using the Statiflux method of crack detection. The static load was held for 15 sec.

study the influence of the time between steps of loading on strain sensitivity showed little change in ϵ_s when the time interval between loadings varied from 8 to 100 sec, and each step of loading increased the load 100 per cent after a complete removal. The influence of time between steps of load on ϵ_s probably will be larger when the additional increment of load is less than 100 per cent.

As a consequence of his study of creep in Stresscoat Stokey† recommends waiting four times the loading time between successive applications of load, to eliminate the influence of creep.

26. *Strain Gradient Perpendicular to the Crack.* The standard calibrating beam is a strip 1 in. by 12 in. by $\frac{1}{4}$ in., loaded as a cantilever under a maximum deflection of 0.592 in., and with an effective span of 10 in.

†Stokey, *op. cit.*, p. 185.

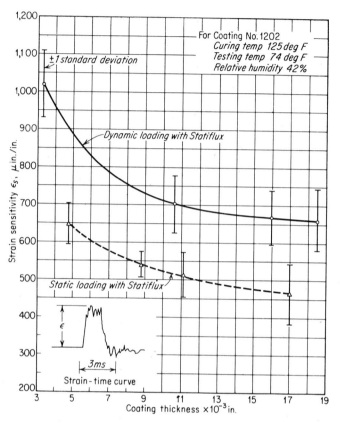

Fig. 16.25. Effect of coating thickness on static and dynamic strain sensitivities using the Statiflux method of crack detection. The static load was held for 15 sec

This loading produces a unidimensional state of stress on the strip. The strain gradient produced by this loading is 0.0002 (in./in.)/in., which corresponds to a stress gradient of 2,000 psi/in. in aluminum and 6,000 psi/in. in steel.

It was necessary to change this gradient conveniently, to study the influence of strain gradient on strain sensitivity. For this purpose the calibrating jig was redesigned. The eccentric wheel, by means of which the deflection is applied, was removed from the axis, and with extra holes the following deflections could be obtained: $\frac{1}{4}$, $\frac{1}{3}$, $\frac{1}{2}$, $\frac{3}{4}$, and 1 times full deflection (see Fig. 16.28).

The results of tests conducted using coating 1204 to 1207 and several curing temperatures are shown in Fig. 16.29 by the family of solid curves. These curves represent the average of all the tests conducted. The broken-

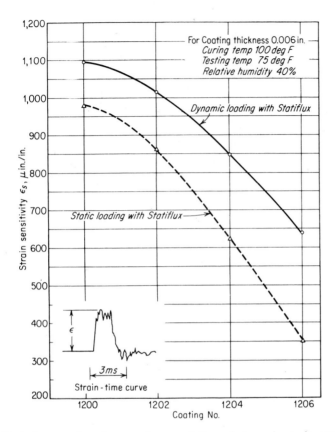

Fɪɢ. 16.26. Influence of coating number on static and dynamic strain sensitivities, using the Statiflux method of crack detection. The static load was held for 15 sec.

line curves have been drawn representing the approximate formula

$$\epsilon_a = \epsilon_s - \frac{2{,}980(2 \times 10^{-4} - x^2)}{(\epsilon_s - 68 \times 10^{-5})^{1/9} + 1.1}$$

where x = strain gradient at investigated point, (in./in.)/in.

    ϵ_s = strain sensitivity of coating when strain gradient is 0.0002 (in./in.)/in.

    ϵ_a = corrected strain sensitivity when strain gradient is x

The curves show that the influence of strain gradient is appreciable for coatings with a low strain sensitivity and that this influence gradually decreases as the strain sensitivity increases. For example, on the bottom curve at 500 psi/in. for aluminum it requires about 31 per cent less strain to crack the coating then at a 2,000 psi/in. stress gradient. The charac-

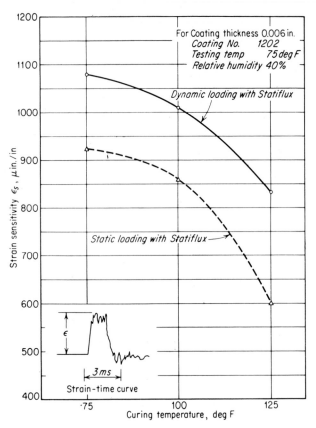

Fig. 16.27. Influence of curing temperature on static and dynamic strain sensitivities, using the Statiflux method of crack detection. The static load was held for 15 sec.

teristic curves within the range of strain sensitivities shown can be interpolated for any strain sensitivity by following the general shape of the nearest curves both below and above the interpolated curve, or they can be computed using the above formula.

The significance of these results in applications is evident: the distance between isoentatics should be taken into consideration to determine the correct coating calibration.

27. *Gradient of Stress in Direction of Coating Crack.* Figure 16.30 shows the dimensions of two hollow cylinders with tapered walls which were used to study the influence of the gradient of stress in the direction of the coating crack. Figure 16.31 is a photograph of one of these cylinders. Both the stresses and the gradient of stresses vary along the length of these tubes for any given internal pressure.

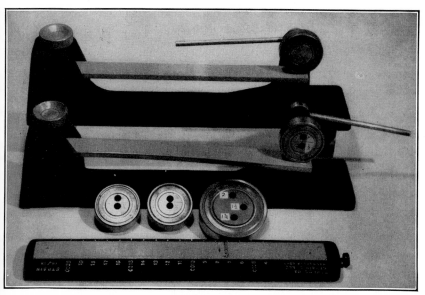

Fɪɢ. 16.28. Calibrating equipment used for brittle coatings. The center beam is being subjected to a "full" deflection of 0.592 in. Using the other wheels with other eccentricities, various fractions and multiples of the full deflection are obtained.

The approximate variation in strain sensitivity may be represented by the empirically obtained linear relation

$$\eta = \eta_0 + m(\gamma - \gamma_0)$$

where $\eta = \dfrac{\text{stress required to crack coating on tube}}{\text{stress required to crack calibration-strip coating}}$

γ = gradient of strain in direction of crack

m = proportionality const

and the subscript 0 refers to any point where values are known. The symbol m may be taken as

$$m = 0.0002$$

Then

$$\eta = \eta_0 + 0.0002(\gamma - \gamma_0)$$

where γ is given in (in./in.)/in.

In the calibration strips there is no gradient of stress in the crack direction. However, no direct comparison with the tube should be attempted because a normal gradient of 2000 psi/in. exists in the strips (aluminum), while that of the tube is zero.

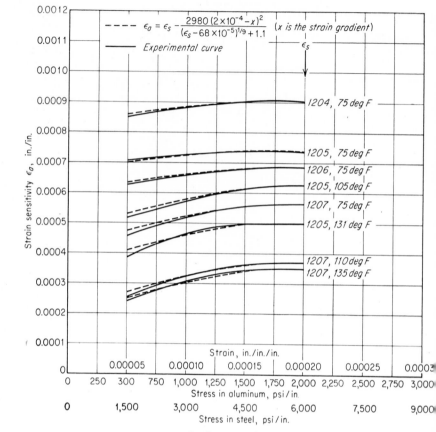

Gradient normal to cracks

FIG. 16.29. Influence of strain gradient perpendicular to the crack on the strain sensi
tivity of Stresscoat in a unidimensional state of stress. Numbers on each curve are
Stresscoat number and curing temperature. Strain sensitivities determined at 75°F
and 40 per cent relative humidity.

The effect of strain gradient perpendicular to the crack is very similar
to the effect of gradient parallel to the crack. The reason for the decreased
strain sensitivity at low values of the strain gradient for both cases is in
all probability the same: the smaller strain gradient produces a larger
zone where the stress is nearly equal to that producing failure in the coating,
and the probability of weak points in the coating is far larger than that
for a small area (corresponding to a larger strain gradient) under stress.

28. *Elastic Constants of the Material under Coating.* According to the
analysis made in the previous chapter, the coating strain sensitivity is
influenced by the difference between the Poisson's ratios of the coating
and the material. For steel and aluminum strips the difference in the

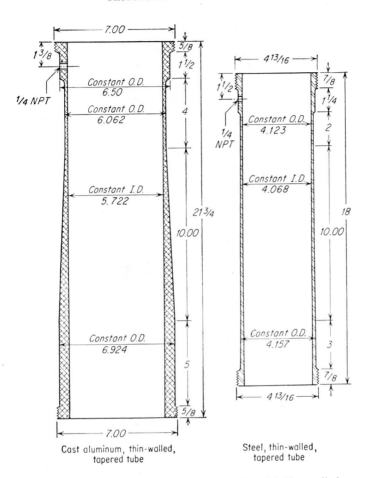

FIG. 16.30. Cross section of thin-walled tubes. Tapered-wall hollow cylinders used to
determine the influence of gradient, in the direction of the crack, and the influence
of biaxiality and triaxiality on strain sensitivity. All dimensions in inches.

coating strain sensitivity would be about 2 per cent, with that of the
aluminum strips being the higher. It is difficult to confirm this conclusion
by tests because the coefficient of variation of the results obtained is of
about the same order as the expected difference.

29. *Biaxiality of Stresses.* The specimens used for some of the tests
conducted to study this variable were the outside walls of the tapered
aluminum cylinder described under item 27 (Figs. 16.30 and 16.31).
Some of the results obtained are presented graphically in Fig. 16.32.
The following conclusions may be drawn:

(a) The primary principal stress in the specimen, σ_1^s, is the governing

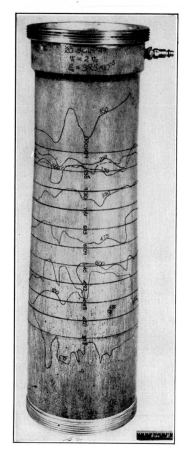

FIG. 16.31. Hollow cylinder with tapered walls used to study the influence of multi-axiality and of the gradient of stress. (See Fig. 15.15 for enlarged view.)

factor in determining coating failure. In the cases reported, σ_1^s varied only from 61 to 83, while σ_2^s ranged between 36 and -245 where the uniaxial state of stress $\sigma_{un} = 100$ (on the strips).

(b) For all cases reported, the stress producing failure was smaller than that required to crack the calibration strips (17 to 39 per cent less).

(c) It takes less stress to produce a crack in a biaxial condition than in a uniaxial condition of stresses.

These tests seem to indicate that the law of failure of Stresscoat is more complicated than the maximum stress law assumed in the previous chapter. The results shown in Fig. 16.32, however, cannot be considered conclusive because all the variables which have an influence on the coating failure were not controlled.

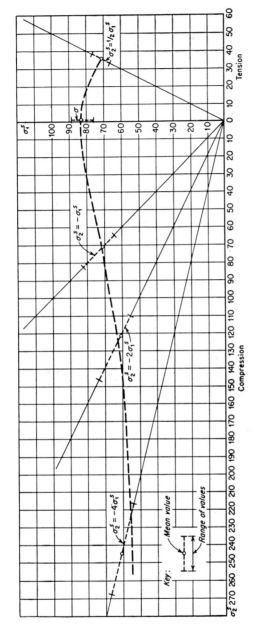

FIG. 16.32. Failure of Stresscoat under biaxial state of stress determined from cast aluminum tapered cylinder loaded by internal hydrostatic pressure and axial compression.

30. *Influence of Hydrostatic Pressure.* Operating instructions provided by the Magnaflux Corporation state that "direct pressure has the effect of sensitizing the coating so that approximately 1500 psi direct pressure will start indiscriminate tension patterns on all coated surfaces even though no strain exists in the structure".† This statement does not seem to be clear and should be interpreted in the light of the following: In experiments conducted with strips, immersed in water, in a vessel under pressure, it was found that the crazing pressures ranged from 500 to 1,000 psi and were dependent on the strain sensitivity of the coating; more sensitive coatings require less pressure for crazing (Fig. 16.33). The coating on these strips is under triaxial compression, the pressure on the surface being the largest of the principal stresses. Apparently in this case the coating cracks because of shear.

31. *Triaxiality of Stresses.* When a surface is loaded in its plane, the coating is subjected to a biaxial state of stress. However, when a normal pressure also acts on the coating, as inside pressure vessels, the state of

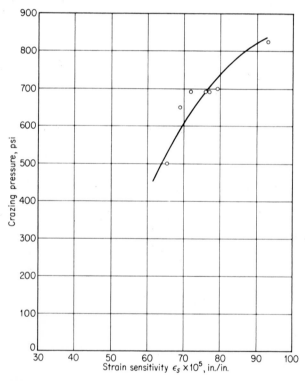

Fig. 16.33. Pressure-crazing the coating as a function of strain sensitivity.

†*Op. cit.*, p. 5.

ress becomes triaxial. The influence of this third principal stress has
een found to be sometimes the most important.

To produce a triaxial state of stress in the coating, the same hollow
ylinder with tapered walls mentioned previously can be used (Figs.
5.30 and 16.31). The inside of the cylinder is coated and then subjected
o internal pressure. The ratio of principal stress in the cylinder walls is
egulated by applying axial loads to the cylinder heads. Loaded in this
manner, the principal stresses are σ_1^s circumferential, or hoop, stress, σ_2^s
ongitudinal stress, σ_3^s internal pressure.

Since the wall thickness of the cylinder varies along the length, the
rcumferential and longitudinal stresses also vary from one cross section
o another. Therefore, the coating cracks first at the thinnest cross
ection, and for any load the cracks progress to that cross section where
ae stress is not sufficiently large to crack the coating.

According to the Magnaflux Corporation "Operating Instructions,"
hen Stresscoat is under direct hydrostatic pressure, the true value of
ress σ^s can be computed from the observed value σ_1^s from the relation

$$\sigma^s = \frac{P_s - P_1}{P_s}\, \sigma_1^s$$

here P_1 = pressure that existed at time coating cracked under load
    P_s = pure hydrostatic pressure producing indiscriminate cracking
his can be stated also as

$$\frac{\sigma^s}{\sigma_1^s} = 1 - \frac{1}{P_s} P_1$$

ince P_s is a constant, σ^s/σ_1^s is a linear function of P_1. In Fig. 16.34 this
s shown for the case where P_s = 800 psi. Experimentally obtained
alues for this case are shown also. It can be seen that the curves generated
y the observed values are not in agreement with the empirical formula.
he vertical-axis intercept was determined from data taken from the
utside of the tube where P_1 = 0. This value was, in general, not equal
o unity, which indicates that the stress required to crack the coating on
ae tube is not the same as that determined by calibration strips. A
econd curve is shown in Fig. 16.34; it was obtained by taking the strain
ensitivity which will normalize the vertical-axis intercept, i.e., using the
utside of the tube for calibration rather than the usual calibration strips.

Different states of stress can be produced in the cylinder walls by con-
rolling the relation of internal pressure and axial compression.

The results obtained from several biaxiality ratios σ_1^s/σ_2^s = ∞, 2, -1,
$-\frac{1}{2}$, $-\frac{1}{3}$, and $-\frac{1}{4}$ showed no discernible effect of biaxiality upon the
ailure of the coating. In all the cases studied all coating failures occurred
etween 250 and 450 psi direct hydrostatic pressure. For these pressures

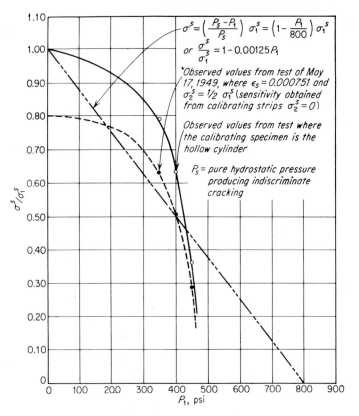

FIG. 16.34. Effect of direct hydrostatic pressure P_1 on the coating, on the stress required to crack it.

the hoop stresses in the cylinder walls at the moment of the coating failure ranged from 70 to 20 per cent of the calibration-strip stresses. The stress required for failure decreased sharply with small increases of internal pressure.

The influence of internal pressure is very critical within the range investigated (250 to 450 psi); this fact limits the accuracy of any determination of σ_1^s from a knowledge of P_1 at failure. It is believed that the values of P_1 will have a larger relative value with respect to σ_1^s in the range of internal pressure below 250 psi.

32. *Second Principal Stress Producing Cracking.* When the two principal stresses are tensile with about the same values, the coating may crack twice, first, because of the maximum principal stress; after this crack is in the coating, a second crack may appear, perpendicular to the first, and produced by the second principal stress.

After the appearance of the first set of cracks the coating is essentially under a unidimensional state of stress, even though the material under the coating is biaxially stressed. This is so because the cracks act as free boundaries and are so close together that, except for a small zone at the bottom of the coating, there are no stresses orthogonal to the cracks. This problem was dealt with in detail in the previous chapter.

33. *Proximity to Free Boundaries.* Near free boundaries, the coating is thicker than inside the field. This can be seen in Fig. 16.6, where the thicknesses have been plotted along a transverse section of a calibrating strip.

Figure 16.35 shows an enlargement of a picture taken with light transmitted through the coating. The number of air bubbles is much larger near the boundary, as could be expected since the thickness is larger near the boundary.

34. *Residual Stresses in the Coating.* Residual stresses may be produced by shrinkage in the coating, when it passes from the liquid to the solid state, or by changes in temperature. These stresses have not yet been measured directly. However, an indirect analysis of the phenomenon can be found in Sec. 15.4.

35. *Drop in Temperature When the Load Is Acting on the Coating.* In the previous chapter it has been shown that a sudden drop in temperature when the load is acting on the coating produces cracks the directions of which coincide with the direction of the principal stresses due to the loading. However, no attempt has been made to calibrate the coating under these conditions. The strain sensitivity should be given as a function of the number of degrees of drop in temperature and as a function of the time during which the coating is kept at the low temperature.

36. *Effect of Application of Etchant.* The sensitivity of the coating can be increased, not only by heat-treating the coating before the test or by refrigeration during the test, but also by etching at the time the load is on the specimen. The degree of sensitization depends upon the strain sensitivity of the coating and the time elapsed between the loading and the application of the dye etchant. According to Magnaflux Corporation, the degree of sensitization is only a function of the above-mentioned variables and is given by Fig. 16.36.

37. *Effect of Application of Statiflux Penetrant.* The sensitivity of the coating can also be increased by the use of Statiflux penetrant on the coating. Tests conducted on coating numbers ranging from 1190 to 1205, curing temperatures of 75, 100, and 125°F, thicknesses of 0.005 and 0.008 in. show that the decrease in the strain sensitivity with the application of the penetrant ranged from 110 to 310 μin./in., with an average difference of 190 μin./in.

38. *Direct Visual Observation.* In static tests the crack pattern will

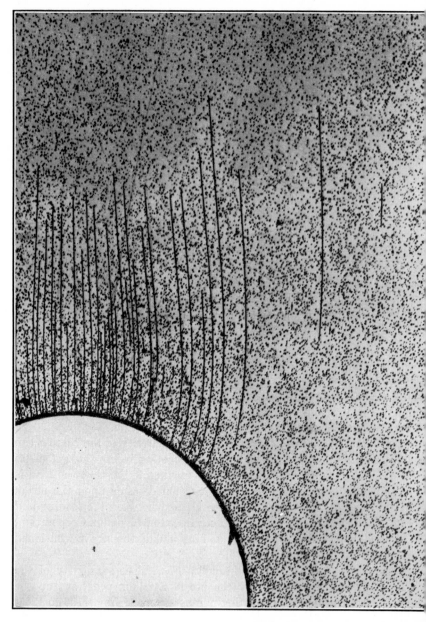

FIG. 16.35. Air-bubble formation at and away from a free boundary. Photographic
enlargement of a picture taken with a light transmitted through the coating. The
number of air bubbles is much larger near the free boundary.

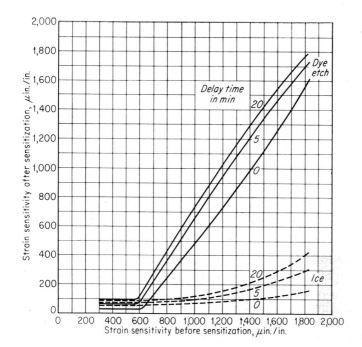

Fig. 16.36. Change of strain sensitivity by sensitizing the coating. (*By Magnaflux Corporation.*) The change in strain sensitivity is given for different lengths of time elapsed between the loading of the specimen and the application of either dye etch or ice.

remain open and visible if the strain sensitivity is less than about 1,000 µin./in. The use of a beam of light with a large angle of incidence and directed perpendicular to the crack aids appreciably in the crack detection. If, however, the strain sensitivity is greater than 1,000 µin./in., the cracks are likely to close and special techniques will be required to detect them.

Under dynamic loading, the limit of the strain sensitivity for which the cracks remain open is lowered from 1,000 to about 600 µin./in.

It has not been definitely established why coating cracks stay open after removal of the load in some cases, while in other cases they close. However, the most plausible explanation is that the coating has tensile residual stresses which are responsible for keeping the cracks open.

39. *The Dye-etchant Method.* Often, when the cracks close upon release of the load, the application of a red-dye etchant aids in detecting the crack pattern. Although no systematic study has been made to determine the best etching technique for each case, it can be stated that in general the older, glossy, and more brittle coatings indicate clearer and sharper crack patterns than the fresh, soft, and dusty coatings. Magnaflux Corporation

recommends the use of a solution of the etchant with SAE 10 oil to detect cracks in the very soft coatings.

Tests conducted using dynamic loading showed that the dye-etchant method cannot detect the last crack in coatings with a strain sensitivity above 800 μin./in.

40. *The Statiflux-penetrant Method.* This is probably the most effective method of crack detection, regardless of the strain sensitivity of the coating. It has been employed with success in locating the crack pattern in coatings with static strain sensitivities up to 1,800 μin./in. In the case of dynamic loading the crack pattern has been located successfully in coatings the strain sensitivity of which was as high as 1,200 μin./in.

The method has two advantages over the dye-etchant method: first, the coating can be used again for successive increments of loading, which is not possible in the case of the dye etchant; second, it requires less time and skill on the part of the operator.

Figure 16.8*a* and *b* shows the difference in appearance of the coating cracks on a set of calibrating strips on which Statiflux penetrant and dye etchant have been used, respectively.

16.5. Simultaneous Study of the Influence of Five Variables on the Strain Sensitivity. In the previous paragraphs the individual influence of 40 variables on strain sensitivity of Stresscoat has been described. A complete systematic study of all the influences of these variables would not be practical. Statistical methods allow a much more efficient determination of the influences. The simultaneous influence of five of the most important variables was determined using the statistical method known as a linear regression of a multivariate universe, which is described in Chap. 11.† The five variables considered were: manufacturer's coating number, testing temperature, testing relative humidity, curing temperature, and coating thickness.

The statistical analysis of the data yielded two regression equations which estimate the strain sensitivity as a linear function of the five variables listed above. The two equations are

$$\epsilon_s = 70,833 - 59.50 \text{ (St. No.)} + 25.4 \text{ (TT)} + 1.48 \text{ (\%H)}$$

$$- 3.85 \text{ (CT)} - 12,920 \text{ (}t\text{)} \qquad (16.1$$

$$\epsilon_s = 98,359.5 - 83.45 \text{ (St. No.)} + 55.6 \text{ (TT)} - 15.0 \text{ (\%H)}$$

$$- 3.17 \text{ (CT)} - 42,330 \text{ (}t\text{)} \qquad (16.2$$

†The method of application of linear regression of a multivariate universe to brittle coating data has been discussed in a paper entitled "Prediction of Brittle Coating Strain Sensitivity Based on a Statistical Regression Analysis" by A. J. Durelli and J. W. Dally which was presented at the Spring Meeting of the Society for Experimental Stress Analysis, Apr. 28, 1955, in Los Angeles, Calif.

where ϵ_s = estimated strain sensitivity, μin./in.

St. No. = manufacturer's number of strain-indicating coating

TT = testing temperature, °F

$\%H$ = per cent relative humidity

CT = curing temperature, °F

t = coating thickness, in.

Equation (16.1) is to be used to predict the strain sensitivity of coating numbers between 1200 and 1210 and testing temperatures between 60 and 105°F. Similarly Eq. (16.2) is restricted to coating numbers between 1170 and 1200 and testing temperatures between 27 and 60°F. Use of the appropriate equation permits the strain sensitivity to be predicted with a reasonable degree of accuracy over the entire range of testing conditions normally encountered in the United States.

Examination of the coefficients of Eq. (16.1) indicates that, on the average, increasing the coating number by 1 will decrease the strain sensitivity by about 60 μin./in. Increasing the testing temperature by 1°F will increase the strain sensitivity by about 25 μin./in. Increasing the relative humidity by 1 per cent, the curing temperature by 1°F, and the coating thickness by 0.001 in. will change the strain sensitivity by about 1.5, -3.9, and -12.9 μin./in., respectively. Similar conclusions can be drawn from the coefficients of regression expressed in Eq. (16.2).

A statistical measure of the reliability of these two equations made by computing the standard error of the estimate (see Sec. 11.10) shows that about two-thirds of the time the value predicted by Eq. (16.1) will be within 91 μin./in. of the true value of the strain sensitivity. Similar calculations indicate that for Eq. (16.2) the value predicted would be within 181 μin./in. two-thirds of the time.

The other statistical measure of reliability, the coefficient of multiple correlation (see also Sec. 11.10), is 0.90 and 0.38 for Eqs. (16.1) and (16.2), respectively, indicating that about 90 and 38 per cent of the variation in the strain sensitivity has been accounted for by the five independent variables considered.

16.6. Influence of the Variables on the Distance between the First Crack and the Continuous Crack. It is a fact that sometimes all the first cracks on the strips are very small and the distance between the very first crack and a crack running, more or less continuously, from one boundary of the strip to the other is about 1 in. At other times, on the contrary, the first crack is large enough to go all the way across the strip. It is believed that the distance between the first crack (FC) and the continuous crack (CC) may be significant and identifies different types of coatings. In particular, it is believed that this distance may give a measure of the brittleness of the coating. Up to the present, however, tests do not seem to substantiate these hopes. Although the distance between the first crack and the second crack is certainly a physical characteristic of the coating, it has not been possible yet to relate it clearly to the variables or to some other properties of the coating.

Also, it is generally believed that the formation of widely separated continuous cracks in an area of low strains is produced by a coating lacking air bubbles. The presence of no or only a few bubbles in a coating results in a very transparent coating, readily distinguishable from a coating with many air bubbles. Coatings have been obtained in which the crack formations are contradictory to general expectation; this leads to the belief that there is a more important factor as yet unknown. Figure 16.37 shows these contradictory coatings. The small white specks are the air bubbles. The very clear strip at the right with no air bubbles (coating heated to very high temperature) shows the same type of crack formation as the left strip, which has a large number of air bubbles.

It is theorized that a crack in a coating lacking air bubbles progresses continuously along the principal stress trajectory into lower strain areas because there are no air bubbles to stop the progressing crack. This condition is considered analogous to the progressive nature of a crack in a piece of glass under stress, which may be stopped by drilling a hole at

Fig. 16.37. Crack formations in coatings of abundant and few air bubbles. The coating on the left, which is full of air bubbles, shows continuous cracks; and the coating on the right, free of bubbles, shows interrupted cracks. This contradicts the assumption that the air bubbles are responsible for crack interruption.

the end of the crack. It may be possible that the presence of air bubbles in some cases does hinder crack propagation. However, Figs. 16.35 and 16.37 show many cracks ending at points where there are no air bubbles.

16.7. Statistical Behavior. A rational way of approaching the failure phenomenon of the coating should include a statistical analysis. The reader is referred to Chap. 11 for the necessary background on statistical methods.

Table 16.3 shows the results obtained from 65 calibrating strips studied statistically. The frequency of the strain sensitivities was represented by a histogram in Fig. 16.38.

If N is the total number of measurements and σ is the standard deviation, the Gauss formula can be represented by

$$y = \frac{N}{\sqrt{2\pi}\,\sigma}\, e^{-(x-m)^2/2\sigma^2}$$

If the Stresscoat-failure phenomenon is "normal," it will follow Gauss's law.

Figure 16.38 shows the relation between the strain sensitivity $x = \epsilon_s$

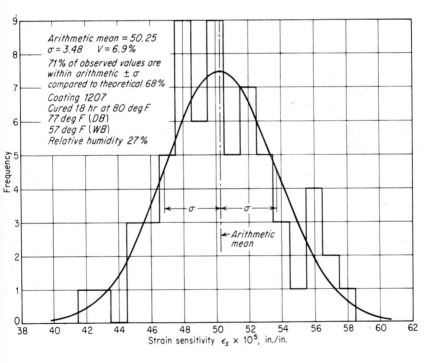

FIG. 16.38. Experimental distribution of data compared with normal distribution. The strain-sensitivity scattering corresponds to a normal distribution.

and the frequency y. Theoretically 68 per cent of the values are inside the range defined by the arithmetic mean $\pm\sigma$. In the test 71 per cent of the experimental values fell inside that range. Figure 16.38 shows the histogram and the curve superimposed. The agreement is good enough to justify the assumption of statistically normal behavior of Stresscoat. Probably the agreement between histogram and curve would have been better if a larger number of specimens had been tested.

Examples of statistical analysis of brittle-coating data can be found in Figs. 16.17 and 16.23 to 16.25.

TABLE 16.3. TABULATION OF THE STATISTICAL BEHAVIOR OF STRESSCOAT

(1) Group, $\epsilon_s \times 10^5$, in./in.	(2) Frequency, f	(1) × (2)	Differences from the average $\bar{x}$,† $x - \bar{x}$	$(x - \bar{x})^2$	$f(x - \bar{x})^2$
42	1	42	−8.25	68.06	68.06
43	1	43	−7.25	52.56	52.56
44					
45	3	135	−5.25	27.56	82.68
46	3	138	−4.25	18.06	54.18
47	5	235	−3.25	10.56	52.80
48	9	432	−2.25	5.06	45.54
49	6	294	−1.25	1.56	9.36
50	9	450	−0.25	0.06	0.54
51	5	255	0.75	0.56	2.80
52	7	364	1.75	3.06	21.42
53	5	265	2.75	7.56	37.80
54	3	162	3.75	14.06	42.18
55	1	55	4.75	22.56	22.56
56	4	224	5.75	33.06	132.24
57	2	114	6.75	45.56	91.12
58	1	58	7.75	60.06	60.06
Σ	65	3,266			775.90

† $\bar{x} = \dfrac{3,266}{65} = 50.25$ (Arithmetic mean).

$$\sigma = \sqrt{\frac{\Sigma f(x - \bar{x})^2}{N - 1}} = \sqrt{\frac{775.90}{64}} = \sqrt{12.11} = 3.48.$$

16.8. Crazing. Crazing is the spontaneous failure of the coating. There are two types of crazing, dry craze and craze produced by thermal or shrinkage stress, or by both. They are characterized by random formation of cracks showing no preferential direction.

Dry crazing may occur on rather thick coatings of normal strain sensitivities. Examples of dry craze may be seen in Fig. 16.39. Dry craze is probably caused by uneven drying of the coating. In a thick coating the outer surface dries first, and some contraction occurs before the coating beneath the top layers has dried. The coating progressively shrinks as the drying continues, but the surface exposed to the air shrinks at a greater rate until it fails in the form of a crack. An equally thick coating with sufficient time between spraying passes does not dry-craze.

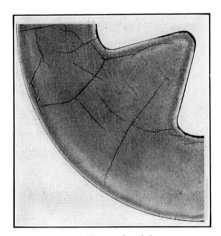

FIG. 16.39. Example of dry craze.

Thermal crazing is the spontaneous failure of a coating due to a temperature change. It is the result of the difference in thermal contraction between the base material and the coating. (The approximate thermal coefficients for steel, aluminum, and Stresscoat are 6.3×10^{-6}, 13.3×10^{-6}, and 60×10^{-6} per degree Fahrenheit, respectively.) Figure 16.40 shows the results obtained from steel, aluminum, and celluloid strips simultaneously sprayed with a low-strain-sensitivity coating, heat-treated at 119°F and later subjected to a temperature of 71°F in order to produce crazing. The coating on the steel and aluminum strips crazed rather severely at this temperature, but the coating on celluloid did not craze. The thermal coefficient of expansion of celluloid is about the same as that of the coating. However, the stresses produced by the drop in temperature are not directly proportional to the difference in thermal contractions because of the tendency of the coating to creep.

The influence of creep on the thermal stresses, producing crazing, can be seen in Fig. 16.41, where the results obtained from strips allowed

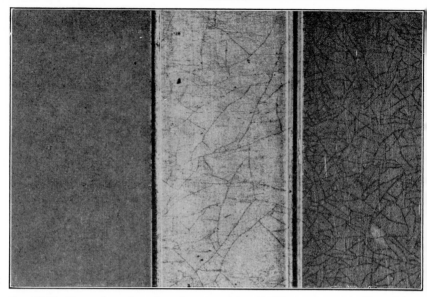

FIG. 16.40. Thermal crazing of coatings on strips of different materials. From left to right the materials are celluloid, aluminum, and steel.

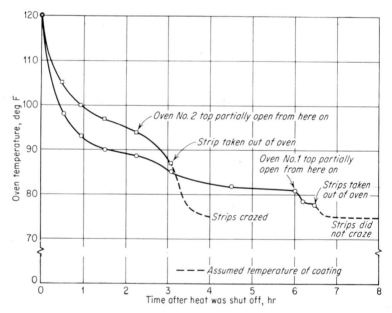

FIG. 16.41. Effect of cooling rate on thermal crazing. Coating 1207. Strips simultaneously cross-sprayed. Cured 17 hr at 120°F and cooled to 75°F dry-bulb and 60°F wet-bulb.

to cool at different rates are shown. The coating with rapid cooling, which therefore allowed more time for the coating to creep, did not craze.

The complete phenomenon of thermal crazing cannot be fully explained by the difference in thermal contractions of the coating and its backing material. For example, heat-treatment of the coating probably affects such mechanical properties as tensile strength, ductility, and modulus of elasticity of the coating; hence this would have an effect on thermal crazing of the coating also. The approximate limit of thermal-craze strain sensitivity in heat-treated coatings is shown in Fig. 16.13.

The coating also may craze when cured and tested at the same temperature and humidity. This crazing has the same appearance as thermal crazing but should be called "shrinkage" crazing since its main cause is the shrinkage produced during curing.

16.9. Closing Up of the Cracks after the Load is Removed. It has been noticed that, in general, when the strain sensitivity is higher than 0.001 the cracks close up after the load is removed. In some cases the same phenomenon takes place with coatings of lower strain sensitivity when the coating is old (3 or more days after spraying). If the temperature is increased after the removal of the load, the cracks close up also. Sometimes this happens with a very slight increase in temperature, as when strips are barely touched with a finger tip.

Results reported in Fig. 16.17 show that tests were carried on for 3 days without any crack closing. Cracks closed however, in coatings tested on the fourth day.

It is believed also that the cracks close up when the load is left on for only a short time (of the order of milliseconds). This point is very important in all impact tests in which crack patterns must be detected after the load has been removed from the specimen.

Figure 16.13 shows the approximate limit line above which cracks close up, after removal of the load in heat-treated coatings. It is likely that residual stress in the coating should be studied carefully in connection with the closing up of the cracks.

16.10. Crack Density. It can be noticed easily by observing any calibrating strip that the spacing between cracks is not constant but varies with the strain. This property can be utilized to determine the strain in the specimen. The number of cracks divided by the base length gives the crack density in cracks per inch. A traversing microscope may be used to count the total number of cracks in a given base length.

Figure 16.42 shows the relationship between strain and crack density in a typical coating 1206, cured at 105°F, and the standard deviation corresponding to determinations on five aluminum strips. The curve proves that crack density increases with strain. The increase is larger at low strains and smaller at high strains. The strain sensitivity of the coating

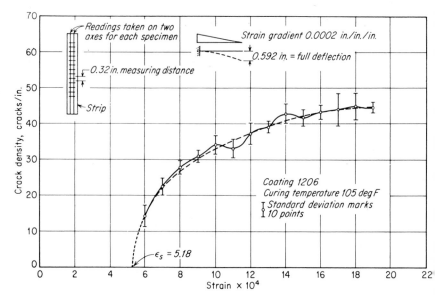

Fig. 16.42. Crack density as a function of strain.

was 51.8×10^{-5}, which is shown by the intersection of the extrapolated curve and the horizontal axis.

Several tests proved that there is no influence of the strain gradient perpendicular to the crack on the crack density. In these tests the standard calibrating jig was used with the modifications indicated in item 26. The test results are summarized in Fig. 16.43, where the intersection of each

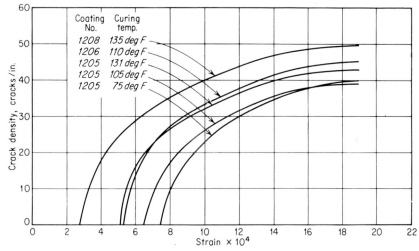

Fig. 16.43. Crack density as a function of strain. Curves plotted for average crack densities on strips loaded under different stress gradients.

curve and the strain axis gives the value of the strain sensitivity. Comparison between the curves of Stresscoat No. 1206 at 110°F curing temperature shows that, for different coatings of the same strain sensitivity, crack density is approximately the same for equal strains. This family of curves therefore defines the relationship between crack density, strain, and strain sensitivity within the range of strain sensitivity investigated and for the coating thickness of approximately 0.007 in.

To study the influence of thickness on crack density, a series of strips of five different thicknesses were sprayed, cured at 115°F, and tested at full deflection at constant temperature and humidity (75°F dry-bulb and 40 per cent relative humidity). The results of these tests in Fig. 16.44

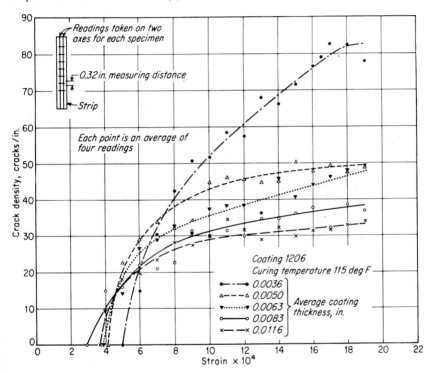

Fig. 16.44. Crack density as a function of strain for different coating thicknesses.

show the crack density to increase inversely with the coating thickness for any constant strain except near the value of strain sensitivity of the coating. The lower four curves, with coating thicknesses from 0.0116 to 0.0050 in., are nearly horizontal at elevated strains; therefore, very little accuracy can be obtained in the high-strain region. However, the curve for a coating thickness of 0.0036 in. exhibits a comparatively large change in crack density per unit strain to an approximate strain of 190×10^{-5}.

This curve is practical for many applications provided that the coating thickness can be kept thin and constant. Figure 16.45 shows the same results plotted as a function of the thickness for four constant strains. This figure indicates that deviations in thicknesses in thin coatings have more influence on the crack density than the same deviations in thick coatings. From these results the conclusion is also reached that the minimum distance between cracks varies from 2.5 to 3.9 times the thickness of the coating.

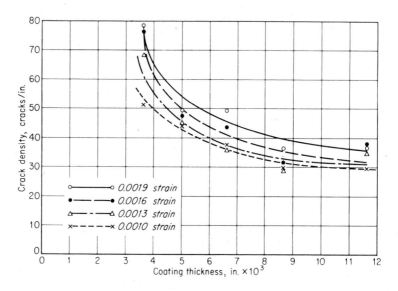

FIG. 16.45. Crack density as a function of coating thickness for different strains.

Figure 16.46 shows the difference in the appearance of the crack density as a function of coating thickness.

In many dynamic applications stresses are not directly proportional to loads, and the techniques of using fractional loads cannot be accurately applied. In the case of materials which creep, the usual method of sketching the family of isoentatics under a series of increasing loads often cannot efficiently be used either. In these cases only one load, viz., the maximum load, can be applied, and only one isoentatic can be obtained. The strains at the points located on this isoentatic can be obtained from the strain sensitivity in the usual manner. This is not possible for points within the cracked zone. However, by employing Fig. 16.45, the strains inside the cracked zone can be obtained in the following manner: Measure the crack densities of the points inside the cracked zone whose strains are desired. From the family of curves in Fig. 16.43 choose the particular

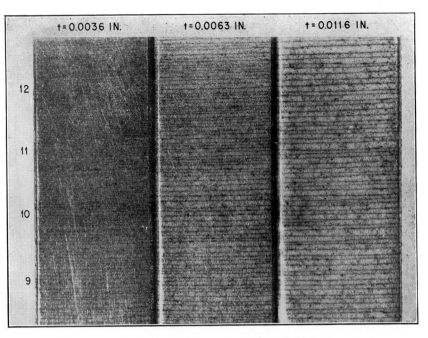

FIG. 16.46. Crack density as a function of thickness.

one which intersects the strain axis at the strain sensitivity of the given coating used. On this curve the values of strain corresponding to the measured crack densities at the points inside the crack zone of the specimen are their maximum principal strains.

The previous analysis assumes that biaxiality of stresses does not influence the crack density. No information is available on this influence. In Japan, however, Nishihara and Taira,† using a different coating, claim that density is directly proportional to strain.

16.11. Flaking. The coating fails by flaking when it separates from the specimen. De Forest, Ellis, and Stern, in the previously mentioned publication, studied the influence of thickness, temperature, humidity, and curing time on flaking sensitivity. They found that the initiation of flaking correlates directly with the amount of compressive strain. The most flaking-sensitive coating starts failing at 0.01 compressive strain. Thickness has little influence on this value. Temperatures above or below 70°F increase the required strain appreciably.

†Toshio Nishihara and Shuji Taira, Strain Determination by Means of Brittle Coating, *J. Soc. Mech. Eng. Japan*, vol. 53, pp. 340–346; September, 1950.

CHAPTER 17

APPLICATIONS OF THE BRITTLE-COATING METHOD

In this chapter three applications of the brittle-coating method will be shown. Two of these applications deal with problems for which the theoretical solution is known so that comparison can be made between theory and experiment. The third application deals with a problem of industrial interest.

In all three cases the refined analysis according to the failure chart is conducted, as well as the approximate analysis using apparent stresses. Comparison is made between the results of these two analyses.

17.1. Determination of the Distribution of Stresses around a Circular Hole in a Finite Plate $(w/d = 11)$ **under a Unidimensional Uniformly Distributed Load.** The brittle-coating test was conducted on a $\frac{1}{4}$-in. aluminum plate with a circular hole whose diameter was approximately one-eleventh of the width of the plate. The dimensions of the plate are shown in Fig. 17.4. A concentrated tensile load was applied at each end of the plate. Two gusset plates were employed to distribute this load uniformly over the width of the plate. The brittle coating used was Stresscoat No. 1207 with no thinner added.

In the direct-load test, the coating was cured at 95°F for 17 hr and then cooled down to room temperature slowly. The test was conducted at room temperature at a relative humidity of 58 per cent. Each load was applied in 15 sec, held for 15 sec, and released in 15 sec. Between each loading the plate stayed unloaded for about 4 min so that the strain in the coating due to creep may be assumed to have completely recovered. After each load the curve connecting the points of the cracks, called isoentatics, was traced directly on both sides of the plate. Each of these isoentatics is denoted by a number which corresponds to the load in thousands of pounds applied to the plate. The crack pattern and the isoentatics on one of the two sides of the plate are shown in Fig. 17.1. An enlarged picture of the region in the neighborhood of the hole is shown in Fig. 17.2. The first crack appeared at a tensile load of 12,000 lb. For those portions of the plate which showed no crack even at the maximum tensile load of 35,000 lb, an air blast, cooled by dry ice, was used to lower the temperature

of the coating.   Cracks practically all over the plate were thus opened
without any further increase in the load.

From time to time, aluminum calibration strips were tested to determine

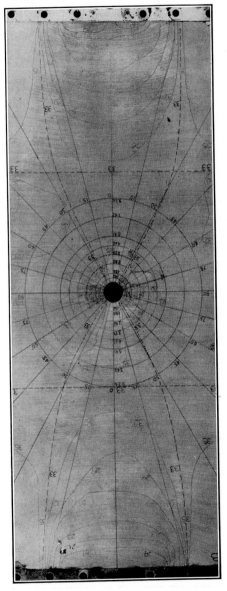

FIG. 17.1. Crack pattern and isoentatics, on one side of a plate with a hole, produced
by direct loading.

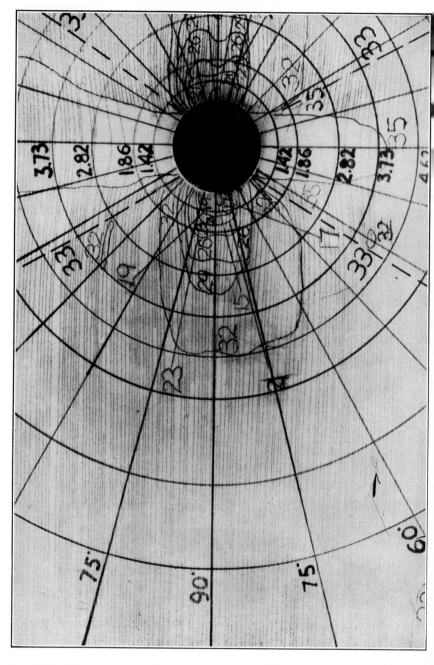

FIG. 17.2. Enlarged picture of the crack pattern and isoentatics of a portion of the plate shown in Fig. 17.1.

the strain sensitivity of the coating at that particular instant. It was noted that the strain sensitivity remained constant (87×10^{-5}) up to the time when the load was 17,000 lb. Then it suddenly increased to about 98×10^{-5} and stayed there for the rest of the experiment. This appreciable change was probably caused by a sudden change in the temperature and humidity of the test room.

Stresscoat creeps under load; hence the time of loading has an appreciable influence on the strain sensitivity. Since the load on the cantilever calibration strips was applied in $\frac{1}{2}$ sec as against the 15 sec used in applying the load on our plate, a correction of 8×10^{-5} (obtained from the time-correction curve supplied by the Magnaflux Corporation) is added to the originally obtained value of 87×10^{-5}, giving 95×10^{-5} as the true strain sensitivity. The correction for the strain sensitivity of 98×10^{-5} is the slightly higher value of 9×10^{-5} (also, obtained from the above curve), giving a true strain sensitivity of 107×10^{-5}.

In the relaxation test the coating was first sprayed on the plate, and a tensile load of 35,000 lb was maintained on the plate while the coating was cured at 90°F for 18 hr. Then the load was reduced to 15,800 lb in 15 sec, held for 15 sec, and loaded back to the maximum 35,000 lb in 15 sec. Again, there was a 4-min waiting period before the next cycle of unloading was begun to avoid the creep effect. The first and only crack appeared when the load was reduced to 5,300 lb in 25 sec. Cool air was then employed to open up cracks all over the plate as shown in Fig. 17.3. The strain sensitivity of the coating, obtained from aluminum calibration strips and corrected for loading speed, is 77×10^{-5}.

a. Computations Using Apparent Stresses. The apparent stresses will be computed first. From the over-all picture (Fig. 17.1), the isoentatic at the uniformly stressed portion away from the disturbances of the holes and of the gusset plates is estimated by interpolation to be 33. The ratio between the apparent stress σ_1^s, normal to the crack at any isoentatic X, and σ_{aG} is therefore given by

$$\frac{\sigma_1^s}{\sigma_{aG}} = \frac{33}{X} \qquad X \geq 19$$

where σ_{aG} is the stress in the uniformly stressed portion of the plate, usually called the average stress across the gross section of the plate. The values of X in the above formula are limited to those values equal to or larger than 19 because the value of the strain sensitivity of the coating as determined on calibration strips had the same value, 107×10^{-5}, between the time when the load was 19,000 lb and the time when the load was 35,000 lb. At the initial stage of the experiment, corresponding to loads of less than 19,000 lb, the strain sensitivity as determined on the calibration strips was 95×10^{-5}. Less stress is therefore required to crack the Stresscoat during the initial period of the experiment than the later period of the experiment. This change in sensitivity is not due to a switch to a different coating, because the same coating was on the specimen all through the direct-loading test. The change was due to a sudden change in the tem-

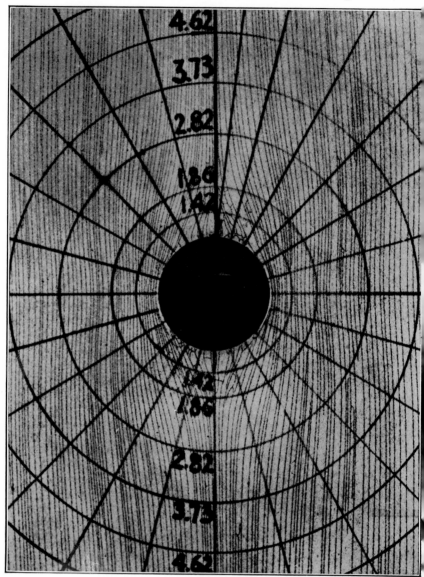

FIG. 17.3. Crack pattern produced by relaxation loading with refrigeration. The only crack that appeared without refrigeration is the small crack shown at the tip of the arrow, and it appeared when the tensile load was reduced from 35,000 to 5,300 lb.

erature and humidity of the testing room, possibly due to the opening
of a door. The ratio between the apparent stress σ_1^s, normal to the crack
at any isoentatic X, and σ_{aG} is therefore given by

$$\frac{\sigma_1^s}{\sigma_{aG}} = \frac{33}{X}\frac{95}{107} \qquad X < 19$$

By means of the above formulas, the apparent stresses at those points
where an isoentatic crosses the minimum section of the plate are calculated
and plotted in Fig. 17.4. The theoretical solution of the stress at the
minimum section, due to Howland,† is plotted in solid curves, while the
experimental results of σ_1^s/σ_{aG} on the two sides of the plate are plotted in
small circles and small squares, respectively.

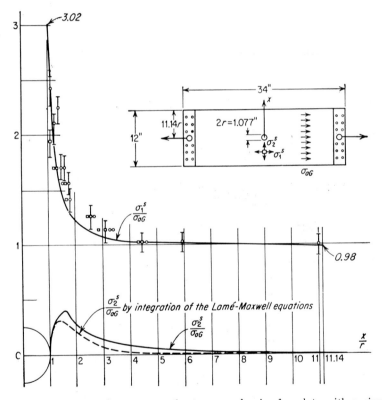

FIG. 17.4. Distribution of stresses on the transversal axis of a plate with a circular
hole, under a unidimensional uniformly distributed load (brittle-coating test). Howland's
solution for the finite plate (width of plate equals 12 diameters of hole) is shown in
solid curve. Aluminum plate used; Poisson's ratio = 0.33.

†R. C. J. Howland, Stress in the Neighborhood of a Circular Hole in a Strip under
Tension. *Trans. Roy. Soc. (London)*, vol. A229, pp. 49–86, 1929.

For the relaxation test, a crack appeared at the edge of the hole under a compressive load of 29,700 lb and ended at approximately $\frac{1}{32}$ in. from the edge of the hole along the longitudinal axis of symmetry. At that point under the 29,700-lb compressive load, the transversal stress is therefore equal to the product of the strain sensitivity of the coating, 77×10^{-5} and the modulus of elasticity of the specimen: $10.3 \times 10^6 \times 77 \times 10^{-5} = 7,930$ psi.

The average longitudinal stress across the gross section of the plate under the compressive load of 29,700 lb is

$$\sigma_{aG} = \frac{P}{A} = \frac{29,700}{3} = 9,900 \text{ psi}$$

where A = area of the gross section of the $\frac{1}{4}$-in. by 12-in. plate.

For a finite plate of the above dimension, the theoretical transversal stress at the edge of the hole along the longitudinal axis of symmetry is very nearly equal to the average longitudinal stress across the gross section of the plate. This transversal stress, however, decreases rapidly as the point in question moves away from the edge of the hole along the longitudinal axis of symmetry. At a distance of $\frac{1}{32}$ in. (0.058 times the radius of the hole) from the edge of the hole, a 25 per cent decrease of stress is predicted by Kirsch's[†] formula. The decrease observed in the above test is

$$\frac{9,900 - 7,930}{9,900} = 20\%$$

The error is 5 per cent so that the check between theory and experiment is reasonably good.

b. Computations Using the Maximum-tensile-stress Law of Failure. Using the same experimental data, we shall now compute the stresses on the assumption that the brittle coating fails according to the maximum-tensile-stress law of failure.

Since, at the minimum section, no cracks perpendicular to σ_2^s appeared without refrigeration under the highest direct load and highest relaxation load of 35,000 lb, we can follow the example set forth in Sec. 15.10 and determine the upper and lower limits of both principal stresses.

Since the specimen and calibration strips are made of the same material Eq. (15.11) can be used to obtain

$$\sigma_0^d = (10.3 \times 10^6)(95 \times 10^{-5}) = 9,780 \text{ psi} \quad \begin{cases} \text{for an external load less} \\ \text{than 19,000 lb} \end{cases}$$

$$\sigma_0^d = (10.3 \times 10^6)(107 \times 10^{-5}) = 11,030 \text{ psi} \begin{cases} \text{for an external load equal} \\ \text{to or greater than 19,000 lb} \end{cases}$$

[†] G. Kirsch, Die Theorie der Elastizität und die Bedürfnisse der Festigheitslehre, *Z. Ver. deut. Ing.*, vol. 42, p. 797, 1898.

At the uniformly stressed portion of the plate, σ_2^s is assumed to be zero so that the average stress across the gross section is

$$\sigma_{aG} = \sigma_0^d$$

When the external load is 33,000 lb,

$$\sigma_{aG} = \sigma_0^d = 11,030 \text{ psi}$$

A sample calculation of the stresses will be conducted on isoentatic 26.

$$\alpha = \beta = \frac{35,000}{26,000} = 1.35$$

$$\beta \frac{\epsilon_s^d}{\epsilon_s^r} = 1.35 \times \tfrac{107}{77} = 1.88$$

Assuming $k = 0.6$, $\nu_c = 0.42$ for the Stresscoat No. 1207 used,

$$\frac{\alpha}{1 - k\nu_c} = \frac{1.35}{1 - (0.6 \times 0.42)} = 1.81$$

From the curve $\nu_c = 0.42$, $\nu_s = 0.33$ of Fig. 15.8, we obtain the upper and lower limits of σ_1^s/σ_0^d and σ_2^s/σ_0^d as the coordinates of the points corresponding to $\alpha/(1 - k\nu_c) = 1.81$ and $\beta(\epsilon_s^d/\epsilon_s^r) = 1.88$,

$$\left.\begin{aligned} 0.90 < \frac{\sigma_1^s}{\sigma_0^d} < 1.07 \\[2ex] -0.65 < \frac{\sigma_2^s}{\sigma_0^d} < 0.88 \end{aligned}\right\} \text{ when external load } = 26,000 \text{ lb}$$

Using the value of 11,030 as σ_0^d, we obtain

$$\left.\begin{aligned} 9,930 \text{ psi} < \sigma_1^s < 11,830 \text{ psi} \\ -7,180 \text{ psi} < \sigma_2^s < 9,700 \text{ psi} \end{aligned}\right\} \text{ when external load } = 26,000 \text{ lb}$$

or

$$\left.\begin{aligned} 12,600 \text{ psi} < \sigma_1^s < 15,000 \text{ psi} \\ -9,100 \text{ psi} < \sigma_2^s < 12,300 \text{ psi} \end{aligned}\right\} \text{ when external load } = 33,000 \text{ lb}$$

Dividing the above by 11,030, we obtain the range of the stress ratios,

$$1.14 < \frac{\sigma_1^s}{\sigma_{aG}} < 1.36$$

$$-0.82 < \frac{\sigma_2^s}{\sigma_{aG}} < 1.12$$

The range of the stress ratios is calculated for each isoentatic and plotted in Fig. 17.4. Only the range of σ_1^s/σ_{aG} is shown, the range of σ_2^s/σ_{aG}

being too wide to be of any use. These ranges have no connection what-soever with the range of the scatter of experimental results but depend mainly on the values of $\alpha/(1 - k\nu_c)$ and $\beta(\epsilon_s^d/\epsilon_s^r)$. A slightly narrower range can be obtained if loads higher than 35,000 lb are used as the maxi-mum load.

In the absence of any further information on the values of σ_2^s, we would have chosen the mean of the two extremities of each range as our best estimate of σ_1^s/σ_{aG}. In most instances, this mean will be close to our apparent stress calculated from the assumption that σ_2^s is zero. However, some knowledge of σ_2^s can be obtained by an examination of the isostatic pattern so that a better estimate of σ_1^s/σ_{aG} is possible. This will be shown in the following paragraphs.

At the minimum section denoted by the line marked 90° in Fig. 17.3, the transversal direction is perpendicular to the cracks produced by relaxation loading. Hence σ_2^s, the algebraically smaller principal stress, is along the transversal direction. The radius of curvature of the iso-statics, S_1, is seen to be zero only at a point about 1.3 radii from the center of the hole. By property 2 (Sec. 8.3 in the chapter on special families) σ_2^s is therefore maximum or minimum only at that point. By property 3 (in the same section), since σ_1^s is tensile, σ_2^s must also be tensile near the edge of the hole. Hence σ_2^s must start from zero at the edge of the hole, become tensile immediately, reach its maximum at about 0.3 radius from the edge of the hole, and decrease to zero at the edge of the plate. The value of σ_2^s is therefore never negative.

The range shown in Fig. 17.4 was calculated in the absence of any knowledge of σ_2^s so that the upper limit was defined as the ordinate of the point on the curve $\nu_c = 0.42$, $\nu_s = 0.33$ (Fig. 15.8) at which $\beta(\epsilon_s^d/\epsilon_s^r)$ is equal to the experimentally determined values. Now that we know σ_2^s is never negative, obviously all those points to the left of the (σ_1^s/σ_0^d) axis (Fig. 15.8) cannot be used, and the upper limit of σ_1^s/σ_0^d must be unity, corresponding to $\sigma_2^s = 0$. The stresses calculated on the basis of $\sigma_2^s = 0$ are precisely the apparent stresses obtained previously. Hence the revised ranges of the stress ratios (Fig. 17.4) can be narrowed down into the interval between the previously calculated lower limit and the dots or squares instead of the previously calculated upper limit. Near the edge of the plate where σ_2^s is estimated to be small, our best estimate for σ_1^s will be the apparent stress itself. At other points, our best estimate will be the mean value of the revised range. The faired curve passing through these means is given in Fig. 17.5a.

The value of σ_2^s can be obtained by integration of the Lamé-Maxwell equations. This will be done by following the procedures outlined in Sec. 15.11, in the chapter on stresses and strains in brittle coatings. The radii of curvature ρ_1 of the isostatics S_1 crossing the minimum section are measured from an enlarged picture of Fig. 17.3 and plotted in Fig. 17.5b. The value of σ_1^s is taken from Fig. 17.5a. The integration is made along the minimum section, starting from the edge of the hole, where σ_2^s is zero, to the edge of the plate, where σ_2^s is again zero. A check is thus obtained, and the small error is distributed along the path of integration. The values of σ_2^s obtained by integration are shown in Fig. 17.4 in dashed line.

17.2. Determination of the Distribution of Stresses in a Ring under Diametral Compression. The distribution of stresses in a ring whose outside diameter is twice its inside diameter and loaded under concentrated compression has been treated quite extensively by S. Timoshenko and

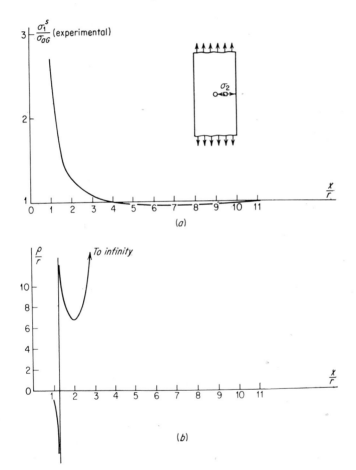

Fig. 17.5. Intermediate steps for the computation of σ_2^s at the minimum section of a plate with a hole, by the integration of the Lamé-Maxwell equations. (a) Best estimate of σ_1^s/σ_{aG} based on the experimental data. (b) Radius of curvature of the isostatics crossing the minimum section, measured from an enlarged picture of Fig. 17.1.

M. Frocht, among others. This allows rather easy checks on the result obtained using the brittle-coating method.

Two separate tests, one a direct-loading test, the other a relaxation loading test, were conducted on a ring made of 24-ST aluminum. The dimensions of the ring are shown in Fig. 17.6. The crack patterns and isoentatics are shown in Figs. 17.7 to 17.9, where the numbers on the isoentatics represent loads in thousands of pounds. Cracks beyond the last isoentatic appeared after refrigeration. The strain sensitivities corrected for the difference between the loading speeds of the ring and of the aluminum calibration strips are 47×10^{-5} and 75×10^{-5}, respectively, for the direct loading and the relaxation loading.

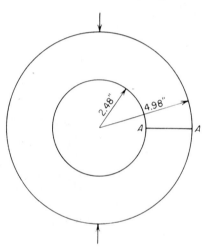

FIG. 17.6. Dimensions of an aluminum ring loaded under diametral compression. Thickness of ring is 1.02 in.

The isostatic pattern on one quadrant of an aluminum ring (obtained by direct loading) is shown in Fig. 17.7a. Figure 17.7b shows the isostatic pattern for the same loading on a transparent plastic ring of the same geometry as the aluminum ring. Singular points S_1 are of the interlocking type. Singular points S_2 are of mixed type. (There is a slight asymmetry on the load which brings S_1 points below the horizontal axis.) The curves of inflection points (see Sec. 8.12) have been drawn showing the points at which σ_1 values go through a minimum or a maximum.

a. *Computations Using Apparent Stresses.* Since the calibration strips and the specimen are made of the same material, Eq. (15.11) gives the apparent stress as

$$\sigma_0^d = E_s \epsilon_s^d$$

where E_s = modulus of elasticity of aluminum = 10×10^6 psi.

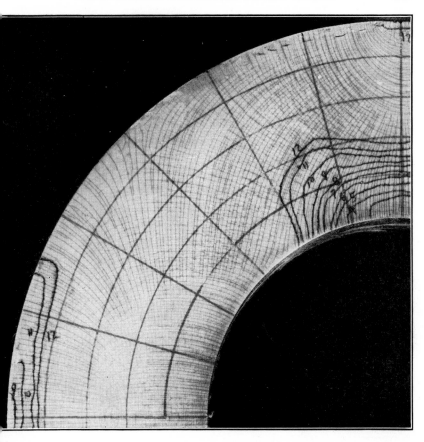

FIG. 17.7a. Crack pattern of a quadrant of an aluminum ring under direct loading. The ring shown in this photograph is not the one used in the analysis in this chapter. It is shown here because of the fine quality of the photographic reproducibility of the crack pattern. Code numbers for different loads on this ring are not linearly proportional to the loads.)

At any point on isoentatic 10 taken from the direct loading test, the maximum principal stress due to a direct load of 10,000 lb is therefore

$$\sigma_1^s = (10 \times 10^6)(47 \times 10^{-5}) = 4{,}700 \text{ psi tension}$$

The average stress across the horizontal section AA (Fig. 17.6) due to the direct load of 10,000 lb is

$$\sigma_{av} = \frac{10{,}000}{2(2.50 \times 1.02)} = 1{,}960 \text{ psi tension}$$

The stress ratio, which is the ratio between the stress at the point in

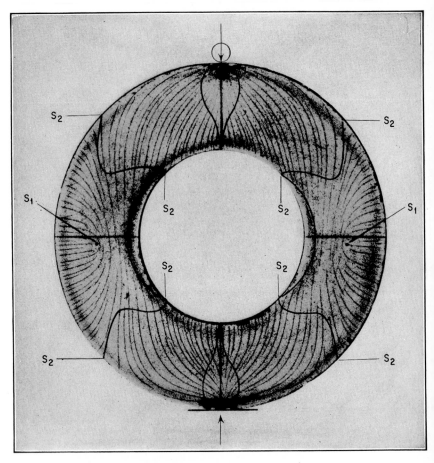

Fig. 17.7b. Isostatic pattern (σ_2 family) obtained from a brittle-coating test on a plastic ring diametrically loaded under compression. Curves of inflexion points have been drawn. Ten singular points are shown.

question and the average stress across the horizontal section due to the same load, is

$$\frac{\sigma_1^s}{\sigma_{av}} = \frac{4,700}{1,960} = 2.40$$

The stress ratio at any point on an isoentatic marked X during the direct-loading test will be given by

$$\frac{\sigma_1^s}{\sigma_{av}} = 2.40 \times \frac{10}{X} = \frac{24.0}{X}$$

Similarly, the stress ratio at any point on an isoentatic marked X in

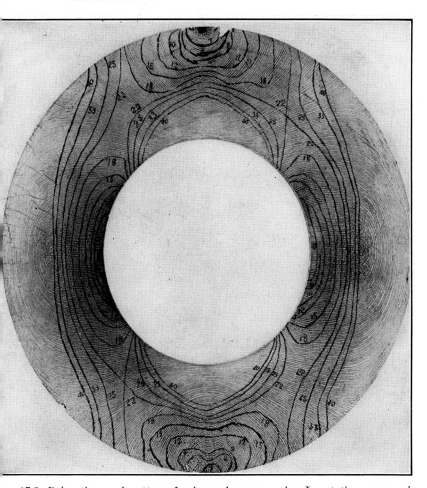

IG. 17.8. Relaxation crack pattern of a ring under compression. Isoentatics correspond
ɔ successive decrements of loading. After the highest load of 40,000 lb was reached,
he specimen was refrigerated and cracks appeared all over the plate.

he relaxation-load pictures (Figs. 17.8 and 17.9) is given by

$$\frac{\sigma_2^s}{\sigma_{av}} = \frac{-38.3}{X}$$

As shown in Figs. 17.7 to 17.9, the inner boundary of the ring is inter-
sected by a number of isoentatics. At these points of intersection, the
stress ratios of the tangential stresses can be determined from the above
formulas. These are plotted in Fig. 17.10, where the points above the
θ axis are the values obtained from the direct-load test, while those below
the θ axis are from the relaxation-load test. The results from a photo-

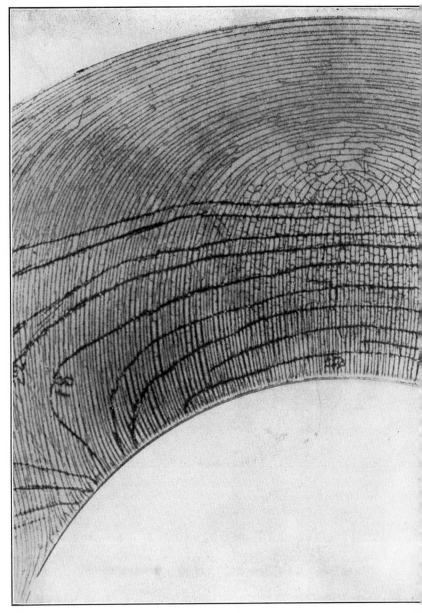

Fig. 17.9. Crack pattern on a portion of a ring under relaxation loading (removal of a diametral compressive load).

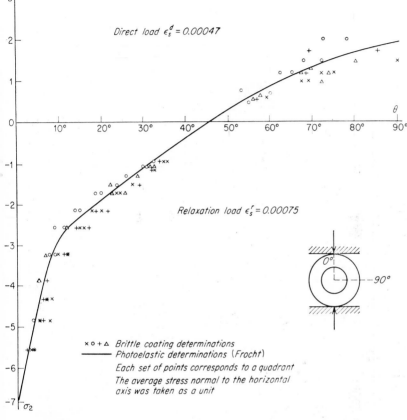

Direct load $\epsilon_s^d = 0.00047$

Relaxation load $\epsilon_s^r = 0.00075$

× ○ + △ *Brittle coating determinations*
——— *Photoelastic determinations (Frocht)*
Each set of points corresponds to a quadrant
The average stress normal to the horizontal
axis was taken as a unit

FIG. 17.10. Stresses tangent to the inner boundary in the closed ring.

elastic determination by Frocht[†] are shown as a full line for comparison with the brittle coating results.

The tangential stresses in the outer boundary, the stresses normal to the horizontal axis, and the stresses normal to the $67\frac{1}{2}°$ axis are calculated in a similar manner and plotted and compared with Frocht's photoelastic results[†] in Figs. 17.11 to 17.13. The curves representing the averages of the brittle-coating data in Figs. 17.10 to 17.12 are plotted in Figs. 17.14 and 17.15. The average of the apparent stresses calculated in a similar manner on the vertical axis is plotted and compared to Frocht's photoelastic results[†] in Fig. 17.16. Because of the yielding of aluminum near

[†]M. M. Frocht, Photoelasticity, pp. 239, 246; On the Optical Determination of Isopachics Patterns, *Proc. 5th Intern. Congr. Appl. Mech.*, 1939, p. 221.

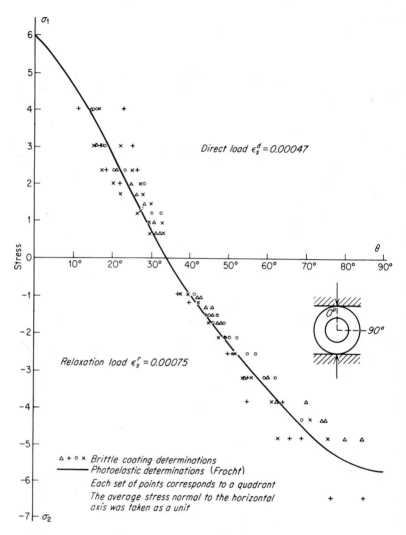

FIG. 17.11. Stresses tangent to the outer boundary in the closed ring.

the concentrated load, the stress distribution in the neighborhood of th
load will not follow the solution of the theory of elasticity for the case c
the concentrated load.

b. Computations Using Maximum-tensile-stress Law of Failure. Usin
the same experimental data, the stresses will be computed assuming tha
the brittle coating fails according to the maximum-tensile-stress law c
failure.

On the free boundaries, one of the principal stresses is zero so that th

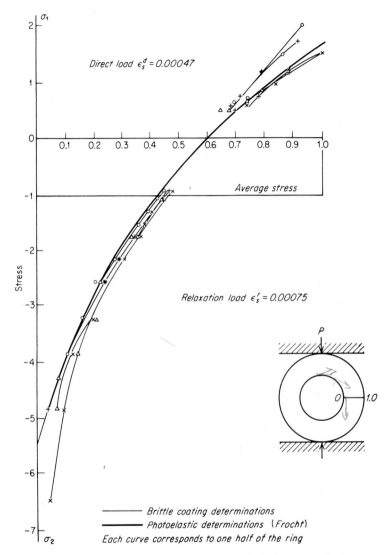

Fig. 17.12. Stresses normal to the horizontal axis in the closed ring.

apparent stress calculated above is identical to the stress calculated from the maximum-tensile-stress law of failure. Figs. 17.10, 17.11, and 17.14 therefore give also the stresses predicted by this law.

On the horizontal axis in Fig. 17.8, at the point where the isoentatic marked 12 intersects this axis, the coating was cracked in one direction by the relaxation load, 12,000 lb, but not cracked in the direction perpendicular to the first by the highest relaxation load of 40,000 lb or by the

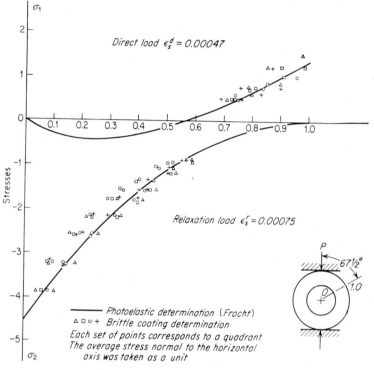

Fig. 17.13. Stress curves for the $67\frac{1}{2}°$ axis of the closed ring.

highest direct load of 47,000 lb without refrigeration. In other words cracks appeared at the above point under a diametral tensile load of 12,000 lb, but no cracks appeared perpendicular to these cracks under the tensile load of 40,000 lb or under the compressive load of 47,000 lb. The strain sensitivity of the tensile-loading test is 75×10^{-5}, while the strain sensitivity of the compressive-loading test is 47×10^{-5}. Assuming $k = 0.6$ $\nu_c = 0.42$, we have

$$\alpha = \frac{40,000}{12,000} = 3.33$$

$$\frac{\alpha}{1 - k\nu_c} = \frac{3.33}{1 - (0.6 \times 0.42)} = 4.5$$

$$\beta \frac{\epsilon_s^d}{\epsilon_s^r} = \frac{47,000}{12,000} \cdot \frac{75 \times 10^{-5}}{47 \times 10^{-5}} = 6.3$$

Note that ϵ_s^d is the strain sensitivity of the coating used in the loading producing a crack at the point in question, while ϵ_s^r is that of the coating

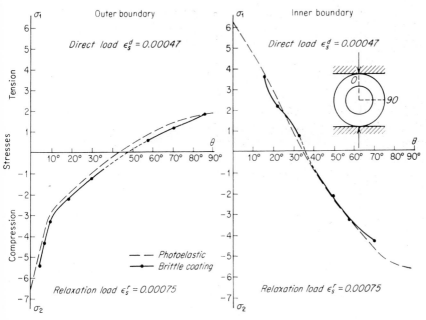

FIG. 17.14. Average of stresses determined by the brittle-coating method compared with photoelastic determinations.

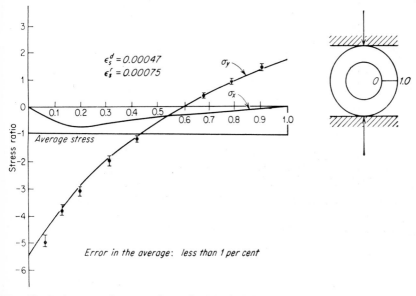

FIG. 17.15. Average of stresses determined by brittle-coating method compared with photoelastic determinations. Horizontal axis of the closed ring.

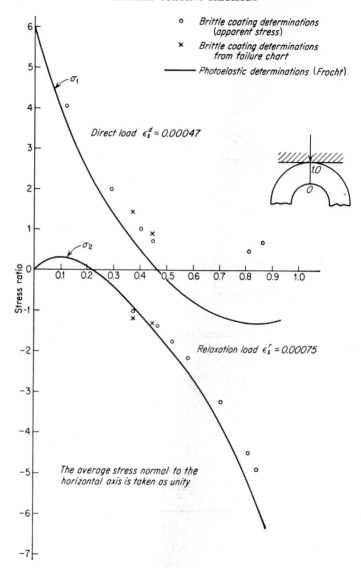

Fig. 17.16. Stress curves for the vertical axis of the ring.

used in the loading which failed to produce a crack perpendicular to the above crack.

From Fig. 15.8 on the line $\nu_c = 0.42$, $\nu_s = 0.33$ the ordinates of the points corresponding to $\alpha/(1 - k\nu_c) = 4.5$ and $\beta(\epsilon_s^d/\epsilon_s^r) = 6.3$ are 0.94 and 1.04, respectively. The apparent stress σ_0^d at any point on the isoentatic 12 in he relaxation loading is, using the dimensions shown in Fig. 17.6,

$$\frac{\sigma_0^d}{\sigma_{av}} = \frac{(10 \times 10^6)(75 \times 10^{-5})}{\frac{12,000}{2(2.50 \times 1.02)}} = 3.18$$

Ience the range of stress is

$$2.99 \leq \frac{\sigma_2^s}{\sigma_{av}} \leq 3.31 \text{ (compression)}$$

Similar calculations are made for the ranges of the stresses at points on ther isoentatics. These ranges are shown in Fig. 17.15.

On the horizontal axis, at a point located at 0.45 of the thickness of the ring from the inner boundary, cracks were obtained both by direct loading and by relaxation loading, so that a determination of both principal stresses s possible. Cracks appeared at this point under a direct load of 32,000 b and a relaxation load of 33,000 lb. Hence

$$\beta \frac{\epsilon_s^d}{\epsilon_s^r} = \frac{33,000}{32,000} = \frac{47 \times 10^{-5}}{75 \times 10^{-5}} = 0.65$$

$$\sigma_0^d = (10 \times 10^6)(47 \times 10^{-5}) = 4,700 \text{ psi}$$

From the line $\nu_c = 0.42$, $\nu_s = 0.33$ in Fig. 15.8, the coordinates of the point $\beta(\epsilon_s^d/\epsilon_s^r) = 0.65$ are -1.7 and $+1.2$. The stresses at point A under the direct load of 32,000 lb are therefore

$$\sigma_1^s = \quad 1.2 \qquad \sigma_0^d = 5,600 \text{ psi (tension)}$$

$$\sigma_2^s = -1.7 \qquad \sigma_0^d = -8,000 \text{ psi (compression)}$$

Under the direct load of 32,000 lb, the average stress in the horizontal axis is

$$\sigma_{av} = \frac{32,000}{2(2.50 \times 1.02)} = 6,270 \text{ psi (compression)}$$

Hence

$$\frac{\sigma_1^s}{\sigma_{av}} = \quad 0.89$$

$$\frac{\sigma_2^s}{\sigma_{av}} = -1.27$$

These stresses are plotted as two crosses in Fig. 17.16; the stresses at a point at 0.36 of the thickness of the ring are calculated in a similar way and plotted also as two crosses in Fig. 17.16.

In the following the failure chart will be constructed using the stress ratios σ_1^s/σ_{av} and σ_2^s/σ_{av} as the ordinate and abscissa.

A quarter of the ring is divided into four zones (Fig. 17.17). In zone 1 no cracks are obtained either under the direct load (diametral compression of 40,000 lb or under the relaxation load (diametral tension) of $-40,000$ lb. The stresses in zone 1 must be represented by points inside zone BH_1B_1' of the failure chart (Fig. 15.7). Under the direct loading of 40,000 lb,

$$\sigma_0^d = 4,700 \text{ psi}$$

$$\sigma_{av} = 7,840 \text{ psi}$$

and

$$\frac{\sigma_0^d}{\sigma_{av}} = 0.60$$

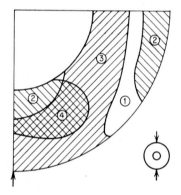

Fig. 17.17. Isoentatic zones.

The scales of both the ordinate and the abscissa of the failure chart are therefore reduced to six-tenths to give the new failure chart, where σ_1^s/σ_{av} and σ_2^s/σ_{av} are the ordinate and abscissa (Fig. 17.18). The abscissa of point M' is -0.6; the abscissa of point M_1' of the line $A_1'B_1'$ defining the failure under relaxation loading is computed as follows:

$$\frac{\epsilon_s^r}{\epsilon_s^d} = \frac{75 \times 10^{-5}}{47 \times 10^{-5}} = 1.60$$

$$\overline{OM_1'} = \frac{\epsilon_s^r}{\epsilon_s^d}\overline{OM'} = 0.96$$

In zone 2 (Fig. 17.17), cracks were obtained under the direct load of 40,000 lb, but not under the relaxation load of $-40,000$ lb. In zone 3, cracks were obtained under the relaxation load, but not under the direct load. In zone 4, cracks were obtained both under the direct load and the relaxation load. The points representing the stresses in these zones will therefore be inside the corresponding zones shown in Fig. 17.18.

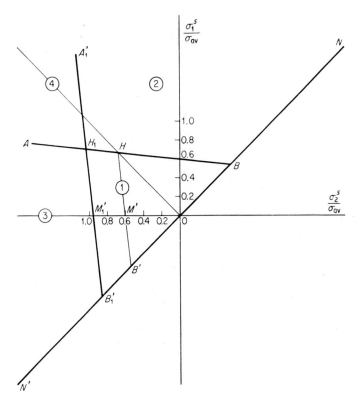

FIG. 17.18. Stress ratios corresponding to the various zones in Fig. 17.17.

17.3. Determination of the Distribution of Stresses in a Track Shoe.

The distribution of stresses in a track shoe is a highly complicated one. To obtain an over-all picture of the surface stresses, the brittle-coating method is the best one to use. Only a direct-loading test was conducted. The shoe model is made of aluminum and loaded under transverse bending, both with pins passing through the holes and without pins. The loading with the pin is shown in Fig. 17.19. The crack patterns and the isoentatics on the two faces of the shoe under the loading without the pin are shown in Figs. 17.20 and 17.21. An enlarged picture of a portion of the shoe is shown in Fig. 17.22. The numbers on the isoentatics represent loads in hundreds of pounds. No cracks beyond the last isoentatic were obtained because no refrigeration was used. The strain sensitivity as obtained from aluminum calibration strips is 66×10^{-5}.

Computations. Only the apparent stress analysis will be made, there being insufficient information for making more elaborate computations. The calibration strips and the specimen are of the same material; hence,

Fig. 17.19. Track shoe under transverse bending (pins passing through the holes).

Fig. 17.20. Crack pattern of the shoe under the loading shown in Fig. 17.19 (without the side pin).

by taking E_s as 10×10^6, we have

$$\sigma_0^d = E_s \epsilon_s^d = 6,600 \text{ psi}$$

At any point on the isoentatic marked 10, the principal stress perpendicular to the crack is equal to 6,600 psi under an external load of 1,000 lb. The principal stress perpendicular to the crack at any point on any isoentatic marked X under the external load of 1,000 lb is therefore

$$\sigma_1^s = \frac{66,000}{X}$$

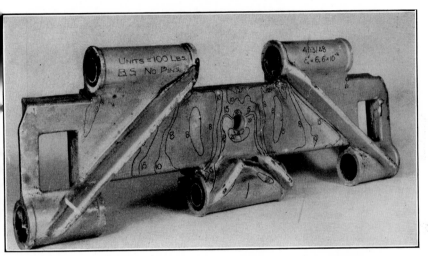

Fig. 17.21. Crack pattern of the back face of the shoe shown in Fig. 17.20.

The maximum principal stress at any uncracked region under the external load of 1,000 lb must be less than 66,000/20, or 3,300 psi.

The first recorded isoentatic is 5. The corresponding apparent stress is 13,200 psi. The maximum stress in the shoe takes place at the fillet, and its value is slightly higher than 13,200 psi. A better estimate of this value can be made by plotting the apparent stresses along a straight line leading to the fillet and extrapolating the values.

The maximum and minimum values of stresses obtained above were used in the redesign of the shoe. It is noticeable that all the ribs on the top side of the shoe are understressed.

Exercises

17.1. Determine the distribution of apparent stresses on the longitudinal axis of a cartridge link.

The results of two brittle-coating tests have been recorded in Figs. 17.24 and 17.25.

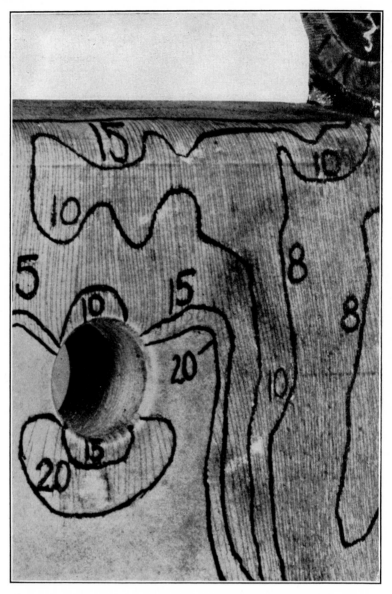

Fig. 17.22. Enlarged picture of the crack pattern of a portion of the shoe shown in Fig. 17.21.

One is a direct-loading test, for which the strain sensitivity was 600 μin./in. The other one is a relaxation test, the strain sensitivity of which was 890 μin./in. The direct-load coating was refrigerated after the test was completed.

Figure 17.23 shows the dimensions of the link, and the following table gives the values of the load corresponding to the isoentatic numbers.

Assume $E_s = 30 \times 10^6$ psi.

Isoentatic numbers	For direct-load test	For relaxation test
1	100 lb	180 lb
2	110 lb	190 lb
3	127 lb	200 lb
4	147 lb	220 lb
5	176 lb	240 lb
6	221 lb	260 lb
7	280 lb	290 lb
8	370 lb	358 lb
9	460 lb	400 lb

The plotting of the stresses should be made neglecting small errors produced by locating isoentatic points on the curved shell, from the photographic record.

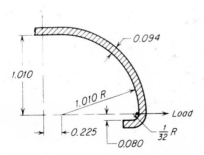

Fig. 17.23. Longitudinal cross section of a cartridge link under pull.

Fig. 17.24a. Isostatics and isoentatics on a cartridge link. Inside view, direct-loading test. The coating was refrigerated after the last isoentatic was recorded. Figures on the isoentatics correspond to amounts of tensile load given in the table in Exercise 17.1.

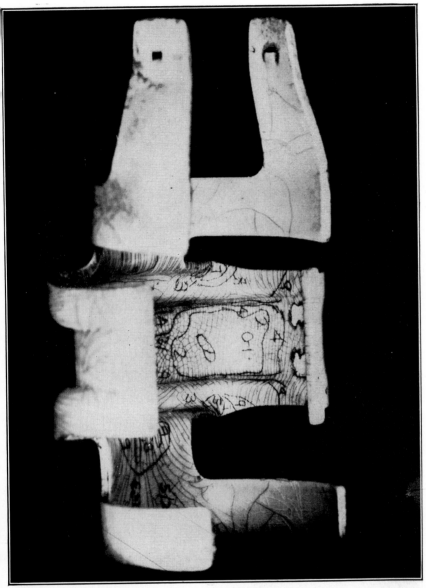

FIG. 17.24b. Isostatics and isoentatics on a cartridge link. Inside view, direct-loading test. The coating was refrigerated after the last isoentatic was recorded. Figures on the isoentatics correspond to amounts of tensile load given in the table in Exercise 17.1.

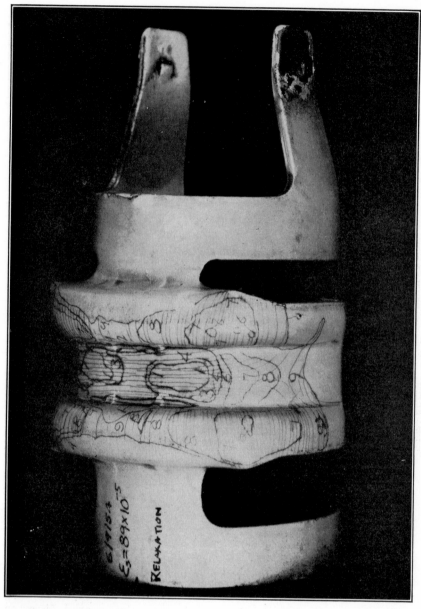

Fig. 17.25a. Isostatics and isoentatics on a cartridge link. Outside view, relaxation test. Figures on the isoentatics correspond to amounts of relaxed tensile load given in the table in Exercise 17.1.

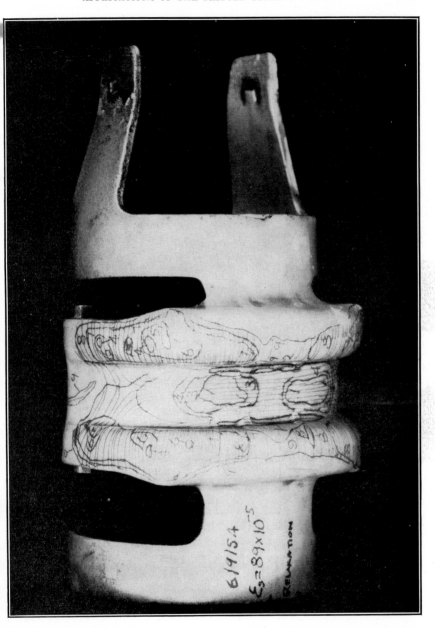

FIG. 17.25b. Isostatics and isoentatics on a cartridge link. Outside view, relaxation test. Figures on the isoentatics correspond to amounts of relaxed tensile load given in the table in Exercise 17.1.

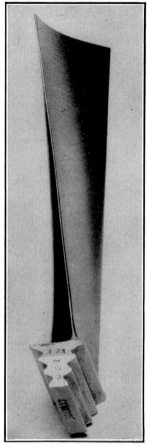

Fig. 17.26. Turbine blade showing blade profile and dovetail root section.

17.2. An uncoated turbine blade is shown in Fig. 17.26. The blade was sprayed with "Stresscoat-1208" and after curing was loaded in the test apparatus shown in Fig. 17.27. The successive increments of bending load were applied and each new isoentatic was given a code number. The results of this brittle-coating test are recorded in Fig. 17.28.

The table on page 465 gives the values of the moments corresponding to the isoentatic code numbers mentioned above. These moments were measured at the top neck section of the dovetail which was arbitrarily selected as the point for the reference moment for this blade.

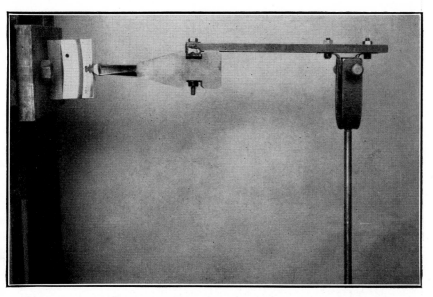

FIG. 17.27. Jig to apply bending loading to turbine blades. The bending load is transmitted to the blade by means of a metal block cast around the tip of the airfoil.

Isoentatic numbers	Moment, in.-lb
1	222
2	260
3	292
4	324
5	370
6	422
7	478
8	530
9	585
10	650
11	747

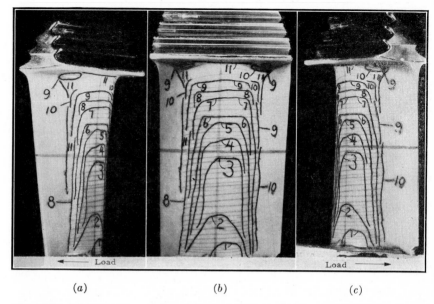

$$(a) \qquad\qquad (b) \qquad\qquad (c)$$

FIG. 17.28. (a) Isostatics and isoentatics on the left of the convex side of a turbine blade subjected to a bending load as shown in the photograph. (b) Isostatics and isoentatics on the front of the convex side of a turbine blade subjected to the same bending load as in a and c. (c) Isostatics and isoentatics on the right of the convex side of a turbine blade subjected to a bending load as shown in the photograph.

Determine the distribution of apparent stresses along the longitudinal and transverse grid lines of the turbine blade as shown in Fig. 17.28, assuming $\epsilon_s = 600$ μin./in. and $E_s = 30 \times 10^6$ psi. Plot these results in graphs for an assumed load of $M = 100$ in.-lb.

Determine the position and value of the maximum apparent stress at the fillet between airfoil and platform, for $M = 100$ in.-lb.

17.3. Determine the angle between the principal stresses and the vertical direction at three vertical cross sections in the simply supported beam subjected to a central load, as shown in Fig. 17.29. Space the three cross sections evenly at a distance of c, $2c$, and $3c$ from the central axis, where c is one-half the height of the beam. The distance between supports is $10 \times \frac{2}{3}c$.

The results obtained should be compared to the angle of inclination of principal stress obtained using elementary strength-of-material formulas.

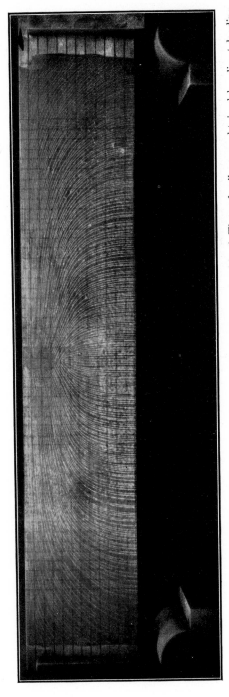

FIG. 17.29. Isostatic pattern in a simply supported beam under concentrated central load. The σ_2 family was obtained by direct loading followed by refrigeration.

467

PART 5

MECHANICAL STRAIN GAGES

CHAPTER 18

MECHANICAL STRAIN GAGES

18.1. Introduction. Mechanical strain gages are instruments which magnify displacements by mechanical means. They are frequently used in experimental-stress-analysis laboratories. The name strain gage is somewhat a misnomer, for the gages measure directly displacements (i.e., relative movements between two points) and not strain, or unit deformation. However, with proper graduation, the scale can be made to indicate strain, and this is done in some cases.

A few of the concepts presented in Chap. 10 will be reviewed here and applied to mechanical strain gages.

In strain-gage terminology the distance whose change is being measured is called the base length. Thus the base length is the distance between the two knives, or needle tips, which in most mechanical strain gages transmit the motion between the two points in the measured specimen. This is also called the gage length. As will be seen, commonly used gages employ base lengths of $\frac{1}{2}$ to 10 in. and larger. When nonuniform fields of strain are present (i.e., gradients of strain exist), the smaller the base length, the more accurate is the determination of strain. In uniform fields of strain the base length is immaterial except that the use of larger gages in some cases increases the precision of the measurement.

The range of an instrument is the difference between the maximum and minimum quantity it can measure. If the range is specified in terms of strain for a mechanical strain gage, it is then the maximum strain the gage can measure. If specified in terms of displacement, the range is analogously the maximum displacement it can measure.

The sensitivity of an instrument is the smallest value of the measured quantity that can be read on the scale. Thus, the term deformation sensitivity is associated with instruments used to measure displacements (deformations), while the sensitivity of a mechanical strain gage used to measure strains is called strain sensitivity. By their definitions, it is seen that strain sensitivity (SS) and deformation sensitivity (DS) are given by the expressions, introduced in Chap. 10,

$$DS = \frac{d}{m} \qquad (10.1)$$

471

$$SS = \frac{d}{mL} \tag{10.2}$$

where d = smallest possible reading on the scale
m = gage mechanical multiplication
L = gage length

As an example, a ruler can be read with skillful eyes to the neares 0.01 in. Its multiplication is unity. If the length over which the change in length is being measured is 100 in., the strain sensitivity is

$$SS = \frac{0.01}{1 \times 100} = 0.0001 \text{ in./in.}$$

This is the smallest value of strain that can be measured with the rule for the given gage length. Its deformation sensitivity correspondingly is

$$DS = \frac{0.01}{1} = 0.01 \text{ in.}$$

A survey of the history of strain gages indicates that practically every conceivable method of mechanical multiplication of displacements has been tried. Many gages have been built using levers and linkages. Others use spur or worm gears, and one employs a twisted strip.

The objective in the design of any mechanical strain gage is to obtain a good combination of the factors (1) accuracy, (2) sensitivity, (3) ruggedness, (4) compactness, (5) ease of handling, and (6) low cost of manufacture. Many gages have been built which have not been used by anyone except the inventors themselves because of failure to reach a satisfactory balance between these factors. A gage developed by Preuss in Germany at the beginning of the century used both mechanical and optical leverage and had the extremely high multiplication of 64,000, while employing a base length as short as 0.028 in. Its strain sensitivity was excellent, and the inventor claimed good accuracy. However, the gage was difficult to handle and was complex and costly.

The gages more commonly used today will be discussed in the paragraphs below, and the advantages and disadvantages of each will be weighed in terms of the above-listed factors. The gages are not listed in any order of preference; however, the topics do progress from the more commonly used gages to those finding less use in the United States.

18.2. Dial Gages. Dial gages are the most common of all displacement measuring instruments, and they have extensive application both within and outside the field of strain analysis. Their wide availability and relatively low cost combined with durability, simplicity, and accuracy make them ideally suited for both laboratory and field work.

A sketch showing the mechanism of a typical 0.001-in. dial gage is given in Fig. 18.1. As is seen, the gage employs a rack and spur gears for mechanical multiplication. Gages with scale graduations in one-thousandths are most common; however, in strain-measurement work, the one ten-thousandth gage is used extensively. The latter has a multiplication of around 800 and a deformation sensitivity of about 0.0001 in. This is too high for most strain analysis; however, in cases where deformations are sufficiently large, the dial gage is generally preferred over many other mechanical gages.

Dial gages are little affected in their accuracy by temperature and moisture changes. This makes them well suited for long-time determina-

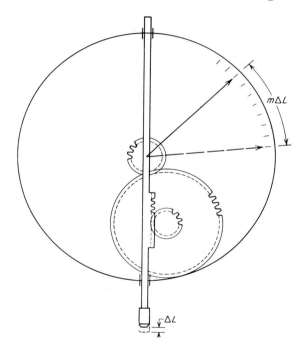

FIG. 18.1. Dial-gage mechanism.

tions. They are almost exclusively used for static measurements, although they can also be used to measure displacement changes of a few cycles per second. In precise work it is advisable to calibrate these gages. The main sources of error are friction in the gears and lost motion. Often these gages are used as an integral part of a more elaborate mechanism that transmits the motion between two points. Some of these gages will be described later.

18.3. Micrometers. This instrument is not so well known as a strain-measuring gage, but it is applicable in some strain-analysis problems. I multiplies displacements by using the screw and vernier principles. I the hands of a good operator, it has the same strain sensitivity as the one ten-thousandth dial gage.

Advantages are ease of handling, low cost, ruggedness, and familiarit to many people.

Disadvantages are high strain sensitivity, necessity for repositionin with every measurement, and restriction of use to simple geometric shape. An example of the application of a micrometer to the measurement o permanent deformations produced in cartridge cases by firing is given in Fig. 18.2.

FIG. 18.2. Application of the micrometer to the measurement of permanent strain in cartridge cases. The numbered rings define the axial position of the micrometer. Marks on the cases define the circumferential position. Diametral measurements are taken before and after firing the case.

18.4. Porter-Lipp Gage. This small lightweight gage employing levers and fulcrums for the multiplication of motion has found extensive application in experimental stress-analysis work. The gage is shown in Fig. 18.3, and its mechanism is sketched in Fig. 18.4.

FIG. 18.3. Porter-Lipp strain gage attached to a tensile specimen.

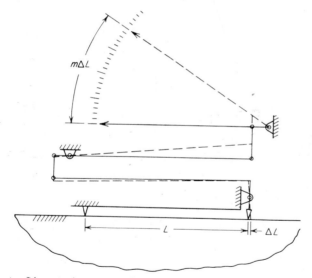

FIG. 18.4. Porter-Lipp strain-gage mechanism. The motion ΔL is multiplied 300 times by means of a series of levers.

It has a base length of 1 in. and a multiplication of 300, and, with scale dimensions readable to the nearest 0.01 in., a strain sensitivity [see Eq. (18.1)] of $0.01/(300 \times 1) = 0.00003$ in./in. With resetting it has a range of 0.008 in.

Its ruggedness, low cost, and ease of handling are also advantages, though its relatively large strain sensitivity and large base length make it unsuitable for many strain analyses.

18.5. The Huggenberger Tensometer. This gage is similar in principle to the Porter-Lipp gage in that it multiplies the displacement through a series of levers and fulcrums. The mechanism is shown schematically in Fig. 18.5, and the tensometer itself is shown in Fig. 18.6.

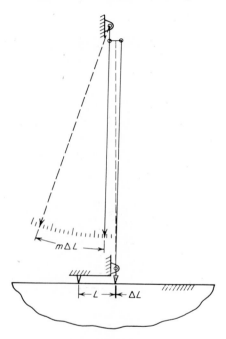

FIG. 18.5. Huggenberger tensometer mechanism. The motion ΔL is multiplied about 1,200 times by means of a series of levers.

This gage is extremely sensitive, with a multiplication of 1,200† and a strain sensitivity of 0.000008 in./in. when used with a 1-in. base length. The base length can be set at $\frac{1}{2}$ in. or 1 in., and extension bars up to 40 inches are available. A range of 0.008 in. is obtainable with resetting. The $\frac{1}{2}$-in. base length is still, unfortunately, large for those strain-analysis applications where large strain gradients are present. The gage, however, finds extensive use because of its accuracy and sturdy construction. Like the Porter-Lipp gage it requires experience by the operator in setting it on the specimen to be studied. The penetration of the movable knife,

†Type A gage.

or its wearing off, should be closely watched since errors in the length of this knife affect the multiplication factor. The gage can be used almost indefinitely and is little influenced by temperature and moisture.

A great assortment of holding devices and other accessories are available, but much of the time the method of adaptation of the gage to a particular problem rests with the ingenuity of the operator. Two holding methods are illustrated in Fig. 18.7, and a third is shown in Fig. 18.17. An application of this extensometer to the measurement of strains on the ribs of a cast-iron plate is shown in Fig. 18.8. Here also two methods of holding the gage can be seen, an extensible clamp provided by the manufacturer of the gage and rubber bands that apply pressure by means of a pin.

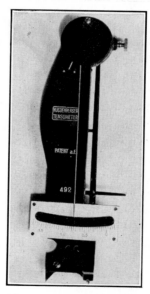

FIG. 18.6. Huggenberger tensometer.

For precise work it is advisable to calibrate these gages periodically. The manufacturer provides a calibrating instrument based on mechanical principles that can be used for this purpose. The most reliable and sensitive calibrating gage system, however, is that employing optical interference fringes. Two optical flats can be attached to the knives of the gage, and the number of fringes passing through a reference line on a telescope focused on these flats when the distance between the flats is changed can be plotted against the corresponding readings on the Huggenberger scale. This was done by Vose with a specially designed fixture.[†]

†R. W. Vose, Characteristics of the Huggenberger Tensometer, *Proc. ASTM*, vol. 34, no. 2, p. 862, 1934.

18.6. Berry Strain Gage. Several gages have been marketed which employ standard-type dial gages with or without previous lever multiplication. The Berry strain gage is one of these and multiplies the displacement five times before transmitting the movement to the dial gage (see Fig. 18.9).

When a dial gage graduated to 0.0001 in. is used, an experienced operator can measure strain to the nearest 0.00001 in./in.; however, the most common application is in field work, where the gage is used on large structures (reinforced-concrete bridges, for example) and at several locations instead of being fixed at one station. Here the errors introduced by the removals between readings reduce the accuracy.

Fig. 18.7. Application of Huggenberger tensometers showing two methods of holding (a) A clamp provided by the manufacturer. (b) Rubber bands.

In such applications small holes are drilled and countersunk, according to the manufacturer's specifications, at each end of the base lengths being studied; and it is necessary to exercise extreme care in the preparation of the holes and in the insertion of the gage contact points.

The gage can be obtained with a 2- or 8-in. base length and in either case with a range of 0.004 in.

18.7. Whittemore Strain Gage. The Whittemore gage employs a dia-

Fɪɢ. 18.8. Use of Huggenberger strain gages in the determination of strains present
n the ribs of cast-iron piano plates. The wiring of electrical strain gages, SR-4's, is
lso visible in the photograph.

age without additional multiplication; it is thus basically a fixture designed
or hand holding a dial gage. The 2-in. and 10-in. base-length gages are
hown in Figs. 18.10 and 18.11. As in the case of the Berry gage, drilled
nd countersunk holes are prepared for insertion of the gage contact
oints at the several locations where the strain is to be measured, and the
age is inserted and removed between readings.

The strain sensitivity of the gage using a 0.0001-in. dial gage is 0.00005
n./in. for the 2-in. base-length gage (i.e., the dial gage sensitivity of
.0001 in. divided by the base length of 2 in.) and 0.00001 for the 10-in.
age. In both cases a gage with a range of 0.024 in. is available.

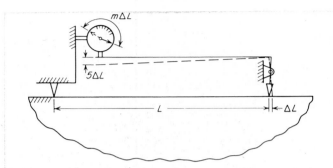

FIG. 18.9. Berry strain gage. The change in distance between the knives is multiplied five times before it is recorded on the dial gage.

FIG. 18.10. Two-inch Whittemore strain gage. The gage has been placed on a mirror to show its top and bottom sides. There is no mulitplication of the displacement between the knives before it is recorded by the dial gage. The jig shown at the right is used to punch the 2-in. gage length holes before drilling and countersinking.

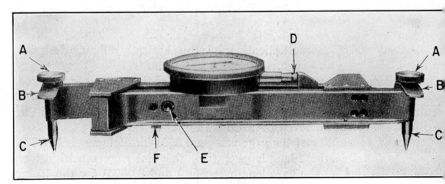

FIG. 18.11. Ten-inch Whittemore strain gage.

Like the Berry gage, its advantages lie primarily in its ruggedness, and hence suitability for field work. Its high strain sensitivity and large base length make it unsuitable for most laboratory strain analyses.

18.8. The Mikrokator. This gage, developed by C. E. Johansson and called the C.E.J. Extensometer by the manufacturer, employs the principle of the twisted strip for mechanical multiplication. The principle is illustrated in Fig. 18.12, and the gage is shown in Fig. 18.13. The metal strip is twisted in one direction from the center to one end of the gage and in the opposite direction from the center to the other end. Linear motion of the right-hand knife-edge (Fig. 18.12) is permitted, while the left-hand knife-edge remains fixed. This results in a stretch of the strip and a consequent rotation of the pointer, which is attached to the strip center.

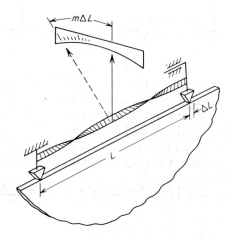

FIG. 18.12. Mikrokator principle as used in the C.E.J. Extensometer. The multiplication of the displacement is obtained by the twisting of a metal strip, without friction or lost motion. The strain sensitivity is of the order of 0.000002.

Extremely large multiplications are possible by this principle. The gage therefore is very sensitive. Two sizes are available, a $\frac{1}{8}$- to $\frac{7}{16}$-in. base-length gage and a 2-in. base-length gage. The latter can be obtained with ranges from 0.0005 to 0.02 in. and has a strain sensitivity of the order of 0.000002 in./in.

This gage has the smallest error due to lag movements, friction, etc., of all mechanical gages. It has been used mainly in the determination of stress-strain curves in the laboratory, but it is also recommended by the manufacturers for outdoor use on large structures.

18.9. Scratch Gage. The deForest scratch gage, while employing no mechanical multiplication, is discussed in this chapter because it is mechan-

FIG. 18.13. The C.E.J. Extensometer. The gage employs the Mikrokator principle
The knife-edges shown can be replaced by other types if desired.

ical in its manner of sensing and recording deformations. The gage (Fig
18.14) consists of three elements, a scratch arm, a friction bar, and a
replaceable target. By means of the three screws, it is attached directly
on the surface being strained, and relative motion over the 2-in. gag
length between the scratch arm and target is recorded by the scratching
of an abrasive, cemented on the tip of the arm, on the polished, chrome
plated surface of the target.

The scratch arm has been ingeniously designed to travel laterall
across the target during the recording through the interaction of th
fulcrum spring and friction bar. The spring is prestressed by bending th
arm to either side before the test, and longitudinal motion of the arr
across the friction bar during the test is then accompanied by latera
motion produced by the restoring force in the spring.

FIG. 18.14. The deForest scratch gage. The relative motion over the gage leng
(2 in.) is recorded by the scratching of the arm tip on the target and is observed und
optical magnification in a microscope.

Dynamic records are thus possible, although it is not possible to obtain the time scale in the recorded strain-time curve.

The scratch trace is either measured or photographed under a metallographic microscope. A typical magnified record is shown in Fig. 18.15. With a 500× magnification and reading of the resulting scratch pattern to the nearest $\frac{1}{20}$ in., a strain sensitivity of SS = $1/(500 \times 20)2$ = 0.00005 in./in. is obtainable.

The gage's simplicity, low cost, and ability to record data make it attractive to field work, and it seems that it deserves to be more popular

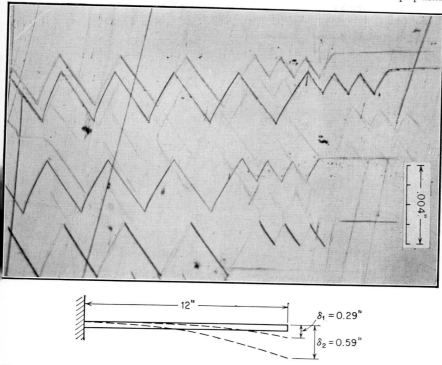

FIG. 18.15. Scratch gage record (500×) with gage mounted on 12-in. by 1-in. by $\frac{1}{4}$-in. strip which was deflected as shown. (See Exercise 18.1 for determination of gage location.)

than it actually is. Unfortunately there is no way to reduce its 2-in. base length, and this in addition to its relatively high strain sensitivity makes it generally unsuitable for laboratory work.

18.10. Examples. As an example of the use of mechanical strain gages in a stress-analysis problem, a test employing Huggenberger gages will be described.

It is desired to study the strain field for the case of the plate of finite width and length with a circular hole at its center as illustrated in Fig. 18.16. The loading will be uniform tension applied in the direction of the plate length. The experimental results can be compared therefore with Howland's theoretical solution for the same case (see Sec. 9.3).

The hole diameter will be chosen as one-twelfth of the plate width, which is the same geometry used in the application of the grid method to

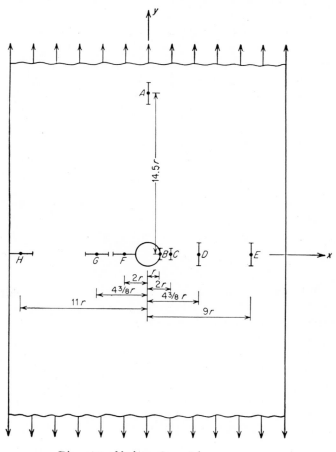

Diameter of hole $= 2r = 1$ in.
Width of plate $= 12$ in.
Thickness of plate $= 0.248$ in.
$$E = \frac{\text{stress at } A}{\text{strain at } A} = 10.1 \times 10^6 \text{ lb/in.}^2$$
Gage length at B and $C = \frac{1}{2}$ in.
Gage length at $A, D, E, F, G,$ and $H = 1$ in.

FIG. 18.16. Position of Huggenbergers in experimental study of plate with central hole.

this problem (see Sec. 13.5), and very close to the geometry used in the application of the brittle-coating method (see Sec. 17.1). Since a $\frac{1}{2}$-in. gage length is the smallest possible with the Huggenberger gage, the plate will have to be large in order to obtain accurate results at locations of high strain gradients; however, the upper limit of size will be determined by the available testing equipment. If a 20,000-lb testing machine can be used, the following steps of calculation show that a 12-in.-wide, $\frac{1}{4}$-in.-thick aluminum plate is suitable for the test.

1. Strain sensitivity of 1-in. base-length Huggenberger gage = 0.000008 in./in.

2. If 0.000400 in./in. strain is applied to the uniform field, then since the 1-in. base-length Huggenberger gage at the uniform field can be read to the nearest 0.000008 in./in., the strain can read to within (0.000008 × 100)/0.000400 = 2 per cent of the total applied strain. This is considered satisfactory.

3. Assume the stress concentration factor is 3; then the maximum stress at the edge of the hole, if aluminum is used, will be

$$\sigma = E\epsilon = 10.1 \times 10^6 \times 0.000400 \times 3 = 12,120 \text{ psi}$$

a satisfactory value, because it is smaller than the elastic limit of the aluminum used.

4. The necessary load to be applied to a 12-in.-wide, $\frac{1}{4}$-in.-thick plate will be

$$P = \sigma A = E\epsilon A = 10.1 \times 10^6 \times 0.000400 \times 12 \times \tfrac{1}{4} = 12,120 \text{ lb}$$

which is well below the maximum capacity of the testing machine.

A sufficient number of tests were conducted to allow the use of two Huggenberger gages at the locations indicated in Fig. 18.16. The loading and unloading were repeated the necessary number of times to relocate the gages and obtain readings at all the locations shown. Figure 18.17 is a photograph showing the two gages clamped at locations B and G. Suitable precautions against bending of the plate out of its own plane were taken; and this was checked by comparing longitudinal strain readings taken on both the front and back of the plate at some of the locations.

The measured strains are plotted in Fig. 18.18. These can be converted to stresses using the stress-strain relations of plane stress derived in Exercise 6.3.

$$\sigma_x = \frac{E}{1 - \nu^2} (\epsilon_x + \nu\epsilon_y)$$

$$\sigma_y = \frac{E}{1 - \nu^2} (\epsilon_y + \nu\epsilon_x)$$

$$\sigma_z = 0$$

It is to be observed that the plotted strains are principal strains since the loading and geometry are symmetrical with respect to the x axis. If this were not so, the use of three, instead of two, strain gages would be necessary to determine completely the states of strain and stress.

At points A and B the stress $\sigma_x = 0$, and the longitudinal stress and strain are related through the further reduced stress-strain relation,

$$\sigma_y = E\epsilon_y$$

The modulus of elasticity E was determined by dividing the applied load per unit area by the strain recorded at point A. Poisson's ratio ν was taken as $\frac{1}{3}$ for aluminum.

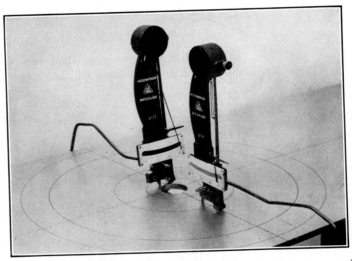

FIG. 18.17. Huggenberger strain gages clamped at two locations on an aluminum plate with a central circular hole.

The distribution of stress on the transverse axis through the center of the hole, according to Howland's solution, is given in Fig. 9.14. This is for the same hole-diameter to plate-width ratio as that for the model in this test. Howland's solution has been converted to terms of strain and drawn in Fig. 18.18 with the Huggenberger results shown in the dots.

As would be expected, the experimentally obtained value of ϵ_y at point B is low. This is because of the large gage length used. The gage measures the average value of strain over the $\frac{1}{2}$-in. gage length and not the maximum which occurs at B. This experimental example illustrates the inability of the mechanical strain gage to record accurately peak values where high strain gradients are involved. Increased accuracy at such points will only

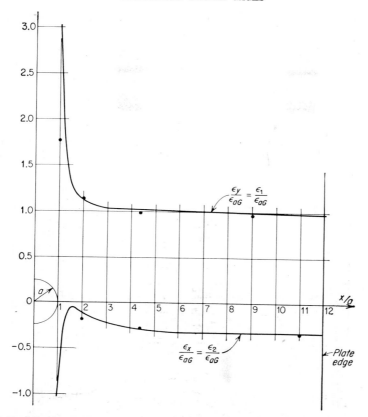

F IG. 18.18. Aluminum plate with a central circular hole, under uniaxial uniform load. Strains along the x axis as determined from Huggenberger measurements. Howland's solution for the finite plate (width of plate equals twelve times diameter of hole) shown in solid curve. Results calculated from Huggenberger measurements shown in dots. Poisson's ratio for aluminum $= \frac{1}{3}$. ϵ_{aG} = average strain at the gross area.

be obtained by increasing the plate size, or by using a Huggenberger with variable base length and evaluating the results using Fischer's method (see Sec. 13.4).

In another experiment dial gages, electrical strain gages, and a brittle coating were all used in the stress analysis of two $\frac{1}{8}$ scale models of a nuclear reactor head.

In Fig. 18.19 the dial gages are shown as used to measure displacement of the head under internal pressure. In Fig. 18.20 the dial gages have been mounted on long lever arms to measure flange rotations with respect to the other flange and with respect to the base.

18.11. Example of Accuracy Determination. Mechanical strain-gage

FIG. 18.19. Test setup for experimental stress analysis of a model of a nuclear reactor head. (The hemispherical head has not yet been perforated.) Dial gages, a brittle coating, and electrical strain gages were used to record the effect of internal pressure.

determinations should be evaluated whenever possible in the light of the considerations developed in Chap. 10 dealing with the precision of measurements. Some systematic studies have been conducted to determine the total error associated with these determinations.

The following example is taken from a report prepared by a committee of the International Federation of the National Standardizing Associations in Great Britain.†

Hollow cast-iron workpieces were prepared and sent to about 20 firms and government agencies to have the external and internal sizes measured

†Quoted in *Chartered Mech. Engineer*, vol. 2, no. 5, p. 255, May, 1955.

FIG. 18.20. Test setup for experimental stress analysis of the reactor-head model shown in Fig. 18.19, after the head has been perforated. The holes in the head were interrupted at the axis of the head thickness to allow the application of internal pressure. The dial gages and the lever arms combine to give a multiplication factor of about 1400 to the displacements (due to rotation) at the periphery of the flange. The effect of bolt loading was also measured.

at specified positions. Micrometers were used for the measurements. The workpieces had previously been measured at the National Physical Laboratory, and the results of these measurements were taken as a standard of comparison.

The standard deviations about the algebraic mean of the errors of measurements are shown in Fig. 18.21. These are total errors produced by several causes: accuracy of the length standards, performance of the equipment, skill of the observer, and temperature conditions.

Exercises

18.1. Determine the location of the scratch gage used in obtaining the record shown in Fig. 18.15.

18.2. Using the results of Howland's solution plotted in Fig. 9.14, verify the values of the strains $\epsilon_1/\epsilon_{a_g}$ and $\epsilon_2/\epsilon_{a_g}$ at positions $x/a = 1$ and 12 in Fig. 18.18.

18.3. Use at least three of the methods described in the chapter to measure displacements and strains in an elastic body under load. Compare the values obtained with each other and with theory.

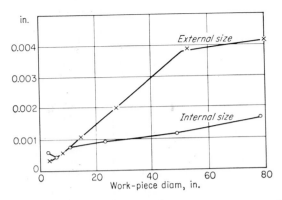

FIG. 18.21. Standard deviation about the algebraic mean of errors of measurements of cast-iron workpieces. Micrometers were used for the measurements (International Federation of National Standardizing Associations).

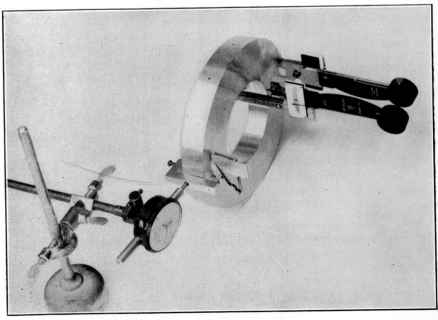

FIG. 18.22. Dial gages and strain gages mounted on a ring to be loaded vertically through the axis.

Figure 18.22 shows a suitable test setup. Here a ring (8 in. OD, 4 in. ID, 1 in. thick) is subjected to a concentrated load through the vertical axis. A Porter-Lipp and a 1-in. Huggenberger are mounted on the opposite sides of the horizontal axis near the outer diameter. A $\frac{1}{2}$-in. Huggenberger is mounted near the inner diameter. The test was run with two dial gages on opposite sides of the horizontal axis (only one is shown), and a dial gage between the two platens of the machine that applied the load (not shown). The results can be compared with the values shown in Fig. 17.12.

18.4. Repeat Exercise 18.3 using an elastic body displaced at some point by a known deflection.

This test can be conducted with the standard Stresscoat calibration strip shown in Fig. 16.28 (also in Fig. 18.15). Mechanical strain gages are mounted in the transverse and longitudinal directions at several points along the axis, and dial gages are used to measure vertical displacements. Strains obtained can be related to the displacements applied to the strip assuming beam theory. Differences between actual distribution of strains and beam theory can be pointed out.

INDEX

DATE DUE

TURNE

DATE DUE

F

)

RE